D1283823

Molecular
Biology of
Bacterial
Viruses

A Series of Books in Biology

EDITORS

Ralph Emerson

Donald Kennedy

Roderic B. Park

George W. Beadle
(1946–1961)

Douglas M. Whitaker
(1946–1966)

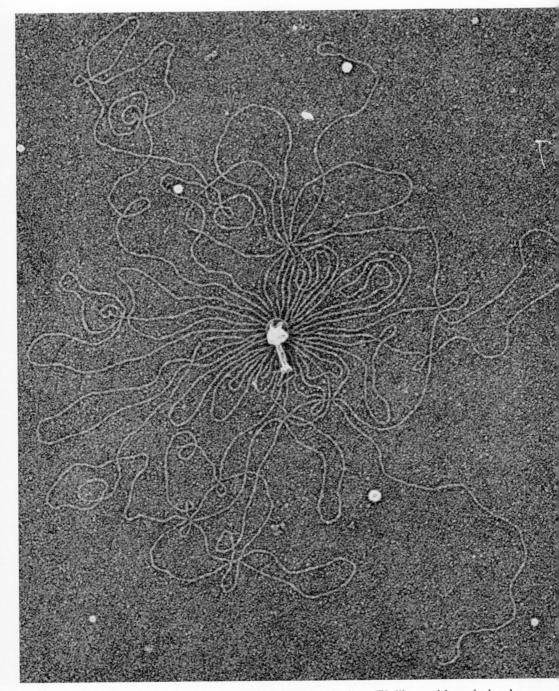

Frontispiece. The DNA macromolecule of bacteriophage T2, liberated from the head of the virus by osmotic shock. *Center:* the phage ghost. *Bottom right and top center:* the two ends of the DNA fiber. Approximate magnification of this electron micrograph: 80,000. [From Kleinschmidt, Lang, Jacherts, and Zahn (365a).]

Molecular Biology of Bacterial Viruses

by GUNTHER S. STENT

UNIVERSITY OF CALIFORNIA

Drawings by JUDITH L. DOHM

W. H. FREEMAN AND COMPANY

San Francisco and London

© Copyright 1963 by W. H. Freeman and Company

The publisher reserves all rights to reproduce this book, in whole or in part, with the exception of the right to use short quotations for review of the book.

Library of Congress Catalog Card Number: 63:12521

Printed in the United States of America   (*C5*)

TO Max Delbrück

Preface

FOURTEEN YEARS AGO, in the summer of 1949, a little group of phage workers were passing the time of day in M. Delbrück's laboratory in Pasadena by filling several blackboards with an outline of all that they then knew of bacterial viruses. It was their hope that an orderly array of all the available facts might perhaps suggest to them new working hypotheses, or make evident hithertofore overlooked clues. Unfortunately, this exercise failed to bring the desired enlightenment. But when it was discovered a few months later that one of them had preserved this ephemeral chalk outline on paper, his notes became the basis of the cooperative "Syllabus on Procedures, Facts and Interpretations in Phage" (59). I have followed here the general plan of this Syllabus, since most of the great advances made meanwhile in the understanding of bacterial viruses have but filled in lacunae of its categories.

Even though bacteriophages have now assumed a position of extraordinary importance in modern biology, only one really comprehensive presentation of bacterial virology, Mark Adams' posthumous *Bacteriophages* (2), has appeared in recent years. This book, completed and edited for publication by friends and colleagues after Adams' death, is an invaluable source of factual, theoretical, and methodological information, and should be in the possession of everyone seriously interested in bacterial viruses. However, *Bacteriophages* is not, in my opinion, particularly suitable for introducing university students or nonspecialists to the subject, and hence I have attempted to fill here the need for an introductory text. Though no doubt self-evident, I would like to call attention to the superficial nature of my treatment; its aim is to give merely a bird's-eye view of what has now become a vast and complex ensemble of facts. This textbook is not intended to be a monograph; rather, its purpose is a preparation for eventual study of more serious works, such as Adams' book, or specialized review articles, or the original literature. In order to facilitate this study, lists of suggested further reading have been appended to each chapter. These lists include the relevant articles whose reprints can be found in the collection *Papers on Bacterial Viruses* (595). Mention should be made here also of two other books useful to the student of bacterial viruses: Luria's *General Virology* (440), an introductory text that juxtaposes homologous aspects of bacterial, plant, and animal viruses for an integrated presentation of the new science of virology and Raettig's *Bakteriophagie* (522), an ecumenical, complete, and cross-indexed bibliography of the literature of bacterial viruses that lists no fewer than 5655 papers and books published on this subject between 1917 and 1956.

Most of this text was written during a sabbatical leave from the University of California. I would like to thank the National Science Foundation for the grant of a Senior Postdoctoral Fellowship; Itaru Watanabe, of the University of Kyoto, and Max Perutz, F. H. C. Crick, and Sydney Brenner, of the University of Cambridge, for hospitable accommodation in their laboratories; and the Provost and Fellows of King's College, Cambridge, for granting me membership in their High Table. I am grateful to my friends A. H. Doermann, J. Weigle, and E. L. Wollman for providing valuable and frequently severe criticisms of the manuscript and to Mrs. Margery Hoogs for her patient editorial help.

February 1963   *Gunther S. Stent*

Contents

CHAPTER

1. The Twort-d'Hérelle Phenomenon   1

  Twort's Glassy Transformation   1
  d'Hérelle's Bacteriophage   3
  Phage Therapy and Prophylaxis   6
  Nature of the Bacteriophage   9
  d'Hérelle's Critics   11
  Origins of Modern Phage Research   15

2. The Bacterial Host Cell   22

  The Group   23
  Cell Structure   26
  Cultivation   29
  Enumeration   32
  Dynamics of Growth   34
  Genetics   36

3. The Infective Unit   40

  Titration   40
  Size   43
  Morphology   46
  Chemical Composition   49
  The Phage DNA   53
  Serology   58
  Internal Structure   63

4. Growth Cycle   70

  One-step Growth   72
  Single Burst   74
  Lysis   77
  Lysis Inhibition   82
  The Eclipse   83

5. Infection   88

    Adsorption   88
    Bacterial Receptors   96
    Phage Growth in Protoplasts   102
    Adsorption Organ   103
    Injection   110

6. Synthesis of Virus Progeny   116

    Incomplete-phage Protein   117
    Incomplete-phage DNA   123
    Phage Precursor Pools   125
    The DNA Pool   126
    The Protein Pool   129
    The Maturation Process   132

7. Metabolism and DNA Replication
    in the Infected Cell   139

    Bacterial Enzymes   139
    The Early Protein   141
    Phage-induced Enzymes   144
    Cell Envelope   152
    Ribonucleic Acid Synthesis   155
    Replication of the Phage DNA   157
    Transfer of DNA from Parent to Progeny Phage   160

8. Mutation and Mixed Infection   175

    Rapid Lysis Mutants   176
    Host Range Mutants   180
    Mutation of the Vegetative Phage   188
    Mechanism of Reproduction of the Viral Genome   190
    Mixed Infection   195
    Partial Exclusion   198
    Phenotypic Mixing   199

9.   Genetic Recombination   202

     The Map   203
     The Visconti-Delbrück Theory   209
     The Circular Map   217
     Copy Choice   222
     Heterozygotes   225
     Negative Interference   230
     Breakage and Reunion   232

10. Genetic Fine Structure and the
     Molecular Basis of Mutation   238

     The Unit of Recombination   239
     The Unit of Mutation   242
     Shortcut Mapping   247
     The Unit of Function   250
     Topography of Genetic Fine Structure   256
     Mutagenesis   259
     Induced Mutation (in vivo)   261
     Induced Mutation (in vitro)   265
     Induced Reverse Mutation   268
     Mutational Heterozygotes   273

11. Radiobiology   277

     Ultraviolet Light   278
     Photoreactivation   282
     Genetic Control of UV Sensitivity   283
     Crossreactivation (or Marker Rescue)   285
     Functional Survival   287
     Multiplicity Reactivation   289
     Effect of UV on Genetic Recombination   292
     Radiophosphorus Decay   293
     X-Rays   297
     Radiosensitivity of the Vegetative Phage   300

12. Lysogeny   306

    Lysogenic Bacteria   306
    The Prophage   309
    Induction   311
    Temperance and Virulence   312
    Curing   315
    Immunity   315
    Nature of the Prophage   317
    Zygotic Induction and the Repressor   323
    Specificity of Prophage Location   324
    Genetic Control of Lysogenization   325
    Chromosomal Attachment of Prophage   328
    Defective Prophages   332
    Conversion   336
    Episomes   338

13. Transduction   341

    The Filtrable Agent   342
    The Transducing Phage   344
    Cotransduction of Linked Markers   346
    Fine-structure Mapping   348
    Abortive Transduction   353
    Specialized Transduction   357
    The Relation of Generalized to Specialized
       Transduction   363

14. Comparative Bacterial Virology   368

    Fate of the Host Cell Nucleus   369
    The Capacity   371
    Autarky   374
    Genetic Interaction Between Phage and Host   374
    Host-controlled Modification   376
    Minute Phages   382
    An Exception that Disproves the Rule   389

15. Expression of the Hereditary Message   391
    General Nature of the Genetic Code   392
    The Messenger   402
    The Adaptor   409
    Synthetic Messengers   412
    Ambivalence   415
    Regulation   420

Postscript   427

Bibliography and Citation Index   429

Subject Index   467

CHAPTER 1

The Twort-D'Hérelle Phenomenon

Twort's Glassy Transformation—D'Hérelle's Bacteriophage—Phage Therapy and Prophylaxis—Nature of the Bacteriophage—D'Hérelle's Critics—Origins of Modern Phage Research

THAT THE submicroscopic, serially transmissible, and potentially pathogenic agents now called **viruses** represent a special class of organisms was first recognized in 1899. In that year, M. W. Beijerinck (45) proposed that the tobacco mosaic virus, which, unlike other microbes, cannot be retained by ceramic filters, or seen in ordinary microscopes, or grown on artificial bacteriological media, is a subcellular form of life, a *contagium vivum fluidum.* The notion of subcellular infectious agents did not, however, find favor with Beijerinck's turn-of-the-century contemporaries, most of whom preferred to think of viruses simply as very small and nutritionally fastidious bacteria that probably *would* grow on artificial media if only the proper nutrients were presented to them.

Twort's Glassy Transformation

Among the numerous bacteriologists then seeking the chimera of in vitro growth of viruses was Frederick W. Twort, the Superintendent of the Brown Institution of London, founded by a benevolent donor for the care and treatment of quadrupeds or birds useful to man. Twort's approach to this problem was rather original; he imagined that pathogenic viruses, which seemed to manifest such reluctance to grow in vitro, are descendants of nonpathogenic, less fastidious viruses, which ought to grow readily on simple artificial media. Hence Twort set to work in the research laboratory of his animal dispensary in quest of these postulated nonpathogenic ancestral viruses, which he thought he

1

might find in cultures of their pathogenic descendants. It was thus that he inoculated nutrient agar with smallpox vaccine fluid, in the hope that a more frugal ancestral form of vaccinia virus might grow up into colonies.

Alas, the only colonies that appeared on Twort's agar plates were those of micrococci contaminating the vaccine lymph. Twort noticed, however, that upon prolonged incubation some of these micrococcal

FREDERICK W. TWORT

[From *Obituary Notices of Fellows of the Royal Society*, **7**:505 (1950–1951).]

colonies underwent a "glassy transformation": they became watery looking and transparent, and could no longer be transferred, or subcultured. Twort then observed that if a healthy, normal micrococcal colony was touched with a trace of the glassy material, the normal colony would in turn undergo the transformation, beginning from the point of contact. The glassy material could still effect this transformation after millionfold dilution and passage through the finest porcelain filters. By successive passages from glassy to normal colonies it was possible to transmit this "disease" of the micrococcus for an indefinite number of generations, but the agent of the "disease" would not grow by itself on any medium, nor would it cause the glassy transformation on heat-killed micrococci. The agent retained its activity after having been stored for more than six months, but lost its activity when heated to 60°C for one hour.

Twort published these findings in a brief note in 1915 (639). In this note Twort advances three possible explanations for his observations. (1) The bacterial "disease" might be a **stage of the life cycle** of the micrococcus itself, which can stimulate fresh cultures of the organism to pass into the same state; in this stage the micrococcus would have to be small enough to pass through the fine filter pores that retain the normal form of the organism and be unable to grow on media that support growth of the normal coccus. (2) The agent of the "disease" might be an **enzyme** secreted by the micrococcus, which leads to its own destruction and production of more enzyme. (3) The agent of the "disease" might be a **virus** that grows on and destroys the micrococci it infects. The latter two alternatives, bacterial enzyme or bacterial virus, were to become the subject of vigorous controversies in the decade following Twort's first (and only) report of this phenomenon.

Shortly after the appearance of this note, Twort's investigations were interrupted by his departure for war duty with the Royal Army Medical Corps. Upon returning to the Brown Institution after World War I, by which time the matter of his discovery had caused an international sensation, Twort did not resume work on this transmissible disease of bacteria. Instead, he continued his attempts to achieve virus growth in cell-free systems. His work came to an end in 1944, when the laboratory of the Brown Institution was destroyed by a German bomb. Twort, after having lived in almost total seclusion for the last thirty years of his life, died in 1950, disappointed that his laboratory was never reconstructed and still of the belief that "my research, offering, I am convinced, such high prospects of success, has in its last stages been foiled" (641).

D'Hérelle's Bacteriophage

Twort's brief 1915 publication remained completely unnoticed for several years, until rescued from obscurity in the aftermath of an entirely analogous discovery by Felix d'Hérelle. D'Hérelle was born in Montreal in 1873, and, like Twort, was trained in medical bacteriology. Unlike Twort, however, who lived almost all of his life in the house in which he was born and worked in the same laboratory for thirty-five years, d'Hérelle was forever on the move, holding a succession of jobs in the Americas, Europe, Africa, and Asia. D'Hérelle also encountered a transmissible "disease" of bacteria, while studying—improbable as it may sound—diarrhea of locusts. This is d'Hérelle's own description of the genesis of his discovery (280):

In 1910, I was in Mexico, in the state of Yucatan, when an invasion of locusts occurred; the Indians reported to me that in a certain place the ground was strewn with the corpses of these insects. I went there and collected sick locusts, easily picked out since their principal symptom was an abundant blackish diarrhoea. This malady had not as yet been described, so I studied it. It was caused by bacteria, the locust coccobacillus, which were present almost in the pure state in the diarrhoeal liquid. I could start epidemics in columns of healthy insects by dusting cultures of the coccobacillus on plants in front of the advancing columns: the insects infected themselves as they devoured the soiled plants.

During the years which followed, I went from the Argentine to North Africa to spread this illness. In the course of these researches, at various times I noticed an anomaly shown by some cultures of the coccobacillus which intrigued me greatly, although in fact the observation was ordinary enough, so banal indeed that many bacteriologists had certainly made it before on a variety of cultures.

The anomaly consisted of clear spots, quite circular, two or three millimeters in diameter, speckling the cultures grown on agar. I scratched the surface of the agar in these transparent patches, and made slides for the microscope; there was nothing to be seen. I concluded from this and other experiments that the something which caused the formation of the clear spots must be so small as to be filtrable, that is to say able to pass a porcelain filter of the Chamberland type, which will hold back all bacteria.

. . . .

On my return to Paris in August, 1915, I was asked by Dr. Roux [the then director of the Pasteur Institute] to investigate an epidemic of dysentery which was raging in a cavalry squadron, then resting at Maisons-Lafitte. I filtered emulsions of the faeces of the sick men, let the filtrates act on cultures of dysentery bacilli and spread them after incubation on nutritive agar in petri dishes: on various occasions I again found my clear spots.

At this time we often got cases of bacillary dysentery in the hospital of the Institut Pasteur in Paris. I resolved to follow one of these patients through from the moment of admission to the end of convalescence, to see at what time the *principle* causing the appearance of clear patches first appeared. This is what I did with the first case which was available.

The first day I isolated from the bloody stools a Shiga dysentery bacillus, but the spreading on agar of a broth culture, to which had been added a filtrate from the faeces of the same sick man, gave normal growth. The same experiment, repeated on the second and third days, was equally negative. The fourth day, as on the preceding days, I made an emulsion with a few drops of the still bloody stools, and filtered it through a Chamberland candle; to a broth culture of the dysentery bacillus isolated the first day, I added a drop of the filtrate; then I spread a drop of this mixture on agar. I placed the tube of broth culture and the agar plate in an incubator at 37°. It was the end of the afternoon, in what was then the mortuary, where I had my laboratory.

The next morning, on opening the incubator, I experienced one of those rare moments of intense emotion which reward the research worker for all his pains: at the first glance I saw that the broth culture, which the night before had been very turbid, was perfectly clear: all the bacteria had vanished, they had dissolved away like sugar in water. As for the agar spread, it was devoid of all growth and what caused my emotion was that in a flash I had understood: what caused my clear spots was in fact an invisible microbe, a filtrable virus, but a virus parasitic on bacteria.

Another thought came to me also: "If this is true, the same thing has probably occurred during the night in the sick man, who yesterday was in a serious condition. In his intestine, as in my test-tube, the dysentery bacilli will have dissolved away under the action of their parasite. He should now be cured." I dashed to the hospital. In fact, during the night, his general condition had greatly improved and convalescence was beginning.

In 1917 d'Hérelle published his first report of this discovery in a note (273) entitled "An invisible microbial antagonist of dysentery bacilli," in which also the following details may be found.

The isolation of the anti-*Shiga dysentery* microbe is simple: one inoculates a broth tube with four or five drops of stool, incubates the tube at 37° for 18 hours, and then filters the fluid through a Chamberland candle. A small quantity of this filtrate added either to a growing broth culture of *Shiga* bacilli or to a suspension of these same bacteria in broth, or even physiological saline, provokes the arrest of the culture, the death of the bacilli, and then their lysis, which is complete after a time lapse varying from several hours to several days, depending on the initial density of the bacterial culture and on the quantity of filtrate added.

The invisible microbe grows in the lysed culture of *Shiga* bacilli, since a trace of this liquid added to a fresh culture of *Shiga* reproduces the same phenomenon with the same intensity: until the present, I have effected more than 50 successive re-inoculations with the first strain isolated. The following experiment, furthermore, supplies manifest proof that the action is produced by a living germ: if one adds to a culture of *Shiga* as little as a millionfold dilution of a previously lysed culture and if one spreads a droplet of this mixture on an agar slant, then one obtains after incubation a lawn of dysentery bacilli containing a certain number of circular areas of 1 mm diameter where there is no bacterial growth; these points cannot represent but colonies of the antagonistic microbes: a chemical substance cannot concentrate itself over definite points.

In the absence of dysentery bacilli the antimicrobe does not grow in any media. It does not attack heat-killed dysentery bacilli, whereas it does grow perfectly well on a suspension of washed bacilli in physiological saline: it follows from these facts that the antidysentery microbe is an obligatory *bacteriophage*.

Thus in this first note, which contains no reference to Twort's publication—by then two years old—d'Hérelle endows the antibacterial virus with the name that it was to bear henceforth: **bacteriophage** (φαγειν = to devour). Later usage shortened this name simply to "phage," and it is in this vestigial form that reference will be made most often to the object of our study in these pages. Nevertheless, the terms "bacteriophage," "bacterial virus," or simply "virus" will also be used here.

FELIX D'HÉRELLE

[Photograph provided by P. Manigault, Institut Pasteur, Paris.]

Phage Therapy and Prophylaxis

From the very start, d'Hérelle left no doubt as to what he believed to be the nature of the bacteriophage: a particulate, invisible, filtrable, self-reproducing virus that is an obligate parasite of bacteria. But philosophical considerations of the true nature of bacteriophages, however cosmic its importance, paled in comparison with what d'Hérelle conceived to be its immense practical significance. This was spelled out in more detail in his second note (274), published in 1918 and entitled "On the role of the filtrable bacteriophage in bacillary dysentery." In it he concluded from the case histories of 34 dysentery patients that "the course of the illness is a result of the interaction of the *Shiga* bacillus and the bacteriophage, the disease and its aggravation corresponding to a deficiency of bacteriophage activity and the amelioration and convalescence to a restitution of the latter. Pathogenesis and pathology of dysentery are dominated by two opposing factors: the dysentery bacillus as pathogenic agent and the filtrable bacteriophage as agent of immunity." From this conception of the bacteriophage as the agent responsible first for recovery from and then for immunity to dysentery, it was but a short step to imagine the bacteriophage as a marvelous gift of nature to medicine: it would only be necessary to cultivate in the laboratory large quantities of the antidysentery bacteriophage and hold them in readiness for administration to patients showing the first symptoms of the disease. In fact, since the bacteriophage should be as transmissible from one individual to the next as the *Shiga* bacillus, the immunity so acquired should be as contagious as the disease itself. Why not, therefore, harness bacteriophages not only for the cure but, even more importantly, also for disease prevention in whole populations endemically afflicted with the pathogenic germs? D'Hérelle at once set to work to generalize his observations and quickly found that in patients recovering from typhoid fever and in chickens afflicted with avian typhosa there also appear bacteriophages capable of destroying the respective pathogenic bacteria.

There is little doubt that it was the emphasis given by d'Hérelle to the medical potential of bacteriophages that drew immediate and widespread attention to his discovery: the Great Hope of Universal Therapy and Prophylaxis. After an initial period of disbelief and ridicule of the announcement that there exists an invisible parasitic virus of microbes, the host of medical bacteriologists everywhere joined in a crusade to exterminate bacterial diseases by means of the bacteriophage. The first results seemed not at all discouraging: bacteriophages active against the bacteria of many diseases—anthrax, bronchitis, diarrhea, scarlet fever, typhus, cholera, diphtheria, gonorrhea, paratyphus, bubonic plague, osteomyelitis—did turn up promptly, and from 1920 onward an avalanche of publications on bacteriophage therapy made its way into the medical literature. This previously undreamt-of way of ridding mankind of some of its most dreaded ills did not fail to fire also the popular imagination, an aspect of the medical Zeitgeist of the 1920's preserved in Sinclair Lewis' novel *Arrowsmith*. Martin Arrowsmith, the hero, is working at a medical research institute in New York where he discovers an "x-principle" capable of serially transmissible lysis of staphylococci. D'Hérelle's first note appears just as Arrowsmith is ready to publish his own findings, and Arrowsmith realizes that his "x-principle" and the bacteriophage are but one and the same thing. After overcoming his disappointment at not being the first to discover bacterial viruses, Arrowsmith sets to work to make phage therapy a practical thing. When bubonic plague breaks out in the West Indies, Arrowsmith heads for the Caribbean to try out there an anti-plague bacillus bacteriophage. Though this trial costs him the lives of his wife and his closest collaborator, Arrowsmith is unable to adduce convincing proof that his ministrations of phage have had any effect on the course of the epidemic. Once more disappointed, Arrowsmith returns to New York, marries a wealthy widow, and resolves to study henceforth the fundamental nature of the bacteriophage rather than its practical applications.

Though Lewis wrote *Arrowsmith* as early as 1924, he allowed his hero to reach what subsequent developments showed to be a most sensible decision: in spite of twenty years' intensive work, bacteriophages never became a successful medical tool. To be sure, many physicians managed to convince themselves of the efficacy of bacteriophage therapy, particularly in the control of cholera (482), but such converts remained everywhere in the minority. Nevertheless, as late as World War II, bacteriophages were said to have found employ in the medical services of the German and Japanese armies, and even today the medical use of bacteriophages still persists in some out-of-the-way places. But ever since antibiotics have shown themselves to be far more efficacious in the control of bacterial diseases than the most fervent proponents of bacteriophage therapy had ever dared hope for their panacea, the strange bacteriophage therapy chapter of the history of medicine may now be fairly considered as closed. Just why bacteriophages, so virulent in their antibacterial action in vitro, proved to be so impotent in vivo has never been adequately explained. Possibly the immediate antibody response of the patient against the phage protein upon hypodermic injection, the sensitivity of the phage to inactivation by gastric juices upon oral administration, and the facility with which (as we shall see presently) bacteria acquire immunity or sport resistance against phages, all militated against the success of phage therapy.

Nature of the Bacteriophage

In spite of his predominant interest in the practical applications of the bacteriophage, d'Hérelle by no means neglected its basic aspects, and during the three-year period 1918–1921 carried out a large number of experiments that went far beyond establishing merely the existence of a filtrable, serially transmissible bacteriolytic principle. This work was published in 1921 in form of the monograph *Le Bactériophage: son Role dans l'Immunité* (277), of which an expanded version, entitled more appropriately *Le Bactériophage et son Comportement* (279), appeared in 1926. In this lengthy and highly polemical book, d'Hérelle vindicates the notion he held from the start: the bacteriophage is nothing else but a **bacterial virus;** he also describes many of the essential features of the phenomenon as we understand it today. For instance, d'Hérelle shows here how to **assay** the concentration of bacteriophage in a lysate. In one assay procedure, the limiting dilution method, sets of identical growing bacterial cultures are inoculated with progressively greater dilutions of the phage lysate. As long as the lysate is not diluted far enough, all of the test cultures ultimately lyse; as soon as the lysate is diluted too far, none of the test cultures lyse. But at the **limiting dilution** some of the test cultures of the set lyse and some do not. This, according to d'Hérelle, can mean only that at the limiting dilution some of the cultures happened to receive one bacteriophage and others none. Thus, in a typical experiment d'Hérelle finds lysis in only 3 of 10 test cultures inoculated with a volume corresponding to 10^{-11} ml of the original lysate. Hence the lysate must contain between 10^{10} and 10^{11} bacteriophages per milliliter. A second assay method takes advantage of the circular clear spots, "taches vierges" or **plaques,** that develop in dense bacterial growth on solid agar inoculated with bacteriophage. D'Hérelle reports that the number of plaques formed is inversely proportional to the dilution of the bacteriophage lysate mixed with the bacterial culture spread on the agar surface, in complete accord with his original proposal that each plaque represents a colony of bacteriophages descended from a single parent virus. Hence the concentration or **titer** of the lysate can be reckoned by simply counting the number of plaques and dividing that number by the volume of the lysate with which the agar surface was inoculated. Assay of one and the same bacterial lysate by limiting dilution and plaque count methods leads to the same value for the bacteriophage titer. The success of these assay methods can mean only that the bacteriophage is "corpuscular" or "discontinuous." To buttress his argument further, d'Hérelle relates that "during my residence at the University of Leiden, in discussing this question with my colleague, Professor Einstein, he told me that, as a physicist, he would consider this experiment as demonstrating the discontinuity of the bacteriophage. I was very glad to see how this deservedly famous mathematician evaluated my experimental demonstration, for I do not believe that there are a great many biological experiments whose nature satisfies a mathematician."

In another chapter of the monograph it is shown that the bacteriophage is first **fixed** to the bacteria it later destroys. In these experiments a phage suspension is mixed with a dense bacterial culture. A few minutes later the bacteria are sedimented into a pellet by centrifugation. Assay of the supernatant fluid then shows that its content of plaque-forming phage is greatly diminished compared to the input. This proves that the phage particles have become attached to the bacterial cells and are then carried down with their host by the centrifugal force. The fixation is **specific,** furthermore, since it occurs only with bacterial races that are sensitive to the action of the phage. D'Hérelle then outlines in these terms what we now know to be the life cycle of the bacteriophage: "The first act of bacteriophagy consists in the approach of the bacteriophage corpuscle toward the bacteria, then in the fixation of the corpuscle to the latter. . . . The bacteriophage corpuscle penetrates into the interior of the bacterial cell. When, as a result of its faculty of multiplication, the bacteriophage corpuscle which has penetrated into the bacterium forms a colony of a number of elements, the bacterium ruptures suddenly, liberating into the medium young corpuscles which are then ready to continue the action." The sudden lysis of a whole bacterial culture ensuing several hours after its inoculation with a high dilution of a previous bacterial lysate is, therefore, to be interpreted as follows: at the outset, a few of the bacteria in the culture are infected by the few phage particles in the inoculum; intrabacterial multiplication of the infecting phages then yields an issue of many progeny particles, released upon lysis of the infected cell; a much greater number of bacteria is then infected, and the intrabacterial multiplication-lysis-reinfection cycle repeated until a sufficient number of phage particles is produced to infect and finally lyse all the cells of the culture.

Besides these quite lucid expositions, d'Hérelle's book also contains much less clear discussions on the variable virulence of phage strains and the acquisition of phage resistance of bacterial strains, as well as sanguine dissertations on the medical application of the bacteriophage and lengthy philosophical arguments in favor of its "living nature." In spite of many obvious defects, it must be admitted that d'Hérelle's monograph shows that he had better understood what bacteriophagy is all about than most of his numerous adversaries who, by that time, had moved in and all but taken over phage research.

D'Hérelle's Critics

Far from gaining immediate acceptance, d'Hérelle's views found few followers among bacteriologists, "probably," wrote Burnet (114) in 1934, "because of the heterodox nature of these conceptions rather than from any fault in d'Hérelle's logic." Moreover, d'Hérelle's personality seems to have precluded his being considered serious by his fellow bacteriologists; the evident validity of some of his claims appeared to have caused other workers only to redouble their efforts to show d'Hérelle to be wrong. But it was not for suggesting the ultimately fruitless medical applications that d'Hérelle usually came under attack— such applications were probably thought to be of such self-evident merit that d'Hérelle deserved little credit for them anyway. Instead, it was toward his *credo* that the bacteriophage is a virus that some serious bacteriologists showed their greatest disdain. One of the first to join battle with d'Hérelle was the young Belgian André Gratia. In 1920, Gratia drew attention to Twort's forgotten—or, rather, never noted— 1915 note, and declared that the priority of the discovery of transmissible bacterial lysis belonged to Twort, d'Hérelle's contribution to this matter really being confined to coining the word "bacteriophage." D'Hérelle responded to this denouement with the assertion that, though the phenomena described by Twort were certainly of capital interest, they bore no resemblance whatsoever to his own bacteriophage. But Gratia could show that the filtrable agent isolated from "glassy" micrococcal colonies in the manner described by Twort is capable of transmissible lysis of growing liquid cultures of staphylococci, and that an anti-staphylococcus phage isolated by the method of d'Hérelle transforms staphylococcal colonies into Twort's "glassy" material. Gratia had,

ANDRÉ GRATIA

[Photograph provided by P. Frédéricq, University of Liège.]

therefore, good reason to state, "The Twort phenomenon and the d'Hérelle phenomenon are identical. They are two different aspects of one and the same phenomenon: the transmissible lysis of bacteria" (249). Henceforth, for the next decade or so, many bacteriologists preferred to speak of the *Twort-d'Hérelle phenomenon*, rather than risk implied approbation of d'Hérelle by use of his neologism, "bacterio-phage."

D'Hérelle found another, formidable opponent in Jules Bordet, the by then already world-famous director of the Pasteur Institute of Brussels: "According to d'Hérelle, the lysis is due to a living being, to a filtering [*sic*] virus. We, on the contrary, believe that the lytic principle originates from the bacteria themselves, which, when touched by this active substance are capable of regenerating it, the factor responsible for the phenomenon being thus unceasingly reproduced—on the condition, however, that the bacteria be still living and provided with the alimentary substances necessary for their growth" (78). Bordet thus pronounced in favor of Twort's earlier proposal that the agent of the transmissible "disease" is a bacterial enzyme that stimulates its own production.

Nor could Bordet find any merit in d'Hérelle's notion that the lysis of bacterial cultures observed hours after their inoculation with dilute bacteriophage is the final outcome of numerous cycles of intrabacterial growth and multiplication of virus particles. As late as 1932, Bordet still thought that "it would be difficult to suppose that an intrabacterial virus, originally present in small amount and at first allowing the microbes to develop, attacks them all at a given moment, almost simultaneously" (80). But if the transmissible bacterial lysis is due to an enzyme and not to a self-reproducing virus particle, how was one to account for the formation of the plaques formed on bacterial lawns by very high dilutions of bacterial lysates, explained so plausibly by d'Hérelle as colonies of the "discontinuous" bacteriophage virus? Gratia supplied the answer:

> The localization of the lytic action of the dilute bacteriophage can be explained by the hypothesis of a chemical substance as well. It must be kept in mind that a culture is not a homogeneous whole, but made up of organisms showing all kinds of qualitative and quantitative individual differences—that is, as far as their susceptibility to the lytic agent is concerned. When a very concentrated lytic agent is poured over the surface of an agar culture an almost complete dissolution occurs, with the exception of just a few organisms resistant enough to overwhelm the strong action of the lytic agent. On the other hand, when a dilute lytic agent is used only the few extremely sensitive bacteria will be influenced, and each of them becomes a centre of regeneration of the lytic agent, which, diffusing evenly in every direction, produces perfectly round spots of clarification very often surrounded by a kind of halo of diffusion. . . . Further, any substance, living or not, is composed of particles, molecules, atoms or ions. When we pour out a glass of soda water, there appear on the wall of the glass small round bubbles of gas, the size of which increases exactly as the so-called colonies of bacteriophage, and yet gas is not a virus (249).

Besides advancing such specious arguments, the adherents of the view of the serially transmissible bacterial lysis as a self-stimulating lytic bacterial enzyme could point to one very concrete fact in their favor, seemingly impossible to reconcile with d'Hérelle's assertion that the bacteriophage is a self-reproducing virus parasitic on bacteria: from about 1921 onward, an ever-increasing number of **lysogenic** bacterial

strains were discovered that "carry" bacteriophages with lytic activity
for other, sensitive bacterial **indicator** strains. Since it proved impossible
to free many of these lysogenic strains from their associated bacteriophage by any method of purification—such as repetitive single colony
isolation of the bacteria or specific inactivation of the phage—it followed
that the phage could not be a casual contaminant of the lysogenic
culture. Instead, it appeared that lysogenic bacteria reproduce the lytic
principle during their growth without viability of the cell being affected
in the slightest way. That any virus could live in such symbiotic coexistence with its host was, however, in flagrant contradiction with what
contemporary bacteriologists, including d'Hérelle, imagined to be the
morbid essence of virus reproduction. The only recourse available to
d'Hérelle, therefore, was to deny the very existence of lysogenic bacteria
—that is, to assert that the carried bacteriophage was, after all, nothing
but a contaminant of the lysogenic culture, from which the bacteria
could be freed provided that proper precautions were taken during the
purification procedure. This easy solution to the paradox posed by the
existence of lysogenic bacteria still found favor with adherents of the
virus viewpoint long after the study of bacteriophage had already
attained a very much higher level of sophistication than that of its
initial, heroic period.

The views of Gratia and Bordet were presented here in some detail
because their stand represented the most extreme among the author-
itative opposition to the notions of d'Hérelle. There were other important
bacteriologists of the period who seemed willing to go along with
d'Hérelle at least part of the way, admitting, for example, that there *is*
such a thing as a self-reproducing bacterial virus particle, but finding
fault with some other aspect of d'Hérelle's ideas. Thus Bronfenbrenner,
in the United States, thought that "far from being the product of lysis
[the phage] is regenerated during the stage of active multiplication of
susceptible bacteria preceding the lysis. . . . Lysis of the bacteria is
merely a secondary phenomenon which may or may not follow the
accumulation of phage" (105). And, at the Rockefeller Institute,
Krueger and Northrop imagined that the bacteriophage freely passes
into and out of bacterial cells, so that extra- and intracellular phage
particles exist in a state of equilibrium with one another (386). An
interesting intermediate position was taken by the elder Wollmans at
the Pasteur Institute of Paris, for whom the bacteriophage appeared as

a "hereditarily contagious autolysis," mediated by a self-reproducing particle related to the hereditary substance of the bacterium but which derives its lytic power from activation of "autolysins" endogenous to the bacterial cell (686).

Origins of Modern Phage Research

The course taken by "fundamental" phage research during its first twenty years reflects the fact that almost all of its outstanding practitioners seemed to have been extremely opinionated men, whose motivation for the design and interpretation of experiments must have derived more from the desire to vindicate intuition than from finding out, step by step, what things are really like. Two notable exceptions to this generalization must be made for the Australian microbiologist F. M. Burnet and the Hungarian chemist M. Schlesinger, whose work during the early 1930's foreshadowed the rise of bacterial genetics and molecular biology, disciplines that were to reach their heyday only twenty-five years later.

F. M. (LATER SIR MACFARLANE) BURNET

[Photograph provided by the Department of the Interior, Commonwealth of Australia.]

Burnet, while accepting d'Hérelle's basic view of the bacteriophage as a virus, disposed of the idea propagated by d'Hérelle that the phage is to be considered as a single, albeit highly variable, species. Instead, Burnet showed that bacteriophages differ so widely in their physical and physiological properties that a great variety of agents must actually share this common name (114). Study of the immunology of bacteriophages showed, furthermore, that different phage types carry entirely different antigens and that serological cross-reaction, rather than range of sensitive bacterial species, is the best criterion for establishing the relatedness of phage strains. Burnet also investigated the role of the bacterial surface in the fixation, or **adsorption,** of the phage particle to its host cell. In order to explain why each phage type is active on only a rather restricted and characteristic number of bacterial strains, he proposed that the initial contact between infecting virus and bacterial surface is a stereospecific process between complementary structures on virus and cell, analogous to an antigen-antibody reaction, and that phage-resistant variants that appear in bacterial cultures after exposure to phage owe their resistance to a hereditary alteration in the cell surface that no longer permits the specific attachment of the virus particle to its bacterial receptor sites. In support of this idea, Burnet could show that bacterial extracts can fix specifically virus particles to which the intact cell is sensitive, but that similar extracts of phage-resistant bacteria cannot (110, 114). Burnet also devised the progenitor of the modern **single-burst experiment,** by means of which he adduced convincing proof of d'Hérelle's contention that phage particles first accumulate inside the infected bacterium and are then suddenly released by lysis of the cell (109). Most importantly, Burnet brought order into contemporary thinking about lysogeny. He pointed out that the existence of lysogenic bacteria need not disprove the viral nature of bacteriophages: the permanence of the lysogenic character can be explained by assuming that a noninfectious *Anlage* of the phage is present in every cell of the culture, as part of the hereditary constitution of the strain. In his studies of lysogenic bacteria, Burnet also recognized the difference between **resistance** of bacteria at the level of phage adsorption and what was later to be called **immunity** of lysogenic bacteria against infection by a phage homologous to that already "carried" by the strain. Burnet, finally, started phage genetics when he discovered a mutant virus whose capacity for being "carried" in the lysogenic state had been lost permanently and hereditarily (118, 119).

Schlesinger began his work around 1930 at Frankfurt-on-Main and after the Nazi *Machtübernahme* emigrated to London. Like Burnet, Schlesinger accepted d'Hérelle's views of the bacteriophage as a virus.

Schlesinger studied the properties of the virus particles by chemical and physicochemical methods, and provided the first insights into what sort of objects bacteriophage really are. By various indirect means, such as measurement of the capacity of the bacterial cell for phage adsorption or the sedimentation velocity of the phage in centrifugal fields, Schlesinger showed that the virus particle has a maximum linear dimension of the order of $0.1\ \mu$ and a mass of about 4×10^{-16} g (544). Schlesinger

MARTIN SCHLESINGER

[Photograph provided by the National Institute for Medical Research, Mill Hill, London.]

also studied the adsorption mechanism of the virus to its host cell and found that the kinetics of this process imply that Brownian movement brings virus particles into random collisions with the bacterial surface (543). Although their small size renders bacterial viruses invisible under ordinary microscopes, Schlesinger was able to estimate directly the total number of phage particles in a purified virus preparation, by counting the number of bright points produced in a dark-field microscope (546). In this way Schlesinger could establish that the number of physical phage particles in the preparation is roughly equal to the infective titer estimated from d'Hérelle's plaque count assay. Most importantly, Schlesinger managed to purify a "weighable" amount of phage by differential centrifugation and graded filtration of crude phage suspensions, and found by direct chemical analysis of the pure virus that it consists mainly of protein and of deoxyribonucleic acid (or DNA) in roughly equal proportions (547, 548, 548a). Schlesinger was thus the first to discover that the chemical composition of bacterial viruses resembles that of chromosomes, the carriers of the hereditary information of living cells.

In 1936 Schlesinger's premature death ended his work, and Burnet turned from bacteriophages to focus his attention on animal viruses. Since none of their collaborators or disciples continued this truly pioneering work in exact experimentation on bacterial viruses, the continuity of "modern" phage research really dates only from 1938, when Max Delbrück took up work in this field. Delbrück had studied experimental

MAX DELBRÜCK

physics at the University of Göttingen, and returned to his native Berlin to become an assistant to Lise Meitner and Otto Hahn at the Kaiser Wilhelm Institut für Chemie. In Berlin, Delbrück joined a discussion group of physicists, centered on Timofeeff-Ressovsky, who thought that the new quantum physics might offer a way to the understanding of the phenomena of heredity; these discussions induced Delbrück to develop a "quantum mechanical" model of the gene (632). In 1937, just before Hahn and Meitner discovered uranium fission, Delbrück went to the California Institute of Technology as a visiting research fellow, where another research fellow, Emory Ellis, introduced him to bacterial viruses. Realizing that these viruses should make ideal objects for the study of the mechanism of biological self-replication, Delbrück began to work with phage and, in collaboration with Ellis, designed the **one-step growth experiment.** This experiment showed that each phage-infected bacterium liberates some hundred progeny phage after a half-hour **latent period,** and that the end of the latent period and the onset of bacterial lysis occur at the very same moment (158, 201). The one-step growth experiment thus vindicated d'Hérelle's view and brought into focus the central problem of reproduction: how does the parental virus manage to effect its hundredfold replication inside the phage-infected bacterium during the half-hour latent period? At the outbreak of war in 1939, Delbrück did not return to Germany; he remained in the United States, where he now became the focus of a new school of phage workers. The members of this group, many of whom, like Delbrück himself, had been trained in the physical sciences, were interested in bacteriophage neither from the medical nor even from the basic bacteriological point of view, but regarded the phage as merely a tool for the study of hereditary processes. In a relatively short time, this group not only changed the orientation and intellectual climate of phage research but also provided one of the main fountainheads of the then nascent molecular biology. One reason for the rapid progress made by this group was that for the next ten or so years its attention was confined to a very few phage strains active on *Escherichia coli.* Thus the results obtained in different laboratories could be integrated much more readily than the earlier efforts of the "classical" period of phage research, when every investigator seemed to take pains to develop his own virus-host system.

Most of the matter to be presented here derives from the work of Delbrück's school of phage workers, or of persons who were working directly or indirectly under its influence. Hence, in spite of the plethora of phage types that are now known and have been studied at one time or another in the short history of phage research, the remainder of this book is mainly concerned with the favorite experimental material of that school, the seven strains of "T" (for *type*) coli phages (175)—T1, T2, T3, T4, T5, T6, and T7—especially the closely related T-even strains T2, T4, and T6. The only important exception to this source of latter-day phage lore concerns lysogeny; despite Burnet's clear expositions, d'Hérelle's a priori refusal to believe that bacteriophage could live in intracellular symbiosis with their host cells continued to be shared by Delbrück's school for some time, probably because none of the T phages to which its work was restricted happened to exist in the lysogenic state. And so it was not until 1950, when A. Lwoff of the Institut Pasteur

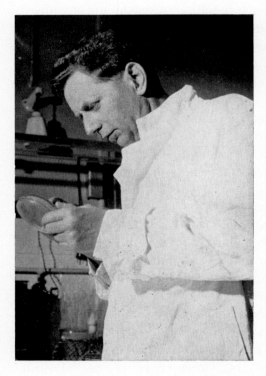

ANDRÉ LWOFF

of Paris finally brought indubitable proof that lysogenic bacteria *do* perpetuate bacteriophage, that the study of lysogeny once more became a "respectable" endeavor. In the discussions of lysogeny and its cognate phenomena, phage types other than the T strains will, therefore, necessarily figure, particularly phages λ and P1 active on *E. coli* and phage P22 active on the bacterial genus *Salmonella*.

Fortunately, this preoccupation with so few bacteriophage types will spare us the tedium of discussing the **taxonomy** of phages, a subject on which very few constructive remarks can be made anyway, despite several attempts to introduce a rational classification of bacterial viruses. [See Chapter XXII in (2).] For lack of any better system, various phage types and strains are now generally designated by numbers, or Roman or Greek letters, or combinations of such symbols, preceded by the name of a bacterial genus on which the phages are active—for example the *Salmonella* phage P22. It so happens, however, that the phages of which we shall speak most often, namely those active on *Escherichia coli*, are usually referred to by the name of the bacterial *species* rather than genus—for example coliphage T2. It seems a pity that the Linnean system of phage classification proposed by Holmes (316) on the basis of no rational taxonomic criteria whatsoever never found favor, since its nomenclature, such as *Phagus minimus*, *Phagus contumax*, or *Phagus futilis*, would have endowed the literature of the genus *Phagus* of the Phagaceae Holmes with much more charm than the workaday designations now in use.

The following chapters shall demonstrate how very far our knowledge of the life of bacterial viruses has progressed in the past two decades and how, in the meantime, the Twort-d'Hérelle phenomenon has become a veritable microcosm of general biology that really brought forth the hoped-for understanding of the structure and function of the hereditary substance of living things.

Further Reading

Twort, F. W., "The discovery of the bacteriophage" (641); d'Hérelle, F. "The bacterio-phage" (280). Two fascinating personal accounts of the discovery of bacterial viruses, by their discoverers, in the popular Penguin Books series *Science News*.

d'Hérelle, F., "The nature of bacteriophage" (278); Twort, F. W. "The bacteriophage: the breaking down of bacteria by associated filter-passing lysins" (640); Bordet, J. and Gratia, A. "Concerning the theories of the so-called 'bacteriophage' " (78, 249). A debate by the principal protagonists in the early controversies on the nature and mode of action of the bacteriophage at the Glasgow meeting of the British Medical Association of 1922.

Bordet, J., "The theories of the bacteriophage" (80); Burnet, F. M. "The bacterio-phages" (114); Delbrück, M. "Bacterial viruses" (160). Three "classical" reviews whose perusal will round out the historical perspective of the ideological and methodological development of bacterial virus research.

Lwoff, A., "Bacteriophage as a model of host-virus relationship" (454). Some reflections on the place of bacteriophages and other viruses in the general scheme of things that led to the conclusion that "viruses are viruses."

CHAPTER 2

The Bacterial Host Cell[*]

The Group—Cell Structure—Cultivation—Enumeration—Dynamics of Growth—Genetics

BETWEEN BACTERIA and other protista such as algae, fungi, and protozoa lies a wide biological gap. Though algae, protozoa, and fungi, considered at the level of the whole organism, are much simpler than metazoa and higher plants, they share with these higher forms a common plan of cellular organization. The nucleus of "higher" cells is surrounded by a membrane and contains the nucleoproteinic chromosomes, which at the moment of cell division are partitioned among the daughter cells by an elaborate mitotic process. The cytoplasm of "higher" cells contains complex subcellular particles, such as mitochondria and chloroplasts, in which specialized enzymatic systems are localized. Bacteria, however, are constructed along simpler lines. Here nucleus and cytoplasm are not clearly delimited; the bacterial hereditary factors reside simply in one or more DNA macromolecules and complex subcellular particles do not appear to be present. It is because of their simplicity, as well as of their small size, that bacteria came to be classified together as a single group; but this group is so heterogeneous in the morphology and physiology of its members that it can hardly represent a "natural" ensemble of related organisms. In this taxonomic respect, bacteria resemble the viruses, which as obligate intracellular parasites have also come to be considered as a single group. But the profound differences that exist between various kinds of viruses make it likely that

---

[*] The main purpose of this chapter is to provide a common basis for discussion with readers not already acquainted with the principles of bacteriology. Hence this chapter, unlike the others, is didactic rather than epistemological in tone and provides no literature references. The presentation is necessarily very superficial, since it compresses the barest of essentials into a few pages. A real foundation for the bacteriological background can be secured by reading Stanier, Doudoroff, and Adelberg's excellent introductory text *The Microbial World* (585).

their similarities derive from convergent evolution rather than common descent. In fact, the bacterial viruses that shall be our concern in these chapters are so different from the viruses infecting animals and plants that it is difficult to avoid the conclusion that bacterial viruses represent a unique biological entity. No doubt the attributes that set bacterial viruses apart from all other viruses find their origin in the very attributes that set bacteria apart from all other cells

The Group

Six major subgroups can be discerned among the bacteria: the **eubacteria** (or **true bacteria**); the **spirochetes;** the **gliding bacteria;** the **budding bacteria;** the **pleuropneumonia** group; and the **rickettsias.** All known bacterial viruses grow on representatives of the first of these subgroups, and no viruses have so far been found that grow on any member of the other five. Our further considerations in this chapter shall, therefore, be limited to the eubacteria. Some of the eubacterial types for which there exist bacteriophages are listed in Table 2-I. Stanier, Doudoroff, and Adelberg (585) characterize eubacteria in the following way:

> These organisms possess cells surrounded by rigid walls. Movement is accomplished by means of flagella, but motility is not an invariable property: many eubacteria are permanently immotile. Cell division always occurs by binary transverse fission.
>
> The great majority of eubacteria are unicellular organisms; the cell is either a sphere (*coccus* type), a straight rod (*bacterium* type) or a curved rod (*vibrio* or *spirillum* types). In many unicellular eubacteria, the daughter cells separate immediately after division, so that the individuals in a population are always isolated. In some, however, the daughter cells have a tendency to remain attached to one another after the completion of cell division, and this results in the formation of many-celled aggregates, often with a very characteristic arrangement. . . . In addition to unicellular forms, the eubacteria include several multicellular representatives, in which the permanent vegetative structure is a simple filament. There is also one large group of eubacteria, the *actinomycetes*, characterized by a mycelial vegetative organization similar to that found in the fungi.
>
> Physiologically speaking, the eubacteria are an extraordinarily varied group: there is almost no known type of biochemical process that cannot be found among them, and they include many organisms with unique biochemical properties. The majority of them are nonphotosynthetic, but the unicellular eubacteria known as *green* and *purple bacteria* carry out a special kind of photosynthesis.

A variety of different eubacteria is illustrated in Fig. 2-1.

TABLE 2-I

Some Eubacteria for Which There Exist Bacteriophages *

Family	Genus	Shape	Habitat
Pseudomonadaceae	Pseudomonas	Elongated rod	Soil and water
	Xanthomonas	Elongated rod	Plants
	Vibrio	Short, curved	Water
Rhizobiaceae	Rhizobium	Rod	Roots of leguminous plants
Micrococcacea	Micrococcus pyrogenes	Spherical	Animal skin and mucous membranes
Neisseriaceae	Neisseria	Spherical	Mammals
Lactobacteriaceae	Streptococcus	Spherical or ovoid	Body fluids of animals
Corynebacteriaceae	Corynebacterium	Straight or slightly curved rod	Animals
Enterobacteriaceae	Escherichia	Short rod	Widely distributed in nature
	Aerobacter	Short rod	Widely distributed in nature
	Klebsiella	Short rod	Found frequently in man, also in animals and materials
	Erwinia	Motile rod	Tissues of living plants
	Salmonella	Usually motile rod	Animals and decomposing foods
	Shigella	Non-motile rod	Bodies of warm-blooded animals
Parvobacteriaceae	Pasteurella	Ellipsoidal to elongated rod	Parasitic on man, other mammals, and birds
	Brucella	Short rod with many coccoid cells	Parasitic, invading all animal tissues
	Hemophilus	Minute rod	Mucosa of respiratory tract or conjunctiva
Bacillaceae	Bacillus	Rod, capable of producing spores	Mostly saprophytes found in soil
	Clostridium	Rod	Soil and human or animal feces
Mycobacteriaceae		Rod	Soil, water and vegetation
Actinomycetaceae		Rod-shaped or spherical filaments	Soil and animals
Streptomycetaceae		Vegetative mycelium	Soil and manure

* Data compiled from *Bergey's Manual of Determinative Bacteriology*, 6th edition, Williams & Wilkins, Baltimore, 1948, and from Raettig (522).

Gram Stain	Other Characteristics	Year of Discovery of Phage	Earliest Reference to Phage
−	Produce water-soluble green pigment; some animal and many plant pathogens	1923	128, 147, 507
−	Plant pathogens causing necrosis	1928	9
−	Some forms causative agents of cholera	1924	209, 473
−	Capable of fixing free nitrogen	1926	253
+	Pathogens; causes of boils and abscesses	1915	639
−	Cause of gonorrhoea	1922	122
+	Some forms pathogenic to animals; others responsible for fermentation of milk	1922	505
+	Produce powerful toxins; responsible for diphtheria	1924	75
−	Found in the intestines of man and sometimes pathogenic to man	1921	83
−	Gas-producing	1927	343
−	Responsible for infections of the respiratory, intestinal, and genitourinary tracts in man	1925	260
−	Pathogenic; produces dry necrosis, galls, wilts, and soft rots in wide range of plants	1938	471
−	Pathogenic for warm-blooded animals; causes typhoid and food poisoning	1918	275
−	The pathogenic species cause dysenteries	1917	273
−	Causes plague in man and rodents	1921	276
−	Pathogenic for animals and causing undulant fever in man	1925	536
−	Causes influenza and respiratory infections in man	1933	540
+	Causes anthrax in man, cattle, sheep, and swine	1926	253
+	Pathogenic for animals; forms powerful botulism exotoxin	1934	148
+	Parasites on animals; causes tuberculosis	1947	233
	Pathogenic for man and cattle; causes ringworm	1940	485
	Antibiotics produced from certain strains	1947	525, 539

Cell Structure

Bacteria are so small that they lie at the limit of resolution of the light microscope; thus information concerning their internal structure was difficult to secure through direct visual observation. However, the perfection in recent years of refined cytochemical techniques, on the one hand, and of specimen preparation for the electron microscope, on the other hand, have made it possible to construct a detailed image of. the anatomy of the bacterial cell, which is revealed in the electron micrograph of Fig. 2-2.

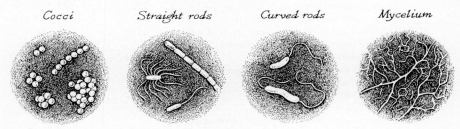

Cocci   *Straight rods*   *Curved rods*   *Mycelium*

Fig. 2-1.   Diagrammatic representations of the principal types of cell morphology found among the eubacteria. [From Stanier, Doudoroff, and Adelberg (585).]

The bacterium is bounded by a rigid **cell wall,** a structure of considerable chemical complexity containing polysaccharides, proteins, and lipids. The precise arrangement of these cell wall components varies among different bacterial types, and endows the cell with the surface specificity that determines its serological reactions and its sensitivity to infection by particular bacteriophages. The cell wall is responsible for the characteristic shape of the cell—coccus, straight rod, or curved rod—and provides the strength necessary for allowing the maintenance of the cell against considerable osmotic pressure. Pressed tightly against the inside of the cell wall is the delicate **cell membrane,** the permeability barrier of the cell, which encloses the **protoplast,** consisting of nucleus and cytoplasm. The eubacteria can be divided into two subgroups, according to the manner in which the cell wall and/or membrane reacts with the stain devised by the Danish physician C. Gram: **gram-positive** bacteria retain the color of the stain in their cell envelope, whereas **gram-negative** bacteria do not. The reaction with the gram

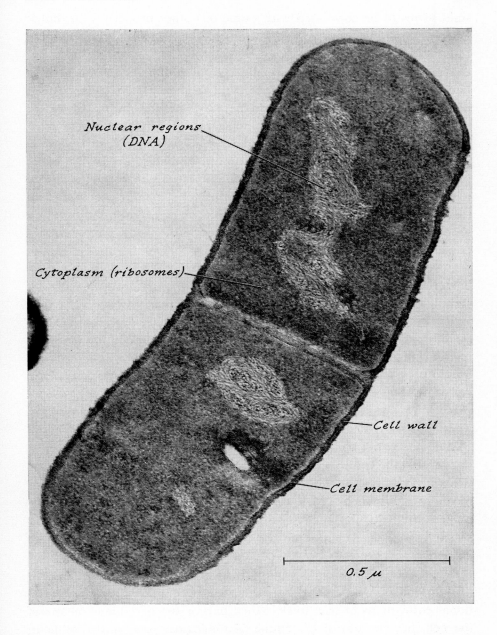

Fig. 2-2. An electron micrograph of a section of *Bacillus subtilis*, showing the principal structural components of the eubacterial cell. [Unpublished photograph provided by C. Robinow and J. Marak, University of Western Ontario.]

stain seems to be correlated with numerous other properties, so that it appears that gram-positive and gram-negative bacteria constitute separate "natural" subgroups.

It is possible to digest away the cell wall of many gram-positive bacteria, such as *Bacillus megaterium*, with the enzyme **lysozyme.** If this digestion is carried out in an ordinary medium, the protoplast bursts, since, deprived of its structural support by the cell wall, the delicate cell membrane cannot withstand the internal osmotic forces. However, if digestion of the cell wall is carried out in a medium of high osmotic pressure, such as a concentrated solution of sucrose, then the bacterium without cell wall survives as a spherical protoplast. This protoplast can still perform most of the functions of the intact bacterium, including growth and division. It can also still support the reproduction of bacteriophage, provided that infection has preceded the enzymatic removal of the cell wall. In the case of rod-shaped, gram-negative bacteria such as *Escherichia coli* it is not possible to remove the cell wall completely by lysozyme treatment; however, enough of the structural wall members can be digested away so that the cell either bursts in a medium of low osmotic pressure, or rounds up into a sphere in a medium of high osmotic pressure. Such gram-negative "spheroplasts" are not true protoplasts, since they still retain a considerable part of the cell wall. The partial removal of the cell wall, however, increases the permeability of the cell, particularly for the penetration of macromolecular substances from the environment.

Whether or not bacteria have a nucleus was for many years a subject of considerable controversy, a controversy which only subsided recently when it became clear that the answer to this question depends on one's meaning of "nucleus." On the one hand, bacteria do not possess a nucleus that, like the nuclei of higher cells, is segregated from its cytoplasm by a nuclear membrane and that encloses typical nucleoproteinic chromosomes. On the other hand, the bacterial deoxyribonucleic acid (DNA) is not uniformly distributed through the cell but is localized in distinct bodies, whose behavior in most respects makes them the functional equivalents of true nuclei: they harbor the hereditary factors of the cell, are in control of cellular physiological functions, double in number in the course of cell division, and are then partitioned among the daughter cells. Because of this functional equivalence, these bacterial DNA bodies are now generally referred to as "nuclei," a convention which shall also be adopted here. The number of nuclei per bacterial cell is not rigidly fixed; it can vary within an almost tenfold range upward from the minimum of one nucleus per cell, depending on the physiological conditions of growth.

The bacterial cytoplasm contains the enzymatic apparatus of the cell. Very little is known of the manner of distribution of enzymes in the bacterial cytoplasm, except that some enzymatic ensembles appear to be localized at the cell membrane. The cytoplasm also contains ribonucleic acid (RNA), most of which is localized in thousands of small spherical bodies, 25 mμ in diameter. These bodies, the **ribosomes,** contain 40% protein and 60% RNA and are the site of protein synthesis in the bacterial cell. Most of the remainder of the bacterial RNA is made up of the "soluble" or "transfer" RNA, which represents a collection of RNA molecules, each capable of combining specifically with one of the common types of amino acids. This combination is thought to be of importance in the mechanism of the predetermined copolymerization of amino acids into the specific polypeptides of enzyme proteins. The total amount of RNA per cell is also subject to wide variations, depending, like the number of nuclei, on the physiological conditions of growth.

Cultivation

Growth Media

There exists an extremely wide spectrum of nutritional requirements among the bacteria. Although bacteria, as all living cells, are composed mainly of the elements carbon, hydrogen, nitrogen, oxygen, sulfur, and phosphorus, and must therefore assimilate these elements from their environment in order to grow and reproduce, bacterial types differ greatly with respect to the kind of chemical compounds that they can utilize as sources of raw material. Bacteria also differ greatly with respect to the external sources of energy on which they can draw to sustain their metabolic activities. Some bacterial types need no organic substances whatsoever for growth; they can extract all of their food from simple inorganic materials and carbon dioxide or carbonate. Most bacterial types, however, require at least some organic compounds as sources of carbon and energy; among these types there are some that

make quite exigent nutritional demands and cannot grow unless they
have access to a complex of sugars, amino acids, heterocyclic compounds,
and vitamins. These nutritional variations reflect, of course, adaptations
to the natural habitat of the bacterial species; bacteria that subsist
autonomously on rocky ledges or in desert wastelands have to be able
to get along on the simplest of substrates, whereas bacteria that live in
intimate contact with living tissues and feed parasitically on components
of their hosts can afford to be more fastidious.

Though *Escherichia coli*, the host bacterium of the bacteriophages that
shall be our principal concern in this book, inhabits the human intestine,
its nutritional requirements are relatively modest. Table 2-II shows the

TABLE 2-II

A Synthetic Growth Medium for E. Coli*

NH_4Cl	1.0 g
$MgSO_4$	0.13 g
KH_2PO_4	3.0 g
Na_2HPO_4	6.0 g
Glucose	4.0 g
Water	1000 ml

* From Adams (2).

composition of a simple chemically defined liquid medium that supports
the growth of *E. coli*. The only organic component of this defined or
"synthetic" medium, glucose, is the source of both carbon and energy;
the mixture of sodium and potassium phosphates serves not only as the
source of phosphorus, sodium, and potassium, but also functions as a
buffer that maintains the medium at a near-neutral pH, in the face of
production of either hydroxyl or hydrogen ions by metabolism of the
growing bacterial culture. Although this simple medium is perfectly
adequate, cultures of *E. coli* are generally maintained in a complex
nutrient broth. In such nutrient broth, *E. coli* bacteria grow more
rapidly than in the synthetic medium, since the bacteria find ready-made
in broth many of the substances that must be homemade in the synthetic
medium. Experiments involving infection of *E. coli* by one of its bacteriophages are most often carried out in nutrient broth, since generally the
virus grows more abundantly when the nutrition of its host cell is
optimal: what is good for the cell is good for the virus, though not

necessarily vice versa. We shall encounter many situations, however, in which cultivation of the bacteria must be carried out in synthetic medium, since the presence of one or another component of the complex nutrient broth would interfere with the particular experimental observations that are to be made.

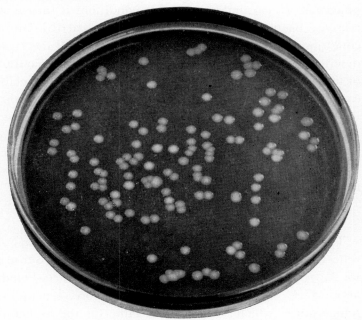

Fig. 2-3. An agar-filled petri plate on which individual bacteria have grown into macroscopic colonies.

Bacteria are grown not only in liquid media, but also on *solid* nutrient surfaces. Such solid media are prepared by adding from one to two percent of agar to nutrient broth or to synthetic media similar to that described in Table 2-II. The most common vessel used in the cultivation of bacteria on solid agar is the **petri plate,** shown in Fig. 2-3.

Aeration

Many bacterial species, like most animals, depend on respiration in the utilization of their sources of energy; such bacteria are called **obligate aerobes,** for they cannot grow, or even survive, in the absence of molecular oxygen. Other bacteria not only do not depend on respiration, but are even inhibited or killed by oxygen; such bacteria are called **obligate anaerobes.** *Escherichia coli* belongs to yet another class of bacteria, the **facultative anaerobes,** that will grow either in the presence or in the absence of air, provided that the proper nutrients are present. Though the synthetic medium of Table 2-II and nutrient broth will support *E. coli* with or without aeration, aerobic growth is very much better than anaerobic growth in these media, and the growth of bacteriophages on *E. coli* under anaerobic conditions is rather poor. For these reasons, bacteriophage work is generally carried out under aerobic conditions, and it is to be understood that in all the experiments to be described in this book, the bacterial cultures are given a plentiful supply of air. Cultures of *E. coli* containing fewer than 10^7 cells per milliliter can derive sufficient oxygen for aerobic growth from the air dissolved in the water of the growth medium; in cultures at higher cell densities an abundant supply of oxygen must be provided, either by bubbling air through the growth medium or by constant shaking of the culture fluid. Bacteria growing on solid agar surfaces obtain, of course, enough oxygen from their direct contact with air.

Temperature

The temperature at which bacteria manifest optimal growth usually reflects the conditions of their natural habitat. The optimal temperature for *E. coli*, as for other bacteria that inhabit warm-blooded animals, is about 37°C. Cultures of *E. coli* are, therefore, generally grown at this temperature, which is maintained either as the air temperature of an incubator chamber or as the water temperature of a constant-temperature bath. When the temperature of incubation is lower than 37°C, the rate of bacterial growth is less than that at the optimum temperature. Bacterial virus growth generally exhibits the same temperature optimum as that of its host bacterium: thus most experiments involving the multiplication of coliphages are carried out at 37°C, though, as we shall see, the use of sub- or supraoptimal temperatures is also of some importance in phage work. *However, unless explicitly stated otherwise, it can be assumed that the temperature of incubation was near 37°C in all the investigations to be described in the following chapters.*

Enumeration

The most direct way of enumerating bacteria is to count the number of cells visible under the microscope. These counts are carried out by means of a special counting chamber, which brings accurately known, very small culture volumes, of the order of 10^{-7} ml, into the microscope field. This method of enumeration is known as the **total cell count.** Accurate total cell counts can be made only on cultures containing more than 10^7 bacteria per milliliter, since at lower cell densities too few bacteria appear in the microscope field.

A second way of enumerating bacteria is to spread a known volume of the culture fluid on the surface of a nutrient agar plate and then to incubate this plate. During incubation, each bacterial cell that comes to rest on the agar surface multiplies and gives rise to a spatially isolated **colony** of descendant bacteria. After a few hours' growth, this colony contains so many cells that it is easily visible to the naked eye (Fig. 2-3). One therefore only needs to count the number of colonies that appear on the agar and then reckon back to the original concentration of bacteria in the culture by dividing this count by the culture volume spread on the plate. This method of enumeration is called the **colony count.** It also goes under the name of **viable count,** since only living cells (those capable of giving rise to an indefinite succession of descendants) will figure here, in contrast to the total cell count, which encompasses both viable and nonviable cells. The colony count method can be used for the enumeration of very few cells, since even a single viable bacterium can be detected in this way; the colony count, however, is equally applicable to very high cell concentrations, since dense bacterial suspensions can first be diluted as necessary so as to produce upon spreading on the agar the optimal number of about 100 colonies per plate. The colony count method is of great importance for bacteriophage work, since, as shall be explained more fully later, one method of assaying virus particles is to determine the number of viable bacteria present in a culture before and after its infection with phage. This difference in the number of viable cells represents the number of cells killed by the virus stock, and hence is directly related to the number of "killing" virus particles present.

Finally, the number of bacteria can also be estimated from the **turbidity** of the culture. Concentrated bacterial suspensions appear turbid because light entering the culture fluid is scattered by the cells, the fraction of the incident light scattered being more or less proportional to the total bacterial mass present. The turbidity can be determined either by a **photometer,** which measures the amount of incident light transmitted, or by a **nephelometer,** which measures the amount of incident light scattered. Turbidity can be related to cell number by carrying out on the same growing culture of bacteria a parallel series of turbidimetric measurements, total cell counts, and colony counts. The normalization obtained in this way is, however, valid only for the precise physiological conditions of the test culture, since the mass per cell is not invariant. The turbidity of a rapidly growing culture of *E. coli* becomes just perceptible to the naked eye at a density of about 10^7 cells per milliliter; it is only above this cell concentration that turbidimetry finds application in the enumeration of bacteria.

Dynamics of Growth

As soon as the growing bacterial cell attains a critical size, it divides to produce two complete individuals. The two daughter cells that result from this binary fission continue to grow at the same rate as their parent, and in due time again undergo binary fission to produce four cells, which in their turn continue to grow and divide, and so on. The rate of multiplication, dN/dt, or the increase per unit of time in the number N of bacteria per unit of volume in a culture of freely growing bacteria, is therefore proportional to the number of bacteria that are already present. Hence

$$dN/dt = QN, \qquad (2\text{-}1)$$

where Q is the rate constant of growth of the culture. Equation $(2\text{-}1)$ is readily integrated to yield the equivalent expressions

$$N = N_0 e^{Qt} \quad \text{or} \quad \log N = \log N_0 + (Q/2.3)t, \qquad (2\text{-}2)$$

where N_0 is the initial number of bacteria when $t = 0$. Because it is described by Equations $(2\text{-}2)$, this kind of growth is usually referred to as "exponential" or "logarithmic" growth, and bacterial cultures that manifest these growth kinetics are said to be in their **exponential** or **logarithmic phase.**

Figure 2-4 presents the growth of two cultures of *E. coli*, one in simple synthetic medium and the other in nutrient broth. In this figure, the logarithm of the number of cells per unit of volume, N, at any time, as determined by the turbidity of the culture, is plotted against the time elapsed, t. It is seen that, as demanded by Equations $(2\text{-}2)$, the plot for both cultures follows a straight line, the intercept with the ordinate at $t = 0$ occurring at log N_0. It follows from Equations (2-2), furthermore, that the **slope** of each of these lines gives the rate constant of growth of the culture, or $Q/2.3$; it is apparent from Fig. 2-4 that the slope of the growth curve of the culture in synthetic medium— that is, its rate constant of growth —is much less than that of the culture in nutrient broth. One convenient way of expressing this rate constant of growth is in terms of the **generation time,** or the period required to produce a twofold increase in the number of cells in the culture. The generation time is the time interval between the moment when the average cell in the culture has just been produced by binary fission of its parent and the moment when it itself has divided to generate its own pair of daughter cells. It can be seen from the data of Fig. 2-4 that the generation time of the culture in synthetic medium is 50 minutes, whereas

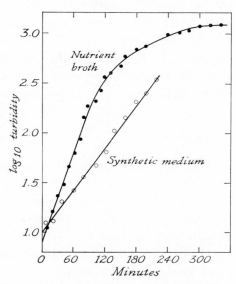

Fig. 2-4. The growth of two well-aerated cultures of *E. coli*, one in nutrient broth and the other in a synthetic medium containing glucose as source of carbon and energy. The ordinate shows the logarithm of the nephelometric turbidity of the cultures, in arbitrary units. A turbidity of 100 units (log turbidity = 2) corresponds to a bacterial density of approximately 10^8 cells/ml.

that of the culture in nutrient broth is only 20 minutes.

It should be clear that a culture of bacteria contained in any vessel of reasonable size cannot continue exponential growth with a generation time of 20 minutes for very long; after 24 hours of such exponential growth, a single *E. coli* bacterium would have given rise to 2^{72}, or about 10^{22}, descendants, weighing some ten thousand metric tons; after another 24 hours of exponential growth, the weight of the descendants would now be several times that of the whole earth! This conversion of our planet into one microbial mass does not occur because, both in nature and in the laboratory, the growth of bacterial populations is self-limiting: as the bacteria increase in number, they exhaust the available nutrients from their environment and excrete products toxic to themselves at an ever-increasing rate. This environmental deterioration soon causes growth to slow down from the maximum rate afforded by the most favorable conditions, until the growth rate finally falls to zero. At this stage, when there occurs no further increase in net number of cells, the culture is said to have attained the **stationary phase** (see Fig. 2-4). Well-aerated cultures of *E. coli* growing either in the simple synthetic medium or in nutrient broth enter the stationary phase when the bacterial concentration has reached the range of $2-5 \times 10^9$ cells/ml.

Genetics

Bacteria breed true, in the sense that the two daughter cells that arise by fission of the parent cell are endowed with and pass on to *their* descendants all of the properties of their progenitor. Each bacterium, therefore, gives rise to a **clone** of descendants, all of which carry the same set of hereditary factors. But if one examines a large population of hundreds of thousands of individuals, all descended from a single cell, a few variant individuals are usually found that differ from the majority of their sib in some character. Such variant individuals are **mutants** that harbor and pass on to their descendants a permanently changed hereditary factor. Many bacterial characters are subject to mutational variation, including the morphology of the colony that the bacterium produces on nutrient agar, the virulence of the bacterium for some host organism, the sensitivity or resistance of the bacterium to drugs, antibiotics, and bacteriophages, and the ability of the bacterium to ferment certain sugars and to synthesize from simple substrates various complex metabolites. These mutations occur spontaneously as **copy errors** during the replication of the bacterial hereditary substance, the bacterial DNA. The probability of occurrence of such copy errors varies over a wide range, from about 10^{-3} to about 10^{-10} per replication act, depending on the particular mutation observed. This mutation frequency can be raised greatly above the spontaneous background by treatment of the culture with various physical and chemical agents, or **mutagens,** such as radiations, heat, peroxides, or alkylating and deaminating agents. The molecular basis of spontaneous and induced mutation will be considered in some detail in Chapter 10. Exigent bacterial mutants that can no longer grow in a simple synthetic medium such as that described in

Table 2-II, unless some organic supplement is added, are called **auxotrophs.** Their less fastidious ancestors (or their reverse mutants) that *can* grow in the simple medium are called **prototrophs.**

For many years bacteria were considered as isolated genetic systems; that is to say, every individual was thought to be the issue of one and only one parent, and it was not supposed that two bacterial cells could ever conjugate like the **gametes** of a higher organism propagating through a sexual mode of reproduction, to beget an offspring that unites within himself the hereditary factors of two different lines of descent. It was recognized that the absence of any sexual mechanism would place bacteria under a severe handicap in natural selection. But it was thought that bacteria, by virtue of their enormous rate of reproduction and their attendant great propensity to sport a vast variety of mutant types, more than make up for any failure to present the ever-changing environment with radically new combinations of hereditary factors through the conjugal pooling of the genetic substance of the species. Later discoveries revealed, however, that the advantages of sexuality had not been overlooked in bacterial evolution and that there exists not only one but three quite different mechanisms by which the genetic factors of two or more ancestral lines can be brought into one bacterial offspring. The first of these processes to be discovered, **transformation,** is certainly the most "primitive," and probably the one of least importance in nature. In transformation, a DNA molecule liberated by lysis of a **donor** bacterium is taken up by a **recipient** cell; some of the hereditary traits inscribed into the donor DNA molecule thereupon appear among the offspring of the recipient cell. A slightly more sophisticated process of genetic transfer in bacteria is **transduction.** Here, a DNA molecule carrying genetic factors of the donor bacterium is transferred to a recipient cell through the vehicle of a bacterial virus particle. Transduction, which shall be discussed more fully in Chapter 13, is probably the very *raison d'être* of bacteriophages. Finally, the most elaborate of the three processes is that of **conjugation,** which comes closest to resembling the sexuality of higher forms.

Bacterial conjugation was first discovered when two mutant strains of *E. coli* that differed from each other in several of their genetic characters were grown together. In this mixed culture there appeared **recombinant** individuals that had obviously obtained some of their genetic characters from one and some of their genetic characters from

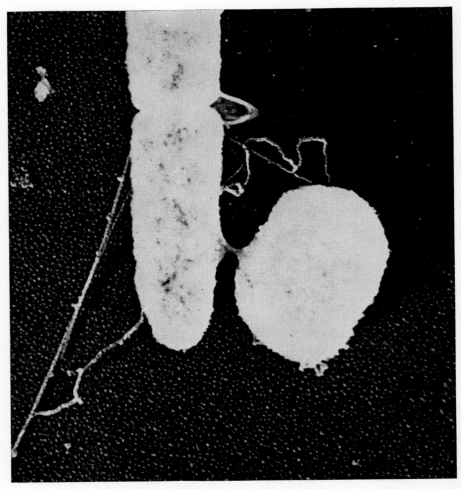

Fig. 2-5.   Electron micrograph of two conjugating *E. coli* bacteria. A slender connecting
bridge has been formed between an elongated Hfr donor cell and a rotund
F⁻ recipient cell. [From Wollman, Jacob, and Hayes (695). Photograph
provided by T. F. Anderson, Institute for Cancer Research, Philadelphia.]

the other of the two parent strains. Subsequent work revealed that
genetic recombination produced by conjugation, unlike that produced
by transformation and transduction, requires contact between the two
bacteria that are to exchange their hereditary substance. As in transformation and transduction, however, one of the two conjugating cells
acts as donor and the other as recipient of a fragment of the bacterial
DNA. But here, this fragment travels from donor to recipient protoplast

through a slender bridge that forms between the two conjugating bacteria (Fig. 2-5). Which of two bacterial strains acts as donor and which as recipient depends on the presence of a fertility agent or F **sex factor:** F^+ bacteria that possess the F sex factor can act as donors, or males, while F^- that lack the F sex factor can only act as recipients, or females. In every culture of F^+ bacteria there is present a small proportion of various **fertility mutants** that, upon contact with an F^- recipient bacterium, begin to transfer their nuclear DNA as a single thread through the intercellular bridge. For any particular type of fertility mutant, this transfer begins at a characteristic point of origin, proceeds in a fixed order, and continues as long as the bridge remains intact. These fertility mutants can be isolated from F^+ populations and grown into pure cultures; such cultures are called **high-frequency recombination** (Hfr) strains. Through study of the manner in which different Hfr strains transfer their nuclear material, it has been possible to show that all the genetic factors of *E. coli* form part of a single, one-dimensional **linkage group,** formally analogous to a single chromosome of higher cells; this single linkage group, furthermore, can be represented by a **circle,** having neither beginning nor end. The disposition on the bacterial "chromosome" of the very numerous genetic factors that have already been identified and localized can be seen in Fig. 12-6, which presents the circular genetic map of *E. coli*, strain K12.

Further Reading

Oginsky, E. and Umbreit, W., *An Introduction to Bacterial Physiology*. Freeman, San Francisco, 2nd edition, 1959.

Luria, S. E. and Delbrück, M., "Mutations of bacteria from virus sensitivity to virus resistance" (445). The famous proof that bacterial mutations occur spontaneously; this paper marks the beginning of bacterial genetics.

Gunsalus, I. C. and Stanier, R. Y., *The Bacteria*. Academic Press, New York, 1960 et seq. The definitive treatise on the structure, metabolism, biosynthesis, growth, and heredity of bacteria, in five volumes.

CHAPTER 3

The Infective Unit

Titration—Size—Morphology—Chemical Composition—The Phage DNA—Serology—Internal Structure

Titration

In his very earliest experiments on the bacteriophage, d'Hérelle had observed "taches vierges" or plaques in areas of dense bacterial growth on nutrient agar surfaces. D'Hérelle found that these plaques represent regions in which bacteria have been destroyed by the growth of bacteriophage colonies descended from parent viruses present in the bacterial inoculum. Since that time, the formation of these easily recognizable plaques has served for the titration of the number of infective units contained in bacteriophage suspensions. Plaques now represent the most important assay tool for bacterial viruses, and it is the simplicity and accuracy of this method that has largely made possible the quantitative investigations to be described in the following chapters.

The plaque assay procedure in general use today, a modification of d'Hérelle's technique introduced by Gratia (250) and by Hershey, Kalmanson, and Bronfenbrenner (304), consists of seeding a few milliliters of melted "soft" agar at 45°C, with about 10^7 host bacteria and an appropriate dilution of the bacteriophage suspension to be titrated. This mixture is then poured over the surface of a solid layer of nutrient agar in a petri plate and the plate incubated after the soft agar top layer has solidified. During the incubation, each bacterium in the inoculum grows into a tiny colony, so that finally 10^7 tiny colonies form a thick, turbid lawn of bacterial growth on the agar surface. At an early stage of the incubation, virus particles present on the plate infect bacteria in their immediate neighborhood and then grow on and lyse those bacteria to produce a crop of progeny viruses. The progeny of

40

each parent virus then infect neighboring bacteria, which in turn are lysed upon the appearance of a second viral progeny generation. These progeny infect more neighborhood bacteria, and the process of phage reproduction and bacterial lysis continues on and on in each focus of infection. Thus as the bacterial lawn grows, holes develop in that lawn. The final diameter of the holes depends on the phage type, the bacterial host strain, and the exact conditions of plating and incubation used, but

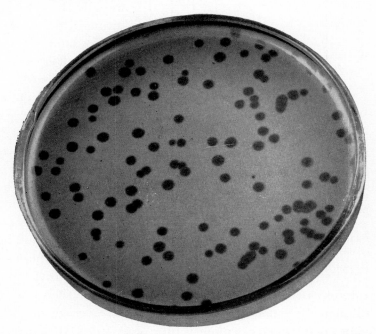

Fig. 3-1. A petri plate showing growth of a lawn of *E. coli* bacteria on which bacteriophage T2 has formed plaques.

it is generally of the order of a few millimeters. Figure 3-1 shows a photograph of an agar plate containing about 100 such bacteriophage plaques.

Each plaque is initiated by a *single* bacteriophage, and not, as would also be theoretically conceivable, by the cooperation of two or more virus particles. This follows from the observation that *the number of plaques formed on any plate is proportional to the volume of a given bacteriophage suspension mixed with the bacterial inoculum.* Figure 3-2 shows the result of an experiment in which equal volumes of increasing concentrations of the same phage lysate were plated on a series of agar plates; it is evident that each twofold concentration increase produced a corresponding twofold increase in average plaque number per plate—that is, plaque number and virus concentration are directly proportional. If more than one virus

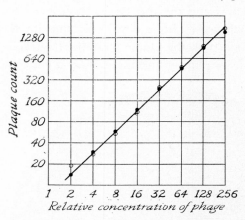

particle were required to initiate a plaque, then the number of plaques in this experiment should have increased more rapidly than the phage concentration; that is, the chance that two or more virus particles happen to fall close enough together on the agar surface to cooperate in the generation of an infection focus would be proportional to the second, or higher power of the average concentration of phages per plate rather than to the first power. Thus, to reckon the infective titer of a phage suspension, it is only necessary to count the number of plaques formed on the assay plate and multiply that number by the

Fig. 3-2. Proportionality of phage concentration to plaque count. Successive twofold dilutions of a phage lysate were plated in duplicate on nutrient agar; 0.1 ml on each plate. The plaque counts per plate from two series of such dilutions are plotted against the relative phage concentration (the reciprocal of the dilution), both on a logarithmic scale. [From Ellis and Delbrück (201).]

dilution made prior to plating. For instance, if 0.1 ml of a 10^4-fold dilution of a phage lysate produced an average of 150 plaques per plate, one would calculate a titer of $(150/0.1) \times 10^4 = 1.5 \times 10^7$ infective units per milliliter.

We may now consider the *efficiency* of this plaque assay method, for even though the proportionality between plaque number and first power of the virus concentration shows that each plaque is initiated by a single phage, this alone gives no clue to the fraction of the virus particles in the assay mixture which actually succeeds in making a plaque. First of all, the *relative* efficiency of the assay must be considered, since one and the same phage suspension does not always give rise to the same number of plaques when plated. Such factors as the composition of the agar on which the assay is carried out and the history of the phage suspension before assay may affect the number of plaques which show up. But of even greater significance is the particular strain of bacteria seeded on the assay plate. As shall be seen presently, different strains of the same bacterial species can vary enormously in their sensitivity to infection by, or in their ability to support the growth of, a given bacterial virus type. Thus, many fewer plaques per virus plated are produced on plates seeded with less receptive or less accommodating bacterial strains than on plates seeded with optimal host bacteria. The variations in plaque count attending different plating conditions are expressed by the **efficiency of plating,** defined as the ratio of the plaque count under a given set of conditions to the plaque count under a standard set of conditions (201).

As the standard set one usually selects those conditions which produce the highest plaque count. What then is the *absolute* plating efficiency under these optimal circumstances, relative to the total number of actual virus particles in the sample? The most reliable method of determination of this absolute efficiency was developed by Luria, Williams, and Backus (452), who counted the number of virus particles visible in electron micrographs of very small samples of phage suspensions (whose volumes were determined by counting the number of visible polystyrene latex reference spheres added to the suspension beforehand in known concentration) and compared these counts with the number of plaque-forming units found by assay of the same phage suspension. In this way it was found that in the best preparations of bacteriophages under optimal plating conditions the ratio of visible particles to plaque forming units is generally less than two; that is, the majority of the phages in the suspension actually initiate a plaque. The plaque count is thus not only a reliable indicator of the relative infective titer of a given phage suspension, but it is a reasonably close approximation to the total number of actual virus particles in the sample.

Probably more than any other single factor, it was the availability of the plaque assay that permitted the extraordinary development of bacterial virus research, and the later extension of this method to the assay of poliomyelitis virus by Dulbecco (193) was to bestow similar benefits to the growth of quantitative animal virology.

Size

Since d'Hérelle had shown that the infectivity of bacteriophage lysates passed through ceramic filters, it was clear from the start that the diameter of bacteriophages must be smaller than about 300 mμ, the size of the biggest filter pores. This diameter approaches the lower limit of resolution of the visible light microscopes, and hence it was not surprising that bacteriophages, like other "filtrable viruses," could not be seen in even the best of these microscopes. However, phages can be made visible in the dark-field microscope, which detects small particles by scattered light. No details of size or shape of the viruses can be discerned in this way, since they simply appear as luminous points. In this way, Schlesinger (546) counted the total number of such points of light produced by a small volume of phage suspension in the dark-field microscope and compared this count with the number of infective units found by plaque assay of the same preparation. This first determination of the absolute plating efficiency yielded results comparable to, though necessarily much less accurate than, the later electron optical procedure of Luria, Williams, and Backus.

Indirect methods, rather than direct observation, had therefore to be employed at first to obtain an accurate idea of the size of the bacteriophages. One of the most successful of these was the method of ultrafiltration, for whose ultimate development Elford (199) was chiefly responsible. In 1907, Bechold, one of the founders of colloid chemistry, had invented a process for the manufacture of collodion filter membranes with graded pore sizes: collodion is dissolved in a volatile organic solvent and a collodion film is formed by allowing evaporation of the solvent. The average pore size of such a collodion membrane depends on the concentration of collodion in the solution and on the nature and rate of evaporation of the solvent, and it can be estimated from the rate at which a known pressure head forces water through the membrane. Elford filtered aliquots of a bacteriophage suspension through such a series of graded collodion filter membranes and assayed each filtrate for its infective titer, in order to determine which of the membranes possessed fine enough pores to prevent passage of the virus particles. The average pore diameter of the membrane just able to retain the virus, so that no phage activity is present in its filtrate, is the **filtration end point.** From that filtration end point, Elford then calculated a diameter for the virus particle by use of an empirical correction factor which relates the average pore size of a collodion filter to the filtrability of test objects of known dimensions. The results of an ultrafiltration study by Elford and Andrewes (200) of several coli or *Shigella* bacteriophage types is presented in Fig. 3-3. Each of the five phage strains examined here is seen to manifest a different filtration end point, ranging from an average pore diameter of 25 mμ for the smallest phage, S13, to 110 mμ for the largest phage, D12. By use of Elford's empirical correction factor, these filtration end points could then be converted into the corresponding

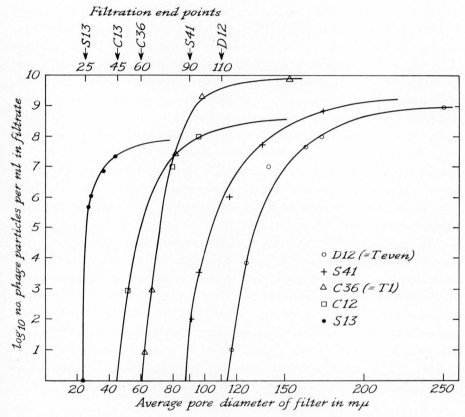

Fig. 3-3. Determination of the filtration end point of some coliphages. [Modified from Elford and Andrewes (200).]

particle diameters of 21 mμ and 90 mμ, respectively. These observations represent the first reliable measurements of phage dimensions, a subject on which there had previously been considerable controversy, since some workers, believing phages to be enzymes, were wont to attribute to them a very much smaller size than that favored by d'Hérelle and other adherents of the viral hypothesis.

Simultaneously with Elford's filtration experiments, Schlesinger (545) determined the size of phage particles by measuring their sedimentation speed in a centrifugal field. Schlesinger centrifuged phage suspensions of known titer in flat-bottomed tubes for various lengths of time in a centrifugal field of about 20,000 times gravity and then decanted and assayed the infectivity of the supernatant fluid. Assuming rapid mixing of the supernatant fluid by convection currents and vibration during centrifugation, Schlesinger derived an equation relating the diameter of a supposedly spherical virus particle to the rate at which plaque-forming units disappear from the supernatant fluid (and appear in the sediment at the bottom of the tube) and to such independently ascertainable parameters as the density difference between phage and suspending medium, the viscosity of the medium, the dimensions of the centrifuge tube, and the gravitational field. On the basis of these sedimentation experiments, Schlesinger calculated a diameter of 90 mμ for the coli phage C16, a close relative of phage D12 studied by Elford and of the present-day T-even strains. This value for the particle diameter of C16 is evidently in agreement with that estimated for D12 from the filtration end point method.

The modern ultracentrifuge with its analytical optical system has made possible much more reliable determinations of the sedimentation rate, and hence of the particle size, of bacteriophages. If determinations of the **sedimentation constant** of the phage (the ratio of its sedimentation velocity to the gravitational force) are combined with measurements of its rate of diffusion, a true particle weight of the phage can be calculated. For the T-even phages, such calculations lead to a weight of 3.3×10^{-16} g or 2×10^8 daltons per particle (518, 519, 621). (A "dalton" is equal to the weight of a hydrogen atom.)

Morphology

The development during the 1930's of the electron microscope, an instrument which produces a magnified image of small objects by deflection of focused electron beams, finally made possible the direct visualization of bacterial viruses. The limits of resolution of the electron microscope extend two orders of magnitude below those of the light microscope, and hence cover the dimensional range of the phages. The first electron micrograph of a bacteriophage was taken by Ruska in Germany in 1940 (532). Two years later, Luria and Anderson (443, 446), using an early American instrument, obtained the first electron micrograph of phage T2, shown here in Fig. 3-4. These still fairly indistinct images revealed that bacteriophage T2 is not a simple sphere but a complex structure, which is endowed with head and tail. Subsequent advances in the design of electron microscopes and in the techniques of preparing specimens for observation have greatly improved the quality of the electron micrographs of bacterial viruses. Of particular importance in this connection has been the invention of methods for circumventing very serious distortions of the virus by surface tension forces attending the drying of the microscope specimen (17, 682, 683) and for heightening the contrast of the electron-optical image of the virus by shadow-casting (685) or "negative staining" (97) with heavy metal atoms. Figure 3-5 pre-

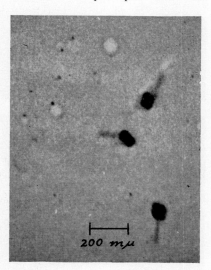

Fig. 3-4. One of the first electron micrographs of phage T2. [From Luria and Anderson (443).]

sents a set of much better electron micrographs of some bacterial viruses. It is evident that whereas all the types shown here possess head and tail, the shape and relative proportions of these two anatomical features can vary within wide limits. At one extreme, the two *Bacillus cereus* phages sport very long and thick tails, one appended to a small spherical head and the other to a larger cylindrical one. At the other extreme, phage T3 is endowed with so short a tail that it was at first overlooked. The T-even phages, on which much of our subsequent discussion will center, possess perhaps the esthetically most pleasingly proportioned head and tail. These excellent pictures naturally allow very much more refined measurements of the dimensions of bacteriophage particles. Table 3-I also lists the results of such estimates, with which the earlier results of indirect methods are in rather good agreement.

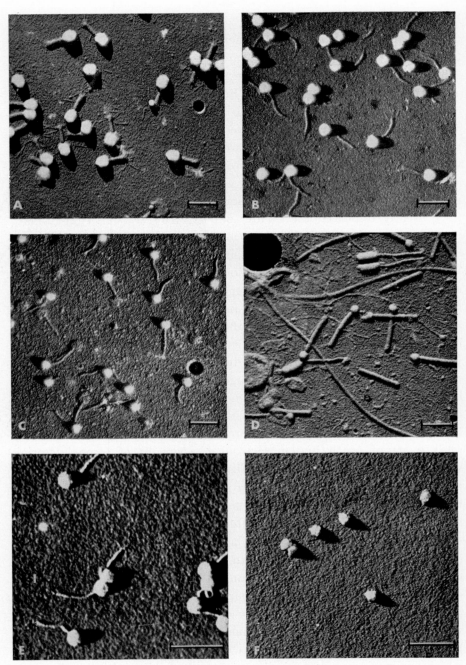

Fig. 3-5. The morphology of some bacteriophage types. **A.** A T-even phage (T2). **B.** Phage T5. **C.** Phage λ. **D.** Two phages carried by a lysogenic strain of *Bacillus cereus*. **E.** Phage T1. **F.** Phage T3. The distance marked on each photograph represents 200 mμ. [**A, B, C,** and **D** from E. Kellenberger, *Nova Acta Leopoldina*, **19:** 55 (1957). **E** and **F** from Williams and Fraser (683).]

TABLE 3-I

Dimensions (in mμ) of Various Bacteriophages

Type	Head		Tail		Reference
	Width	Length	Width	Length	
T2 T4 T6	65	95	20	95	(356)
T5	65	65	10	170	(683)
T1	50	50	10	150	(683)
T3 T7	47	47	10	15	(683)
λ	54	54	?	140	(356)
P22	similar to T3				(69)

Chemical Composition

In order to purify bacteriophages for study of their chemical composition, one must separate the virus particles from the mass of other materials present in lysates of bacteria on which the phages have grown. The first pure bacteriophage preparation was obtained by Schlesinger in 1933, by means of the ultrafiltration technique with collodion filters of graded pore size (547). After first removing all macromolecular debris larger than the virus particles by filtration through membranes with pores just big enough to let the virus particles through, Schlesinger collected the phages on a filter with pores just small enough to retain them. He then washed off the phages from the filter and finally sedimented them into a pellet in a high-speed centrifuge. When the results of Schlesinger's chemical analysis of phage WLL are compared with present-day analyses of its close relatives, the T-even phages, it becomes apparent that Schlesinger's phage preparation was indeed of a high degree of purity. Nowadays, because of the general availability of preparative ultracentrifuges, differential centrifugation is probably the method most widely used for the manufacture of pure bacteriophage stocks. For this purpose, the phage lysate is first centrifuged repeatedly at low speeds to free the suspension of large bacterial debris; the phage particles are then sedimented into a pellet by centrifugation at higher speeds, which leaves in the supernatant fluid all debris smaller than the virus particles. When phages are to be harvested from very large lysate volumes, a preliminary concentration of the virus by precipitation with acid at pH 4 (282) or alcohol (521) out of the lysate is sometimes undertaken prior to the purification by differential centrifugation. In this way, it is not difficult to obtain about 30 mg of pure virus from a liter of culture fluid.

TABLE 3-II

Amino Acid Composition of T2 and T3 Bacteriophages *

Amino Acid†	Amino Acid (in g) per 100 g Virus (dry weight)		
	T2 (8 determinations)	T3 (5 determinations)	Difference (T3 − T2)
	gm	gm	gm
Alanine	3.5 ± 0.14	4.4 ± 0.09	0.9
Arginine	2.3 ± 0.21	2.8 ± 0.23	0.5
Asparagine ⎫ Aspartic acid ⎭	5.3 ± 0.11	5.4 ± 0.03	0.1
Glutamic acid ⎫ Glutamine ⎭	5.4 ± 0.11	5.3 ± 0.07	−0.1
Glycine	4.3	3.8	−0.5
Histidine	0.4 ± 0.02	0.8 ± 0.05	0.4
Isoleucine	3.0 ± 0.04	2.2 ± 0.10	−0.8
Leucine	2.7 ± 0.10	4.4 ± 0.06	1.7
Lysine	2.9 ± 0.16	2.8 ± 0.20	−0.1
Methionine	1.0 ± 0.04	0.9 ± 0.03	−0.1
Phenylalanine	2.5 ± 0.11	1.6 ± 0.04	−0.9
Proline	1.8 ± 0.09	2.1 ± 0.08	0.3
Serine	2.4	1.9	−0.5
Threonine	2.7	3.2	0.5
Tyrosine	2.9	2.4	−0.5
Valine	2.7 ± 0.12	3.0 ± 0.03	0.3
Total	45.7	47.0	

* From Fraser (214).
† Tryptophan and cysteine were not determined.

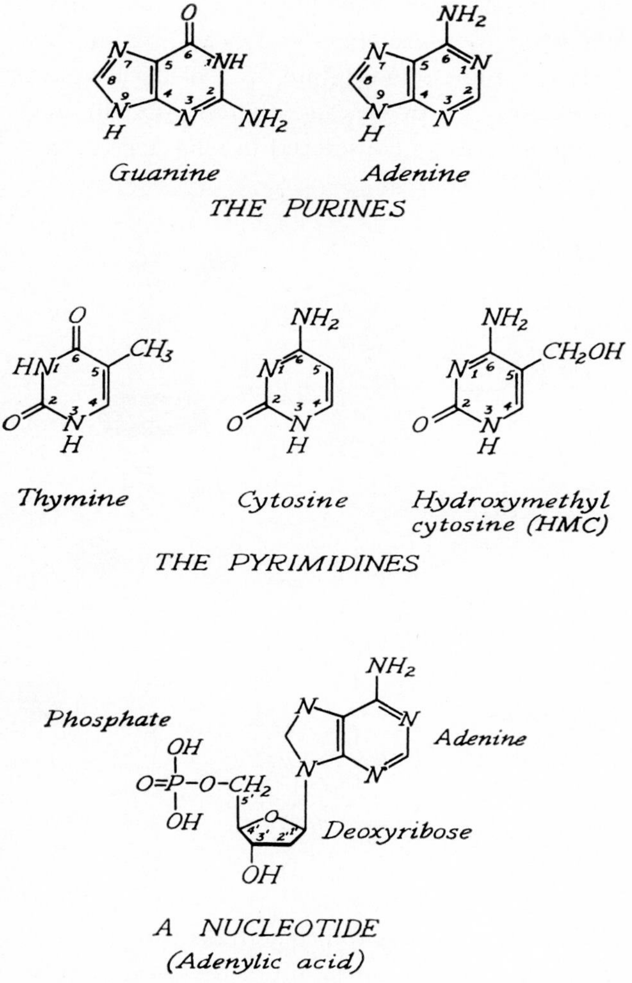
Guanine
Adenine
THE PURINES
Thymine
Cytosine
Hydroxymethyl cytosine (HMC)
THE PYRIMIDINES
Phosphate
Adenine
Deoxyribose
A NUCLEOTIDE
(Adenylic acid)

Fig. 3-6. The chemical structure of purines and pyrimidines and of a deoxyribonucleotide.

Schlesinger found that phage WLL contained 42% carbon, 13.2% nitrogen, 6.4% hydrogen, and 3.7% phosphorus, and that it gave positive reactions in the xanthoproteic test specific for protein and in the Feulgen test specific for deoxyribonucleic acid, or DNA. On the basis of these tests and the relatively high phosphorus content of his preparation, Schlesinger concluded that this bacteriophage is a deoxyribonucleoprotein (548, 548a). Since Schlesinger's time, numerous types of bacterial viruses have been purified and analyzed; the general finding has been that protein and DNA, present in roughly equal amounts, indeed comprise more than 90% of the weight of the particle. Bacterial viruses do not, in general, contain any ribonucleic acid, except for the phage type to be considered in Chapter 14.

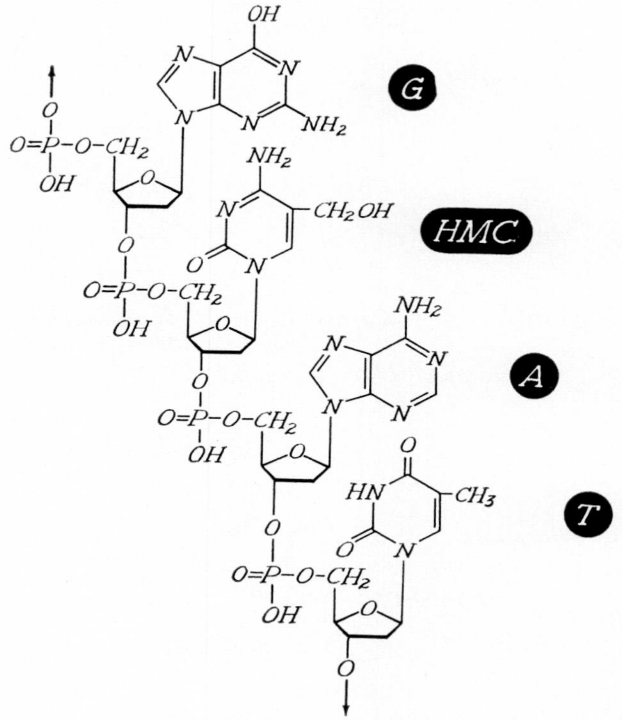

Fig. 3-7. A short segment of a deoxypolynucleotide chain, containing the nucleotides guanylic (G), hydroxymethylcytidylic (HMC), adenylic (A), and thymidylic (T) acids.

Once chromatographic methods came into general use in the 1940's, the amino acid composition of the protein of bacterial viruses could be readily determined. Table 3-II presents the results of an amino acid analysis of the protein of the coli phages T2 and T3. (The structural formulas of the amino acids are shown in Table 10-I.) As can be seen, these two rather different phage types do not differ very markedly from one another in the relative abundance of the individual amino acids in their proteins, although some minor differences are clearly manifest. It should be noted, however, that the amino acid composition of these phage proteins is very different from that of histones and protamines, the proteins that make up the protein moiety of deoxyribonucleoproteins of higher organisms.

The Phage DNA

The DNA of bacterial viruses, just like the DNA found in the nuclei of bacteria or of higher forms, is a polymer of very high molecular weight. Its basic building block is the **nucleotide,** which consists of three basic components: one molecule of phosphoric acid, one molecule of the pentose **deoxyribose,** and one molecule of one of the two purine bases **adenine** and **guanine** or of the two pyrimidine bases **thymine** and **cytosine** (Fig. 3-6). Tens or hundreds of thousands of such nucleotides, each joined to the next through a phosphate diester bond linking successive deoxyribose residues, make up the **polynucleotide** chain of which the DNA macromolecule is composed (Fig. 3-7). Though the basic chemical constituents of DNA were already known by the time Schlesinger demonstrated its presence in bacteriophages, its macromolecular character was not appreciated for another decade. And the actual molecular architecture of DNA was recognized only in 1953, when Watson and Crick (658, 660) inferred from X-ray diffraction patterns secured by Wilkins and his collaborators (681) that DNA consists of not one but two helically intertwined polynucleotide chains running in opposite directions, as shown in Fig. 3-8. (The direction of a polynucleotide chain is defined by the manner in which the phosphate bonds of the chains are linked to the hydroxyl groups of the adjacent deoxyribose residues.) At each nucleotide level, the two polynucleotide chains are held together by hydrogen bonds between a **complementary pair** of purine and pyrimi-

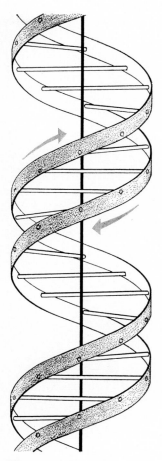

Fig. 3-8. A diagrammatic representation of the double-helical DNA molecule. The two ribbons symbolize the two deoxyribose-phosphate diester chains, and the horizontal rods the pairs of hydrogen-bonded bases holding the chains together. The vertical line marks the fiber axis of the molecule. [From Watson and Crick (658, 659).]

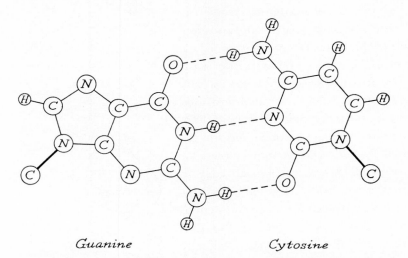

Fig. 3-9.   Pairing of adenine and thymine and of guanine and cytosine in
the double-helical DNA molecule. Hydrogen bonds are shown
as dotted lines. The 1' carbon atom of the deoxyribose residues
is also shown.

dine bases on opposite chains, as shown in Fig. 3-9. That is, opposite
every adenine residue on one chain there is a thymine residue at a corresponding place on the other chain, and a similar complementary relation
holds between the guanine and cytosine residues of the two chains. The
discovery of this complementary relation explained the rather puzzling

fact (131) that in most samples of DNA subjected to quantitative analysis for their content of purine and pyrimidine bases, the molar proportion of adenine was found to be equal to that of thymine, and the molar proportion of guanine equal to that of cytosine. A drawing of a space-filling model of a short section of the DNA macromolecule is presented in Fig. 3-10.

The first chromatographic analyses of the purine and pyrimidine base composition of the DNA of the T-even bacteriophages led to conflicting results. While some workers claimed to find the pyrimidine base cytosine together with the three ordinary DNA bases adenine, guanine, and thymine, others noticed that cytosine did not appear to be present (470). These contradictions were finally resolved when it was discovered that instead of cytosine the DNA of the T-even phages contains a previously unknown pyrimidine base, the cytosine analogue 5-hydroxymethyl cytosine, or HMC (698) (see Fig. 3-6). The results of analyses of the total amount of DNA per phage particle and of the purine pyrimidine base composition of the DNA of some bacteriophage types are presented in Table 3-III. As can be seen in this table, phage types other than the T-even strains do not contain HMC; instead, they contain the ordinary base cyto-

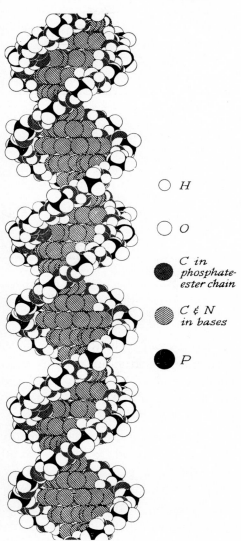

○ H

○ O

● C in phosphate-ester chain

◑ C & N in bases

● P

Fig. 3-10. A space-filling model of the double-helical DNA macromolecule. The size of the circles representing various kinds of atoms reflect their van der Waal's radii. [Drawn after Feughelman, Langridge, Seeds, Wilson, Hooper, Wilkins, Barclay, and Hamilton, *Nature*, **175**: 834 (1955).]

TABLE 3-III

DNA Content and Composition in Various Bacteriophages *

Phage	Approximate DNA Content (g per particle)	Nucleotide Composition in Mole Percent				
		Adenine	Thymine	Guanine	Cytosine	5-Hydroxy-methylcytosine
T2	2.3×10^{-16}	32.5†	32.5	18.2	0	16.8
T4	2.5×10^{-16}	32.3	33.3	18.1	0	16.3
T6	—**	32.4	33.4	17.7	0	16.5
T5	1.8×10^{-16}	30.3	30.8	19.5	19.5	0
T1	0.7×10^{-16}	27	25	23	25	0
T3	0.9×10^{-16}	22.8††	27.8	23.5	26.1	0
T7	0.6×10^{-16}	26.0	26.0	24.0	24.0	0
λ	1.2×10^{-16}	21.3††	28.6	22.9	27.1	—
P22	0.7×10^{-16}	25††	25	25	25	—

* Modified from Sinsheimer (576).
† DNA also contains 0.45 moles of 6-methylaminopurine per 100 moles of adenine.
** The DNA content of T6 is usually considered to be very similar to that of T2 and T4.
†† "Preliminary" or "tentative" data.

sine. It is evident, furthermore, that as demanded by the Watson-Crick double helical structure of DNA, the molar proportion of adenine is very nearly equal to that of thymine, and the molar proportion of guanine equal to that of cytosine (or of its analogue, HMC), in all these different bacterial virus types.

Upon closer examination, the nucleic acid moiety of the T-even phages was found to possess another highly unusual property: in addition to the pentose deoxyribose, the hallmark of DNA, the T-even phage DNA also contains the hexose **glucose,** attached to the hydroxy-methyl group of the HMC pyrimidine (347, 572). The three T-even phage strains differ, however, in their relative content and manner of distribution of the glucose in the viral DNA. In T2, 25% of the HMC residues are free of glucose, 70% carry one molecule of glucose and 5% carry two molecules of glucose; in T4, 100% of the HMC residues carry one molecule of glucose; in T6, 25% of the HMC residues are free of glucose, 3% carry one molecule of glucose, and 72% carry two molecules of glucose (348, 408, 572). Furthermore, the character of the bonds by which the glucose molecules are attached to HMC also differs among the T-even strains. As shown in Fig. 3-11, in T2 and T6 both monoglucosyl and diglucosyl residues are bound to the hydroxymethyl group in an α-glycosidic linkage; in the diglucosylated HMC residues, the second glucose is bound to the first by a β linkage. In T4, only 70% of the monoglucosyl residues are attached to HMC in the α configuration, whereas 30% of the monoglucosyl residues are attached to HMC in the β configuration (408).

Serology

It was first shown by Bordet and Ciuca (83) in 1921 that injection of rabbits with phage lysates stimulates development in the serum of these animals of antiphage **antibodies** that are capable of neutralizing the infectivity of homologous phage particles. The proteins of bacterial viruses, like many other proteins foreign to the injected animal, are, therefore, **antigens;** that is, they elicit an immune response, resulting in the formation of a new species of serum globulin that possesses a specific affinity for their three-dimensional structure. Since antibacterial anti-bodies formed by the rabbit in response to its injection with uninfected phage-sensitive *bacteria* do not, in general, react with phage particles, it can be concluded that bacteriophages manifest a serological autonomy vis-à-vis their host cells: the phage antigens that evoke the neutralizing antiphage antibodies are not already present in the uninfected bac-terium. Different phage types, furthermore, carry different antigens, since the antibodies evoked by immunization of a rabbit with one kind of phage usually cannot neutralize the infectivity of another kind of phage. But in the case of some phages, an antiserum containing anti-bodies developed against one strain does neutralize the particles of another strain; phage strains that *crossreact* in this manner carry common antigens and are therefore said to be serologically related. Serological crossreaction, rather than range of sensitive bacterial hosts or mor-phology of plaque, provided the first (and for many years the only) valid method for establishing whether different types of bacterial viruses are really generically related (3, 113, 114). And thus it was by virtue of their serological crossreaction that among the seven T phages active on *E. coli*, the T-even strains T2, T4, and T6 (whose original assignment of even numbers occurred quite by chance) were first considered to be closely

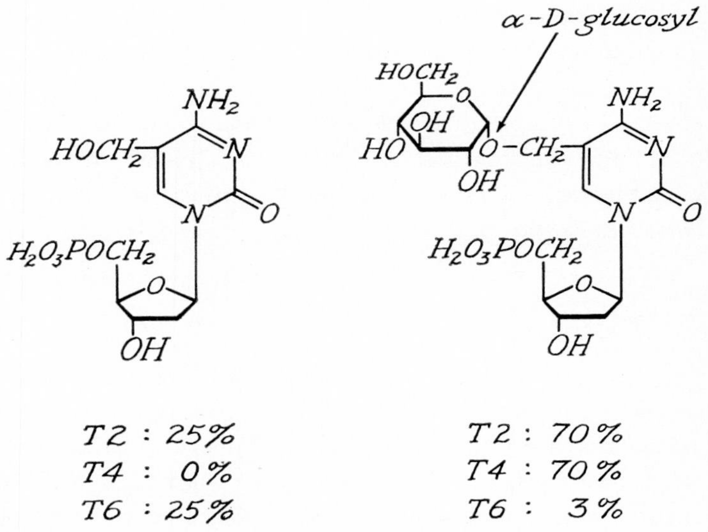

Fig. 3-11. Glucosylation patterns of HMC and their relative frequency in the DNA of T2, T4, and T6 bacteriophages.

related to each other and unrelated to the other four T strains. Later physical, physiological and, above all, genetic studies, were to justify fully this familial grouping.

When a phage population is mixed with a homologous antiserum obtained by bleeding an immunized rabbit, the number of infective (that is, plaque-forming) virus particles decreases continuously with time. The kinetics of this inactivation process can be followed by diluting samples of the phage-antiserum mixture at various times after the start of the reaction and plating the diluted samples on sensitive indicator bacteria for plaque assay. Since dilution of the mixture effectively stops further neutralization and since the reaction of the phage with its neutralizing antibody is usually irreversible (283) [though, depending on the kind of antibody, not invariably so (346)], the number of plaques formed in this way indicates the number of phages in the mixture not yet neutralized by the serum at the moment of dilution. A typical result of such a neutralization experiment of phage T4, employing three different concentrations of a homologous anti-T4 antiserum, is presented in Fig. 3-12**A**. As is evident in this figure, the logarithm of the fraction, *s*, of surviving phage decreases linearly whit the β-D-glucosyl

HOCH₂
OH
HO
OH
$H_2O_3POCH_2$
OH

β-D-glucosyl   α-D-glucosyl

HOCH₂
OH
HO
HO HO
OH
$H_2O_3POCH_2$
OH

T2 : 0%
T4 : 30%
T6 : 0%

T2 : 5%
T4 : 0%
T6 : 72%

time, t, the slope of the survival curve being inversely proportional to the dilution, D, of the antiserum in the reaction mixture. The neutralization kinetics may, therefore, be described by the relation

$$\log s = -\frac{K}{2.3D}\,t, \tag{3-1}$$

where K is a constant that depends on the physicochemical conditions, such as temperature (117) and ionic strength (344), under which the reaction is carried out, but, more importantly, reflects the neutralizing **potency** (that is, both the quality and quantity of antiphage antibodies present) of the particular antiserum used. The constant K (when tested under a standard set of conditions) is called the **titer** of the serum. According to this definition, the anti-T4 serum employed in this experiment can be reckoned to have a titer of 500 per minute.

Figure 3-12**B** presents the result of a neutralization test in which different samples of the same dilutions of the anti-T4 serum ($D = 1000$) were mixed not only with a population of the homologous T4 phage, but also with populations of T1, T2, T3, and T6 phages. It can be seen, first of all, that all three T-even phages are neutralized by the anti-T4 serum; however, T2 and T6 populations evidently lose their infectivity more slowly than the T4 population, anti-T2 and anti-T6 titers of the anti-T4 serum being only 150 per minute and 40 per minute, respectively. It follows, therefore, that though the T-even phages are serologically related, they are, nevertheless, not identical, for the neutralizing antibodies evoked by the T4 antigens react less rapidly with T2, and even less rapidly with T6, than with their homologous T4 virus particles. Second, it can be seen that the infectivity of neither T1 nor T3 phages is in any way diminished by the presence of anti-T4 serum, demonstrating that these two phage types are *not* serologically related to the T-even phages. Cross-neutralization tests more elaborate than those shown in Fig. 3-12**B** have shown that the T coliphages constitute four

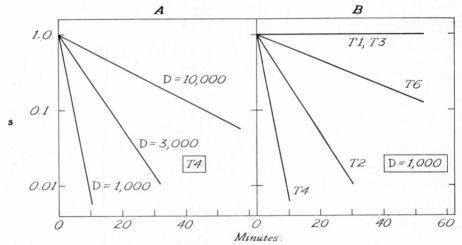

Fig. 3-12. Antiserum neutralization of T-even bacteriophages. **A.** Kinetics of neutralization of T4 by three different dilutions of an anti-T4 rabbit serum. **B.** Neutralization of T2, T4, and T6 by a 1000-fold dilution of the same anti-T4 serum. The ordinate shows the fraction of the initial phage population surviving as plaque formers (plotted on a logarithmic scale) after the number of minutes shown on the abscissa have elapsed between the moment of addition of antiserum to the phage and the moment of dilution of the reaction mixture for plaque assay.

distinct serological groups (165): (1) T1; (2) T2, T4, T6; (3) T5; and (4) T3, T7. Besides having no neutralizing antigens in common, phages belonging to different groups of this classification also differ, as has already been seen in Fig. 3-5, in their morphology and, as shall be seen later, in their biological behavior.

The exact mechanism by which antibodies neutralize phage particles is not yet fully understood. The logarithmic kinetics of antiserum neutralization stated in Equation (3-1) would suggest that the loss of infectivity of the virus results from the collision and subsequent fixation of a single antibody molecule with a phage particle. Since it can be demonstrated, however, that antibody molecules can attach themselves to virus particles without necessarily causing loss of infectivity, it would follow that inactivation results only from the fixation of an antiphage antibody to a "critical site" on the virus. In the case of T2 phage, this "critical site" must reside in the phage *tail*, since Lanni and Lanni (393) found that whereas head and tail of the virus carry entirely distinct antigens, the neutralizing antibodies represent only those directed against the tail antigens. Fixation of antibody to the "critical site" appears to prevent an early step in the viral life cycle, since the virus becomes refractory to antiserum neutralization as soon as it has infected the bacterial host cell (162). This antiserum-sensitive early step does not, however, appear to correspond to the initial fixation, or adsorption, of the phage to its host cell, since neutralized virus particles can still attach themselves to sensitive *E. coli* bacteria (113). Any proposed mechanism of antiserum neutralization must also render account of an assortment of strange facts. For instance, the logarithmic inactivation kinetics described by Equation (3-1) are usually valid only for the neutralization of 90% or 99% of the phage population; the remaining 10% or 1%, which do not appear to represent an a priori antiserum-refractory part of the population, are neutralized at a much slower rate than the majority (21, 162). Furthermore, phage particles surviving the neutralization reaction are no longer "normal," since some of their physiological properties have been altered by the exposure to the antiserum (22, 345). Despite the failure so far to comprehend the exact nature of the reaction, neutralization of phage by antiphage antibody has been an extremely useful tool in bacterial virus experimentation.

Though neutralization offers the most sensitive test for antiphage antibodies, their presence can also be detected by the specific **agglutination,** or precipitation, of the homologous virus. That is, if a concentrated phage suspension is mixed with a strong antiphage antiserum, a visible precipitate is formed containing both phage particles and antibody molecules, which slowly settles to the bottom of the tube (112). This **immune precipitate** contains aggregates composed of very many virus particles, held together by **bivalent** antibodies that carry not one but two sites capable of specific reaction with their homologous antigen and hence attach themselves to two phage particles. And since each phage particle can fix many antibody molecules, a phage-antibody network, in which every virus is joined through a serum globulin ligature to several other viruses, develops in the phage-antiserum mixture; this network, because of its enormous molecular size, then settles out of the suspension. Figure 3-13 shows electron micrographs of

Fig. 3-13.   Differential immunochemical agglutination of T2 phages. **A.** Head-to-head agglutination by an anti-head serum. This serum was prepared by injecting rabbits with the empty phage heads or "doughnuts" (described in Chapter 6). **B.** Tail-to-tail agglutination by an anti-T2 phage serum, from which anti-head antibodies have been previously removed by exhaustion with purified "dougnuts." [Unpublished electron micrographs, provided by F. Lanni, Emory University, and A. E. Vatter, University of Illinois.]

relatively small immune aggregates of T2 phage. One of these preparations has been agglutinated with a special anti-T2 antiserum, containing only antibodies directed against the phage heads; hence the phage particles are seen to stick together by their heads. The other preparation has been agglutinated with another special antiserum, containing only antibodies directed against the phage tails; here the phage particles are seen to stick together by their tails.

Chemical analysis of such serological phage precipitates—after correction of the results for any contributions to the analysis of the serum globulin antibodies in the precipitate—provided one of the early methods for determining the composition of the virus particles. For instance, on the basis of nitrogen determinations of serological precipitates, Hershey, Kalmanson, and Bronfenbrenner (304) estimated in 1943 that the amount of nitrogen per infective T2 particle is about 10^{-13} mg, a figure that direct analysis of purified phage suspensions substantiated in later years. Upon the availability of radioactive tracer isotopes for phage research, it became very much easier to estimate the amount of phage material contained in a serological precipitate; thus, if the phage suspension agglutinated by the antiserum contains a radioactive label, the quantity of virus in the precipitate can be readily determined by counting its total radioactivity (461, 462).

It must be borne in mind, however, that before an antiphage antiserum is actually used for specific agglutination of virus particles from a crude suspension such as a phage lysate that contains also bacterial debris, a preliminary **exhaustion** of the serum with bacterial antigens is necessary. Since the phage preparations used as antigens in the immunization of rabbits are usually contaminated with nonviral antigenic materials derived from the bacteria on which the phages were grown, the immune serum generally contains not only antiphage antibodies but also antibacterial antibodies evoked by these contaminants. Thus addition of such an antiserum to a crude phage lysate would produce a precipitate that contains not only the virus particles but also some of the host cell debris. But if the antiserum is first treated repeatedly with debris obtained by artificial disruption of uninfected bacteria, all antibacterial antibodies are removed from the serum, leaving behind only the antiphage antibodies that can now effect specific precipitation of their homologous virus particles, even from crude mixtures of viral and nonviral host cell antigens.

Internal Structure

The key to the topological relation between the two principal viral components, phage DNA and phage protein, was provided in 1949 by a discovery of T. F. Anderson that failed to arouse much excitement at the time: Anderson found that T-even phages lose their infectivity when subjected to the **osmotic shock** attending a sudden dilution into distilled water from a suspension in concentrated salt solution, such as 4 M NaCl. Electron micrographs showed that this inactivation derives from the rupture of the phage head and concomitant release of the viral DNA into the ambient medium (15, 16, 18, 20). The effects of osmotic shock can be seen in Fig. 3-14, which presents an electron micrograph of a T6 phage particle shocked in situ on the electron microscope specimen holder. In this picture DNA fibrils released from the disrupted phage head are clearly evident. The discovery of osmotic shock suggested, therefore, that the phage head is constituted of an outer semipermeable proteinaceous membrane and an inner core of viral DNA.

Osmotic rupture of the phage head renders the viral DNA accessible to hydrolysis by the enzyme deoxyribonuclease (DNase), from whose

Fig. 3-14. Electron micrograph of a T6 phage shocked in situ on the electron microscope specimen holder. The empty, broken phage head and the phage tail are at the bottom of the picture. The strands of phage DNA released from the head are spread out over most of the field. [From Fraser and Williams (216).]

action it is normally protected in the intact virus particles. Thus, it is possible to prepare DNA-free phage **ghosts** of T-even particles by digestion of osmotically shocked phage suspensions by DNase. These ghosts, which represent about 95% of the total phage protein (290), can still adsorb to, and even sterilize, sensitive *E. coli* (279). But the way in which such T-even phage ghosts kill bacteria has little resemblance to the destruction of the host cell by intact, infective T-even viruses (77, 230); hence the statement sometimes encountered in the phage literature that the killing power of T-even phages, or their "virulence," resides in their protein coat should not be taken very seriously. The bulk of the ghost, and hence of the entire phage protein, is made up of the semipermeable membrane, the so-called **head protein,** that encloses the viral DNA. The head protein itself is composed of some 1000 subunits of a single type of polypeptide of molecular weight about 80,000 g/mole (101, 646), whose amino acid composition is essentially that given in Table 3-II for the whole T-even phage. The rest of the ghost is made up of the proteinaceous phage *tail*, an organ of considerable complexity that shall be discussed in more detail in Chapter 5.

As seen in Table 3-III, the T-even phages contain about 2×10^{-16} g of DNA per particle, corresponding to a total molecular weight of the order of

$$2 \times 10^{-16} \text{ g/particle} \times 6.02 \times 10^{23} \text{ particles/mole}$$
$$= 120 \times 10^6 \text{ daltons.}$$

How many macromolecules, or subunits, actually make up this complement of 120×10^6 daltons of DNA in the phage head? When this question was first posed in the early 1950's, it was reasonable to suppose that there are somewhere between 10 and 100 macromolecules of viral DNA in the T-even phage head, since the first physicochemical studies of DNA extracted from various natural sources, such as calf thymus or trout sperm, had indicated that DNA polynucleotides attain sizes in the range of 1×10^6 to 10×10^6 daltons. It should have been a simple task, therefore, to determine the number of DNA molecules per phage by releasing the viral DNA from the phage head by osmotic shock and then ascertaining the molecular weight of the liberated polynucleotide molecules by one of the then conventional methods, such as light scattering, viscosity, or sedimentation velocity measurements (see 533).

This project turned out to be more easily conceived than done, however, and the first measurements of the molecular weight of the T-even phage DNA were secured not by use of one of these conventional methods but by means of a special autoradiographic technique developed by Levinthal (418) especially for this very purpose. Levinthal labeled the DNA of T2 phage with the radiophosphorus isotope P^{32} at a specific radioactivity sufficiently high that each phage contained hundreds of the radioactive atoms. He then embedded the ratioactive virus particles in a sensitive photographic emulsion, allowed radioactive decay to proceed, and then counted the number of β-ray tracks found to be

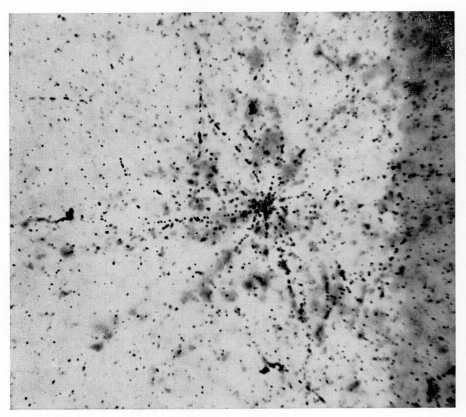

Fig. 3-15. Molecular autoradiography. β-rays emanating from a point source, or "star," produced by the decay of P³² atoms of a radioactive virus embedded in a sensitive photographic emulsion. Because of the small depth of focus, only a few of the many tracks originating from the particle are visible in this micrograph. [From Levinthal and Thomas (423).]

emanating from point sources after photographic development of the exposed emulsion (Fig. 3-15). Since every track represents the decay of a single P³² atom, the total phosphorus content of each point source can then be estimated from the number of its tracks, the exposure time, the known decay rate of the isotope, and the specific radioactivity of the virus particles. Levinthal also embedded the free viral DNA released by osmotic shock from the P^{32}-labeled, T2 phage particles in the photographic emulsion. Here each radioactive DNA macromolecule acted as its own point source of β tracks, so that the phosphorus content, and hence the molecular weight, of the individual DNA molecules could be determined. These experiments led Levinthal to conclude that the DNA complement of the T-even phage is **bipartite,** consisting of one large single molecule of molecular weight of about 45×10^6 daltons and of some 10 to 20 smaller molecules, each no larger than about 10×10^6 daltons (423, 629).

But these first autoradiographic molecular weight estimations, as well as most earlier "conventional" physicochemical size determinations of DNA, were carried out in unawareness of the extreme fragility of DNA macromolecules under hydrodynamic shear (154). It transpired later that all these studies had involved *breakage* of the molecules during the preparation and mensuration of the DNA and did not, therefore, reveal the true state of the native polynucleotides in the virus head. When this complicating factor was at last appreciated and the DNA extracted from the head of the T-even phage by methods more gentle than osmotic shock and handled during the subsequent measurements in a manner that minimized exposure to any shear gradients, both autoradiographic as well as physicochemical methods showed that the entire T-even phage DNA complement is but one **single, giant macromolecule** of molecular weight 130×10^6 daltons, larger by far than any polynucleotide hithertofore known (107, 123, 155, 297, 530). The single DNA molecule of phage T2 can be seen in the electron micrograph of the frontispiece. Contour measurement of the continuous fiber, from its one free end seen in the lower right corner of this picture to its other free end seen in the top center, shows that the viral DNA complement has a length of about 50 μ.

A careful study by Hershey (290, 294) of the products of osmotic shock revealed that some other materials, comprising a few percent of the total weight of the virus particle, are in fact released together with the viral DNA from the head of the disrupted T-even phage. These *minor components* include an **internal protein** that, though insoluble in cold acid, is too small to be sedimented in centrifugal fields sufficient to bring down the rest of the proteinaceous phage ghost; an **acid-soluble peptide** containing mainly the amino acids aspartic acid, glutamic acid, and lysine; and two other acid-soluble nitrogenous compounds that were later identified as the **polyamines** spermidine and putrescine (6, 7):

$$NH_2(CH_2)_3NH(CH_2)_4NH_2 \qquad\qquad NH_2(CH_2)_4NH_2$$
$$\text{spermidine} \qquad\qquad\qquad \text{putrescine}$$

The presence of these very basic polyamines in the phage head is readily explained by supposing that their function is to neutralize, in consort with other divalent ions such as Mg^{++}, the very high density of negative charges accumulated by the acidic phosphate residues of the DNA polynucleotide chain (6). Tremendous repulsive forces would be sure to exist between different parts of the viral DNA molecule tightly packed into the phage head unless these negative charges were neutralized. In any case, the exact amount and relative proportion of the two polyamines in the phage head is not invariant and depends on the physiological conditions both under which the virus particles are grown and to which they are subjected after their release from the host cell.

When the internal protein, which represents about 3% of the total protein of the phage, was later studied in more detail by Levine, Barlow, and Van Vunakis (415), it was discovered that the internal protein represents an antigen that is entirely distinct from the external head and tail proteins of the phage: antisera obtained from rabbits immunized with preparations of osmotically shocked phage contain antibodies that react specifically with the internal protein. Such anti-internal-protein antibodies are absent from antisera elicited by immunization with *intact* phage particles, no doubt because the internal antigen of the injected intact phages is covered up and not accessible to the cognitive system of the animal responsible for regulating the synthesis of specific serum globulins. Surprisingly, Levine and his collaborators found that the internal proteins of T2 and T4 do not at all cross-react serologically— that is, represent two species of proteins so different structurally that they share no common antigenic sites—even though, as we have already had occasion to observe, the *external* head and tail proteins of all the T-even viruses *are* antigenically related. The internal protein is a basic polypeptide and hence possesses an affinity for the acidic phage DNA; in solutions of low salt concentration, internal protein and phage DNA associate, but increasing concentrations of salt bring about their dissociation, which is complete in 0.2 M NaCl.

Having formed an idea of the general nature of the infective bacterio-phage and of the methods by which it can be detected and assayed, we are now ready to consider the manner in which the virus particles achieve their growth and reproduction.

Further Reading

Adams, M., *Bacteriophages* (2). Chapters III, IV, V, VII, VIII. These chapters furnish more details on the enumeration, size and morphology, inactivation by physical and chemical agents, chemical composition, and antigenic properties of bacterial viruses than the rapid survey of the preceding pages.

Davidson, J. N., *The Biochemistry of the Nucleic Acids* (152). An excellent Methuen mono-graph that provides the novice with a short and painless introduction to nucleic acids.

Thomas, C. A., Jr., "The organization of DNA in bacteriophage and bacteria" (630). An account of how, after many false starts, the true molecular weight of the viral DNA was finally determined.

CHAPTER 4

Growth Cycle

THE BASIC MANIFESTATION of bacteriophagy can be described in these terms: A growing bacterial culture is inoculated with an emulsified sample of the natural environment of the particular bacterial species, whereupon lysis of the infected culture suddenly ensues several hours later. A second bacterial culture is now infected with a very high dilution of this lysate, whereupon lysis of the second culture also ensues suddenly after several hours. The process of lysing bacterial cultures by inoculation with high dilutions of previous lysates can be continued indefinitely; that is, the lytic principle, or bacteriophage, is serially transmissible. From the very beginning, d'Hérelle (279) interpreted this phenomenon as the following sequence of events: (1) infection of a few bacteria of the culture by a few virus particles in the inoculum; (2) intrabacterial multiplication of the infecting viruses to yield an issue of more progeny viruses; (3) release of these progeny by lysis of the infected bacteria; (4) reinfection of a greater number of bacteria by the progeny; (5) repetition of the intrabacterial-multiplication-lysis-reinfection cycle, until a number of phage particles have been produced sufficient to infect and finally lyse all of the cells of the culture. Simple enough as this idea now seems, it was slow to find acceptance among d'Hérelle's contemporaries, even though there existed good experimental support for this view. D'Hérelle had shown by periodic titration of the phage content of an infected bacterial culture that multiplication of the bacteriophage from a small inoculum of a few particles to the final yield of a million progeny proceeds in a stepwise manner in the culture, each step requiring 75 minutes and producing an approximately 20-fold increase in total virus concentration. In 1929,

Burnet (109) was able to bring more convincing proof of the stepwise nature of phage multiplication by an improved experimental arrangement. Burnet incubated a large number of very small samples of a phage-infected bacterial culture, each sample containing at the outset an average of only one phage, and plated the total content of several samples for plaque assay at regular intervals. The result of this experiment is presented in Table 4-I. The data of this table show that for the

TABLE 4-I

Stepwise Multiplication of a Staphylococcus Phage*

PROCEDURE :   A growing *Staphylococcus* culture is infected with an average of 1 phage particle per 0.03 ml. Aliquots of 0.02 ml of the infected culture are then each drawn into one of 60 calibrated capillary pipettes and incubated in a water bath at 37°C. Six lots of 10 capillary pipettes are withdrawn from the bath at various times after addition of the phage to the culture and the contents of each pipette blown on one agar plate seeded with the sensitive indicator bacteria. The plates are incubated overnight for plaque count.

RESULTS:

Time after Addition of Phage (minutes)	Number of Plaques Obtained from Each Specimen									
32	0	1	0	0	2	2	1	0	1	2
67	0	20	1	0	0	0	1	0	0	—
97	71	75	0	11	0	0	0	0	1	1
127	0	0	0	0	1	45	0	0	0	0
180	0	2	+++	0	0	0	1	1	73	—
240	10	0	0	0	+++	39	0	38	—	—

* From Burnet (109).

+++ = too many plaques to count.

first hour following infection of the bacteria, each sample contained either none or only one or two plaque-forming units, but that after one and a half hours had elapsed, many of the samples suddenly contained many more plaque-forming units. Burnet concluded from these results that d'Hérelle's conception of phage multiplication was correct; for the first hour the infecting virus particle multiplies under some spatial constraint—that is, inside the bacterium; that restraint is suddenly

released when the infected bacterium ruptures and liberates the clone
of progeny particles into the surrounding medium.

One-step Growth

In 1939, Ellis and Delbrück (201) devised their **one-step growth**
experiment, which demonstrated even more clearly that the progeny of
the infecting bacteriophage particle appear only after a period of
constant virus titer; it also provided proof that no further production
of bacteriophages takes place if reinfection by phage progeny of any
uninfected bacteria in the culture is prevented. The one-step growth
experiment, which marked the beginning of modern phage work, is still
today the basic procedure for studying bacterial virus multiplication: a
suspension of growing bacteria is infected with a suitable number of
phages, incubated for a few minutes to allow fixation to the bacteria of
most of the phage particles, and then diluted from ten thousand to one
million fold into nutrient medium. The diluted culture is now incubated
further and aliquots plated on sensitive indicator bacteria from time to
time for plaque assay of the instantaneous number of infective units in
the culture. The protocol and the results of a typical one-step growth
experiment are presented in Fig. 4-1.

As can be seen, the number of plaque-forming units in the culture
remains constant for the first 24 minutes after infection. This initial
interval during which the infective titer shows no increase is the **latent
period.** After some 24 minutes have elapsed, the number of plaque-
forming units in the culture begins to rise rapidly, until a final plateau
is attained some ten minutes later, when no further increase in infectivity
occurs. The time interval during which the number of plaque-forming
units increases is the **rise period,** and the ratio of the final titer of the
plateau to the initial titer of phage-infected bacteria is the **burst size.**
The latent period thus represents the time which elapses between the
moment at which the bacterial culture is infected with a phage stock
and the moment at which the first infected cells in the culture lyse to
liberate into the medium a crop of progeny phage particles. The rise
period represents the time span during which more and more of the
infected bacteria lyse, and the final plateau of infectivity is attained when
all the infected bacteria which are going to lyse have lysed; no further
phage multiplication occurs after this stage, since progeny phage and

residual uninfected bacteria in the culture have been separated from each other by the high dilution of the culture made shortly after the initial infection. The burst size corresponds to the average number of progeny virus particles produced per infected bacterium, which in the experiment presented here amounts to about 100 phages per cell.

Fig. 4-1. The one step growth curve of bacteriophage T4. [Experimental data of Doermann (181).]

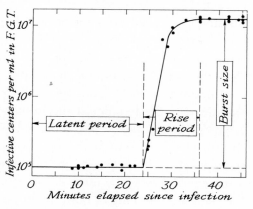

Procedure: *E. coli* growing exponentially in a glycerol-casamino acids medium are concentrated by centrifugation to a density of 10^9 cells/ml and infected with an average of one T4 phage/cell. The mixture is incubated with aeration for 2 minutes, during which time at least 80% of the phage input becomes fixed to the bacterial cells. The infected bacteria are then diluted 40-fold into an appropriate concentration of anti-T4 serum in order to neutralize any remaining free phage particles. A few minutes later, the infected bacteria are diluted 250-fold into fresh growth medium to reduce the anti-serum concentration to a very low level. The tube containing this dilution (*first growth tube*, or *F.G.T.*) and another tube containing a 20-fold further dilution of the first growth tube (*second growth tube*) are incubated, and samples from both tubes are plated periodically for plaque assay on sensitive indicator bacteria. During the latent period and early in the rise period, the titer of infective centers shown on the ordinate of the graph is estimated from plaque counts obtained by assay of the first growth tube; thereafter, the titer is reckoned from plaque counts obtained by assay of the second growth tube.

Let us now clarify further the nature of the plaque-forming units appearing on the assay plates of the one-step growth experiment of Fig. 4-1. Evidently, the plaques produced upon plating aliquots of the infected culture *during* the latent period derive not from individual free virus particles but, instead, from phage-infected bacteria that may already contain within them very many progeny viruses. Nevertheless, the plating of each such phage-infected bacterium prior to the end of the latent period gives rise to only a single plaque, because the solid agar of the assay plate confines the hundred or so progeny viruses ultimately liberated from that cell to a single focus of infection. Only after the conclusion of the latent period, when the intracellular phages have escaped from the host cell into the culture medium, can each

progeny virus form its own focus of infection on the agar surface. The
term **infective center** is used to describe the unit which forms a single
plaque; thus an infective center may represent either a single, free phage
particle or a phage-infected bacterium.

The parameters of phage multiplication defined by the one-step
growth experiment may differ very much depending on the exact
physiological conditions under which phage growth is allowed to proceed. The latent period, as might be expected, is longer at lower
temperatures of incubation; for instance, Ellis and Delbrück (201) found
that the latent period of their coliphage was 30 minutes at 37°C,
60 minutes at 25°C, and 180 minutes at 16°C. Maaløe (460), who
examined in greater detail the influence of lower temperatures on the
latent period of phage T4, observed that the temperature effect is not
the same at different points in the latent period, as if the successive
steps of intracellular phage multiplication possess very different temperature coefficients. The nutrition and physiological state of the bacterial
host cells can also affect both latent period and burst size; for example,
in a poor growth medium or in "old" bacterial cultures that have passed
the phase of their most active growth, the latent period is usually longer
and the burst size smaller than in cultures growing rapidly on a favorable
substrate (159, 271). Latent period and burst size also differ widely for
various strains of bacteriophages, and even for variants of the same
phage strain or for various strains of host bacteria. Latent period and
burst size do not, however, depend in any very striking way on the
number of phage particles with which each bacterial cell has been infected;
the time of the first appearance of the progeny phages and their final
yield per infected cell is about the same whether the concentration of
infecting phages is much less than that of the host bacteria (in which
case each bacterium that is infected at all is infected with only a single
phage particle) or whether the concentration of infecting phages exceeds
that of the host bacteria (in which case every bacterium in the culture
is infected with several phage particles) (168).

Single Burst

The one-step growth experiment examines the events in thousands of
phage-infected bacteria. The latent period is a *minimum* parameter,
reflecting the time elapsed between infection and lysis in those infective

centers in which phage development has progressed most rapidly, whereas the burst size is an *average* parameter, giving no insight into how many progeny viruses are actually liberated by individual bacteria. In addition to the one-step growth procedure, Ellis and Delbrück (201) also invented the single-burst experiment, which renders it possible to study phage growth in individual infected cells. For this purpose, numerous small aliquots of a high dilution of a bacterial suspension infected with phage under the conditions of the one-step growth experiment are distributed among a set of vials well before the end of the latent period, so that each vial contains on the average less than one infected bacterial cell. If the average number of infected bacteria per vial is n, then the fraction of the vials, p_r, that received r infected cells is given by the Poisson law (506):

$$p_r = \frac{n^r}{r!} e^{-n}. \qquad (4\text{-}1)$$

Hence, provided that n is sufficiently small, most of the vials which have received any infected bacterium will have received only one. The vials are then incubated until lysis of all the infected bacteria is certain to have occurred and the total contents of each vial plated for plaque assay of the number of infective centers. The result of a typical single burst experiment is presented in Table 4-II. It can be seen that 25 out of the 40 vials, or a fraction $p_0 = 0.62$, showed no plaques upon assay; evidently these vials did not receive any infected bacteria at all; for them, $r = 0$. Since, according to Equation (4-1),

$$p_0 = \frac{n^0}{0!} e^{-n} = e^{-n}, \quad \text{or} \quad n = -\ln p_0, \qquad (4\text{-}2)$$

one can then estimate that in this experiment n, the average number of infected bacteria per vial, was

$$n = -\ln 0.62 = 0.47.$$

The remaining 15 vials showed anywhere from 1 to 190 plaques; according to the Poisson law, about 12 of these vials should represent the yield from single infected bacteria and 3 the yield from two or more infected bacteria. These results show that the final phage yield of individual infected cells varies within very wide limits.

An average phage yield per cell may also be calculated from the single

TABLE 4-II

A Single-burst Experiment*

PROCEDURE: A culture of *E. coli* is infected with a high dilution of a filtered phage lysate. After 10 minutes have been allowed for adsorption of the phage particles to the bacteria, the infected mixture is diluted more than 100-fold. Forty samples of 0.05 ml each of this dilution are placed into small vials and incubated for 200 minutes. The entire content of each vial is then plated for plaque count on agar seeded with *E. coli*.

RESULTS:

Vial No.	1	2	3	4	5	6	7	8	9	10
No. of Plaques	0	130	0	0	58	26	0	0	0	0

Vial No.	11	12	13	14	15	16	17	18	19	20
No. of Plaques	123	83	0	9	0	31	0	0	5	0

Vial No.	21	22	23	24	25	26	27	28	29	30
No. of Plaques	0	0	0	53	0	0	48	1	0	72

Vial No.	31	32	33	34	35	36	37	38	39	40
No. of Plaques	45	0	0	0	0	0	190	0	9	0

* From Ellis and Delbrück (201).

burst data, if the total number of plaques on all plates is divided by the number of infected bacteria in which the entire brood of progeny found on the assay plates was produced. This ratio is usually found to be similar to the burst size estimated directly from a one-step growth experiment carried out on the same infected culture. From the data of Table 4-II the average yield is reckoned as follows.

Total number of plaques: 883
Total number of infected cells: $40 \times 0.47 = 18.8$
Average yield or burst size: $883/18.8 = 47$

The very broad distribution of phage yields by individual infected bacteria seemed rather puzzling at first. Delbrück (161) noted that the variation in length of individual cells of the infected culture was probably not the factor involved in the yield variation. It now seems likely that it is the very complexity of the process of intracellular phage growth itself which is responsible for the wide fluctuations in individual yields. If the final number of infective progeny viruses liberated at the time of lysis depends on a number of consecutive and concurrent reactions, then relatively minor perturbations in any one of these steps can easily lead to a very considerable diminution of the maximum number of phage particles of whose synthesis the cell is optimally capable. Indeed, mathematical analysis of the model of intracellular phage growth to be developed in subsequent chapters shows that the high variance in number of phage progeny produced by individual cells is only to be expected (590).

Lysis

The kinetics of bacteriophage growth may be followed not only by assaying the number of infective centers in one-step growth but also by observation of the lysis of the infected cells, either through direct microscopic observation of individual bacteria, or through observation of the macroscopic turbidity of the bacterial culture. In such studies it is necessary, of course, that nearly all of the bacteria be infected with phage at the outset, since a preponderance of uninfected cells would render it difficult to observe by either method the lysis of a minority of the individuals in the culture. Before considering such experiments we shall, therefore, first discuss the relation existing between the fraction of infected bacterial cells and the **multiplicity of infection,** which is defined as the ratio of the number of phages (strictly speaking, the number of *adsorbed* phages) in the inoculum to the number of bacteria in the culture.

The infecting phage particles can be considered to distribute themselves nearly at random over the bacterial cells, and hence the fraction of bacteria, b_0, that receives no phage particles at multiplicity of infection m is approximated closely by the Poisson law; by analogy with Equation (4-2),

$$b_0 = e^{-m}. \tag{4-3}$$

Since every phage-infected bacterial cell is killed by the virus, b_0 can also be determined directly by spreading aliquots of the culture on nutrient agar plates before and after its infection; the fraction b_0 of uninfected bacteria is then equal to the fraction of the cells still capable of forming a colony after infection of the culture. Such measurements of colony survival can also be used as an independent assay of the number of virus particles in a phage suspension, as shown in the example presented in Table 4-III. In general, the "killing titer" of a phage

TABLE 4-III

Assay of "Bacterial Killing" Titer of a Phage Suspension According to the Method of Delbrück and Luria (168)

PROCEDURE: A suspension of *E. coli* in nutrient broth is diluted 10^5-fold in physiological saline, and 0.1 ml of this dilution is spread on a nutrient agar plate (Plate A). A 1.9 ml sample of the original bacterial suspension is infected with 0.1 ml of a filtered (bacteria-free) lysate of T2 phage. Phage and bacteria are allowed to react in this mixture for 8 minutes. The infected suspension is then diluted 10^4-fold in physiological saline and 0.1 ml of this dilution is spread on a nutrient agar plate (Plate B). (Plate B contains anti-T2 serum, so that any progeny phages liberated upon lysis of the infected bacteria are neutralized before they can infect any surviving, uninfected bacteria in their vicinity.) Plates A and B are incubated overnight and the number of bacterial colonies appearing on each counted.

RESULTS:

	Colony Count	Titer of Surviving Bacteria in Original Mixture (cells/ml)	Fraction of Surviving Bacteria (b_0)
Plate A	135	1.35×10^8	1.0
Plate B	63	6.3×10^6	0.047

$$m = -\ln b_0 = -\ln 0.047 = 3.1 \text{ phages/cell}$$

Killing titer of original phage suspension:

$$3.1 \times 1.35 \times 10^8 \times (2.0/0.1) = 8.4 \times 10^9 \text{ phages/ml.}$$

suspension determined in this way equals the infective titer estimated from the plaque assay (168). As will be seen in subsequent chapters, however, certain physical or chemical treatments of phage populations may reduce the infective titer more than the "killing" titer; in other words, the ability of the virus to kill bacteria may, in some circumstances, be less sensitive to inactivation than its reproductive potential.

Figure 4-2 presents the result of an experiment in which a culture of bacteria was infected at an average multiplicity of five T4 phages per cell (so that according to the Poisson law only 0.007 of the bacteria should have remained uninfected), and the turbidity of the culture was observed continuously by measurement of the amount of light scattered. Simultaneously, the number of infective centers in the culture was followed by periodic plaque assays of aliquots. As is evident from Fig. 4-2,

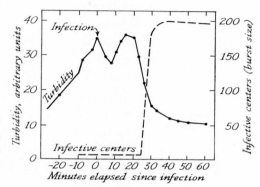

Fig. 4-2. The turbidity and infective center content of an *E. coli* culture at various times after its infection with an average of five T4 phages per cell. [Data from Doermann (180).]

the turbidity of the culture manifests an immediate drop upon phage infection, but soon regains again its initial, preinfection level. This transient reduction in light scattering reflects changes in the optical properties of the infected cell produced by the enzymatic modifications of the bacterial envelope to be considered in Chapters 5 and 7. But precisely at the conclusion of the latent period (as revealed by the sudden rise in infective centers) the culture suddenly experiences a second, much more extensive and permanent loss in turbidity. The turbidity reaches its minimum—that is, the culture clears—when all the bacteria that are going to lyse have lysed (180). Analogous results are reached by direct microscopic observations of phage-infected cultures; the onset of lysis or disappearance from the microscope field of individual bacteria coincides with the first rise in infective centers signaling the end of the latent period (159).

The mechanism by which the phage-infected bacterial cell is lysed has been the object of numerous investigations since the first days of bacteriophage research. Some of the early observations were bedeviled by the circumstance that there exists not one but two rather different processes by which bacteriophages can lyse sensitive bacterial cells (159). One of these is **lysis-from-without,** which represents an immediate dissolution of the host bacteria, often encountered when the multiplicity of infection is much greater than one phage per cell (35, 386, 478, 496).

Loss of the infecting phages, rather than their multiplication, is connected with this form of lysis, which not only proceeds in, but is even favored by, the absence of an active metabolism of the host cell (270). It seems very likely that lysis-from-without results from the digestion of the bacterial cell wall by lytic enzymes present in phage lysates either in "soluble" form or attached to phage particles (41, 328a, 368, 513, 664). Since this type of lysis has nothing to do with phage multiplication, it is really only the second of the lytic processes, or **lysis-from-within,** which plays an important role in phage growth.

Direct microscopic observation of the lysis of phage-infected, rod-shaped bacteria was first carried out by d'Hérelle, who noticed that the cells assume a spherical, swollen form shortly before their dissolution (146, 277). Use of microcinematography shows that the dissolution of the bacteria and the release of their contents resembles an explosion, as if the final act of cell lysis is the bursting of the cell envelope by internal pressure (44, 105). It is probable that intracellular phage multiplication first engenders a weakening of the structural members of the bacterium, so that, in the case of rod-shaped bacteria, the cell loses its rigidity and shortly before its end assumes the spherical shape of least surface to volume ratio, before the tensile strength of the envelope falls below the stress exerted by the osmotic forces.

The weakening of the bacterial structures connected with lysis-from-within is evidently the work of lytic enzymes, or **lysins,** that are synthesized in the infected cell and whose function is to digest away parts of the cell wall. The first to discover the existence of such a phage-induced lysin was Sertic (559, 560), who noticed in 1929 that the plaques formed by phage Fcz on *E. coli*, strain Fb, were surrounded by large haloes or zones of partial bacterial lysis (Fig. 4-3). Sertic found that infective Fcz phages were present only in the small central area of these plaques and that the haloes were free of phage. He succeeded in extracting a non-infective lysin from the haloes that was capable of inducing the lysis of chloroform-killed *E. coli* cells. There was good reason to believe that this lysin, contrary to what other phage workers then thought (81, 82, 105, 687), does not represent merely the phage-induced release of a lytic enzyme endogenous to the bacterium, because: (1) neither lysin nor any substance related antigenically to lysin can be extracted from normal, uninfected *E. coli* Fb cells; (2) some phage types other than Fcz elicit no lysin from strain Fb and produce only very small, halo-free plaques on it; and (3) the plaques of some phage types that, like those produced by phage Fcz, are surrounded by large haloes, contain a lysin whose activity is more resistant to heat inactivation than that of the lysin associated with the plaques of phage Fcz (564). Thus, both quantity and quality of the lysin produced depend on the type of phage infecting the host bacterium, and hence Sertic was justified in concluding

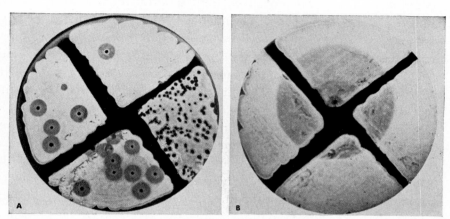

Fig. 4-3. The discovery of phage *lysin* (or phage lysozyme). **A.** Plaques formed by a phage on *E. coli* after incubation for 24 hours. The number of phage particles inoculated in each agar quadrant increases counterclockwise. Each plaque proper is bounded by a white ring and surrounded by a large phage lysin halo of partial bacterial lysis. **B.** A single phage plaque after incubation for 9 days. The central plaque is no larger than the plaques formed after 24 hours, but the lysin halo has now spread to all four quadrants. [From Sertic (559).]

that his lysin was an enzyme whose formation is induced by the phage; that is, "in the course of its metabolism, the bacteriophage, like other living beings, gives rise to products with enzymatic activity."

In subsequent years, many similar instances of the appearance of phage lysins were reported (251, 328a, 472, 524, 553), but students of the T coliphages were slow to manifest very much interest in these enzymes. In 1945 T. F. Anderson (10) found that irradiation of T2 phages releases a soluble bacteriolytic substance from the virus particles, and later Koch and Weidel (369) and Barrington and Kozloff (41) showed that a lytic enzyme appears to be attached to the phage particles. In fact, the chemical action of this enzyme on the bacterial cell wall closely resembles that of the bacteriolytic enzyme lysozyme that Fleming

(208) had discovered in 1922 in the secretions and tissues of animals. But only after it was finally shown that T4 phage lysates contain large quantities of the same enzyme in soluble form and that certain hereditary variants of the phage unable to synthesize the enzyme cannot lyse their host cells (616) did the idea gain currency that this is the lysin that digests the cell wall of T4-infected *E. coli* from within and thus allows escape of the phage progeny from the bacterium in which they were hatched. The T-even phage lysin now goes under the name of **phage lysozyme,** in part because its digestive function as well as its detailed chemical structure resembles very closely those of egg-white lysozyme (188, 366, 669) and in part because its latter-day rediscoverers had apparently never heard of either the work or the terminology of their predecessors.

Initiation of the reactions leading to lysis-from-within requires not only phage infection of the host cell but also onset of intracellular phage development: bacteria do not lyse that have been infected with nonmultiplying virus particles, such as certain kinds of ultraviolet-irradiated, mutant, or host-modified bacteriophages to be discussed in later chapters. But formation of infective phage progeny does not seem to be a prerequisite for lysis-from-within. For instance, as shall be seen presently, in the presence of the acridine dye proflavin T-even-phage-infected bacteria lyse at the normal time without yielding any intact virus particles. In the course of normal phage growth, the lytic reaction seems to be initiated about halfway through the latent period; after that time a rapid degeneration of the host cell sets in, which leads to its lysis a few minutes later, even if further phage multiplication is arrested by chilling the culture in ice or by adding such metabolic poisons as cyanide (48, 460).

Lysis Inhibition

There exists a "natural" way in which the imminent disintegration of a phage-infected bacterium can be staved off at almost the last moment. This is the phenomenon of **lysis inhibition,** discovered by Doermann in 1948 (180). If bacteria infected with one of the T-even phages are *superinfected* with additional phage particles before the end of the normal latent period, then the appearance of progeny phages is delayed by several minutes, and the overall lysis of the culture, as reflected by its turbidity, is retarded by as much as an hour. When lysis-inhibited bacteria finally do lyse, they yield a very high burst of progeny phages, sometimes as many as 1000 phages per cell. One may infer, therefore, that secondary infection of a bacterium in which intracellular growth of a primary T-even phage has already reached a late stage of its latent period gives renewed vigor to the cell, or at least retards its further degeneration. Possibly superinfection temporarily antagonizes the lytic action of the phage lysozyme, and thus postpones the moment of final disruption of the cell by its internal pressure. Lysis inhibition, although its mechanism is still poorly understood, has been an extremely useful tool in both genetic and biochemical studies of bacteriophage reproduction, since it allows the harvest of additional infective progeny particles constituted from bacteriophage precursors already present in the cell at the time of normal lysis (424, 602).

The Eclipse

The one-step growth experiment demonstrated clearly the general nature and overall kinetics of the multiplication of bacterial viruses on their bacterial hosts. It thus brought into focus a question of fundamental biologic interest: what is going on *inside* the infected cell during the latent period while the parental phage particle manages to cause its own several hundredfold replication? The first point relevant to this question that we shall now consider concerns the manner in which the number of phage particles present within the infected cell increases from the moment of infection until the time of lysis. This information can be obtained by breaking open the infected cells during the latent period and assaying for the infectivity of the material released by premature, artificial lysis. Such an experiment was first realized in 1948 by Doermann (179, 181), who infected bacteria with T4 phages under the conditions of the one-step growth experiment and at various times after infection induced lysis-from-without of the infected bacteria by addition of cyanide and a large excess of T6 phages to aliquots of the culture. Doermann then assayed these artificial lysates for their content of infective T4 particles on agar plates seeded with a T4-sensitive strain of indicator bacteria resistant to infection by the T6 phages added to the culture only for inducing lysis-from-without. The result of Doermann's experiment is presented in Fig. 4-4.

As can be seen from the data of Fig. 4-4, Doermann's experiment led to a most surprising finding: the infectivity associated with the original T4 parental bacteriophage is lost at the outset of the reproductive process, since no infective T4 phages whatsoever were found in any

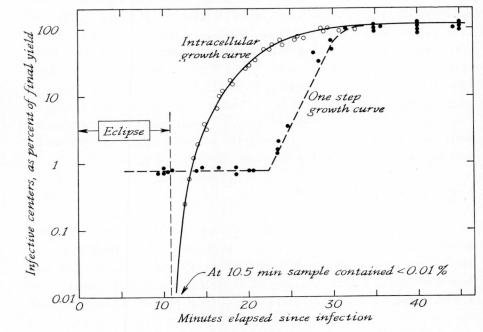

Fig. 4-4. The intracellular growth curve of bacteriophage T4. [Experimental data of Doermann (181).]

> *Procedure:* The same as that described in the legend to Fig. 4-1, except that here at various times after infection aliquots of the first growth tube are diluted 20-fold into a *lysing medium* containing 4×10^9 T6 phages/ml and M/100 KCN. After standing in the lysing medium for at least 30 minutes, samples of these dilutions are plated on agar seeded with a T6-resistant T4-sensitive strain of *E. coli*.

of the infected bacteria lysed-from-without within the first ten minutes following infection. After more than ten minutes have elapsed, however, an ever-increasing number of infective T4 phages is seen to have made its intracellular appearance, until the same final crop of progeny has been produced which would have been released by the spontaneous lysis of all the infected bacteria at the end of the normal latent and rise periods. The time intervening between infection and the first intracellular reappearance of infective phage particles—the stage of intracellular bacterial virus growth during which the infected host cell contains no material capable of initiating a plaque—is called the **eclipse** (436). The discovery of the eclipse confirmed a ten-year-old observation of the elder Wollmans (689), who had lysed phage-infected, gram-positive *megaterium* bacilli by lysozyme digestion of the cell wall and noticed that the infectivity associated with the parental phage particles could not be recovered from the lysate. The Wollmans inferred from their finding that the infecting bacteriophage passes through a non-infective or "cryptophagic" phase during its intracellular growth.

Since Doermann's original experiment, other methods for premature lysis of phage-infected bacteria have been devised, such as sonic oscillation (19) and explosive decompression from a nitrous oxide pressure bomb (213). Perhaps the easiest method for opening phage-infected bacteria (and the most widely used at present) is to shake the culture with a few drops of chloroform (556); chloroform treatment ruptures the bacterial cell wall, provided that enough of the phage lysozyme has already accumulated within the infected cell, without harming the intact phage particles which may be present. All these methods reveal exactly the same sequence of events of intracellular phage growth: the infectivity associated with the parental phage particle at first disappears and only later, after an eclipse lasting for about half of the latent period, do infective progeny particles appear within the cells.

The data of Fig. 4-4 show that after the termination of the eclipse, the number of intracellular phage progeny increases at a *constant* rate until the end of the latent period. These linear growth kinetics represent, of course, only an average over the entire infected culture; it would be possible, therefore, that in individual infected cells the increase in intracellular progeny phages follows quite different kinetics—for example, exponential. In order to study the time course of phage growth within the individual bacteria, the techniques of premature lysis and of single burst were combined by Bentzon, Maaløe, and Rasch (48). A very large number of tubes, each containing on the average slightly less than one phage-infected bacterium, were incubated and premature lysis was induced at various times after infection in different sets of these tubes. Plaque assays of each set of premature lysates of single infected cells showed, first, that the moment at which different individual bacteria contain their first infective phage is distributed over many minutes;

second, that after the termination of the eclipse, each infected bacterium passes through phases in which it first contains a few and later many progeny phages; and third, that the intracellular appearance of infective phages in individual cells indeed follows *linear* and not exponential kinetics.

The discovery of the eclipse temporarily complicated the conclusions which one might have hoped to draw from Doermann's intracellular growth curve, for the question now posed itself as to just when during the latent period the actual multiplication of the infecting phage particle takes place. Does the eclipse period represent a waiting stage for the infecting phage particle, during which it is "masked," while the host cell undergoes some necessary renovations preliminary to the onset of intracellular phage growth? In this case, the first infective phage particle present within the bacterium at the termination of the eclipse would be the original, once more "unmasked" parental phage, which might then proceed to grow and divide as any other microbe. The daughter viruses of the first division would in turn divide, until through successive division cycles the final crop of several hundred viruses had been attained by the end of the latent period. One might anticipate that such a geometric mode of growth of intracellular infective progeny should follow exponential rather than, as actually found, linear kinetics. But since the bacterial cell is a *bounded system*, it would not be surprising that the limiting conditions imposed by this fact force intracellular phage growth to proceed at a constant, rather than ever-increasing rate.

An entirely different explanation of the significance of the eclipse is that—far from being a stage of waiting—it is precisely that part of the latent period during which the substance of the bacteriophage progeny is constructed. In that case the increase in intracellular progeny does not at all represent the multiplication of the parental virus but constitutes rather a terminal process of the completion of previously synthesized phage constituents into intact virus particles. The results of investigations to be discussed in subsequent chapters have established that it is this latter point of view which is correct; the infecting virus particle not only metamorphoses into a noninfective form at the outset of its infection of the host cell but it also multiplies in this form to yield at first noninfective progeny structures, whose assembly, or **maturation,** into intact progeny viruses signals the end of the eclipse. This non-

infective form is called the **vegetative phage,** in contradistinction to
the resting, mature, infective phage particle (182). The vegetative phage
is thus the connecting link between parental and progeny viruses, and
the elucidation of its structure and function is the central problem of
bacterial virus growth.

Further Reading

Ellis, E. L. and Delbrück, M., "The growth of bacteriophage" (201); Delbrück, M.,
  "The growth of bacteriophage and lysis of the host" (159). These papers describe
  the invention of one-step growth and single-burst experiments and clarify the relation between phage growth and bacterial lysis.

Doermann, A. H., "The intracellular growth of bacteriophages" (79). The discovery of
  the noninfective eclipse phase of intracellular phage growth.

Luria, S. E., "Bacteriophage: An essay on virus reproduction" (436). A perspicacious
  analysis of the problem of phage multiplication as it appeared in 1950, written on
  the eve of the important discoveries to be recounted in later chapters.

CHAPTER 5

Infection

Adsorption—Bacterial Receptors—Phage Growth in Protoplasts—
Adsorption Organ—Injection

Adsorption

When bacterial viruses are mixed with a suspension of sensitive bacteria, the phage particles diffuse through the suspending fluid and collide with the cells. As a consequence of these collisions the phages become fixed, or **adsorbed,** to the cell surfaces. The extent to which adsorption occurs in any mixture of phages and bacteria can be determined in several ways. One common method is to centrifuge the mixture at low speed, so that only the bacteria, but not the free virus particles, sediment into the pellet. The number of infective centers in pellet and supernatant fluid can then be assayed by the plaque-count method; the supernatant infectivity represents the number of virus particles remaining unadsorbed, whereas the pellet infectivity represents the number of adsorbed phages—or rather the number of infected bacteria—present in the mixture at the time of centrifugation. Another method, which directly measures the number of infected bacteria without centrifugation, is to add an antiphage serum to the phage-bacterium mixture. The antiphage antibodies in the serum rapidly neutralize the free virus particles but do not inactivate the infective centers constituted by phage-infected bacteria. Plaque assays of adsorption mixtures after antiphage serum treatment thus count only *adsorbed* phages (162). A third method, which measures directly the number of *unadsorbed* phages, is to shake the adsorption mixture briefly with a few drops of chloroform; chloroform does not affect the viability of the free virus particles but destroys all phage-infected bacteria as infective centers. Hence, plaque counts made after chloroform treatment of the mixture represent only those phages which were not yet adsorbed to bacteria at the moment of chloroforming (218). (If adsorption proceeds under physiological conditions that allow intracellular phage development, then it is necessary, of course, that the adsorption mixture be centrifuged, antiserum neutralized, or chloroformed *before the end of the eclipse.* Otherwise liberation of intracellular infective progeny phages by the infected bacteria will interfere with any measurement of adsorbed or unadsorbed virus particles.)

The kinetics of phage adsorption were first studied by Krueger (384) and Schlesinger (104, 105), who determined the fraction of the input phage particles remaining unadsorbed at various times after phage and bacteria had been brought into contact. The results of such an experiment, in which T4 phage was mixed with *E. coli* suspensions of various cell densities are presented in Fig. 5-1. These data show that the log-

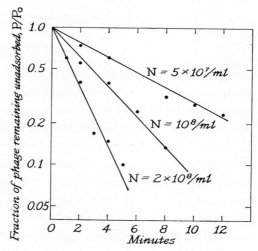

Fig. 5-1. Kinetics of adsorption of bacteriophage T4 to suspensions of *E. coli* at various cell densities, N. The ordinate presents the fraction of the initial infective centers that can still form plaques upon chloroform treatment of the adsorption mixture at various times after mixing phage and bacteria.

arithm of the fraction of phage particles remaining unadsorbed decreases linearly with the time allowed for adsorption. Further, the adsorption *rate*—that is, the slope of the free phage survival curve—is proportional to the concentration of bacteria in the mixture: the higher the bacterial density, the faster the rate of adsorption. Phage adsorption thus appears to follow the kinetics of *first-order reactions* and can therefore be described by the relation

$$-dP/dt = kNP, \qquad (5\text{-}1)$$

where P is the number of phage particles remaining unadsorbed after a time t, N the concentration of bacterial cells in the adsorption mixture, and k the **adsorption rate constant.** Integration of this differential equation leads to the expression

$$\log P/P_0 = -(1/2.3)kNt, \qquad (5\text{-}2)$$

which states that the logarithm of the fraction of initial phage particles, P_0, remaining unadsorbed decreases linearly with time, at a rate proportional to the concentration of adsorbing bacteria in the mixture.

Schlesinger, who postulated that contact between phage and bacterium arises from random collisions of the two bodies, analyzed the adsorption process in terms of the von Schmoluchowski equation (549), which describes the coagulation kinetics of colloidal suspensions. Phage adsorption can then be treated as the diffusion of small virus particles toward large, essentially stationary bacteria, to which the phages become fixed at a fraction f of all collisions. The von Schmoluchowski equation predicts the value of the adsorption rate constant, k, of Equation (5-1) as

$$k = 4\pi RCf, \qquad (5\text{-}3)$$

where R is the radius of a sphere whose surface area is equal to that of the bacterial cell, and C is the diffusion constant of the virus. Since the area of the bacterial surface, and hence the parameter R, can be estimated from the known size of the bacterium, and since the viral diffusion constant, C, can be determined directly by physicochemical measurements, it is possible to calculate from Equation (5-3) a theoretical value for the ratio k/f and compare it with the experimental value of k found from adsorption rate measurements. Such calculations for optimal adsorption conditions of phage T4 are presented in Table 5-I; they show that the theoretical value of k/f and the experimental value of k are similar in magnitude; that is, f appears to be of the order of unity. In other words, nearly every collision between a T4 phage and an *E. coli* bacterium seems to result in fixation of the virus particle (158, 606).

Schlesinger also determined **adsorption capacity** of bacterial cells for phage particles (544). For this purpose, he added increasing numbers of WLL phages to a suspension of *E. coli* and noted that point at which additional phages could no longer become attached to the bacteria. He thus found that the adsorption capacity of the bacteria reaches saturation when about 300 virus particles have been added for every bacterial cell

TABLE 5-I

Comparison of Observed and Calculated Adsorption Rates of Phage T4

1. Radius of sphere equivalent in surface area to *E. coli* cell:

$$R = 8 \times 10^{-5} \text{ cm.}$$

2. Diffusion constant of T-even phages [from Putnam (519)]:

$$C = 2.4 \times 10^{-6} \text{ cm}^2/\text{min.}$$

3. Theoretical value (according to Equation 5-3):

$$k/f = 4\pi \times 8 \times 10^{-5} \text{ cm} \times 2.4 \times 10^{-6} \text{ cm}^2/\text{min}$$
$$= 0.24 \times 10^{-8} \text{ cm}^3/\text{min.}$$

4. Experimental value of the adsorption rate constant (from Fig. 5-1):

$$k = 0.25 \times 10^{-8} \text{ cm}^3/\text{min.}$$

in the suspension. Schlesinger then estimated the diameter of the WLL phage by assuming that the bacterial adsorption capacity is saturated only when the entire cell surface is covered with a close-packed, single layer of some 300 virus particles. That is, since p close-packed spherical viruses of diameter δ cover an area $p\delta^2$, it would follow that at saturation

$$\delta = \sqrt{A/p_s}, \qquad\qquad (5\text{-}4)$$

where A is the surface area and p_s the number of saturating phage particles per bacterium. The particle diameter of 60–120 mμ calculated for WLL phage in this way is in rather good agreement with modern electron-optical determinations of the diameter of the head of the closely related T-even strains; it may be inferred, therefore, that each *E. coli* bacterium can adsorb as many T-even phage particles as are able to get to its surface.

The attachment process of phage to bacterial surface must be of a highly stereospecific nature. First of all, the range of bacterial strains to which a given bacteriophage type adsorbs—that is, which are *receptive* to the virus—is quite restricted. Second, a bacterium receptive to several different strains of phage may sport mutants among its descendants to which one phage strain can no longer attach but to which the other phage strains are still readily adsorbed. Such mutant bacteria are, of course, resistant to infection by the phage strain which they no longer adsorb. As will be seen in a subsequent chapter, the phage strain excluded from the resistant bacterium may in its turn sport a mutant virus which is once more adsorbable to, and hence can infect, the mutant cell. Such mutant viruses possess a structural modification of their adsorption organ which compensates in some manner for that alteration in the surface of the mutant cell which is responsible for resistance to infection by the original virus strain. This delicate hereditary control of cell receptivity and viral adsorbability renders it probable that a "lock and key" type of fit, possibly similar to the interaction between antigen and antibody, is involved in the fixation of phage to host cell surface.

Whether and how well adsorption occurs depends not only on the strains of phage and bacteria in question but also on the composition of the medium in which the two bodies encounter each other (279, 305, 562, 563). In particular, pH and ionic composition play an important role here; none of the T-series phages is fixed to normally receptive *E. coli* bacteria suspended in distilled water or in saline buffered at a pH below 5 or above 12. All of these phage strains are adsorbed at maximum velocity at neutral pH, but the optimal cationic composition differs for the various types. For instance, optimal adsorption of phage T1 requires a concentration of 0.001 M divalent, or of 0.01 M monovalent cations, whereas the T-even strains adsorb most rapidly in the presence of 0.1 M monovalent cations (514, 635). The role of the cations probably derives from their neutralization of electrostatic repulsive forces, which would otherwise prevent the approach of the negatively charged virus particles to the negatively charged bacterial surface (517). But, as will be seen presently, cations may also bring about some subtle structural changes in the virus required for the adsorption process. In any case, it is of great practical importance in bacteriophage work to ascertain the optimal ionic conditions for adsorption of any virus strain under study, since (depending on the circumstances) it is sometimes essential to achieve rapid infection of bacterial cultures, and at other times highly desirable to create conditions which *prevent* rather than promote optimal phage adsorption.

Thus far in our discussion we have not taken any pains to distinguish clearly between adsorption of the virus and infection of the cell, for the reason that attachment of the phage particle to the bacterial surface usually leads to infection. In this event, adsorption is necessarily **irreversible,** not only because firm chemical bonds are formed between cell surface and virus, but also because, as will become evident later in this chapter, the phage particle itself experiences a profound structural modification that precludes the possibility of its desorption as an intact, infective unit from the cell. However, under certain conditions, phages *can become reversibly* adsorbed to bacteria; in this case, the virus particles are held at the cell surface without causing infection. Such reversibly adsorbed phages may be detected by centrifuging an adsorption mixture at a low speed, resuspending the bacterial pellet in fresh medium, and then once more centrifuging the resuspended pellet. Any free virus particles present in the supernatant fluid of the second centrifugation must represent phages which were first reversibly attached to, and hence carried down with the bacteria of the original adsorption mixture and later eluted from the bacteria after resuspension of the pellet in fresh medium. Various workers have observed reversibly adsorbed phages in this way. For instance, Schlesinger (543) found that about 0.1% of WLL phages adsorbed to *E. coli* in broth could be eluted, and Hershey, Kalmanson, and Bronfenbrenner (305) noticed that about half of the T2 particles attached to bacteria in salt-free broth desorb again upon dilution of the mixture. Garen and Puck (234, 238) found that phage T1 undergoes an almost completely reversible attachment to *E. coli* cells in normal media at 0°C, or in the presence of zinc ions at 37°C. On the basis of these observations, Garen and Puck concluded that a reversible attachment of phage to bacterium precedes every irreversible attachment and is thus the *first step* in the infection of the host cell (238, 513). Although this view may be entirely correct, particularly in the case of phage T1, there is as yet no evidence that the transition from reversible to irreversible attachment is actually possible without prior desorption of the virus particle from the cell surface. Hence it must still be considered an open question whether a state of reversible attachment is an obligatory prelude to irreversible adsorption, and hence an essential step in the cell invasion sequence, or whether it merely reflects some other interaction between virus and cell surface irrelevant to the infection process (292).

Further studies (606) on the kinetics of adsorption of phage T4 showed that the mechanism of phage adsorption must be more complex than the simple collision-fixation picture conceived by Schlesinger. First, although the rate of phage adsorption increases proportionally to the bacterial concentration at low cell densities, it was found that a *maximum* adsorption velocity is reached when more than about 5×10^8 bacteria/ml are present in the adsorption mixture. That is, the adsorption rate of phage T4 shows no further increase after the density of receptive cells exceeds this limit, even though collisions between phage and bacteria ought to become still more and more frequent the higher the bacterial concentration. Second, it was found that the rate constant, k, of adsorption of phage T4 decreases by more than a factor of 10 if the temperature of the adsorption mixture is lowered from 25°C to 5°C. Since the diffusion constant, C, of the T4 particles changes very little within this temperature interval, collisions between phage and bacteria are nearly equally frequent at the high and the low temperature. Hence it may be concluded from Equation (5-3) that f, the fraction of collisions resulting in fixation of the phage, is the temperature-sensitive factor mainly responsible for the lower adsorption rate constant at 5°C. These findings lead to the idea that phage adsorption involves at least *two* steps; that is, in addition to collision between virus and cell another reaction must play an important role in phage adsorption. It is this second step which becomes the rate-limiting reaction at high bacterial concentrations and which is much more sensitive to temperature changes than the collision frequency. Three alternative possibilities have been envisioned for the nature of this second step (606).

1. It is possible that each phage particle oscillates between one of two states: an "active" state, in which every collision with a receptive bacterium leads to irreversible adsorption, and an "inactive" state, in which no collision can lead to adsorption. At very high bacterial concentrations the "active" fraction of the phage population becomes irreversibly fixed almost at once, and the remainder of the phages can be adsorbed no faster than the rate at which they make the transition from "inactive" to "active" state. The tenfold reduction in the adsorption rate constant attending the lowering of the temperature from 25°C to 5°C implies in this case that the fraction of phages in the "active" state is ten times greater at 25°C than at 5°C.

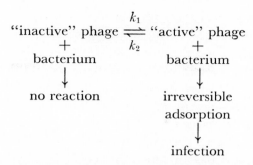

$$k_1 = \text{maximum adsorption rate at high cell densities}$$

$$k_1/(k_1 + k_2) = f$$

2. It is possible that the phage particles can collide with bacteria in two different ways: one "good," which adsorbs the phage irreversibly, and one "bad," which fixes the phage reversibly to the surface of the cell without allowing it to become irreversibly adsorbed. At high bacterial concentrations, nearly all the phages become immediately attached to cells. However, only a minor fraction of the particles is initially adsorbed in the "good" or irreversible way, the rate of irreversible adsorption of the remainder being limited by the rate of *desorption* of the reversibly held particles. The ten-fold reduction of the adsorption rate constant attending the lowering of the temperature implies in this case that the fraction of "good" collisions is ten times greater at 25°C than at 5°C.

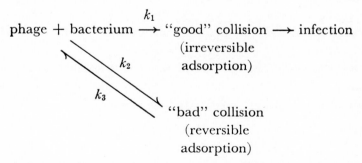

$$k_3 f = \text{maximum adsorption rate at high cell densities}$$

$$k_1/(k_1 + k_2) = f$$

3. Finally, it is possible that at each collision phage and bacteria enter a potentially reversible attachment. While thus reversibly held to the

cell surface, the phage may either become fixed irreversibly, or it may desorb from the bacterium before becoming irreversibly fixed. At high bacterical concentrations, nearly all the phage particles immediately enter the reversibly adsorbed state, so that the rate of irreversible fixation at the bacterial surface becomes the rate-limiting reaction in the overall adsorption velocity. The tenfold reduction in the adsorption rate constant attending the lowering of the temperature from 25°C to 5°C here implies that in this interval the surface fixation reaction has a temperature coefficient ten times greater than the desorption process.

$$\text{phage} + \text{bacterium} \underset{k_2}{\overset{k_1}{\rightleftharpoons}} \begin{matrix} \text{reversible} \\ \text{adsorption} \end{matrix} \overset{k_3}{\longrightarrow} \begin{matrix} \text{irreversible} \\ \text{adsorption} \end{matrix} \longrightarrow \text{infection}$$

$$k_3 = \text{maximum adsorption rate at high cell densities}$$
$$k_3/(k_2 + k_3) = f$$

It is not possible at present to decide which of these alternatives of the two-step nature of phage adsorption corresponds most nearly to the truth. On the one hand, as we shall see presently, there is some reason to believe now that T-even phage particles can oscillate between an "active" and an "inactive" state, in support of the first of these alternatives. On the other hand, the demonstration that a state of reversible phage adsorption does exist might lead one to favor either the second or the third of these alternatives. Puck and Garen's proposal that reversible adsorption is the *first* step in infection is, of course, identical with the third of these alternatives. It is not excluded—indeed, it seems probable—that different types of phage are adsorbed to the surface of their hosts by different mechanisms, so that one or the other of these alternatives may apply to any particular case.

Bacterial Receptors

The bacterial host cell does not appear to play any active, metabolic role in the adsorption of most phage strains since the virus particles are fixed irreversibly not only by heat-killed or cyanide-poisoned bacteria but even by fragments of lysed or disrupted cells. The bacterial cell wall must, therefore, contain some phage-specific **receptor sites** that are able to undergo a spontaneous, irreversible chemical reaction with the attachment organs of the virus particle. The first attempts to identify these phage receptor sites were made more than twenty-five years ago (115, 116, 416), but, besides demonstrating that such receptors exist, little progess was made until the very complex structure of the bacterial cell wall was clarified in the 1950's (534). The principle underlying the identification and isolation of phage receptors is to prepare an extract of receptive bacterial host cells, to add to this extract a phage suspension of known titer, and then to assay the residual infective titer of the mixture. If the extract contains active phage receptors, then these will fix, and hence neutralize the phage particles of the test suspension. In this way, active phage receptors make their presence known, in Burnet's terminology, as phage-inhibiting agents, or PIA (115). When Weidel perfected methods for isolating and purifying whole *E. coli* cell walls (Fig. 5-2), he found that these empty walls still adsorb the T coliphages as efficiently and specifically as the living bacteria (664, 665). Except for phage T1, fixation of virus particles to the empty walls is irreversible, and hence such walls constitute PIA.

Chemical fractionation of the *E. coli* cell wall led Weidel to propose that it is constructed of at least three entirely distinct layers (668). Two outer layers, one a **lipoprotein** and the other a **lipopolysaccharide,** provide a plastic cover for the cell. An inner or "R layer," is completely buried under the plastic outer layers, and comprises little more than 10% of the weight of the whole wall. This inner R layer provides the rigid framework responsible for the characteristic blimp shape of the *E. coli* cell. A **mucopolymer** plays a key role in the chemical architecture of the rigid, inner R layer; the mucopolymer, an enormous macromolecule whose subunits are held together by covalent bonds, is assembled from mucopeptide units which contain five characteristic components: muramic acid, glucoseamine, alanine, glutamic acid, and the unusual amino acid $\alpha\epsilon$-diaminopimelic acid (697) found only in bacterial cell walls. Upon testing the PIA activity of the different chemical fractions of the cell wall, it was found that only the two outer layers carry phage receptors, each layer being capable of adsorbing a different class of phages: the lipopolysaccharide layer fixes phages T3, T4, and T7, whereas the lipoprotein layer fixes phages T2 and T6. The third and innermost layer, never being exposed to the outside world, is devoid of phage receptors.

Each of the phage types whose receptors are located on the same cell wall layer nevertheless engages a different class of specific receptor site. For example, saturation of the "polyvalent" lipoprotein receptor complex with T2 phage does not preclude subsequent adsorption of the heterologous T6 phage to the same layer. In fact, the biosynthesis of

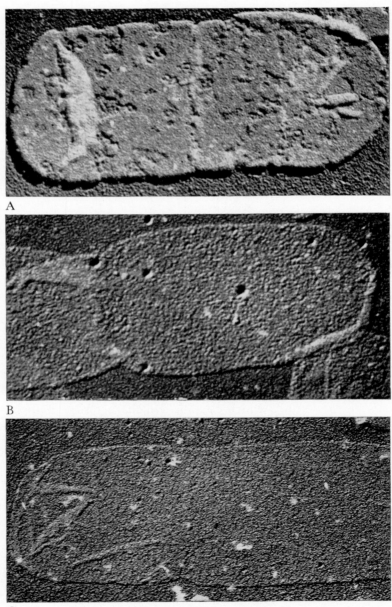

A

B

C

different kinds of phage receptors must involve different enzymatically controlled reaction steps, since genetic mutations in the nucleus of *E. coli* can eliminate any one of the various kinds of receptor activity from the bacterial cell wall without necessarily affecting the other receptor activities: bacterial mutants occur whose lipoprotein layer can fix T2 phage but not T6 phage, whereas other mutants can fix T6 but not T2. But the receptor activity for several different phage types can also be wiped out simultaneously by a single mutation, if their receptors all form part of the same chemical complex. Thus, *E. coli* mutants selected for resistance against any one of the three phage types T3 or T4 or T7 frequently turn out to be resistant also to (that is, no longer adsorb) the other two phage types (175). In these particular mutants the structure of the whole lipopolysaccharide layer, in which the receptors for all three phage types reside, has been profoundly altered (666).

In addition to the "polyvalent" lipopolysaccharide and lipoprotein layers, the *E. coli* wall comprises also a "monovalent" type of phage receptor component that combines only with phage T5. This T5 receptor is easily removed from the cell wall with dilute alkali. Electron micrographs show the receptor to be a sphere of about 30 mμ in diameter (Fig. 5-3), and chemical analysis reveals that it is composed of a lipopolysaccharide nucleus surrounded completely by a lipoprotein shell that carries the structural configuration necessary for fixation of the attachment organs of the T5 particle (670, 671).

One may thus imagine the bacterial surface as a *mosaic* of various phage receptor sites, each receptor being capable of forming a highly specific bond with the phage type to which it is receptive. The structure

---

Fig. 5-2. The *E. coli* cell wall and its component layers. **A.** Cell wall of *E. coli*, strain B. The normally smooth surface shows cavities produced by localized removal of parts of the outer plastic layer in the preparative procedure. Lipoprotein and lipopolysaccharide components of the outer plastic layer possess different phage receptor activities. **B.** Exposure of the rigid inner R layer after removal of outer plastic layer. This residual structure is now devoid of phage acceptor activity. The regular surface pattern is produced by protein units held by covalent bonds to the mucopolymer framework. **C.** The mucopolymer framework after removal of its protein by digestion with a proteolytic enzyme. Lysozyme causes complete dissolution of this giant, blimp-shaped macromolecule by hydrolytic cleavage of the mucopeptide polymer chains. [Unpublished micrographs provided by H. Frank, Max Planck Institut für Biologie, Tübingen.]

of each receptor site can be modified by hereditary changes in the bacterial nucleus so that an irreversible union between cell wall receptor and its homologous phage no longer takes place.

The chemical nature of the receptors for phage T1 has thus far proven rather elusive. Since it has not been possible to find anti-T1 PIA in *E. coli* extracts, no isolation or identification of the receptors could even be attempted. The failure to find T1 receptors in bacterial extracts could

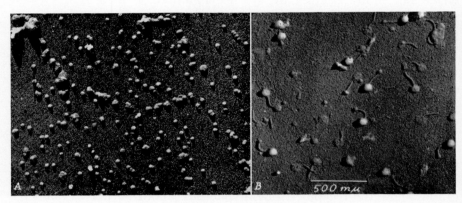

Fig. 5-3. **A.** Purified T5 receptors extracted from the *E. coli* cell wall. **B.** T5 phages to which T5 receptors have been added and of which more than 99% have lost their infectivity; phage particles with intact and empty heads are visible; the receptor spheres are attached to the phage tails. [From Weidel and Kellenberger (670).]

conceivably mean that T1, alone among the T phages, actually requires some active metabolic participation on the part of the bacterial host for its irreversible adsorption. This requirement would also account for the surprising but rarely stated fact that T1 adsorbs exclusively to "living" bacteria and is only fixed *reversibly* to bacteria sterilized by ultraviolet light or poisoned by cyanide. The adsorption mechanism of T1 may, therefore, be quite different from that of its fellow T phages, in which case inferences drawn from adsorption studies of T1 (238, 514) would not be directly applicable to other phage types.

As soon as a T-even virus has attached itself to the *E. coli* surface, the lysozyme carried by the phage particle starts digesting the bacterial cell wall (369, 664). Weidel and his collaborators (512, 672) have shown that it is the rigid, innermost layer of the wall that is attacked by the phage lysozyme, which splits off the amino acids, the muramic acid, and the glucoseamine of the mucopolymer. In agreement with the view that phage receptors reside in the other two layers of the cell wall, phage-lysozyme digestion of the mucopolymer does not result in the loss of phage receptor activity (349, 670); this is consonant with the fact that a bacterium already infected by a T-even phage can still adsorb further phage particles. It is still not entirely clear if digestion of the muco-polymer at the time of infection is an essential part of the invasion process of the host cell or, indeed, if the lysozyme carried by the virus forms really an integral part of, or is only casually adsorbed to, the phage particle. Weidel is of the opinion that the rigid mucopolymer presents an obstacle that must be overcome by the phage in its entrance into the bacterium, and therefore must be pierced by the enzyme at the outset of infection. But since T4 mutant phages unable to synthesize any active lysozyme (and hence presumably devoid of this enzyme in their extra-cellular form) are nevertheless capable of infecting *E. coli*, it would seem possible that the virus can invade its host even without digesting part of the rigid innermost layer of the cell wall. In any event, it is apparent that the enzymatic weakening of the bacterial structures attending the normal lysis-from-within, as described in the preceding chapter, must correspond to the splitting by the phage-induced intracellular lysozyme of the glycosidic bonds holding the glucoseamine backbone of the mucopolymer together. Once the rigidity of the innermost layer of the wall has been destroyed enzymatically, the cell becomes incapable of resisting the osmotic pressure and bursts open, or lyses.

The lysozyme carried by the T-even particles no doubt accounts for the phenomenon of lysis-from-without. When a single phage particle infects a bacterium, only a relatively small fraction of the bacterial wall is digested and the cell remains intact long enough for successful intra-cellular phage growth. Nevertheless, even this limited digestion produces a noticeable increase in permeability of the infected cell immediately after infection, so that various cytoplasmic constituents leak into the growth medium (515, 516). This leakage is, most probably, also re-sponsible for the immediate postinfection drop in the turbidity of T-even infected bacterial cultures evident in Fig. 4-2. Soon after the onset of phage growth, leakage ceases and the cell regains its previous imperme-ability and albedo by resynthesis of the digested cell wall components. When very many virus particles simultaneously infect a single bacterium, however, then the fraction of the rigid cell wall layer from which the mucopeptide subunits have been digested away by the phage lysozyme is so great that the wall can no longer withstand the osmotic forces, and the cell bursts open before intracellular phage growth can get under way. Such lysis-from-without is all the more effective if a metabolic poison such as cyanide is added at the time of infection, since any resealing efforts by the cell through mucopolymer resynthesis will thus be forestalled.

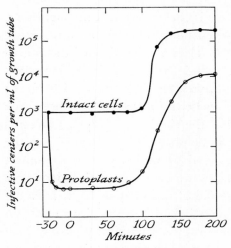

Fig. 5-4. One-step growth curves of bacteriophage C on intact cells of *Bacillus megaterium* and on protoplasts. [From Brenner and Stent (100).]

Procedure: A culture of *B. megaterium* is grown in a synthetic medium to a density of $5 \cdot 10^7$ cells/ml, centrifuged, and resuspended in half of its original volume of 5% peptone water. The culture is then infected with about $2 \cdot 10^6$ phages of strain C per milliliter. After incubation for 5 minutes, more than 90% of the phages are adsorbed. The culture is centrifuged, washed, and resuspended in sucrose-buffer. One aliquot of this suspension is digested at room temperature with 10 μg/ml lysozyme. Microscopic examination indicates protoplast formation to be complete after 30 minutes. A second aliquot of the suspension of infected cells remains untreated. At time $t = 0$, both aliquots are diluted 1000-fold into sucrose-buffer-peptone maintained at 25°C, and sampled and assayed periodically for infective centers.

Phage Growth in Protoplasts

Although digestion of the cell wall by the phage lysozyme normally brings the latent period to term, the presence of the outer cell wall is not absolutely essential for intracellular phage growth: bacteriophage development can proceed in cell-wall-less **protoplasts** of the gram-positive *Bacillus* species *megaterium* and *subtilis* (100, 490, 535). As stated in Chapter 2, the cell wall of many gram-positive bacteria can be completely removed by lysozyme digestion; the cells then survive as spherical protoplasts as long as they are maintained in concentrated sucrose solution. Such protoplasts do not *adsorb* phages to which the intact cell is sensitive (663), showing that also in these bacterial species the cell wall encompasses the phage receptor sites. But in spite of their physiological phage resistance, it is possible to study phage growth in protoplasts by *first* infecting the phage-sensitive intact bacteria and *then* converting them by lysozyme treatment into protoplasts immediately after infection.

Figure 5-4 presents the result of an experiment in which one part of a phage-infected culture of *B. megaterium* was converted into protoplasts and both intact bacteria and protoplasts were maintained at 25°C in concentrated sucrose broth; aliquots of both cultures were diluted and plated for plaque count on nutrient agar at various times after infection. It can be seen that at the outset of phage growth, less than 1% of the infected protoplasts register on the assay plate as infective centers. Sixty minutes later, there begins a rapid rise in the number of infective centers in the protoplast culture, until a titer is reached fourteen times higher than the original concentration of infected cells. The initial failure of the protoplasts to register as infective centers constitutes, in effect, another demonstration of the eclipse phenomenon; upon dilution from the sucrose broth, the infected protoplasts lyse at once, and, as long as they harbor no intracellular intact progeny phages, they are lost as infective centers. The later increase in infective centers in the protoplast culture is a reflection of the successful intracellular growth and maturation of vegetative phage in the cell-wall-less bacteria.

Since only part of the cell wall of the gram-negative *E. coli* can be removed by lysozyme digestion, it has not yet been possible to examine the ability of the T phages to grow in true, cell-wall-less protoplasts. However, osmotically sensitive "spheroplasts" produced by lysozyme treatment of *E. coli* in sucrose broth (see Chapter 2) are able to support growth of T3 and the T-even strains (215, 469). Hence it can be concluded that the integrity of the lysozyme-sensitive R layer of the *E. coli* cell wall is not essential for intracellular virus development, as long as the external osmotic pressure of the growth medium is high enough to counterbalance the internal osmotic pressure of the infected cell.

Adsorption Organ

In order to understand just how the virus attaches itself to its bacterial receptor site, we must now consider the anatomy of the phage particle in more detail. The first important step in this direction was made in 1952 by T. F. Anderson, who showed by use of his then newly developed "critical point" technique for avoiding surface tension artifacts in electron microscope specimens (17) that *bacteriophages are adsorbed by their tail* (18) (Fig. 5-5). It is thus the phage tail which carries the organelles responsible for the specific fixation of virus to host cell receptors. Weidel and Kellenberger were able to confirm this conclusion for phage T5 in a slightly different way (670). Instead of virus adsorbed to intact bacteria, they examined suspensions of T5 phage that had been

Fig. 5-5. Electron micrograph of an *E. coli* cell to which T5 phages have adsorbed by their tail. [From Anderson (18).]

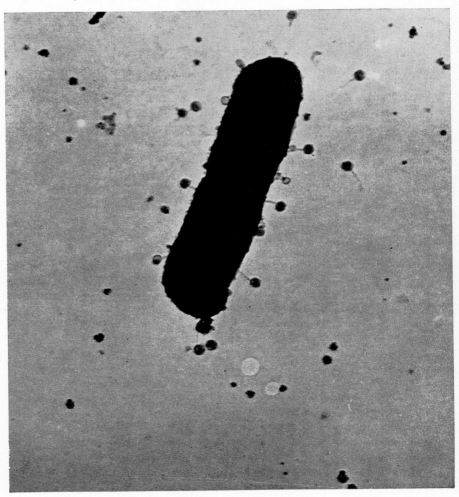

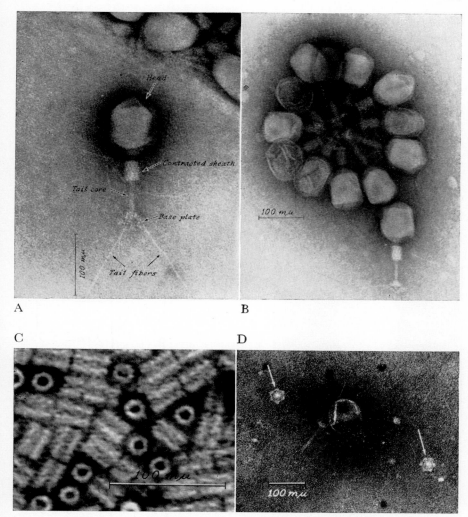

Fig. 5-6. Structural components of the T-even phage. **A.** A T-even phage particle
observed in the electron microscope after "negative staining" with phos-
photungstic acid; the sheath has been made to contract by treatment of
the virus with hydrogen peroxide. **B.** Rosette of T-even phages treated with
hydrogen peroxide: both normal and altered particles with shortened and
thickened sheaths are visible. **C.** Purified contracted sheaths isolated from
the tails of T-even phages; several sheaths can be seen standing upright,
revealing a "cog wheel" arrangement of the polypeptide subunits of the
structure. [**A, B,** and **C** from Brenner, Streisinger, Horne, Champe, Barnett,
Benzer, and Rees (101).] **D.** Two isolated hexagonal base plates of T4.
[Unpublished photograph provided by E. Boy de la Tour, University of
Geneva.]

allowed to react with isolated T5 receptors. Their electron micrographs show (Fig. 5-3**B**) that the spherical cell receptors form an irreversible union with the tip of the T5 tail. Studies made possible by further advances in electron microscopy and dissection of virus particles later revealed that the phage tail is, in fact, a rather complex organ. Largely through the work of Williams and Fraser (684), Kellenberger (359), Brenner (101), and their collaborators, it is now known that the tail of the T-even phages is assembled from at least four proteinaceous components: a **sheath**, a **core**, a **base plate**, and six **tail fibers** (Fig. 5-6). All of these tail proteins differ chemically from each other, as well as from the *head protein*, the major protein constituent of the phage. An image of the assembled structure of the entire T-even virus particle is presented in Fig. 5-7. By breaking up the tail in various ways and testing

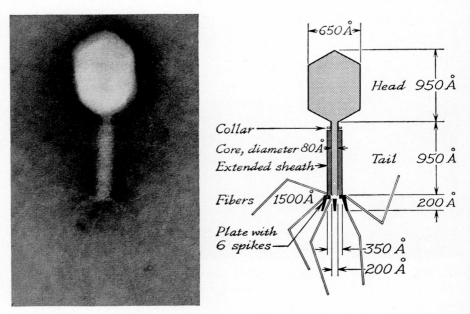

Fig. 5-7. The detailed structure of the T-even phage particle. [From Kellenberger (356).]

separately the adsorbability of the different isolated components, it was found that it is only the *tail fibers* that are specifically fixed to bacteria. (That is to say, the tail fibers are adsorbed to phage-sensitive bacteria but are not adsorbed to phage-resistant bacterial mutants.) Neither isolated sheaths nor core proteins—nor, understandably, head protein or the DNA it encloses—are in any way fixed by phage-sensitive bacteria. It would seem, therefore, that the adsorption organelle of the phage tail resides in the tail fibers, whose specific, lock-and-key bond to the bacterial receptor sites anchors the virus to the bacterial surface. No experiments on the adsorbability of isolated tail plates have as yet been reported, and it is possible that the tail plate also has an affinity for bacterial receptor sites and plays a role in the attachment reaction.

It was discovered in 1945 that certain strains of the T-even phages will not adsorb to their normal *E. coli* host unless they have been previously "activated" by contact with certain amino acid cofactors, the most effective of which is tryptophan (11, 12, 13). The detailed study of the reversible activation of such "cofactor-requiring" phages turned out to be an exercise in complicated reaction kinetics and suggested that the cooperation of about five tryptophan molecules is necessary for rendering the virus particle adsorbable (604, 605, 696). When Sato subsequently found that *permanent* activation of cofactor-requiring phages can be achieved by treatment of the virus with urea, it seemed likely that the reaction with cofactor produces a structural change or "denaturation" of the tail proteins that form part of the phage adsorption organ—for example, the tail fibers (537). Finally, it was shown that the cofactor molecules do not promote the reaction between cell surface and tail fibers but rather *prevent* an interaction between tail sheath and tail fibers (96, 212). Electron micrographs show that in the absence of cofactor the six tail fibers of cofactor-requiring strains of T-even phages are not free but tightly wound around the tail sheath. Since the adsorption organs are thus folded back, the virus particle cannot attach itself to the host cell. Reaction of the tail with tryptophan cofactor molecules liberates the tail fibers from embracing the sheath, and the phage becomes adsorbable. If the simultaneous freedom of all six fibers were required for adsorption, the need for the cooperation of about five or six cofactor molecules in the activation process would be explained, provided that each molecule liberates one fiber from contact with the sheath. An earlier observation by Jerne (345) that anti-T4 sera can achieve a permanent activation of cofactor-requiring T4 particles is now also accounted for; some of the antiphage antibodies become attached to the sheath and cover up sites for which the tail fibers otherwise have an affinity.

The tail fibers of non-cofactor-requiring T-even phages have also some affinity for their tail sheaths, so that even in these strains only a fraction of the phage population has all of its tail fibers extended (that is, is adsorbable) at any one moment. Hence, it is probable that the liberation of tail fibers from their attachment to the sheath is the second, temperature-sensitive step that becomes the rate-limiting reaction at high bacterial densities envisaged by the first of the three alternative explanations of the two-step nature of phage adsorption discussed earlier in this chapter. It is also possible that the influence of ionic composition and pH on the adsorbability of phages reflects an electrostatic interaction not only between phage and bacterial surface but also between tail fibers and tail sheath.

A most surprising fact came to light when it was discovered that the tail of the T-even phages is a *contractile organ:* such treatments of T-even phages as incubation with hydrogen peroxide or zinc cyanide, heating gently, or freezing and thawing, cause the sheath to contract toward the phage head, exposing the tail core as a spike at the tip of the tail (357, 382) (Fig. 5-8). A similar contraction of the sheath is observed when the phage particles react with isolated bacterial cell walls (357). In the electron micrograph shown in Fig. 5-9, it can be seen that the proximal part of the phage tail has become shorter and thicker and that the tail core has actually penetrated through the cell wall.

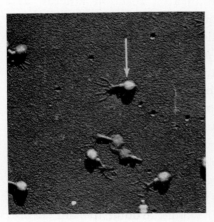

Fig. 5-8. T2 phage particles after peroxide-induced contraction of the tail sheath and exposure of the tail core. [From Kellenberger and Arber (357).]

It may be inferred, therefore, that after the tail fibers have firmly anchored the T-even virus particle to the bacterial receptor sites, contact of phage tail with cell surface causes the sheath to contract, forcing the tail core toward the interior of the host cell. The modus operandi of the T-even phage tail thus resembles that of the sort of hypodermic syringe whose needle is pushed under the skin by release of a built-in spring.

The nature of the contractile reaction of the sheath is not yet entirely clear. It has been proposed that the sheath is a small muscle, whose contraction resembles the interaction between the muscle proteins actin and myosin (378), since ethylene diaminetetra-acetate (EDTA), an agent known to prevent the contraction of actomyosin, inhibits both infection of bacteria by T-even phages and contraction of the tail

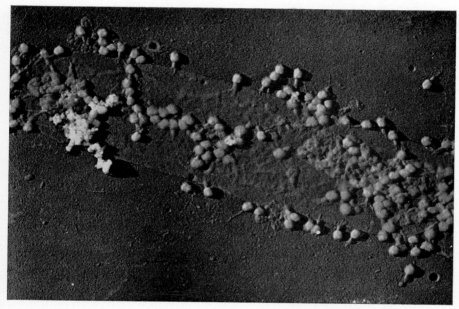

Fig. 5-9.   Empty cell wall of *E. coli* to which T2 phages have adsorbed. The penetration of the cell wall by the tail core is clearly visible. [From Kellenberger and Arber (357).]

sheath after adsorption of virus particles to isolated cell walls (379). There is, furthermore, a small but significant amount of adenosine triphosphate (ATP) present in the phage tail which is hydrolyzed to adenosine diphosphate (ADP) at the moment of infection, just as though the actomyosin system were at work (381). It must be said, however, that the chemical composition and structure of the sheath protein does not in any way resemble that of actomyosin (101). But whether the sheath is a muscle or not, in all of biology there can hardly exist an example of active movement at a level of structural complexity lower than that of the contractile phage tail.

Injection

Since the reproduction of the infecting phage particle proceeds *inside* the bacterium, it follows that after its adsorption to the bacterial surface the virus must somehow penetrate into the interior of the host cell, if it is to set in motion there the train of events that culminate in the construction of infective progeny phages. The experiment that finally led to the understanding of just how bacterial viruses manage to get into bacteria is one of the great milestones in the history of bacteriophage research. Three discoveries by T. F. Anderson were of undoubted heuristic value for the conception of this experiment: namely, that osmotic shock ruptures the phage and produces an empty-headed phage "ghost," that phages adsorb to bacteria by their tail and thus form what ought to be a dynamically unstable union with the host cell surface, and that violent agitation in a Waring blendor of mixed suspensions of phage and sensitive bacteria prevents infection (15). According to Hershey (293), it was an appreciation of these facts, and of a later finding (281) that the "ghosts" are protein structures from which the phage DNA has been released in a DNase-sensitive state, that "literally forced" him and Chase to perform in 1952 the **blendor experiment** (301). This experiment showed that upon infection, just as upon osmotic shock, the phage DNA leaves the phage head and is the only, or at least the principal, viral component that gains entrance into the host cell, the bulk of the phage protein remaining outside, beyond the wall. Before we can consider the experiment of Hershey and Chase in detail, however, a brief discussion on the use of radioactive tracers in phage research is required.

If a culture of bacteria grows in a chemically defined medium such as that described in Table 2-II, containing phosphoric acid and sulfuric acid as only sources of phosphorus and sulfur, then any radiophosphorus P^{32} or radiosulfur S^{35} (the two radioisotopes of the greatest importance for our discussion) added to the medium as $H_3P^{32}O_4$ or $H_2S^{35}O_4$ is incorporated into all of the phosphorylated or sulfurylated constituents of the cells. The ratio of radioactive to stable isotopes of phosphorus or sulfur—that is, the *specific activity* of these cellular constituents—will be the same as that of the phosphate and sulfate of the growth medium. If, furthermore, such radioactive bacterial cultures are infected with bacteriophage, then the progeny phage grown on these bacteria also contain the radioisotope in their phosphorylated or sulfurylated components. After phage growth, the labeled virus particles can be readily separated by differential centrifugation (see Chapter 3) from the other contaminating radioactive materials in the lysate, such as the residual unassimilated phosphate or sulfate of the growth medium and the bacterial debris. In this way it is quite easy to obtain a pure suspension of isotopically labeled phages whose radioactivity emanates exclusively from the virus particles themselves. Fortunately, it turns out that the two isotopes, P^{32} and S^{35}, are specific labels for DNA and protein, the two principal components of the phage. Since the DNA contains practically all of the phosphorus of the virus (in polynucleotide phosphate diester bonds) and the protein all of the sulfur (in the two amino acids methionine and cysteine), a phage labeled only with P^{32} harbors all its radioactivity in DNA, whereas a phage labeled only with S^{35} harbors all its radioactivity in the protein.

Hershey and Chase thus infected different aliquots of an *E. coli* culture with purified stocks of P^{32}- or S^{35}-labeled T2 phage. After allowing a short time for adsorption of most of the virus particles, they separated the infected cells from any unadsorbed phage by low-speed centrifugation and resuspension in fresh medium. This suspension was then agitated violently for various lengths of time in a Waring blendor, in order to subject the phage-infected cells to the very strong shearing forces generated in the fluid by that device. After blendor treatment the survival of the infective centers was determined by plaque assay. At the same time, the infected bacteria were centrifuged once more at low speed and the fraction of the total radioactivity that remained in the supernatant fluid or sedimented into the bacterial pellet was determined in a radiation counter. It is, therefore, possible to measure by means of this procedure how much of either P^{32} or S^{35} label initially adsorbed to the bacteria with the infecting phage particles is again stripped off by violent agitation and how many of the infected cells can still continue to produce infective progeny viruses after the blendor treatment. The result of this experiment is presented in Fig. 5-10, and can be summarized as follows: (1) The survival of the infective centers is not affected by the blendor treatment. (2) The shearing forces strip off 75–80% of the adsorbed S^{35} from the infected cells. (3) Only 20–35% of the adsorbed P^{32} can be removed from the bacteria; of that fraction, half has been already

liberated into the medium before the blendor is turned on. It is, therefore, possible to infer that most of the phage DNA enters the bacterium
at the outset of infection, whereas most of the phage protein remains at
the cell surface. The shearing forces of the blendor break the tail by
which the "phage ghost" is still held to the cell wall and thus liberate
into the medium only the empty head membrane, devoid of the phage
DNA it once enclosed. Since the infective centers survive the blendor

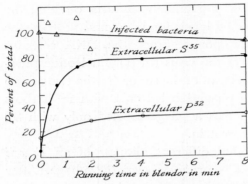

Fig. 5-10. The blendor experiment. The ordinate presents the percent of S^{35} and P^{32} removed from bacteria infected with radioisotope-labeled T2 phage, and the percent of infected bacteria surviving as infective centers, after the time of agitation in a Waring blendor, is shown on the abscissa. From Hershey and Chase (301).

Procedure: Broth-grown *E. coli* are infected with S^{35}- or P^{32}-labeled phage in buffered saline, the unabsorbed material is removed by centrifugation, and the cells are resuspended in water containing per liter 1 mM $MgSO_4$, 0.1 mM $CaCl_2$, and 0.1 gm gelatin. This suspension is agitated in a Waring blendor at 10,000 rpm. The suspension is cooled briefly in ice water at the end of each 60-second running period. Samples are removed at intervals, assayed for plaque count to determine the number of bacteria capable of yielding phage, and centrifuged to measure the radioactivity in the supernatant fluid, i.e. the proportion of radioisotope released from the cells.

treatment it can be inferred that the bulk of the phage protein has no
further function in the intracellular reproduction process after the
proteinaceous tail has anchored the virus particle to the bacterial surface
and safely "injected" the phage DNA into the host cell. Hershey and
Chase further substantiated the inference that the phage DNA leaves
the protective envelope of phage head membrane at the moment of
infection by showing that the T2 DNA is rendered accessible to the
hydrolytic action of DNase upon adsorption of the phages to isolated
bacterial cell walls or heat-killed bacteria, or upon freezing and thawing
T2-infected bacteria. In the case of adsorption of phages to isolated
bacterial cell walls, the phage DNA is "injected" into the medium on
the other side of the wall; in the case of infection of bacteria which
have been either heat-killed before infection or frozen-thawed after

infection, the bacterial cell membrane is rendered permeable to DNase enzyme molecules.

Before dismissing altogether the phage protein from further consideration, some mention must be made of that 20% of the phage sulfur which is not removed from the infected cells by the blendor treatment. Much of this sulfurylated protein fraction probably represents parts of phage tails which adhere too firmly to the bacterial surface to be shaken loose; in support of this notion, electron micrographs show that the material stripped off the infected cells looks exactly like phage ghosts with shortened tails (422). The notion that at most a minor fraction of the "nonstrippable" 20% of the phage protein actually enters the infected cell was also buttressed by the observation that no more than 1% of the methionine or lysine of the parental T2 phage protein reappears in the protein of the progeny phages (227, 301), in contrast to the constituents of the parental phage DNA, which *do* enter the host cell and which, as shall be seen in a later chapter, *are* transferred efficiently to the DNA of the progeny. But one proteinaceous, albeit minor, component of the infecting phage that does enter the host cell with the viral DNA is the *internal protein* already mentioned in Chapter 3 (294, 297, 415). This protein carries some 7% of the total sulfur of the T2 particle (480), and hence must represent about one third of the "nonstrippable" phage S^{35} of the blendor experiment. In spite of its entry into the bacterium at the time of infection, however, the internal protein is *not* transferred to the progeny viruses (480). Thus the argument that the nontransfer of most of the other "nonstrippable" protein proves its failure to enter the host cell is not wholly rigorous. The other two minor internal components of the T2 phage mentioned in Chapter 3, the acid-soluble peptide and the polyamines, also find their way into the infected cell, but since they contain no sulfur they make no contribution to the "nonstrippable" S^{35}.

How does the single, enormous viral DNA macromolecule, seen in the electron micrograph of bacteriophage T2 of the frontispiece, manage to travel from the phage head into the interior of the host cell? It seems likely that the mechanical penetration of the cell wall by the tail core upon contraction of the tail sheath and, possibly, the digestion of the inner mucopolymer layer by the phage lysozyme in the tail after adsorption provide the necessary breach in the cell integument. The tip of the phage tail must then become uncorked, probably by removal of the core, so that the DNA is free to pass through the channel provided by the sheath into the host cell cytoplasm. Since the width of the hole in the sheath is little larger than the 20 Å diameter of the DNA molecules themselves, the DNA would have to pass through the sheath as a single thread. The nature of the moving force of this process, whose dynamics would be roughly equivalent to quickly pushing a 10-meter length of string 1 mm thick through a narrow straw, is less clear. In any case, the energy-yielding reactions of the host cell do not seem to be called upon for this purpose, since the DNA is ejected from the phage head after adsorption to either heat-killed bacteria or isolated cell walls or after various chemical and physical treatments of the free phage particles. One may imagine, therefore, that the DNA is packed into the phage head under constraint and forces its own way out through the sheath after the contraction and "uncorking" reactions of the tail are triggered.

The discovery that most or all of the DNA, and only very little of the protein, of the parental phage enters the host cell at the moment of infection thus showed that it must be the DNA which is the carrier of the hereditary continuity of the virus; that is, it is the **germinal substance** of the extracellular phage. (The 20–35% of adsorbed phage P^{32} liberated from infected bacteria in the blendor experiment probably represents the DNA complement of a minor fraction of the phage population which fails to infect, or properly inject its DNA into, the bacterial hosts.) The release of the phage DNA from its protein coat at the very moment of infection evidently accounts for the eclipse period at early stages of intracellular virus development, when, as Doermann's premature lysis experiment showed, no infective virus particles can be recovered from the infected cell. For, having just been divested of its attachment and injection organs, the DNA of the parental phage is of course now unable to gain entrance into any further bacteria to which it might be presented in the infectivity test after its release upon artificial lysis of the host cell.

Hershey and Chase's attribution of a germinal role to the viral DNA was thus in perfect harmony with the earlier discovery of Avery, MacLeod, and McCarty (33) that in bacterial transformation the hereditary factors of the donor bacillus are transferred to the genome of the receiver cell through the exclusive vehicle of bacterial DNA molecules. Now in retrospect it seems odd that, though in 1952 the genetic role of bacterial DNA had already been known for eight years, the notion that viral DNA is also the hereditary material of bacterial viruses did not figure prominently in any of the numerous hypotheses on the nature of phage previously considered. Perhaps, the idea that DNA is the germinal substance of the virus, if it was ever proposed, had been rejected as too hopelessly naive. In any case, it was Hershey and Chase's experiment that suddenly brought enlightenment to all but the most obdurate regarding the true nature of the functional differentiation of the two principal viral components, nucleic acid and protein. Four years later, the doctrine that the nucleic acid is the carrier of viral heredity was generalized with the discovery that the tobacco mosaic virus reproduces only from its ribonucleic acid complement and can dispense with its protein for infection (211, 242). At present there can be little question of the validity of this doctrine, as more and more examples of bacterial, plant, and animal viruses have been provided in which the pure viral nucleic acid, stripped of its protein envelope, is an infectious agent that is competent to induce synthesis of structurally intact viral progeny in the host cell.

Further Reading

Schlesinger, M., "Adsorption of bacteriophages to homologous bacteria" (544). The first physicochemical analysis of bacteriophage adsorption [reprinted in English translation in (595)].

Hershey, A. D. and Chase, M., "Independent functions of viral protein and nucleic acid in growth of bacteriophage" (306). The paper that demonstrated that DNA is the germinal substance of the bacteriophage; a milestone in phage research.

Garen, A. and Kozloff, L. M., "The initiation of bacteriophage infection" (237); Tolmach, J., "Attachment and penetration of cells by viruses" (634); Hershey, A. D., "Bacteriophages as genetic and biochemical systems" (292); Weidel, W., "Bacterial viruses (with particular reference to adsorption/penetration)" (667). Specialized reviews devoted to the subject of this chapter.

CHAPTER 6

Synthesis of Virus Progeny

Incomplete-phage Protein—Incomplete-phage DNA—Phage Precursor Pools—The DNA Pool—The Protein Pool—The Maturation Process

THE DIVORCE of parental nucleic acid and parental protein at the moment of infection reflects a most characteristic trait of viruses; in their life cycle, viruses pass through a stage in which the genetic substance is the only material link connecting one generation to the next. The entire bacteriophage is thus reproduced only from its DNA, which, once injected into the host cell, is committed to two principal tasks: (1) its own several hundredfold replication to generate the genetic substance with which the progeny viruses are to be endowed and (2) the manufacture of several hundred replicas of the phage protein to provide heads, tails, and internal proteins for the somatic substance of the progeny. To achieve this end, the infecting phage DNA diverts the anabolism of the bacterial host cell away from the making of autochthonous bacterial constituents into new channels leading to the construction of viral components. This synthesis of materials foreign to the uninfected cell is carried out in part by the existing metabolic apparatus of the host and in part by new protein and nucleic acid species whose synthesis is also induced by the phage DNA in the infected cell but which are not themselves destined to become part of the infective progeny particles. We shall now recount in more detail those events that unfold within the phage-infected bacterium during the phage latent period.

We saw in Chapter 4 how Doermann had studied the intracellular growth of bacteriophage by breaking open infected cells at various stages of the latent period and assaying these premature lysates for the number of infective phages present. His experiment thus followed the appearance of progeny particles already endowed with the power of self-reproduction, the most complex of all the attributes of the virus particle. Later investigations revealed, however, that in artificially induced lysates of phage-infected bacteria there are also present "incomplete" phage structures which possess one or another of the properties of the virus without as yet being capable of causing the formation of plaques when plated on sensitive indicator bacteria. The study of these "incomplete" phage structures showed that the actual synthesis of the substance of the phage progeny proceeds already during the eclipse period and that the intracellular appearance of infective progeny represents only the *maturation* of previously formed phage components into morphologically intact, infective units.

Incomplete-phage Protein

The bacteriophage protein, as already discussed in Chapter 3, is an excellent antigen and exhibits a rigorous serological autonomy vis-à-vis the proteins of the host cell. It is, therefore, possible to search for the existence of incomplete phages by examining lysates of infected bacteria for the presence of noninfective materials that react specifically with the antiphage antibodies of sera from animals immunized with purified phage stocks. For instance, if an antiphage serum (from which all antibodies directed against bacterial antigens have been removed through exhaustive adsorption with bacterial debris) is added to a phage lysate, then any material in the lysate capable of reacting with phage antibodies settles into an immune precipitate, whereas all other materials devoid of phage-specific antigens remain in suspension. A search for incomplete phages, which took advantage of this immunospecific precipitation, was carried out by Maaløe and Symonds (462). They infected bacteria growing in a radiosulfur S^{35}-labeled medium with T2 phages, lysed the bacteria artificially at various times after infection, and then counted the radioactivity in the protein that could be specifically precipitated from the lysates with anti-T2 phage serum. It was discovered in this way that some noninfective, serum-precipitable phage protein actually appears in the infected cells several minutes before the end of the eclipse period. If the amount of precipitable phage protein detected at various times after infection is expressed in multiples of the total sulfur content of a single, intact T2 bacteriophage—that is, in

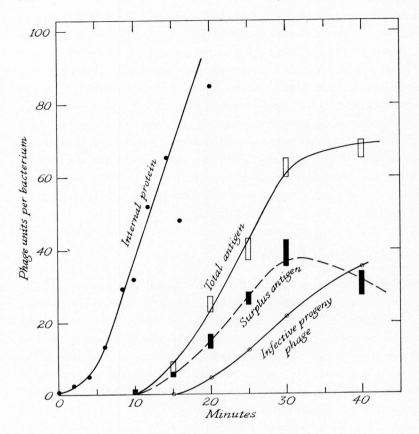

Fig. 6-1. Appearance of incomplete-phage protein in T2-infected bacteria. The curve labeled "total antigen" represents the amount of S³⁵-labeled material specifically precipitable by anti-T2 serum that is liberated by premature lysis-from-without of *E. coli* infected with an average of five T2 particles per cell. The infected bacteria are growing in a synthetic medium to which S³⁵-sulfate is added at the moment of infection. The points on the curve labeled "surplus antigen" represent the difference between number of phage units per cell of "total antigen" and the number of intracellular infective progeny per cell present at various times. [Data from Watanabe (654).] The curve labeled "internal protein" represents the amount of antigenic material reacting with anti-T2-internal-protein antibodies liberated by sonic disruption of T2-infected *E. coli*. The infected bacteria are growing in broth. [Data from Murakami, Van Vunakis, and Levine (488).]

terms of *phage units*—then the infected cell already contains approximately 10–20 phage units of antigenic phage protein when the first infective progeny particles make their appearance. After the termination of the eclipse (after intracellular infective phage progeny have appeared), the amount of incomplete phage protein, or **surplus antigen,** can be estimated by subtracting the number of infective centers found upon infectivity assays of the lysates from the total number of phage units of antigenic sulfur precipitated. As can be seen in Fig. 6-1, the incomplete or *surplus* phage antigen attains a maximum of 30 to 40 phage units per infected cell 20 minutes after infection and then remains at this level throughout the remainder of the latent period (299, 462, 654).

Phage antigens can reveal their presence not only through specific antiserum-precipitability but also through *interference* with antiserum neutralization of a test population of the same phage strain. That is, any materials having the same antigenic structure as those parts of the phage tail that ordinarily react with the neutralizing antibodies can themselves combine with, or adsorb out, the neutralizing antiphage antibodies and hence diminish the neutralizing potency of an antiphage serum. The **serum-blocking-power** (**SBP**) of a suspension of phage antigens can be estimated quantitatively by comparing the reductions in neutralizing titer produced in a serum upon addition of the antigens and upon addition of a known number of intact phage particles. One phage unit of SBP thus corresponds to the reduction in neutralizing titer engendered by treatment of the serum with one phage particle. In this way Burnet (111) discovered in 1933 that there exist incomplete phage antigens in T-even phage lysates: after having removed all intact, infective virus particles from the lysates by ultrafiltration, a significant amount of SBP activity was still present in the filtrates. Twenty years later, these investigations were continued by DeMars (171), who confirmed, first of all, that from 10 to 25% of the total SBP of T-even phage lysates is in an incomplete form—that is, is not part of intact phage—since this fraction of the SBP passes through filter membranes that retain the virus particles and cannot be sedimented in centrifugal fields that bring down the virus particles. More importantly, DeMars studied the appearance of neutralizable phage antigens in T2-infected bacteria by ascertaining the total SBP liberated from infective centers lysed at various times after the onset of intracellular phage growth. His experiments showed that the first nonsedimentable SBP appears within the infected cells between the

9th and 10th minute, or some 2 to 3 minutes prior to the debut of the first infective progeny. They showed, furthermore, that at later stages of the latent period, after the end of the eclipse, the total SBP of the lysates then increases steadily, concomitantly with the rise in titer of intra-cellular infective progeny; the total number of phage units of SBP, however, is always in excess of the number of infective progeny phages. Since the neutralizable antigens of the T-even virus reside in the tail of the phage particle (393), the incomplete SBP material detected in this experiment no doubt represents phage tail protein which has not yet become part of structurally intact, infective units. These incomplete SBP materials are probably included in the antiserum-precipitable surplus antigen fraction of Maaløe and Symonds.

The antisera employed in the experiments on serum-precipitable surplus antigens are, as a rule, obtained from animals immunized with purified stocks of intact T-even phages and contain, therefore, no antibodies against the antigenically distinct *internal* protein of these viruses. Antibodies against the internal protein can only be elicited, as already explained in Chapter 3, by immunizing with preparations of osmotically shocked or otherwise disrupted phage. Sera prepared in this way also contain, of course, antibodies directed against the external antigens of the phage, but these antibodies can be removed by exhaustive adsorption with intact phage particles, leaving behind only anti-internal protein antibodies. The amount of internal phage protein present in any preparation can then be estimated by adding to it such an adsorbed serum and measuring the extent of the antigen-antibody reaction. Levine and his collaborators (488) used this assay to investigate the intracellular appearance of the internal protein in T2-infected bacteria, and their results are also presented in Fig. 6-1. It can be seen that within 2 to 3 minutes after the onset of intracellular phage growth an increase in the amount of internal protein over that introduced into the cells by the parental phage is already manifest, and that by the time the first infective progeny appear at the end of the eclipse period, more than 50 phage units of internal protein are already present in the infected cells.

The electron microscope offers another method of searching for incomplete bacteriophage structures, quite independently of serological techniques. Whereas only the intact phage particles themselves show up in electron micrographs of *purified* phage suspensions, a variety of other objects can be discerned in pictures of *crude lysates* of phage-infected bacteria. It was first pointed out by Wyckoff (699) and by Hercik (272) that the resemblance of the shape of some of these objects to the characteristic morphology of parts of the intact bacterial virus suggests that they represent incomplete forms of the virus. Particularly prominent here are certain rings or "doughnuts," whose diameter is about the same as that of the electron-dense head of the intact phage particle but which are not attached to any tail and are also much less electron-dense. That these doughnuts are indeed related to intracellular phage growth was shown by Levinthal and Fisher (421), who lysed T2-infected bacteria at various times after the onset of phage growth and counted the number of doughnuts visible in electron micrographs of the crude lysates. At early stages of the latent period they saw no doughnuts or any other structures not also liberated from uninfected *E. coli* cells similarly lysed. However, about 3 minutes before the debut of morphologically intact phages and the termination of the eclipse, doughnuts began to appear in their lysates and then increased in number at about the same rate as the intracellular infective progeny, until a maximum of about 35 doughnuts per infected bacterium had been attained. The number of doughnuts then remained at this level, while the number of intact, infective phage particles continued to rise. These "doughnuts," as T. F. Anderson (20) could show, are in fact *empty phage heads*, which look like flat disks rather than rings when the electron microscope specimens are dried by methods that avoid surface tension distortions. As would be expected, the empty heads neither adsorb to sensitive bacteria nor carry any SBP antigens, since, having no tails, they lack the adsorption organ and site of neutralizable antigens of the phage. Each empty head has about 25% of the total mass of the intact virus, and carries most of the viral protein (about 75% of the total viral sulfur) but very little, if any, of the viral DNA (less than 15% of the total virus phosphorus) (172). There is little doubt that these empty heads account for the bulk of the sulfurylated serum-precipitable "surplus" antigens mentioned earlier in this chapter. Further experiments by Kellenberger and Séchaud (359) confirmed the kinetics of the appearance of empty T2 phage heads and also demonstrated the presence in premature lysates of certain "rods," which resemble the T2 phage tail in structure and dimensions. Unlike empty phage heads, the rods appear only after the termination of the eclipse and finally reach an average level of about

30 rods per bacterium. The rods cannot be complete phage tails, however, since they do not carry any T2 SBP antigens and, though reversibly adsorbed to bacteria, do not become irreversibly fixed to the host cell surface. Figure 6-2 is one of Kellenberger and Séchaud's

Fig. 6-2. Electron micrograph of a crude lysate of T2-infected *E. coli*. Structurally intact phages, empty heads ("doughnuts"), and tails are visible. The tangled filaments in the upper part of the picture probably are DNA. [From Kellenberger and Séchaud (359).]

electron micrographs on which structurally intact T2 phages, empty heads, and tail cores are visible.

Serological and morphological observations thus agree in showing that components of the viral protein appear in an incomplete form in the phage-infected bacterium before the emergence of the infective progeny and that these incomplete forms continue to accumulate in the cell after the end of the eclipse. However, these studies do not yet clarify the relation that such incomplete forms bear to the structurally intact virus particles which follow in their wake. We shall temporarily defer our discussion of this important question.

Incomplete-phage DNA

For some time it proved more difficult to find the phage DNA in an incomplete form than the phage protein. When S. S. Cohen, one of the first workers to apply the methods of modern biochemistry to the problem of phage growth, first studied the nucleic acid metabolism of T2-infected bacteria in 1947, he found that net DNA synthesis in the culture comes to a halt immediately after infection, and that some 5 or 6 minutes later DNA synthesis resumes at a rate greater than that obtaining just before infection (137, 138). If, as Cohen assumed, all of this postinfection DNA synthesis concerns the manufacture of phage DNA, then a considerable fraction of the newly formed phage DNA must be in incomplete form, since the amount of DNA per infected bacterium at all times greatly exceeds that which can be accounted for by intracellular infective progeny particles. In order to detect such incomplete forms of the phage DNA, a search was made for noninfective, DNA-containing materials in phage lysates which possess either the *antigenicity*, or the *sedimentability*, or the *adsorbability* of the phage. (It should be noted here that T-even phage particles not only differ from any constituent of the host cell in their antigenic structure but, because of their size, shape, and density, also possess a characteristic sedimentation velocity unlike that of any part of the bacterium, and, because of the attachment organ in their tail, are specifically adsorbable to bacterial cells.) An experiment was, therefore, carried out in which T2-infected *E. coli* growing in a P^{32}-labeled medium were lysed artificially at various times after the onset of intracellular phage growth and count was then made of the P^{32} radioactivity which could either be specifically precipitated from the lysates with anti-T2 antibodies or be specifically sedimented from the lysates by differential centrifugation in gravitational fields bringing down only the virus particles, or be specifically adsorbed from the lysates to a test suspension of T2-sensitive *E. coli* cells (461). The results of this search were distinctly negative: during the eclipse period of T2-infected bacteria, no radioactive phosphorylated material (that is, DNA) could be found which was serum-precipitable, sedimentable, or adsorbable like the intact virus. After the end of the eclipse period, furthermore, the only phosphorylated structures found to be endowed with these characteristics were the infective progeny particles themselves. In other words, there do not appear to exist any incomplete, DNA-containing phage structures which possess (a) the antigens, or (b) the size, shape, and density, or (c) the attachment organs of the intact virus. These observations are, of course, in harmony with the finding that the serum-precipitable incomplete phage protein occurs mostly in the form of *empty*, DNA-free phage heads.

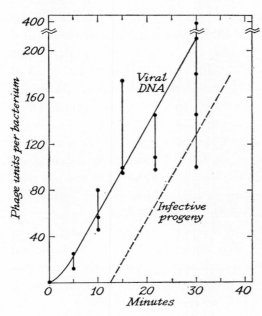

Fig. 6-3. Appearance of viral DNA in T2-infected *E. coli* growing in broth. The number of phage units of DNA per cell has been computed from the amount of HMC recovered by chromatography after acid hydrolysis of a DNA extract of the infected cells. Each point represents the analysis of a different culture. [Data from Hershey, Dixon, and Chase (302).]

The discovery (698) that the DNA of the T-even bacteriophages contains the unusual pyrimidine, 5-hydroxymethylcytosine (HMC), in place of cytosine, the more common base found in the DNA of the *E. coli* host, now made it possible to examine phage-infected bacteria for the presence of phage-specific DNA at various stages of intracellular growth. The first investigation of this sort was carried out by Hershey, Dixon, and Chase (302), who infected *E. coli* bacteria with T2 phages, extracted the DNA of the infected culture at different times after the onset of phage growth, and analyzed the extract for its content of HMC, cytosine, and the other purine and pyrimidine bases. These analyses then permitted an estimate of the number of phage units of HMC-containing DNA present at any time, based on the total nucleic acid and relative HMC content of the intact T2 phage particle. The results of such an experiment are presented in Fig. 6-3, where it may be seen that the synthesis of bacteriophage (that is, HMC-containing) DNA commences between the 6th and 7th minute after infection and then proceeds so rapidly that a few minutes later, when the first infective progeny make their appearance, already some 40–80 phage units of HMC-containing DNA are present within the infected cell. The synthesis of phage DNA then continues at a more or less constant rate throughout the remainder of the latent period, so that there is always an excess of about 80 phage units of HMC-containing DNA over the total number of infective progeny which accumulate in the cells during that time. This "surplus," incomplete phage DNA found in the premature lysates is "free" in the sense that, as we have already seen, it does not sediment in centrifugal fields capable of sedimenting intact virus particles, and that it is sensitive to the hydrolytic action of DNase (288). These findings thus show that synthesis of not only the viral protein but also of the viral DNA commences during the eclipse, well before the first appearance of structurally intact, infective progeny.

Phage Precursor Pools

Since the incomplete forms of viral protein and DNA appear in the lysates before the infective progeny, the thought readily comes to mind that they are **phage precursors** and in some way represent developmental stages in the ontogeny of the virus particle. This notion cannot be simply taken for granted, however, since instead of being phage precursors, these incomplete structures could also be *by-products* of phage reproduction or abortive attempts to assemble intact phages, in which case they would never be destined for integration into the future infective progeny. In order to qualify as a phage precursor, a structure encountered in an incomplete state at an early stage of intracellular growth must, therefore, be shown to become part of infective progeny phage at a later time. Fortunately, this point can be settled by use of tracer atoms; if an isotopic label added to the infected culture first shows up in an incomplete structure and afterwards enters intact phage—that is, if the label "flows" through it—then the structure really is a phage precursor. This, as the following discussion shows, is actually the case for the incomplete-phage protein and DNA described in the preceding paragraphs.

The DNA Pool

Isotopic tracer experiments on bacterial virus reproduction began in 1948 with an experiment of S. S. Cohen, which at last laid to rest an idea propounded repeatedly since the discovery of the bacteriophage. This notion, borrowed from the autocatalytic conversion of trypsinogen into trypsin, envisaged that there are already present within the normal host bacterium *bacteriophage precursors* whose metamorphosis into the "lytic principle" is merely triggered by the infecting phage (245, 385, 387). Cohen's experiment (139), which has since its time served as the paradigm of the testing of postulated precursor relations, simply asked the question whether the phosphorus atoms of the DNA of the progeny viruses are already within the bacterial cell at the time of its infection, as would be demanded by the precursor hypothesis. Two cultures of *E. coli* were grown for this purpose, one in medium labeled at a known specific activity of P^{32}, and the other in nonlabeled medium. After growth, the bacteria were centrifuged out of their original culture fluids, the labeled cells resuspended in nonlabeled growth medium, and the nonlabeled cells resuspended in labeled growth medium. Both cultures were then infected with T2 phage at a multiplicity of infection of several phages per cell and incubated until complete lysis. The progeny phages grown in each culture were finally isolated, purified, and assayed for their specific content of the P^{32} label. The result of this experiment was that the DNA phosphorus of the phages grown on labeled bacteria in nonlabeled medium possessed only one-third of the specific activity of the P^{32} introduced, whereas the DNA-phosphorus of the phages grown on nonlabeled bacteria in labeled medium possessed two-thirds of the specific activity of the P^{32} introduced. Cohen thus demonstrated that most of the phosphorus of the phage DNA has not yet been assimilated from the growth medium at the moment of infection and hence that the phage particles cannot derive exclusively from pre-existing precursors in the host cells. Nevertheless, one-third of the atoms of the phage progeny DNA *has* already been assimilated before infection. This fraction, the **bacterial contribution,** is not, as Cohen originally supposed (139), supplied preferentially by low molecular weight intermediates of bacterial nucleic acid metabolism present in the bacterium at the moment of infection. Instead, as was shown by growing T-even phages on bacteria whose purines or pyrimidines were specifically labeled with radiocarbon C^{14}, it is the bacterial DNA which is the chief provenance of the bacterial contribution (303, 377, 662). A minor fraction of the bacterial contribution, however, is also derived from the host ribonucleic acid. In thus contributing their substance to the DNA of the progeny phages, the bacterial nucleic acids are broken down to low-molecular weight fragments subsequently repolymerized into phage-specific polynucleotides (302, 303). A biochemical route for the bacterial contribution other than breakdown and resynthesis would, in any case, be difficult to imagine, since the purine-pyrimidine base composition of the bacterial DNA is qualitatively different from that of the DNA of the T-even phages, in particular in that the former contains cytosine and the latter HMC. During the course of intracellular phage growth, more than 85% of the host (that is, cytosine-containing) DNA disappears, most of which ultimately reappears in phage (HMC-containing) DNA. In this process, bacterial cytosine is directly converted into viral HMC (141).

The complete kinetics of assimilation of phage DNA phosphorus atoms were later studied by two modifications of Cohen's experiment. First, P^{32} label was either added to nonlabeled bacterial cultures or withdrawn from labeled cultures *at various times before and after their infection* with T2 phages. Second, one aliquot of these cultures was lysed prematurely shortly after the termination of the eclipse and another aliquot was allowed to proceed to spontaneous lysis. In this way, the fraction of the total phage phosphorus assimilated by the time of addition or removal of the P^{32} could be estimated from the specific P^{32} content of the DNA of the phage yields produced, both for the earliest phages to appear within the cells and for the final crop of progeny viruses. The results of this experiment are shown in Fig. 6-4. If we focus attention first on curve B, describing the specific P^{32} content of the final phage progeny, we notice that prior to infection the bacteriophage phosphorus is assimilated at the rate of bacterial growth, confirming the inference that end products of bacterial synthesis such as nucleic acids, and not metabolic intermediates, are the source of the bacterial contribution. The intersection of curve B at the time of infection with the ordinate at the 0.3 level corresponds to Cohen's original finding that one-third of the phosphorus of the phage progeny is present in the cell prior to infection. Immediately after infection, however, the rate of phage phosphorus assimilation is seen to increase sharply, indicative of a sudden alteration in the metabolism of the infected cell, which channels almost all the newly assimilated phosphorus atoms into the pathway of phage DNA synthesis. Assimilation of the phage phosphorus is seen to be nearly complete 20 minutes after the onset of phage growth, although, as shown in curve C, infective progeny continue to make their appear-

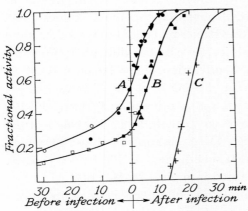

Fig. 6-4. Assimilation of bacterio-phage phosphorus by *E. coli* before and after their infection with T4. Curve A. Fraction of phosphorus incorporated into the DNA of the first 15% of the progeny phages to mature. Curve B. Fraction of phosphorus incorporated into the DNA of the progeny phages of the final yield. Curve C. Fraction of final phage yield present intracellularly as infective progeny. The bacteria are growing in a synthetic medium of low total phosphorus content, to which P³² is added (solid symbols) or from which P³² is withdrawn (open symbols) at the time indicated on the abscissa. [From Stent and Maaløe (602).]

ance in the cells for at least another 10 minutes. We may now consider curve A, which describes the relative content of P³² label in the first few progeny per cell to appear. Curve A evidently runs above and parallel to curve B, showing that on the average the phosphorus of the first infective progeny is assimilated earlier than that of the final progeny. At the time of infection, curve A intersects the ordinate at 0.6. Thus a greater fraction of the phosphorus of the DNA of the first phages to mature has already been assimilated from the medium before infection; that is, the bacterial contribution appears preferentially, though not exclusively, in the first progeny. The horizontal distance between curves B and C indicates that phosphorus atoms assimilated from the medium after infection spend an average "development time" of about 14 minutes in the cell prior to their incorporation into the DNA of infective progeny phages. The parallelism of curves A and B implies, however, that individual development times of different phosphorus atoms are widely distributed about this average; in other words, phosphorus of the bacterial contribution and phosphorus assimilated at various times after infection are *mixed* in the course of intracellular phage growth. This finding led to the idea that the phage DNA phosphorus passes through one or more intrabacterial pools, whose size and number is reflected by the observed degree of mixing (602).

These experiments were extended by Hershey (288), who examined, under a variety of labeling programs, the time course of the specific P^{32} content of not only intact progeny phages but also of incomplete or "free" phage DNA present in T2-infected cells. Hershey's experiments showed that the incomplete phage DNA is indeed the precursor of the DNA of the infective progeny viruses. A pool of this phage precursor DNA, whose phosphorus is derived both from the breakdown products of the host DNA and from the growth medium, is built up in the bacterium during the first 10 minutes of intracellular phage growth. At the end of the eclipse period, phage DNA begins to be withdrawn at random from this pool for incorporation into intact progeny viruses. From that point onward, synthesis of phage DNA and formation of infective progeny proceed at more or less the same rate, so that the pool of phage precursor DNA retains a constant size of about 50–100 phage units per cell for the remainder of the latent period. Once a phosphorus atom has been built into an intact phage particle, it does not reappear in the phage DNA precursor pool, showing that incorporation of DNA into the progeny virus is *irreversible*. This process, furthermore, is also very *efficient*, since more than 90% of the phosphorus atoms that enter the phage DNA precursor pool manage to be incorporated into intact phage particles at some later time. About half of the average "development time" of 14–16 minutes spent by the phosphorus atoms on their way from the medium to intact phages is required for the trip from medium to phage DNA precursor pool, and the other half for the rest of the journey.

The Protein Pool

The source of the atoms of the phage progeny protein has been studied in a manner similar to that just described for the assimilation of phage DNA phosphorus, except that S^{35}-, N^{15}-, or C^{14}-labeled amino acids, instead of P^{32}, were used as the tracer materials. These experiments proved that *very little, if any, of the viral protein is derived from the protein of the host cell*—there is no important bacterial contribution to the protein of the virus progeny (380, 567). The kinetics of assimilation of the raw materials for phage protein were studied by Hershey (303), who allowed T2-infected bacteria to take up S^{35} label from their growth medium for 5-minute intervals at various stages after the onset of phage development and then determined the amount of S^{35} subsequently incorporated into the mature intact virus particles and into the general bacterial protein. This experiment showed that the total amount of radioisotope which enters intrabacterial protein during a 5-minute exposure to labeled growth medium is more or less the same at all stages of the latent period, as well as also being equal to the labeling attained during the same interval by an uninfected bacterial culture. An earlier finding by S. S. Cohen (137, 138) that total protein synthesis proceeds in the host cell at the same rate before as after infection was thus confirmed. The proportion of the total assimilated S^{35} that finds its way into virus protein, however, varies greatly at different stages of the latent period. Very little of the sulfur assimilated during the first 5 minutes after infection ultimately enters the protein of the phage progeny, whereas at least 60–70% of the total sulfur taken up during any 5-minute interval after the 10th minute of phage growth is destined for the mature virus particles. These results indicate that two classes of protein, one phage precursor and the other not, are synthesized in the infected host cell and that the maximal rate of precursor protein synthesis is not reached until the latter part of the eclipse period.

However, it is apparent that synthesis of different particular components of the phage precursor protein starts at different times in the latent period. For, as the data of Fig. 6-1 show, new internal phage protein is already discernible in the infected cells 3 minutes after the beginning of phage growth, at a time when very little of the total sulfur assimilated is evidently consigned to phage precursor protein. Minagawa (480) could demonstrate the validity of this inference directly by undertaking short, transient exposures of an *E. coli* culture to S^{35}-labeled medium at different times after its infection with T2 phage and fractionating by osmotic shock the protein of the progeny phage particles ultimately formed into internal protein and phage ghost, comprising the head and tail protein. He then determined the relative amount of S^{35} present in the two components under various labeling programs and found that T2 particles produced in bacteria given a transient exposure to S^{35} immediately after infection contain labeled internal protein but essentially unlabeled head and tail proteins. In contrast, T2 particles produced in bacteria exposed briefly to S^{35} after the 20th minute of intracellular phage growth were found to contain a higher specific S^{35} activity in their head and tail proteins than in their internal protein. There can be little doubt therefore that in the T2-infected cell, construction of the polypeptide chains of the internal protein of the phage progeny starts well before synthesis of any polypeptides of viral head and tail proteins has begun.

The most complete studies of the kinetics of phage precursor protein synthesis were carried out by Koch and Hershey (367), who determined the rates of incorporation and disappearance of C^{14}-labeled arginine or S^{35} into and from various protein fractions found in lysates of T2-infected bacteria; in particular they focused their attention on the total protein of the cell, the intact phages, the antiphage serum-precipitable "surplus" antigens, and a "soluble" protein which cannot be precipitated with antiphage antibodies. The results of one of their experiments, in which S^{35} was fed to T2-infected bacteria from the 20th to the 25th minute of phage growth, is presented in Fig. 6-5. First, it may be noted that about 19 phage units of sulfur enter the total protein of the cells during the time that S^{35} is fed to the culture; after that

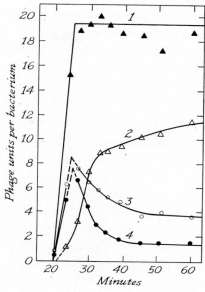

Fig. 6-5. Incorporation of S^{35}, fed from the 20th to the 25th minute of infection, into various proteinaceous fractions of T2-infected *E. coli* growing in a synthetic medium of low total sulfur content. The ordinate presents the amount of sulfur assimilated during the labeling period (a phage unit being 1.5×10^{-12} μg of sulfur) that has reached a given fraction by the time indicated on the abscissa, when the culture is lysed-from-without. Curve 1. Total protein of the infected cells. Curve 2. Protein of intact progeny phages. Curve 3. "Soluble" protein not precipitable by anti-T2 antibodies. Curve 4. Serum-precipitable "surplus" phage antigens. [From Koch and Hershey (366).]

period, label neither enters nor leaves the protein with further growth. Second, it is evident that about 12 phage units per bacterium of the sulfur assimilated during the 5-minute labeling period are ultimately incorporated into phage particles, corresponding to a rate of synthesis of phage precursors of 2.4 phage units per bacterium per minute. Of these 12 units of labeled protein per bacterium assimilated, 10 units appear in phage particles only after the end of the labeling period, the half-time of this incorporation process being about 5 minutes. Third, at all times subsequent to the labeling period, the sum of the S^{35} content of the three fractions—phage particles, serum-precipitable "surplus" antigen, and nonprecipitable "soluble" protein—is constant, showing that the sulfur incorporated into phage particles is derived exclusively from the other two fractions. Thus the "surplus" antigen, as well as the nonprecipitable "soluble" protein, is indeed a precursor of the protein of the infective progeny particles. Since the flow of S^{35} into and out of these two precursor fractions is virtually simultaneous, it seems unlikely that the nonantigenic soluble protein is itself a precursor of the serum-precipitable "surplus" antigen; instead, both fractions appear to be direct precursors of the mature virus.

The Maturation Process

We may now form an image of that last act of intracellular phage growth which permanently encloses the phage precursor nucleic acid into a protein head membrane and endows the intact head with a tail—that is, the *maturation* of the infective unit. Some insight into this process, which, Hershey (292) thought in 1957, "presents a more complicated problem, at least conceptually, than vegetative [phage] reproduction," was provided by electron-optical observation of phage-infected cells. The desirability of looking at what can be seen by means of the electron microscope inside bacteria at various stages of phage growth had, naturally, been long appreciated by phage workers. But for many years the interior of the phage-infected cell remained veiled to the electron microscopist since the thickness of the intact bacterium renders it quite opaque to the electrons of his microscope. Finally, the formidable technical obstacles in the way of electron-optical observations of phage-infected cells were overcome by Kellenberger (355), who developed a superior method of slicing infected bacteria into ultrathin sections transparent to the electron beam.

Kellenberger and his collaborators (360, 557), first of all, could confirm in this way the earlier findings (157, 449, 489) made in the ordinary, visible light microscope that (as discussed more fully in Chapter 14) the bacterial nucleus, site of the bacterial DNA, disintegrates and its material becomes dispersed during the first few minutes of intracellular phage growth. (The cytologically manifest destruction of the host nucleus by T-even phages is, of course, in perfect harmony with the inference from isotopic tracer experiments that most or all of the host DNA is broken down to low molecular weight materials to provide the bacterial contribution to the progeny phage DNA.) At later stages of the latent period, Kellenberger observed events hithertofore invisible; onward from about the 8th minute, the bacterial cytoplasm begins to fill up with characteristic fibrils, whose dimensions suggest that they are the "incomplete" molecules of the phage DNA precursor pool. For the remainder of the latent period, some of these DNA fibrils continue to be present. At about the 10th minute, well before the end of the eclipse period, a new type of structure appears in the sections—electron-dense bodies exhibiting the polyhedral shape of the head of intact T2 phage particles (Fig. 6-6). The number of such polyhedral bodies per cell visible at various times in the latent period always exceeds the total number of empty phage heads and intact phage particles per cell present in premature lysates of the same population of infected cells. Some of the polyhedral bodies, therefore, cannot be *structurally intact* heads belonging to either mature phages or to incomplete phage precursors but correspond to an as yet earlier stage in the ontogeny of the virus particle. It is these bodies that must hold the key to the maturation problem.

According to Kellenberger (356), one may envisage the maturation of the intact phage particle in the following terms. The first step of this process is the **condensation** of the single viral DNA macromolecule from the vegetative phage DNA precursor pool into one of the polyhedral bodies visible in electron micrographs of ultrathin sections of infected cells. This condensation, which is certain to involve considerable losses in entropy, is achieved by means of a proteinaceous "condensation principle" that establishes cross-ties between different segments of the very long polynucleotide molecule and allows, or guides, its package

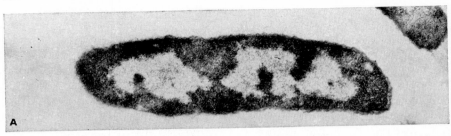

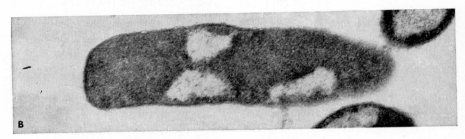

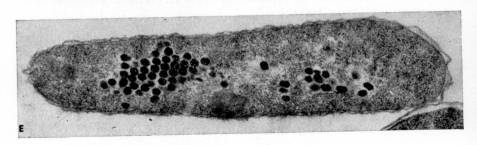

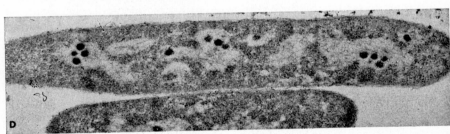

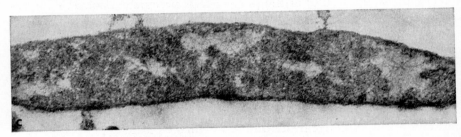

into a compact polyhedron. The *internal protein* of the T-even phages would commend itself for the role of this condensation principle. The other minor components present within the phage head, the acid-soluble peptide and the polyamines, probably serve to neutralize the high density of negative charges of the acidic polynucleotide, which unneutralized would present a formidable energetic barrier to its condensation. These polyhedral DNA condensates are not yet stable upon disruption of the host cell and appear as free DNA molecules in lysates. The second step in the maturation is the growth of the proteinaceous head membrane around the polyhedral DNA condensate, through aggregation or crystallization, of the thousand or so identical head protein subunits drawn from the phage protein precursor pool. These tailless phage precursor heads also are not yet stable structures; their internal condensed polynucleotide leaches out of the head membrane upon lysis of the infected cell, so that they give rise to empty phage heads—the "doughnuts" and the serum-precipitable "surplus antigens"—and to free viral DNA molecules. The third step is the endowment of the nascent phage head with the tail, an engine whose assembly from its diverse constituent protein subunits is probably even more intricate than the construction of all the rest of the phage particle. Even at this stage, the nascent virus is still not stable and disintegrates upon lysis of the infected cell into the various structural components visible electron-optically (Fig. 6-2) or detectable as surplus precipitable or SBP antigens. Finally, as the last step, the completely assembled progeny particle attains maturity when some cement holding all of its components together has "set" and its structural integrity as an infective unit survives lysis of its native host cell.

One of the first clues to the nature of the maturation process was

---

Fig. 6-6. Electron micrographs of ultrathin sections of T2-infected *E. coli* at various stages of intracellular phage growth. **A.** At the moment of infection; the normal bacterial nuclei are visible as electron-transparent areas. **B.** Two to four minutes after infection; the nuclei have changed their form and migrated towards the cell wall. **C.** Ten minutes after infection; the nuclei have disappeared and, instead, vacuoles filled with fibrillar material (phage DNA) have made their appearance. **D.** Fourteen minutes after infection; the first condensates of phage DNA have been formed. **E.** Forty minutes after infection; many condensates and structurally intact phage heads are present. [From Kellenberger, *Scientific American*, **204**, No. 6:93 (1961).]

already secured in 1946 when Delbrück and Bailey (167) observed an anomalous plaque assay behavior of phages liberated from bacteria mixedly infected with T4 and T2 phages. Novick and Szilard (497) investigated this anomaly further and found that joint growth of T2 and T4 phages within the same bacterium produces some hybrid phage particles that have themselves the adsorption organs characteristic of T4 (that is, are adsorbable to the T2-resistant bacterial host strain B/2) but carry the germinal material of T2, since their own progeny have the adsorption organs of T2 (that is, are not adsorbable to the T2-resistant B/2 host). This phenomenon, which evidently gives rise to phage particles that possess the adsorption organs of one but the germinal material of another parent, is called **phenotypic mixing** (308). Phenotypic mixing has been observed not only for the host-specific adsorption character but also for the serum-neutralizable antigens (611) and adsorption cofactor requirements (90) of the T-even phages. From detailed studies of phenotypic mixing, Streisinger (611) concluded that among the issue of a bacterium infected jointly with two different parental phage types, adsorption specificity and neutralizable antigen characters are nearly randomly associated with the corresponding germinal material. Since the specific adsorption organs and the neutralizable antigens of the virus particle are carried in its tail protein and the hereditary factors of the phage are carried in its DNA, phenotypic mixing reveals the free association of tail protein with phage precursor DNA in the maturation process. Or, in terms of Kellenberger's maturation model, we may say that in an infected bacterium harboring a mixed population of T2 and T4 phage precursor DNA molecules and of T2 and T4 tail protein subunits, tail protein subunits of one type are free to associate themselves with nascent polyhedral head bodies enclosing the condensed phage precursor DNA of the other type, and thus generate progeny particles that manifest the somatic character of one parental phage and the genetic character of the other.

Another observation of rather long standing pertaining to phage maturation is that in the presence of the acridine dye **proflavine** T2-infected bacteria lyse after the normal latent period without releasing any infective progeny (210). If proflavine is removed from the growth medium of the culture a few minutes before the end of the normal latent period, however, a considerable number of infective progeny is produced, suggesting that proflavine blocks a rather late step in phage reproduc-

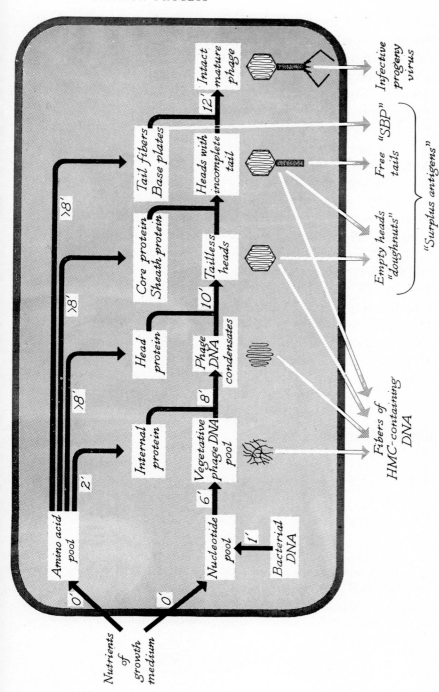

Fig. 6-7. Flow sheet summarizing the ontogeny of T-even phages, indicating the time after infection at which the reaction steps are thought to commence. The lower part of the diagram traces the origin of various incomplete-phage materials found in lysates of phage-infected bacteria.

tion. Electron-optical, immunological, and chemical studies support this view, since proflavine lysates, though devoid of any infective units, do contain the "incomplete" phage structures mentioned earlier in this chapter; empty phage heads (or doughnuts), serum-precipitable and serum-blocking (SBP) phage antigens, internal proteins, and phage (HMC-containing) DNA are all present in amounts similar to those found in lysates of infected bacteria growing in the absence of the drug. No particles are present in proflavine lysates, however, that exhibit the morphology of intact phages (171, 172, 361). One is thus led to conclude that while proflavine allows the synthesis of all the known major constituents of the phage, it inhibits in some way their maturation into the intact virus. Since the characteristic polyhedral bodies do appear in electron micrographs of sections of infected bacteria growing in the presence of proflavine, it cannot be the condensation of the phage precursor DNA into the head configuration with which the drug interferes (360). Instead, it is probable that proflavine prevents the final cementing of already assembled parts of the progeny virus.

The ideas brought forward in this chapter are summarized schematically in Fig. 6-7, which presents a no doubt greatly oversimplified flow sheet of the path along which the precursors of the progeny particles are processed on their way to virushood in the phage-infected bacterium.

Further Reading

Cohen, S. S., "Synthesis of bacterial viruses; origin of phosphorous found in desoxyribonucleic acids of T2 and T4 bacteriophages" (139). The first application of radioisotopes to phage research, which showed that most of the phosphorus of the phage DNA is assimilated from the growth medium after infection.

Hershey, A. D., "Nucleic acid economy in bacteria infected with bacteriophage T2. II. Phage precursor nucleic acid" (288); Koch, G. and Hershey, A. D., "Synthesis of phage precursor protein in bacteria infected with T2" (367). Analyses of the kinetics of synthesis of viral DNA and protein.

Kellenberger, E. and Séchaud, J., "Electron microscopical studies of phage multiplication" (359, 360). Excellent electron micrographs of the structures pertaining to vegetative phage growth.

Kellenberger, E., "Vegetative bacteriophage and the maturation of virus particles" (356). A concise review that covers also the intracellular growth of phage types not mentioned in this chapter.

CHAPTER 7

Metabolism and DNA Replication in the Infected Cell

Bacterial Enzymes—The Early Protein—Phage-induced Enzymes—Cell Envelope—Ribonucleic Acid Synthesis—Replication of the Phage DNA— Transfer of DNA from Parent to Progeny Phage

WE SHALL now consider the biochemical events that unfold in the phage-infected cell during the synthesis of the precursor materials from which, as was seen in the last chapter, the progeny of the infecting virus are finally assembled. In particular, we shall first enquire into the metabolic machinery which carries out the reproductive sequence initiated by the infecting viral DNA. A rough calculation shows that the total synthetic power required of the phage-infected bacterium is similar in magnitude to that achieved by the uninfected cell: the viral substance represented by the several hundred T2 progeny phages synthesized per cell during the half-hour latent period of phage growth is comparable in weight to the bacterial protoplasm synthesized by the cell during its normal half-hour division period. The apparatus already existing in the host cell for supplying the raw materials and energy of general anabolism ought, therefore, to be equal to the demands of phage reproduction.

Bacterial Enzymes

Studies of the metabolism of phage-infected bacteria began in 1946. During that year Cohen and Anderson (142) examined the rate of respiration of T2-infected *E. coli* cultures and hence, indirectly, of the overall energy supply furnished to the cell by its enzymatic ensemble involved in uptake of oxygen, transport of electrons, oxidation, fermen-

139

tation of carbohydrate substrates, and formation of energy-rich phosphate bonds. This study showed that T2 infection of bacteria immediately stops the formation of further respiratory enzymes, so that respiration of (and hence energy flow into) the cells proceeds at a *constant* rate for the entire latent period. Interference with this energy flow by respiratory poisons such as cyanide instantly arrests the progress of phage development, a fact which, as we already noted in Chapter 4, was utilized by Doermann in the design of his probe into the kinetics of intracellular phage growth. At about the same time as these experiments, Monod and Wollman (481) showed that phage-infected *E. coli* bacteria can no longer be induced to form their enzyme β-galactosidase. Subsequent studies on the formation of a variety of other enzymes of whose synthesis the uninfected cell is capable showed the same general picture: infection by T-even phages causes the synthesis of bacterial enzymes to come to a sudden and complete halt; throughout the latent period, the activity of bacterial enzymes remains at its preinfection level (50, 139, 140, 500, 501, 566).

This sudden halt of enzyme synthesis has important practical consequences, particularly in the case of **inducible** or **repressible enzymes,** whose presence in the cell depends on the previous history of the culture. Thus, phage multiplication cannot proceed in a bacterium which *prior* to infection has not already been allowed to form all those inducible or repressible enzymes that may be required for growth under the conditions obtaining *after* infection. (For instance, no T2 phage are produced in *E. coli* grown in a glucose-supplemented medium before infection and then transferred to a medium containing lactose as the only carbon-energy source after infection, since the β-galactosidase necessary for hydrolysis of the lactose is absent from the glucose-grown cells.) An apparent exception to the rule that synthesis of bacterial enzymes ceases upon T-even phage infection was discovered by Pardee (388, 502) who found that the activity of bacterial DNase increases several fold soon after infection of an *E. coli* culture with T-even phage. At first, it was attempted (377) to reconcile this seemingly exceptional finding with the general phage-induced arrest of enzyme synthesis by proposing that the observed increase in activity of DNase does not derive from its post-infection synthesis, but rather from the phage-induced destruction of a species of bacterial ribonucleic acid (RNA) inhibitory to the hydrolytic action of DNase. But though the activity of bacterial DNase is indeed subject to partial inhibition by bacterial RNA (65), later work (609) failed to substantiate this proposal. Rather, it now appears that the postinfection stimulation of DNase activity was actually the first observed instance of what was later to be called the "virus-induced acquisition of metabolic functions" (205).

Not only does phage infection stop the formation of bacterial enzymes, but it also arrests production of "structural" proteins such as the protein moiety of the bacterial ribosomes, which contain about 10% of the total protein of the bacterial cell and which, as shall be considered in more detail later, play an important role in the process of protein synthesis itself. It is most likely that this dramatic cessation of synthesis of bacterial proteins is the consequence of the destruction of the host cell nucleus at the outset of intracellular phage growth mentioned in Chapter 6. Inasmuch as the integrity of the bacterial DNA is necessary for the continued synthesis of bacterial protein (see Chapter 15), it is small wonder that no further increase in the amount of bacterial enzymes or structural protein is observed as the host nucleus is being broken down into nucleotide raw materials for the construction of viral DNA. Thus, whatever bacterial enzymes are to be utilized for the metabolic reactions of phage growth must already be present in the host cell prior to infection.

The Early Protein

In their first studies on the metabolism of T2-infected cells, Cohen and Anderson (142) also measured the *total* amount of protein in the bacterial culture and found that overall protein synthesis in the bacteria is by no means inhibited by phage infection and continues at its preinfection rate throughout the latent period. Thus phage infection has no immediate effect on the *quantity* of protein formed in the host cell, but only engenders important changes in its *quality*. Much of the protein synthesized after the 12th minute of phage growth is phage precursor protein (see Fig. 6-5); in fact, more than 60% of the total protein then synthesized in the cell concerns one single species of phage precursor protein—the polypeptide subunit of the phage head membrane. However, at early stages of the eclipse period only a very minor fraction of the total de novo protein (that small amount represented by the *internal* protein of the phage) is a precursor of intact phage progeny particles. It might be thought, therefore, that the nonprecursor protein synthesized in the cell in the time intervening between infection and onset of massive precursor manufacture is not directly connected with the process of phage reproduction. But this "early" protein cannot, of course, reflect the temporary continuation of the formation of normal bacterial proteins, whose synthesis, as already mentioned, ceases abruptly at the outset of infection. Moreover, formation of most of this early protein must actually be induced by the viral DNA, since T2-infection of *ultraviolet-irradiated E. coli*, whose endogenous protein synthesis has been very greatly reduced by the radiation, causes an immediate acceleration of net protein synthesis, which then proceeds at the rate characteristic of normal infected cells (655). The experiments to be recounted now show that the non-precursor proteins appearing in the host cell immediately after infection represent molecular species that are in fact essential factors in phage growth.

In 1947, Cohen and Fowler (145) observed that no phage reproduction takes place if the tryptophan analogue 5-methyl tryptophan, which blocks the biosynthesis of tryptophan and thus the formation of protein, is added to bacterial cultures at the moment of their infection with T2 phage. This interference with phage growth produced by the amino acid analogue cannot simply be due to the prevention of the synthesis of phage precursor protein; instead, it must represent the blockage of a very early step in vegetative phage development, since not only protein but also DNA synthesis by the infected cells is likewise suppressed under these conditions. After removal of 5-methyl tryptophan from the culture,

$$H_3C-\underset{\underset{H}{|}}{\underset{N}{\bigcirc\!\!\!\bigcirc}}-CH_2-\underset{\underset{NH_2}{|}}{CH}-COOH$$

5-methyl tryptophan

phage development commences, leading to a burst of progeny phages after a normal latent period reckoned from the time of removal of the analogue. Subsequent refinements and extensions of this type of experiment showed that no synthesis of phage-specific (HMC-containing) DNA occurs in T-even phage-infected bacteria in which protein synthesis has been suppressed from the very start, either by the presence of an inhibitory amino acid analogue or the antibiotic *chloramphenicol*, or by the absence of a required amino acid. If, however, the bacteria are infected under normal conditions and protein synthesis is stopped by

$$O=C-CHCl_2$$

$$O_2N-\left\langle\bigcirc\right\rangle-\underset{\underset{OH}{|}}{\overset{\overset{H}{|}}{C}}-\underset{\underset{H}{|}}{\overset{\overset{NH}{|}}{C}}-CH_2OH$$

chloramphenicol

any of these methods only a few minutes after the start of intracellular phage development, then synthesis of HMC-containing phage DNA does proceed without formation of any further protein, and the *rate* of such DNA synthesis per cell is the greater the later protein synthesis has been arrested (Fig. 7-1). No infective progeny particles are, of course, formed under these conditions until the inhibitory factor has been removed and synthesis of phage precursor protein allowed to take place. These experiments show, therefore, that the appearance of some nonprecursor protein is required in the infected cell before replication of the bacteriophage DNA can commence. Once some of this "essential" protein has been formed, synthesis of the viral DNA can proceed in the absence of further protein synthesis (121, 307, 474, 637).

The data of Fig. 7-1 show that T2-infected bacteria to which chloramphenicol is added at late stages of the eclipse period can accumulate considerable amounts of HMC-containing DNA in the presence of the antibiotic. This DNA is really phage precursor DNA, since, if radiophosphorus P^{32} is added to the infected cells only during the time of chloramphenicol inhibition, the labeled phage DNA synthesized in the presence of the antibiotic later enters the structurally intact progeny phages that mature after protein synthesis has been allowed to resume. In fact, phage DNA formed after removal of the chloramphenicol appears to be mixed with the phage precursor nucleic acid pool of previously synthesized DNA (307). The phage DNA formed in the absence of protein synthesis is not only a phage precursor but is also "functional," since the phage particles which draw such DNA molecules for their germinal substance are fully infective (636). Furthermore, both *mutation* and *genetic recombination*—processes which, as we shall see presently, are associated with the replication of the viral genetic material —occur during phage DNA synthesis in the presence of the antibiotic

(99, 296, 428). The great excess in amount of phage precursor DNA over phage precursor protein which can thus develop in chloramphenicol-inhibited infected cells shows that the replication of the phage DNA does not have to proceed *within* any structure composed of phage precursor protein. Electron micrographs of ultrathin sections of T2-infected bacteria synthesizing phage precursor DNA in the presence of chloramphenicol manifest the intracellular accumulation of the characteristic DNA fibrils, but show none of the polyhedral DNA condensates which are otherwise visible before the end of the eclipse period of normal growth (Fig. 7-2) (358). Soon after the removal of the antibiotic and resumption of protein synthesis, however, polyhedral DNA condensates do make their appearance. The necessity of protein synthesis for formation of these condensates supports, or rather was the stimulus for, Kellenberger's conception of the proteinaceous condensation principle mentioned in Chapter 6. Evidently synthesis of the condensation principle is required before phage DNA can be removed from the vegetative phage DNA pool and condense into the structure later to be encapsulated into the phage head membrane of the mature intact progeny virus particle.

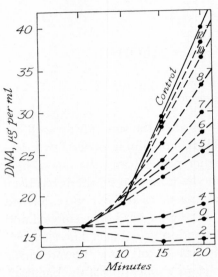

Fig. 7-1. The effect of chloramphenicol on the synthesis of DNA in T2-infected bacteria. *E. coli* grown in broth to a density of 3 × 10⁸ cells/ml are infected with an average of four T2 phages/cell. After the elapse of the number of minutes indicated on each curve, 30 μg/ml chloramphenicol is added to a sample of the infected culture (the sample labeled "control" receives no chloramphenicol). At the time indicated on the abscissa, the total amount of DNA/ml in each sample is determined by means of the colorimetric diphenylamine reaction specific for DNA. [From Tomizawa and Sunakawa (637).]

Phage-induced Enzymes

The nature of the "early" protein essential for phage DNA replication became greatly clarified when Flaks and Cohen, Kornberg and his

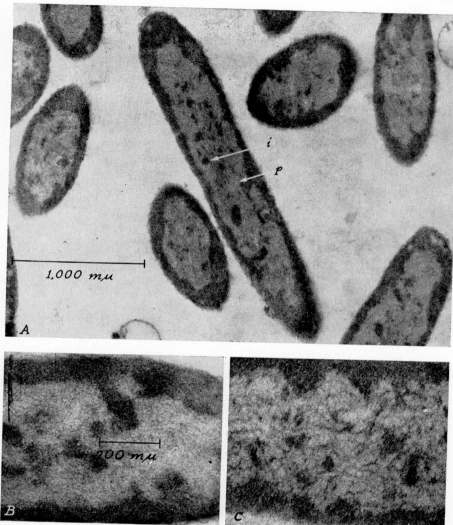

Fig. 7-2. Electron micrographs of the pool of vegetative phage DNA. *E. coli* are infected with an average of three T2 phages per cell and 25 μg/ml chloramphenicol is added 8 minutes after infection. The infected bacteria are fixed and prepared for ultrathin sectioning 75 minutes later. **A.** The giant DNA pool (*p*), composed of thin filaments, nearly fills the whole cell; the denser islets (*i*) in the pool represent transverse cuts of cytoplasmic protrusions. **B.** Detail of the pool; its aspect is very similar to that of bacterial nuclei. **C.** Detail of the pool in bacteria in which the DNA filaments have been aggregated by treatment with a chelating agent. [From Kellenberger, Ryter, and Séchaud (358).]

Fig. 7-3. Virus-induced acquisition of metabolic function in the T-even-infected bacterium. The numbered arrows (except Nos. 10 and 11) represent enzymes whose formation is induced by T-even phages. (ATP = adenosine triphosphate; UDPG = uridine diphosphate glucose.)

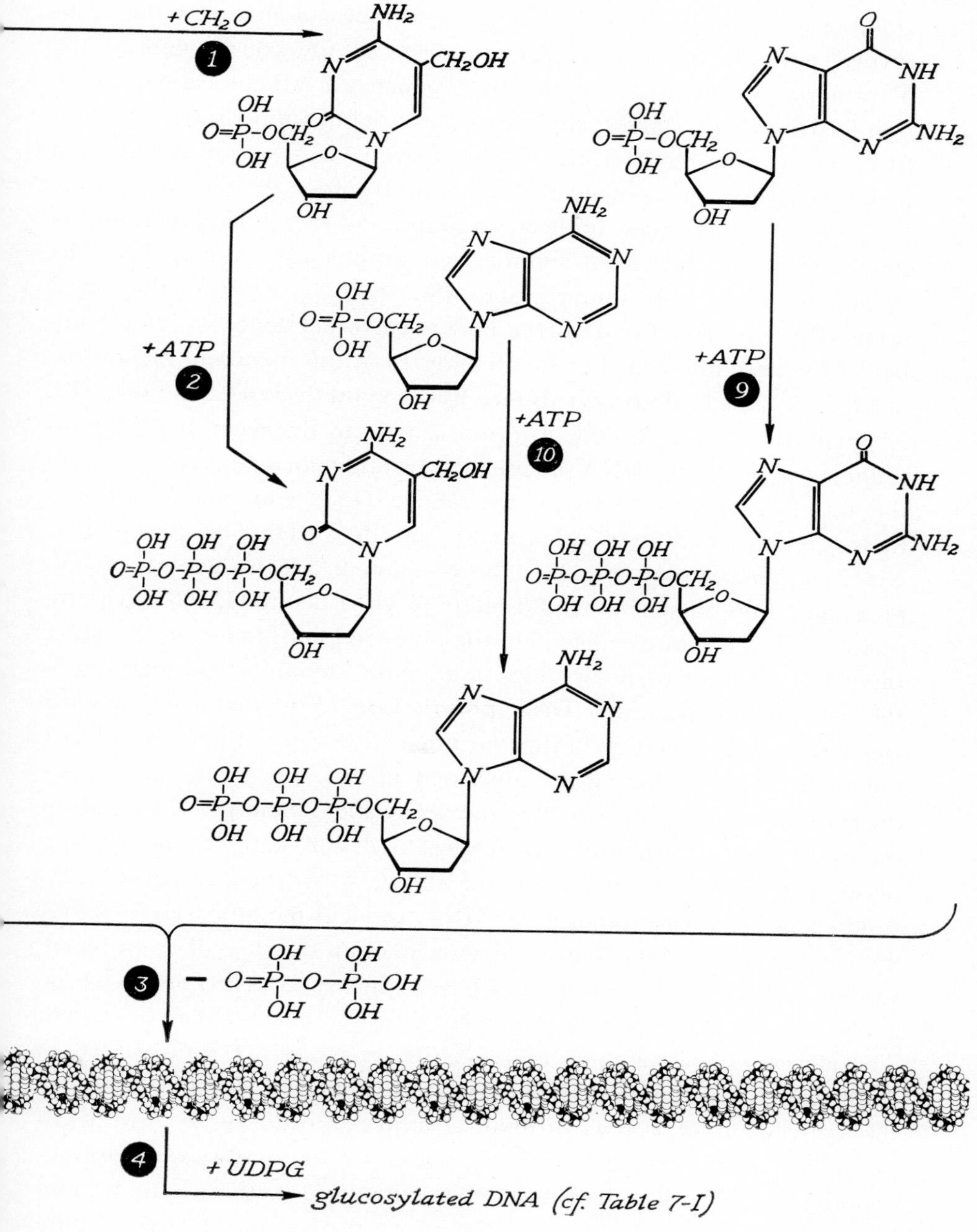
+ CH₂O
1
+ATP
2
+ATP
10
+ATP
9
3
4
+ UDPG
glucosylated DNA (cf. Table 7-I)

collaborators, and others discovered a number of new enzymes concerned with the intermediary metabolism of the constituents of the T-even phage DNA. These enzymes, which are absent from normal, uninfected *E. coli*, make their intracellular debut immediately after infection of the host bacterium by the T-even virus and thus represent new species of protein molecules synthesized under the direction of the phage DNA. This "virus-induced acquisition of metabolic functions" of the infected cell has been summarized graphically in Fig. 7-3. The following enzymes are found among the "early" protein of the initial stages of phage growth, numbered here in correspondence with the number of the reaction step that each catalyzes in the metabolic panorama of Fig. 7-3. No. 1: **deoxycytidylate hydroxymethylase** (205, 207, 372, 579) catalyzes the addition of formaldehyde to deoxycytidine-5'-phosphate, converting this DNA precursor nucleotide normally synthesized in the uninfected bacterium into the phage DNA component deoxy-5-hydroxymethyl-cytidine-5'-phosphate (or deoxy-HMC-5'-phosphate). No. 2: a **kinase** that catalyzes the reaction between deoxy-HMC-5'-phosphate and adenosine triphosphate to yield deoxy-HMC-5'-triphosphate (372); the latter, like the analogous triphosphates of the other three DNA precursor nucleotides of adenine, thymine, and guanine, is the substrate of No. 3: a **DNA polymerase** (371) that catalyzes the ordered copolymerization of the four nucleotide triphosphates into DNA polynucleotide, by linking the innermost of their three phosphates in a diester bond to the 3'-hydroxyl of the deoxyribose moiety of the adjacent nucleotide. No. 4: **glucosyl transferases** (372, 408) catalyze the reaction between uridine-diphosphate-glucose and the 5-hydroxyl group of HMC residues of *intact*, macromolecular DNA, to yield the glucosylated DNA molecules typical of the T-even phages. Each of the three T-even phage strains induces the formation of different glucosyl transferases, to whose action the specific glucosylation pattern shown in Fig. 3-11 can be traced. The characteristics of these glucosylating enzymes are summarized in Table 7-I. No. 5: **deoxycytidine pyrophosphatase** (370, 372) catalyzes the conversion of deoxycytidine-5'-triphosphate to deoxycytidine-5'-phosphate. This enzyme is a specific poison for the synthesis of cytosine-containing DNA, since it reverses the activating function of the normal kinase of uninfected bacteria that converts deoxycytidine-5'-phosphate to the triphosphate substrate of the bacterial DNA polymerase. The appearance of deoxycytidine triphosphatase ensures that no cytosine finds its way into DNA molecules synthesized after the onset of phage growth, unless the hydroxymethyl group has first been added to the 5-position of the pyrimidine residue. No. 6: **deoxycytidylic deaminase** (353) catalyzes the removal of the 6-amino group of deoxycitidylic acid —that is, the conversion of deoxycytidylic into deoxyuridylic acid. No. 7: **thymidylate synthetase** (40, 206) catalyzes the addition of formaldehyde to the 5-position of deoxyuridine-5′-phosphate. The appearance of enzyme No. 6 and its partner, No. 7, establishes a new metabolic pathway of thymine biosynthesis in the infected cell. The creation of this pathway accounts for an earlier, and at the time rather surprising, observation (39) that, upon T2 infection of thymine-requiring auxo-

TABLE 7-I

HMC-Glucosyl Transferases that Appear in T-even Infected E. coli*

PROCEDURE: Growing cultures of *E. coli* were infected with an average of 3–4 T2, T4, or T6 phages per cell and intracellular phage development allowed to proceed for 15 minutes. The proteins of the infected bacteria were then extracted and fractionated by ion-exchange column chromatography. The glucosyl transferase activity in the fractionated extracts was studied by measuring the transfer of C^{14}-glucose from uridine-diphosphate-glucose to the HMC residues of an acceptor DNA added to the test system. The glucosylated acceptor DNA was degraded enzymatically to mononucleotides and the extent and character of the C^{14}-glucosylation determined by chromatography and specific hydrolysis with α- and β-glucosidases of the C^{14}-glucosylated hydroxymethylcitydilic acid residues. The acceptor DNA used in these tests was either a *synthetic*, initially nonglucosylated DNA prepared by the action of DNA polymerase on the deoxynucleoside triphosphates of adenine, guanine, thymine, and HMC, or a *natural*, already glucosylated phage DNA extracted from one of the three T-even phage types.

Transferases Found in Extracts of Infected *E. coli*	Extent of C^{14}-glucosylation of Acceptor DNA			
	Synthetic HMC-DNA	T2 DNA	T4 DNA	T6 DNA
	% of total HMC residues glucosylated			
T2-HMC-α-glucosyl	50–58	< 1	< 1	< 1
T4-HMC-α-glucosyl	60–75	7	< 1	< 1
T6-HMC-α-glucosyl	50–71	7	< 1	< 1
T4-HMC-β-glucosyl	70–78	28	< 1	25
T6-glucosyl-HMC-β-glucosyl	< 1	70	70	< 1

THE DATA OF THIS TABLE

LEAD TO THE FOLLOWING CONCLUSIONS:

1. α-Glucosyl transferases appear in T2-, T4-, and T6-infected *E. coli* that glucosylate 50–75% of the HMC residues of synthetic, initially glucose-free acceptor DNA. These transferases transfer little or no glucose to the glucose-free HMC residues of the natural T2 and T6 acceptor DNA. This suggests that the specificity of the α-glucosyl transferases allows them to add glucose only to a restricted class of HMC residues of the DNA polynucleotide chain.

2. A β-glucosyl transferase appears in T4-infected bacteria that adds glucose to the glucose-free HMC residues of T2 and T6 acceptor DNA. The specificity of the T4-β-glucosyl transferase thus permits it to glucosylate that class of HMC residues of the DNA which the α-glucosyl transferases cannot glucosylate, thus accounting for the complete glucosylation of all HMC residues of the natural T4 DNA.

3. A glucosyl-β-glucosyl transferase appears in T6-infected bacteria that cannot add glucose to the glucose-free synthetic acceptor DNA, but can add a second glucose molecule to all of the monoglucosylated HMC of T2 acceptor DNA and to 70% of the monoglucosylated HMC of T4 acceptor DNA. The specificity of this enzyme evidently allows glucosylation of an HMC-α-glucosyl residue, but does not allow glucosylation of glucose-free HMC or HMC-β-glucosyl residues. T6-induced α-glucosyl and glucosyl-HMC-β-glucosyl transferases acting in tandem thus account for the diglucosylated HMC residues that predominate in natural T6 DNA.

---

* From Kornberg, Zimmerman, and Kornberg (373).

trophic mutants of *E. coli*, phage growth and synthesis of thymine-containing phage DNA can proceed perfectly well in the absence of an exogenous supply of the thymine growth factor.

In addition to these enzymes, whose activity represents a totally new metabolic function foreign to the uninfected bacterium, there are also several enzymes already present prior to infection whose activities increase significantly in the course of intracellular phage growth. This second class includes the **deoxyribonuclease** mentioned earlier in this chapter (388, 502) and Nos. 8 and 9, which are **kinases** (72, 73, 372) that catalyze the reaction of deoxythymidylic-5′-phosphate and deoxyguanylic-5′-phosphate with adenosine triphosphate to yield, respectively, deoxythymidylic-5′-triphosphate and deoxyguanylic-5′-triphosphate, the substrates of the polymerase in the copolymerization of the DNA polynucleotide. Does this postinfection increase in activity of enzymes whose function is native to the uninfected cell represent merely a phage-induced stimulation of pre-existing enzyme species? Or does it, just as the appearance of phage-induced enzymes whose activity is foreign to the normal cell, represent the synthesis of a new class of enzyme proteins under the direction of the viral DNA? It seems likely that it is the latter alternative that is correct: the postinfection increase in enzyme activity seems to reside in new proteins whose function merely resembles rather closely that of autochthonous bacterial enzymes but which upon closer examination show distinct behavioral differences from their bacterial analogues (72, 73, 609).

The only enzymes of DNA metabolism that do *not* show any increase in their activity after T-even phage infection are the *kinases* Nos. 10 and 11, which catalyze the conversion of deoxyadenylic and deoxycytidylic acids into their triphosphates (372). Of these two, adenylic kinase already exists in the uninfected bacterium at a level much higher than any of the corresponding other kinases (372) and hence is apparently already sufficiently abundant for the later demands of phage growth. And cytidylic kinase, in any case, becomes *de trop* as soon as HMC replaces cytosine as a basic constituent of DNA anabolism.

Why synthesis of the early protein should be a prerequisite for synthesis of the viral DNA is now explained: if appearance of these metabolic enzymes is prevented by inhibiting protein synthesis at the time of infection, then some reactions essential for the construction of viral DNA cannot be carried out and synthesis of phage-specific DNA is a fortiori out of the question. Once these enzymes are present in the cell, however, then they can continue to catalyze their respective reactions, and replication of viral DNA can proceed without any further formation of enzymes—that is, in the absence of further protein synthesis. The discovery of the phage-induced enzymes of phage DNA metabolism taught two important lessons on the function of the genetic material of viruses. First, the viral DNA induces in the infected cell the synthesis not only of the materials which are to make up the intact, mature progeny virus particle (of the phage precursors) but also of enzymes which pertain only to the vegetative phage and do not appear in the infective unit. Second, the synthesis of virus-induced enzymes may proceed in the infected cell *prior* to the onset, and hence in the absence of, viral DNA synthesis. The process, therefore, which "reads off" the instructions from the genetic material and translates them into physiological function by directing the construction of specific proteins (see Chapter 15) does not require the concomitant replication of the viral DNA.

Though de novo formation of enzymes of phage-specific DNA metabolism adequately explained the necessity for protein synthesis prior to onset of intracellular T-even phage growth, some votaries of the early protein thought that one of its components might have some intimate connection with the very replication of the hereditary material; for instance, it seemed conceivable to them that the ordered copolymerization of the viral DNA molecule from its nucleotide building blocks might involve a proteinaceous **template** of which the early protein forms part (593, 594). They were encouraged in this belief by the observation that synthesis of an essential protein is also required before replication of the genetic material of the coliphages T1 and λ can get under way (631, 642). Unlike the composition of the DNA of the T-even strains, that of the DNA of T1 and λ does not seem to be qualitatively different from that of the DNA of the host bacterium, and hence it is not obvious what new metabolic enzymes would be necessary here before polymerization of the viral DNA could proceed. Furthermore, the early protein also figures in the evolution of the radiation resistance of T-even-infected bacteria (see Chapter 12), in a manner that cannot very readily be accounted for in terms of the mere appearance of enzymes of metabolism of phage DNA constituents (511, 637, 642, 643). But whatever as yet unknown components the early protein might actually comprise, it now seems clear that the transcription of the hereditary factors of the infecting phage to a proteinaceous template cannot be an essential prelude to the replication of the viral DNA molecule. For it has been demonstrated that in a bacterium infected with two related but genetically distinct phage particles, the early protein synthesized under the influence of *only one of them* can serve for the subsequent replication of the genetic material *of both* (203, 631).

Cell Envelope

The enzymatic processes related to the synthesis of phage-specific DNA are not the only metabolic functions acquired by the infected cell. Another series of reactions initiated by T-even phages concerns the cell envelope. One of these reactions *strengthens* the envelope and heals the postinfection trauma of the bacterium. As mentioned in Chapter 5, this phage-induced synthesis of cell wall components stops cytoplasmic leakage and concomitantly restores to the infected culture its preinfection turbidity. The progress of this reaction also makes known its presence by means of another phenomenon that shall now be considered.

Exclusion and Superinfection Breakdown

If a T2-infected bacterium is superinfected with a second T2 particle at various times after the onset of growth of the first phage, we observe the progress of an exclusion reaction that prevents participation of the secondary virus in the reproductive events of the infected cell. Thus, in the event that primary and secondary virus differ from one another in some genetic character, fewer and fewer infective centers liberate phage progeny bearing the genetic character of the secondary phage as more and more time has been allowed to elapse between primary and secondary infection (192, 248). Exclusion of 50% of the superinfecting phage is already achieved by the first minute and of about 95% by the tenth minute of primary phage growth, although it is still possible—by massive superinfection with several hundred secondary phages per cell—to introduce secondary genetic characters into most of the infective centers at late stages of the latent period (649). This exclusion of genetic character of the secondary phage is paralleled by *breakdown* of the superinfecting phage DNA, as can be demonstrated by superinfecting (with P^{32}-labeled secondary T2 particles) bacteria already infected with non-labeled primary T2 phage. If a period of more than 2 minutes intervenes between primary and secondary infection, then most of the P^{32}-labeled secondary DNA is no longer injected into the bacterium; about half of the labeled DNA is degraded and appears in the medium in a low-molecular-weight form, while the rest remains at the cell surface (413, 414). Superinfection breakdown of the secondary DNA can be prevented by adding streptomycin to the medium or by reducing the concentration of Mg^{++} below $10^{-5} M$ (229). Since streptomycin and low Mg^{++} concentration are known to inhibit the action of DNase, it appears likely that breakdown of the DNA of the secondary phage is connected with the previously mentioned phage-induced stimulation of DNase synthesis by growth of the primary T-even virus.

Nevertheless, neither stimulation of DNase synthesis nor superinfection breakdown can be the fundamental cause of the exclusion phenomenon, since the genetic character of the superinfecting phage is excluded whether or not action of DNase is inhibited. Instead, it appears likely that, immediately after infection, growth of the primary phage induces the formation of a metabolic system that stimulates vigorous synthesis of either cell wall or cell membrane, so that the bacterial envelope soon becomes less permeable and entrance of the secondary DNA is obstructed. Partially released from the phage head after contraction of the phage tail sheath has been triggered by adsorption, the secondary phage DNA becomes accessible to enzymatic degradation at the host cell surface. This strengthening of the cell envelope is also reflected by a waxing resistance of the infective centers to lysis-from-without: multiplicities of infection of T2 phage high enough to bring about immediate lysis-from-without of uninfected bacteria no longer produce such lysis when added to cells in which intracellular phage development has already progressed for a few minutes (649).

Lysozyme

Besides setting in train a series of reactions that strengthen the cell envelope, the phage also induces synthesis of another enzyme that undoes again the constructive effort of these first reactions and ultimately produces the final dissolution of the infected cell. This enzyme is the phage lysozyme that digests from within the structural members of the cell wall and thus prepares the bacterium for lysis and liberation of intracellular phage progeny at the end of the latent period. It is possible to study the kinetics of intracellular appearance of phage lysozyme by breaking open T4-infected bacteria at various stages of the latent period and assaying the concentration of enzyme liberated. (The amount of lysozyme present can be estimated from the speed with which samples of the lysate can lyse heat- or chloroform-killed test bacteria or, better yet, can dissolve isolated bacterial cell walls.) Such studies reveal that the lysozyme is not among the early proteins but starts to make its intracellular appearance only half-way through the latent period, about the time that the first components of the phage tail protein can be detected (486). This finding is, of course, in perfect agreement with the earlier physiological observations that the lytic reaction appears to be initiated about half-way through the latent period. No doubt the delayed start of synthesis of the phage lysozyme is almost a necessity for successful phage multiplication; for if the lytic enzyme were among the early phage proteins formed soon after infection, it would commence erosion of the cell envelope too soon and thus cause lysis of the infected cell before any structurally intact, infective phage progeny had been produced.

Ribonucleic Acid Synthesis

In contrast to his finding that net synthesis of protein continues at its preinfection rate, Cohen observed in his first metabolic experiments that the synthesis of ribonucleic acid (RNA) comes to a sudden halt immediately after infection of bacteria with T2 phage (138). Very little, if any, increase in the total amount of RNA per cell occurs during the remainder of the latent period, while intracellular multiplication of the virus is actively under way. This stoppage in RNA synthesis reflects, in the first place, the phage-induced termination of the formation of **bacterial ribosomes,** the ribonucleoprotein particles which harbor about 80% of the total RNA of the bacterial cell (542), and which, as shall be explained more fully in Chapter 15, play an essential role in protein synthesis. Thus, whatever ribosomal particles are to be used for the processes of viral growth must, like the bacterial enzymes, already be present in the cell before infection. This is an inference which can be tested in another way, since the number of ribosomal particles relative to other constituents of the bacterium can be varied within rather wide limits, depending on the physiological conditions of growth of the culture before infection. Such experiments show that the rate of phage multiplication and the final phage yield in T2-infected bacteria is less the lower the preinfection level of ribosomes, so that finally no phage growth at all (**abortive infection**) is observed in bacteria which, though still perfectly viable, have been deprived of virtually all their ribosomes before infection.

RNA is the principal phosphorylated constituent of *E. coli* bacteria and hence the destination of most of the phosphorus assimilated by the cells during their normal growth. The blockage of RNA anabolism upon phage infection therefore allows synthesis of DNA to proceed at a much greater rate after rather than before infection without there being any necessity for the cell to raise the rate of its phosphorus uptake from the growth medium. This sudden switch in the distribution of newly ingested phosphorus from the pathway of RNA to that of DNA synthesis is evident in the data of Fig. 6-4, where the sharp upward turn of the phage phosphorus assimilation curve at the time of infection indicates that from this moment on a much greater fraction of the assimilated phosphorus is channeled toward phage DNA precursors.

But when Hershey (288) carried out some experiments in which P^{32} was added to bacterial cultures only after their infection with T2 phage, he found that during phage growth a small but significant amount of label enters the RNA fraction of the infected cell. Hence some RNA synthesis actually does go on in the infected cell. Volkin and Astrachan (651) could not only confirm these findings but also showed by measurement of the incorporation of P^{32} into the four individual ribonucleotides —adenylic, guanylic, cytidylic, and uridylic acids—generated by hydrolysis of the postinfection RNA that the label does not enter each of these four ribonucleotides at the same rate at which the ribonucleotides of uninfected *E. coli* bacteria would have acquired P^{32} under analogous labeling conditions; that is, the postinfection synthesis concerns a species of RNA of base composition different from that of the overall host cell RNA (Table 7-II). It is apparent that the purine-pyrimidine base com-

TABLE 7-II

Comparison of the Purine-Pyrimidine Base Composition of Postinfection RNA with that of Host RNA and Viral DNA*

Nucleic Acid	Nucleotide Composition (mole percent)					
	Adenylic (A)	Uridylic (U)	Thymidylic (T)	Guanylic (G)	Cytidylic (C)	Hydroxymethyl-Cytidylic (HMC)
Postinfection RNA in T2-infected bacteria	29	29	—	25	17	—
Normal *E. coli* RNA	23	22	—	32	23	—
T2 phage DNA	32	—	32	18	—	17

* From Volkin and Astrachan (651).

position of the postinfection RNA rather resembles that of the T2 phage *DNA*, provided that, for the purpose of this comparison, uridylic and cytidylic acids of the RNA are considered the equivalents of their structural analogues thymidylic and hydroxymethylcytidylic acids of the viral

DNA. The amount of postinfection RNA present at any time is rather small compared to the total RNA content of the bacterium, but, if expressed in multiples of the weight of nucleic acid per T2 phage particle, it nevertheless attains a level of about 20 phage units per cell. This phage-induced species of RNA is in a state of rapid metabolic turnover; if P^{32} label is first added and then withdrawn from a culture at various times after infection, it can be seen that phosphorus atoms continuously enter and leave the postinfection RNA species (32). The bulk of the RNA of normal, rapidly growing *E. coli* cells, in contrast, exhibits no such turn-over (289).

This virus-induced postinfection RNA cannot, of course, be a direct precursor of infective progeny phage, since T2 particles contain no RNA (518, 652). Nor does it represent the synthesis and rapid turnover of a small number of phage-specific ribosomes, since the P^{32} label enters an RNA fraction which does not exhibit the physical or chemical charac-teristics of ribosomal RNA. Instead, it appears that the postinfection RNA plays that most important role of the "messenger" by which the DNA of the infecting virus arrogates the host cell cytoplasm for the synthesis of viral proteins. This role shall be examined in more detail in Chapter 15.

Replication of the Phage DNA

Once it had been established that the phage DNA is the germinal substance of the virus, it became pertinent to ask just how hereditary information could actually be inscribed into a DNA macromolecule. The only answer to this question which has so far been conceived is that it is the *exact sequence* of purine and pyrimidine bases along the poly-nucleotide chains which endows different DNA molecules with their individuality; that is, the long DNA macromolecule corresponds to a scroll on which information is recorded in a language employing the four-letter alphabet *A*denine, *G*uanine, *C*ytosine, and *T*hymine. Since the base sequence of the two helically intertwined polynucleotide chains of each DNA molecule is complementary—that is, since every base on one chain determines some particular base on the other chain, it follows that every DNA molecule carries its hereditary information not once but twice, although the two chains do not record this information in the *same language*.

We learned in the preceding chapter that the DNA molecule of the infecting T-even bacteriophage enters the bacterial host cell and generates during the next half hour several hundred replicas identical to itself, to furnish the phage precursor DNA molecules with which the progeny viruses are to be endowed. And we saw in earlier sections of this chapter that prior to the onset of DNA replication, the infecting virus induces in the host cell the formation of an ensemble of new enzymes that function in the synthesis and polymerization of the specific building blocks of the viral DNA. But how are the four different deoxyribonucleotide building blocks—adenylic (A), guanylic (G), thymidylic (T), and cytidylic (C) acid—actually joined into macromolecules in an order identical to the specific nucleotide sequence of the DNA introduced by the parent virus? The complementary arrangement of purine and pyrimidine bases of the two polynucleotide chains of DNA at once suggested to Watson and Crick (659) that the DNA molecule might replicate itself directly by having each chain serve as a **template** for the formation of its complement. The two strands of the original double helix, they thought, separate, and each purine or pyrimidine base attracts and holds in place by means of specific hydrogen bonds a complementary free nucleotide available for polymerization within the cell. These free nucleotides, in the form of deoxyribonucleotide-5′-triphosphates, already possess the necessary free energy for polyesterification and are joined to one another by the DNA *polymerase* enzyme (407) after having been held in place on the parental template chain to form a new polynucleotide molecule of the required nucleotide sequence (Fig. 7-4). Thus, after growth of complementary de novo replicas has taken place along both parental polynucleotide chains, two DNA molecules are now present that are identical in regard to their exact permutation of the four purine and pyrimidine bases, and hence in informational content, with the parental DNA double helix. At this point one cycle of replication is complete. For the next replication cycle, the four polynucleotide chains of the two daughter molecules again separate, so that each can act as a template for growth of further complementary chains, to generate four DNA molecules identical with the original parental structure. In this way, the vegetative pool of phage precursor DNA would be built up and maintained by successive cycles of complementary polynucleotide chain separation and growth.

The Watson-Crick replication mechanism makes an important prediction about the distribution of the *substance* of the parental molecule over the replica duplexes, a prediction of which, it is fair to say, no one would have thought prior to Watson and Crick's discovery of the DNA double helix. Since in the act of serving as templates for the growth of new replica chains the two parental polynucleotide chains separate, the atoms of the parental double helix become equally distributed over the two daughter molecules of the first replication cycle. In subsequent rep-

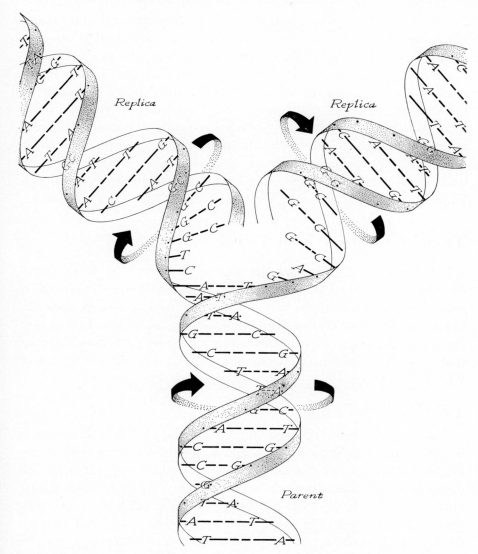

Fig. 7-4. Replication of DNA, according to the mechanism of Watson and Crick.

lication cycles, however, no further dispersal of the original parental DNA atoms should occur, since the individual polynucleotide chains of the parental DNA molecule remain intact. For instance, among the four daughter molecules generated by the second replication cycle, there are present two molecules which each contain one of the parental poly-nucleotide chains and one de novo chain, and two molecules which contain only nonparental substance. More precisely, in every one of the $2n + 1$ replica molecules generated by n synchronous replication cycles of a parent DNA molecule, one chain has been synthesized in the very last cycle and the other chain has been synthesized with probability 2^{-i} in the ith cycle before the last. This mode of distribution of the parental atoms is called **semiconservative,** in contradistinction to a **conservative** distribution, which entirely conserves the integrity of the parental DNA in the replication process (169). Under conservative replication, there is among the daughter DNA molecules generated by one or more replication cycles always one individual whose atoms are entirely parental while the substance of all the other individuals is entirely de novo (Fig. 7-5).

Transfer of DNA from Parent to Progeny Phage

It was evident that it should be possible to probe into the nature of the phage DNA replication process by following the fate of the DNA molecules injected into the host cell by the infecting virus particle. In particular, one should be able to ascertain whether or not the atoms of the parental phage DNA molecule really become partitioned over its replicas in the semiconservative manner predicted by the mechanism of Watson and Crick.

Extent and Specificity of Transfer

Studies on the fate of the infecting T-even phage DNA in the course of intracellular phage growth had begun already three years prior to the proposal of Watson and Crick, when Putnam and Kozloff (520) invented their *transfer experiment* directed toward the question of how many, if any, of the atoms of the parental DNA appear in the DNA of the progeny phages. The procedure of this transfer experiment is to infect bacteria under conditions of the one-step growth experiment with phage particles whose DNA is labeled with radiophosphorus P^{32} or radiocarbon C^{14} and

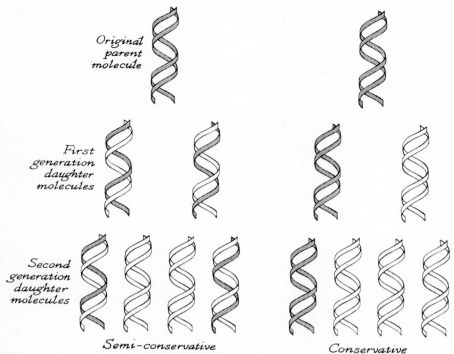

Fig. 7-5. Semiconservative and conservative distribution of the two parental polynucleotide chains as possible alternatives in the replication of DNA.

then to harvest, purify, and assay for its content of parental radioisotope the phage yield issuing from these infected host cells at the end
of the normal latent period. Putnam and Kozloff found in this way that
about 30–40% of the labeled atoms of the parental phage DNA are
transferred to the progeny. Subsequent investigations employing improved experimental techniques confirmed the transfer of an appreciable
fraction of the atoms of the infecting DNA and revealed that the transfer
efficiency can amount to as much as 50%. The remaining, nontransferred half of the labeled parental DNA atoms of the lysate is usually
found to be in part attached to bacterial debris (10%) and in part
liberated into the medium, either as macromolecular, free DNA (30%)
or as low-molecular-weight, acid-soluble compounds (10%) (229, 296,
301, 377, 463, 661).

Why, one may ask, is the transfer incomplete? Why do only 50% of
the parental DNA atoms appear among the progeny phages? Kozloff
(376, 377) favored the idea that phage reproduction involves no direct

transfer of specific parental DNA at all; instead, the parental DNA molecule might be degraded in the course of the latent period, and its degradation products introduced into the synthetic pathways of the infected cell and built up, along with other nucleic acid precursors, into new, phage-specific progeny DNA. However, closer study of the chemical and genetic details of DNA transfer rendered the hypothesis of indirect transfer by breakdown and resynthesis quite unlikely. For instance, it was found that all four kinds of purine and pyrimidine bases of the parental DNA are transferred with the same efficiency as the phosphorus atoms, and that addition of an excess of the unlabeled pyrimidine deoxyribonucleosides thymidine and uridine to the phage-infected bacteria during intracellular phage growth does not suppress the transfer of paren`al labeled pyrimidines to the progeny DNA (303). This result suggests that the parental DNA is not broken down into *nucleosides* during transfer, since pyrimidine nucleosides added to the infected culture *do* compete with pyrimidine nucleosides generated by the phage-induced breakdown of the *bacterial DNA* and interfere with the incorporation of host pyrimidines into the phage DNA as part of the "bacterial contribution." Moreover, studies involving joint growth in the same cell of labeled and unlabeled phage particles show that a considerable fraction of the atoms of the infecting DNA remains associated with recognizable physiologic or genetic characters of the labeled parent, in contrast to the more or less random partition of the parental atoms to be expected from transfer by breakdown and resynthesis. For instance, DNA phosphorus atoms of ultraviolet-inactivated, P^{32}-labeled, parental phage particles, infecting bacteria jointly with active, nonlabeled viruses, appear to carry the radiation lesions along through the transfer process, since most of the transferred label reappears in *dead* progeny particles. And transfer measurements after mixed infection of bacteria with related but genetically different labeled and unlabeled parents show that most of the parental label stays "true" to the genetic character with which it is introduced into the cell (296, 303).

Another conceivable interpretation of the incomplete transfer might be that the phage DNA consists of two portions, one predestined to be transferred and another predestined to be lost. This idea was tested by carrying out a transfer experiment through *two successive cycles of phage growth*. If the transferred atoms represent a special "transferable" part of the viral DNA, then the labeled atoms introduced by the original parent phage should become concentrated in the transferable sector of the first generation progeny and hence be transferred to a second generation progeny with much higher efficiency during the next growth cycle. However, the same transfer efficiency of original parental label was found in both first and second cycles (308, 463). This experiment was later extended to a third generation transfer (603), the results of which can be schematized as follows:

parent (label = 100%)

$\longrightarrow$ 1st generation progeny (label = 50%)

$\longrightarrow$ 2nd generation progeny (label = 25%)

$\longrightarrow$ 3rd generation progeny (label = 12%).

It may be concluded, therefore, that the parental phage DNA that is transferred neither originates from a preferentially transferable part which remains intact nor is preferentially destined for a part which is preferentially lost in the next growth cycle. It would appear, rather, that the reasons for the incompleteness of the transfer must be sought among *random losses* experienced by the entire parental phage DNA in the course of infection, replication, and maturation, as well as among certain technical difficulties inherent in the transfer measurements themselves (291, 296). One may suppose, therefore, that those atoms which are passed on from one phage generation to the next constitute a representative sample of *all* the DNA molecules that initiated a successful infection.

Further insight into the transfer process can be obtained by breaking open bacteria infected with P^{32}-labeled phages at various stages of the latent period and examining the intracellular state of aggregation of the parental DNA. Such experiments show that during the eclipse period most of the parental label remains part of free DNA molecules, the remainder being broken down to low-molecular-weight compounds (656). After the end of the eclipse, the parental label is reincorporated into the first mature progeny phages to make their intracellular appearance, each phage particle receiving on the average 2% of the parental label. Phages maturing at later times receive less and less of the parental label until transfer is essentially complete by the time that about 100 mature, infective progeny particles are present per cell (229, 288, 661)

(Fig. 7-6). At no time during the latent period dces there appear to exist an important fraction of the parental DNA which forms part of structures intermediate in size between free DNA molecules and mature bacteriophage particles (656). The fact that the parental phage DNA

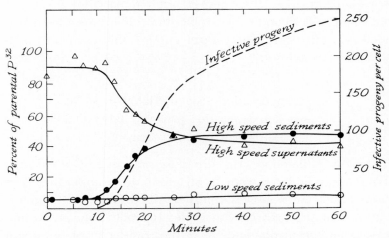

Fig. 7-6.   The kinetics of transfer of P^{32} from parent to progeny phage. *E. coli* are grown to a density of 2×10^8 cells/ml and infected with an average of five P^{32}-labeled T2 particles per cell. After the elapse of the minutes indicated on the abscissa, a sample of the infected culture is lysed-from-without by addition of cyanide and an excess of UV-killed T2 phages. The lysate is digested with deoxyribonuclease and subjected to two cycles of differential centrifugation, the first cycle at 3000 times gravity producing the "low-speed sediment" and the second cycle at 12,000 times gravity producing the "high-speed sediment" and the "high-speed supernatant." The P^{32} activity found in the "low-speed sediment" represents nuclease-resistant parental phosphorus attached to bacterial debris; that found in the "high-speed sediment" represents parental phosphorus transferred to progeny phages; and that found in the "high-speed supernatant" represents the remainder of the nontransferred parental phosphorus. [From Hershey (288).]

persists as the free nucleic acid and that it, like all other viral DNA precursors present in the host cell at early stages of infection, reappears preferentially in the first progeny phages to mature, leads one to infer that the transferred parental DNA simply forms part of the general intrabacterial pool of viral precursor DNA which it initiates and from which it may later be withdrawn for condensation, encapsulation into phage precursor protein, and finally rematuration as a structurally intact, infective unit.

Distribution of Transferred Material

The experiments just described revealed that most of the transferred parental DNA remains part of specific polynucleotides throughout the intracellular reproductive processes. Hence study of the *distribution* of the transferred parental atoms should really provide some valid answer to the question of whether or not replication of the viral DNA engenders a semiconservative repartition of the parent substance. Thus, if the entire DNA complement of one parental virus is transferred intact to a single progeny virus, then it would be inferred that replication is conservative; if just half of the atoms of the parental DNA complement are passed on together to individual progeny particles, then replication would be thought to be semiconservative; if, finally, the atoms transferred from one parental virus are scattered over many progeny particles, then replication, one might conclude, is neither conservative nor semiconservative but, instead, **dispersive** (169). Unfortunately, however, the interpretation of the observed distribution of the transferred parental phage DNA over the progeny phages turns out to be more complicated than is suggested by these simple considerations, for, as we shall see presently, processes other than replication can also contribute to dispersing the DNA complement of the infecting virus during intracellular phage growth.

In order to determine the distribution of the transferred parental DNA atoms over the progeny phages it is necessary to measure the amount of parental label in *individual* virus particles, instead of, as was the case in all the radioactive tracer experiments discussed up to this point, simply counting the average isotope content per particle among the members of a very large phage population. Since, in the case of radiophosphorus label, no more than about 3000 atoms of P^{32}, producing less than six radioactive disintegrations per hour, can be incorporated into the DNA complement of a single T-even parent phage, it is not possible to measure the distribution of the transferred P^{32} by placing individual progeny phages before conventional radiation counters. More sophisticated experimental procedures had, therefore, first to be invented before this problem could be fruitfully studied. Two very different techniques, each capable of estimating the P^{32} content of individual virus particles in a heterogeneously labeled phage population, finally revealed just how the transferred parental atoms are distributed over the progeny particles. The more direct of these techniques, an autoradiographic method developed by Levinthal (418), involves measurement of the label of individual phages by embedding the radioactive virus particles in a sensitive photographic emulsion, as described in Chapter 3. The second, much less direct, method measures the P^{32} content of individual phages by observing the *lethal effects* of the decay of the radioactive atoms (601). As will be discussed in more detail in Chapter 11, one out of every ten P^{32} disintegrations that take place in the T-even phage DNA is lethal to the particle, and hence the rate of inactivation with radioactive decay of a population of labeled phages is proportional to the content of radioactive isotope of the individuals.

Experiments were made in which *E. coli* bacteria were infected with highly P^{32}-labeled T-even phage particles, and the content of transferred isotope of individual progeny phages was then estimated by one of these techniques; the results showed that the integrity of the parental DNA is not conserved in the course of the reproductive process. Instead, it was found that the DNA atoms transferred from each parent virus are scattered over numerous descendants. This dispersive distribution of the parental label is, however, far from uniform: about half of the transferred atoms appear in progeny particles which harbor as much as 10–20% of the entire DNA complement of a single parent phage, whereas the remaining half of the transferred atoms are found in progeny endowed with very much smaller fragments of the polynucleotide patrimony. Further experiments were carried out in which the first generation progeny carrying the transferred parental atoms were passed through a second cycle of growth and the distribution of grandparental DNA atoms was studied among the *second generation progeny*. The second generation transfers showed that the second growth cycle does not appear to produce any further dispersal of the large 10–20% fragments that had already survived the first growth cycle intact (418, 601, 603).

The meaning of these results is still not entirely clear. They certainly show that the parental phage DNA complement is subject to a dispersive force during its sojourn in the vegetative pool. This dispersive force does not appear to act randomly and repeatedly on the transferred polynucleotide chains, however, for if such random force were at work a further dispersal of the parental substance should occur during the second growth cycle. At the time these transfer distributions were secured, they were generally interpreted to mean that the DNA complement of T-even phages is a *bipartite* structure, consisting of two parts that are a priori destined to be transferred as large and small fragments respectively. This bipartite hypothesis, furthermore, received strong support from the finding that the DNA of T-even phages also appears to comprise two parts of strikingly different sensitivity to ultraviolet light (296). Later studies showed that the DNA complement of not only the parent but also of the progeny phages does not remain in the vegetative phage precursor pool as one single, integral structure, since progeny DNA polynucleotides formed at different times of the latent period come together for maturation in the same intact virus particle (375, 636). It then seemed most plausible to believe that the dispersal of the parental nucleic acid in the transfer process reflects only the dissociation of the infecting DNA complement into the large and small subunits from which it was assembled in the previous growth cycle. But it is not obvious now how such a postulated assembly of subunits can be reconciled with the fact mentioned in Chapter 3, that the entire DNA complement of the T-even virus is but one giant molecule, unless it were supposed that both of the two polynucleotide strains of this macromolecule do not represent a covalent continuum but contain staggered interruptions, in the manner first proposed by Dekker and Schachman (156) soon after the discovery of the Watson-Crick structure.

In any case, the problem of the repartition of the substance of the parental T-even phage DNA molecules engendered by the elementary replication act was not settled by these transfer distribution experiments. Evidently it is necessary to examine the distribution of the transferred atoms, not over individual progeny phage particles, but over segments of individual progeny DNA *molecules*. Such studies became possible after Meselson, Stahl, and Vinograd (476) had shown that the effect of stable tracer isotopes on the *density* of DNA can be used to measure the isotope content of individual molecules. By use of their technique of **density gradient equilibrium sedimentation** Meselson and Stahl (475) then proved that the replication of the DNA of *E. coli* does indeed result in the semiconservative distribution predicted by the mechanism of Watson and Crick: after growth for two generations of heavy nitrogen N^{15}-labeled bacteria in a culture medium containing the ordinary, light isotope N^{14}, half of the bacterial DNA molecules are of a density corresponding to the isotope ratio 50% N¹⁵ and 50% N¹⁴, while the other half of the molecules have a density corresponding to 100% N¹⁴ (Fig. 7-7). Though analogous density label experiments on the transfer of T-even phage

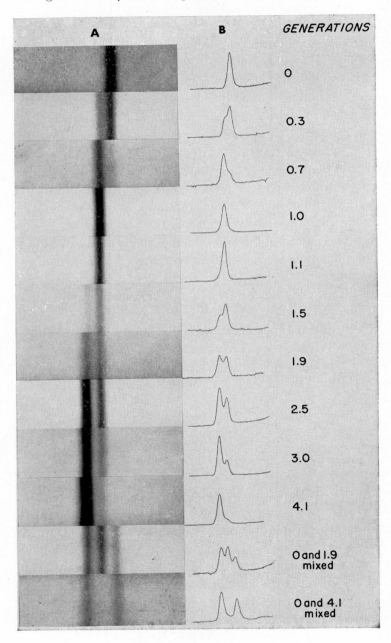

DNA present greater technical difficulties than those on the replication of *E. coli* DNA, Meselson's student Roller (528) was able to ascertain the distribution of the parental atoms over the progeny phage DNA molecules in phage transfer experiments by use of the heavy isotopes of nitrogen and carbon, N^{15} and C^{13}. Her work was repeated by Kozinski (374), who employed the thymine analogue 5-bromouracil as a density label instead of the heavy isotopes of nitrogen and carbon. (As will be considered in more detail in Chapter 10, 5-bromouracil is readily incorporated into the phage DNA in place of thymine; phage DNA molecules containing the brominated pyrimidine are much denser than the normal polynucleotide molecules.)

In these transfer experiments, *E. coli* growing in a "heavy" medium—containing either the isotopes N^{15} and C^{13} as the only nitrogen and carbon sources, or bromouracil—were infected with P^{32}-labeled "light" T4 phages containing the normal isotopes N^{14} and C^{12} and thymine in their DNA. The progeny phage issuing from the "heavy" bacteria at the end of the normal latent period, to which, as usual, about half of the parental P^{32} had been transferred, were then harvested and purified, their DNA molecules extracted, and the density of the DNA molecules carrying the

---

Fig. 7-7. The demonstration of semiconservative replication of *E. coli* DNA. **A.** Ultraviolet absorption photographs of an ultracentrifuge cell, in which DNA molecules are banded in a density gradient established in a concentrated cesium chloride solution. Each frame represents the bands formed by DNA extracted from an initially N^{15}-labeled *E. coli* culture after growth in an N^{14}-labeled medium for the number of generations indicated. The density of the cesium chloride solution increases to the right, regions of equal density occupying the same horizontal position on each photograph. **B.** Densitometer tracings of these photographs, where the height of the densitometer curve is proportional to the concentration of DNA. The relative content of N^{15} and N^{14} isotopes of a molecular species is indicated by the position of its band in relation to the bands of fully N^{15}- and fully N^{14}-labeled DNA shown in the lowest frame. It can be seen that after 1.0 generation of growth, all the DNA is found in a *hybrid* band, characteristic of the density of molecules containing equal proportions of the two nitrogen isotopes. After 1.9 generations, half of the DNA is present in a hybrid band and half is present in a band characteristic of molecules containing only N^{14}. A test of the inference that the DNA in the band of intermediate density contains just equal proportions of the two nitrogen isotopes is provided by the frame showing the bands obtained by centrifugation of a mixture of DNA extracted from bacteria after 0 and 1.9 generations. [From Meselson and Stahl (475).]

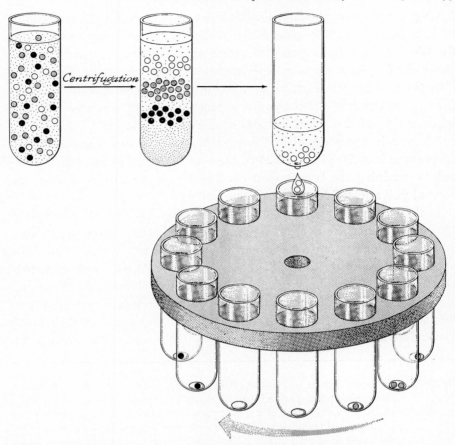

Fig. 7-8. Analysis of bands formed in cesium chloride density gradient sedimentation. A mixture of "heavy" (solid dots), "hybrid" (stippled dots), and "light" (open dots) DNA molecules is dissolved in a concentrated solution of cesium chloride (tiny dots). Upon centrifugation the cesium chloride forms a density gradient, the salt being concentrated toward the bottom of the tube; each species of DNA forms a band at that level at which the cesium chloride solution has its own density. When the sedimentation process has reached near-equilibrium, the centrifuge is stopped, a hole is punched through the bottom of the centrifuge tube and the contents of the tube collected drop by drop in a fraction collector. Each drop is then analyzed for its content of radioactivity in a radiation counter and for its absorption of ultraviolet light in a spectrophotometer. [Modified from Sinsheimer, *Scientific American*, **207**, No. 1:113 (1962).]

transferred parental P^{32} atoms determined by means of a modification of the original density gradient equilibrium sedimentation method. This modification, which was first used by Weigle (in connection with an investigation to be presented in Fig. 13-7), extends analysis of contents of bands formed in density gradient centrifugation to almost any property, such as radioactivity or infectivity. The principle of this method, as applied to the experiment under discussion here, is illustrated in Fig. 7-8.

The outcome of one of these transfer distribution experiments is presented in Fig. 7-9. As can be seen, the P^{32} atoms transferred from the "light" parental DNA molecules are found to reside in DNA molecules that possess very nearly the fully "heavy" density of the progeny DNA molecules synthesized after phage development in the "heavy" host cells. This finding, therefore, confirmed the earlier inferences from radioautography and P^{32} decay inactivation that the transferred parental atoms are rather widely dispersed—so widely dispersed, in fact, that not enough parental DNA atoms are transferred *en bloc* so that they can make an appreciable contribution to the density of the progeny DNA complement of which they happen to form part. However, when the density determinations were undertaken only after *fragmentation* of the viral DNA molecules extracted from the progeny phages to molecular weights of the order of 10^7 daltons, then most of the transferred P^{32} atoms were found to reside in molecules of *hybrid density*, halfway intermediate between that of the fully "light" parental DNA and that of the fully "heavy" progeny DNA. Hence the dispersal of the transferred DNA is by no means complete; sufficiently long chains of the parental polynucleotide are transferred intact to dominate the density of molecular fragments of the order of 5–10% of the whole viral DNA complement.

The hybrid density of the transferred parental DNA fragments thus reveals that the atoms of the DNA molecule of the parent T4 virus are indeed distributed semiconservatively over their vegetative replicas. It is the further fragmentation experienced by the parental DNA molecules in the course of intracellular phage growth that causes these half-old, half-new parental hybrid DNA molecules to be dispersed over the DNA complement of many progeny virus particles, in which the transferred patrimony appears in segments embedded in entirely de novo progeny polynucleotides. Hence it can be concluded that the semiconservative replication envisaged by Watson and Crick is really at work during the synthesis of the phage precursor DNA in the vegetative pool of the infected bacterium. Though the causes and mechanism of the fragmentation of the T-even phage DNA during its sojourn in the vegetative pool have not yet been adequately explained, the genetic consequences of this fragmentation have been in part elucidated and shall be of importance in our discussion of genetic recombination (Chapter 9).

*   *   *

In the latter part of the 19th century, Darwinian thought brought recognition of the evolutionary principle that allowed the growth of

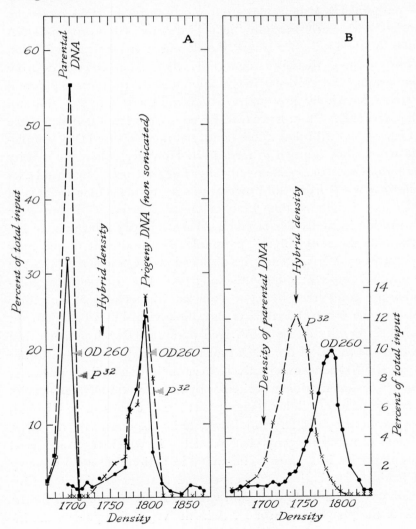

modern biology into a unitary science. In conformity with Hegelian dialectics, this synthesis soon engendered thesis and antithesis, as *biochemistry* and *genetics* came into flowering at the turn of this century. Of these two complementary methods of study of living matter, biochemistry evolved as a specialized branch of chemistry not very different in either concepts or methodology from its heuristic ancestor. Genetics, on the other hand, began as a completely new and entirely formal discipline, whose radical notion of the "Mendelian factor" or *gene* is an abstraction, independent of any real physical or chemical entities. Indeed, because of its formal character, genetics owed more to mathematics than to any other science for intellectual succor during most of its short history. Thus, for about fifty years, biochemistry and genetics ran a parallel

---

Fig. 7-9. The distribution of P^{32} transferred from parent to progeny phage. A culture of *E. coli* growing in a synthetic medium supplemented with bromodeoxyuridine (the deoxynucleoside of bromouracil) is infected with an average of three P^{32}-labeled T4 particles per cell. The culture is incubated until complete lysis, at which time each infected bacterium has liberated an average burst of 200 bromouracil-labeled progeny phages. These "heavy" progeny, to which about 40% of the parental P^{32} has been transferred, are then purified. **A.** Density-gradient centrifugation in a concentrated cesium chloride solution of DNA extracted from "light" parental and "heavy" T4 progeny phages. The drops are analyzed for their optical density (OD 260) to ultraviolet light at 260 mμ (indicative of the *total* content of progeny phage DNA) and for their P^{32} activity (indicative of their content of *transferred* parental DNA). The ordinate of the graph indicates the percentage of total DNA, or of P^{32}-labeled DNA, introduced into the centrifuge tube found in drops whose density is indicated on the abscissa. The optical density determinations show that the "light" parental phage DNA is considerably less dense than the "heavy" bromouracil-labeled DNA of the progeny. The congruence of P^{32} determinations with the optical density determinations shows that individual progeny DNA molecules harboring the transferred parental phosphorus atoms carry so few of the "light" parental thymine residues that the density of these molecules is essentially that of the fully bromouracil-substituted progeny DNA. The arrow labeled "hybrid density" indicates the position expected of a band of DNA molecules half of whose thymine residues are replaced by bromouracil. **B.** Density analysis of the progeny DNA after sonic fragmentation. The density of the bulk of the progeny DNA is unchanged, as revealed by optical density determinations. But measurement of P^{32} activity reveals that the transferred parental phosphorus now resides in DNA ragments that possess a *hybrid* density halfway intermediate between the fully "light" parental DNA and fully "heavy," bromouracil-substituted progeny DNA. [From Kozinski (374).]

course without any conceptual bridge that allowed comprehension of the phenomena described by one in terms of the doctrines of the other. At last, it fell to the students of the bacteriophage to help provide that bridge and to create from thesis and antithesis their synthesis—now called "molecular genetics."

Up to this point, our discussions on the nature and life of the bacteriophage have been concerned mostly with the biochemical aspects of the virus—that is, with the statement of thesis. We shall now abandon temporarily this line of inquiry and proceed to examine antithesis, or phage genetics.

Further Reading

Adams, M. H., *Bacteriophages* (2). Chapters XII, XIII, XIV, and XV supply further information on cytologic changes in the infected cell, isotopic tracer studies, nutritional and metabolic requirements for phage production, and chemical interference with phage growth.

Kornberg, A., Zimmerman, S. B., Kornberg, S. R., and Josse, J., "Enzymatic synthesis of deoxyribonucleic acid. VI. Influence of bacteriophage T2 on the synthetic pathway in host cells" (372). The discovery of some of the "early" enzymes of T-even phage growth.

Watson, J. D. and Crick, F. H. C., "The structure of DNA" (660). A summary description of the double helical structure of DNA and of its postulated mechanism of replication.

Watson, J. D. and Maaløe, O., "Nucleic acid transfer from parental to progeny bacteriophage" (661). The unequivocal demonstration that part of the parental phage DNA is transferred to its progeny.

Hershey, A. D. and Burgi, E., "Genetic significance of the transfer of nucleic acid from parental to offspring phage" (296). An attempt to distill some meaning out of the confusing mass of data on the transfer of phage DNA from parent to progeny.

Delbrück, M. and Stent, G. S., "On the mechanism of DNA replication" (169). An appreciation of the Watson-Crick structure of DNA and of its significance for the growth of bacteriophages.

Meselson, M. and Stahl, F. W., "The replication of DNA in *Escherichia coli*" (475). The proof of semiconservative DNA replication, by use of heavy isotopes and cesium chloride density gradient equilibrium sedimentation.

CHAPTER 8

Mutation and Mixed Infection

Rapid Lysis Mutants—Host Range Mutants—Mutation of the Vegetative Phage—Mechanism of Reproduction of the Viral Genome—Mixed Infection—Partial Exclusion—Phenotypic Mixing

"IF THESE d'Hérelle bodies were really genes, fundamentally like our chromosome genes, they would give an utterly new angle from which to attack the gene problem," wrote the geneticist H. J. Muller (487) prophetically in 1922. The next chapters will demonstrate that bacteriophages do indeed resemble chromosomal genes and that the new angle they provided has meanwhile very nearly solved the "gene problem." In preceding chapters there already was occasional reference to genetic aspects of bacterial viruses, as for instance in the pronouncement that the DNA is the carrier of the hereditary continuity of the phage. No experimental evidence has so far been offered, however, that really showed that bacterial viruses possess anything like heredity, or that specific genetic characters are actually passed on from one viral generation to the next. On the basis of most of the facts recounted thus far, one could, on the contrary, still imagine—as indeed not a few workers did during the early days of phage research—that all the "information" for the construction of the virus progeny is already present in the bacterium *before* its infection and that phage synthesis is merely "triggered" by the injection of the parental phage DNA into the host cell. In other words, the parental DNA might play only a "regulatory" rather than an "instructive" role in the physiological processes that ensue in the infected cell.

It was only through the discovery of hereditary variants or **mutants** of bacteriophages that it became clear that these viruses, no less than their bacterial hosts or higher organisms, really do possess a genuine

175

hereditary apparatus. Once established, the genetics of bacterial viruses was not long in becoming responsible for advances so important to the general understanding of the structure and function of the units of heredity that the ideas of the "gene" prevailing as recently as the 1940's now appear, in retrospect and with the wisdom of hindsight, as strangely unsophisticated. It has been asserted that this rapid progress in phage genetics was "due to two major factors, the favorable properties of bacteriophages as materials for genetic research, and perhaps, more important, the fact that the research workers were not trained as classical geneticists" (2).

The early literature is not lacking in reports of "variation" in phage (561) or of the acquisition of new, mutant properties by a virus type under study—d'Hérelle himself believed that all phage types were but variants of a single "species." But the first clear-cut demonstration of the occurrence of phage mutants was provided only in 1936. In that year Burnet and Lush (118) reported that the staphylococcal phage C, which produces plaques containing a dense central growth of phage-resistant bacteria in their center, sports a stable hereditary mutant C′, which produces clear plaques without any central growth. Burnet and Lush showed that this difference in plaque morphology reflected the loss by the C′ mutant phage of the capacity possessed by the normal C phage to induce phage resistance in the phage-sensitive staphylococci. Although the phenomenon of viral mutation and its attendant physiological consequences were very clearly exposed here, this excellent paper did not stimulate any further work with phages as objects of genetic study. And thus the development of phage genetics had to wait for another ten years, until the first mutants of T2 were isolated.

Rapid Lysis Mutants

It was first noticed by Hershey (284) that one out of 10^3 or 10^4 plaques formed by T2 phages on agar plates seeded with the usual host *E. coli*, strain B, looks rather different from the normal plaques which have a small, clear center and are surrounded by a diffuse halo. The rare variant plaque, in contrast, possesses a large, clear center and a sharp edge (Fig. 8-1). When Hershey picked such an unusual plaque from the agar and isolated and replated the phage particles that it contained, he found that all these phages themselves gave rise to variant plaques identical in morphology to the variant plaque in which they had been found. In other words, the phages present in the original variant plaque *breed true*. The occurrence of that first variant plaque thus did not derive from some rare, accidental physiological aberration in plaque development which caused the plaque morphology to be different from the normal. (Such physiological aberrations actually do occur, since the ultimate aspect of the plaque depends on the interplay of a host of variables, such as the

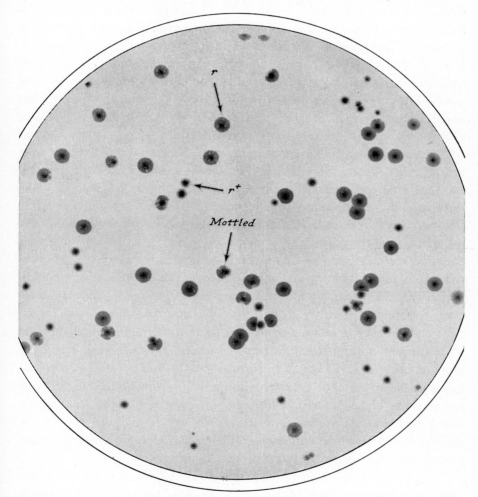

Fig. 8-1. Morphology of the normal T2r⁺ (wild type) plaque and of a variant T2r (rapid lysis mutant) plaque. This plate contains also mottled plaques that owe their characteristic morphology to the joint growth of both r^+ and r genotypes in the same focus of infection.

local water, salt and nutrient content of the agar, and also the physiological state and density of the indicator bacteria.) Instead, the variant
plaque must reflect the presence in the phage inoculum of a hereditary
mutant T2 phage, from which a line of mutant individuals descended
during the growth of the plaque. This phage mutant possesses and passes
on to its progeny the property of forming a plaque different in appearance from that formed by the normal or **wild type** phage (that is, encountered in nature, in the "wild"). The T2 virus must, therefore, carry
some hereditary determinants of its own; it cannot be true that all of
the genetic information for growth and construction of the virus particle
is already contained in the uninfected host bacterium. For if phage
multiplication were merely triggered by the infecting phage, every virus
particle of a given phage strain would only trigger the synthesis of one
and the same type of progeny virus in a given type of host bacterium,
and there could be no hereditary mutants of the phage.

Hershey gave this plaque type mutant the name **rapid lysis,** or **r**
mutant. And in accordance with the nomenclature of classical genetics,
Hershey represented the wild type—the normal, nonrapid lysis T2 phage
forming ordinary plaques—by the symbol r^+. Since later phage workers
followed Hershey's lead, the superscript plus sign on the symbol of some
mutant character now signifies in phage genetics, as in classical, that
the individual is "wild"—that is, does *not* possess the character in question. It is important to remember, however, that in *bacterial* genetics,
which was developed at the same time and by some of the very same
people as phage genetics, a different convention has been adopted: in
bacterial genetics, the superscript plus sign on a symbol means that the
individual *does* possess the character in question, no special nomenclature
being employed to designate the wild type. Thus, Lac^+ refers to a bacterium able to ferment lactose, while a bacterium unable to do so is
described as Lac^-. Unfortunately, it is necessary to use both conventions
in this text. In the remainder of this text the reader will thus have to be
wary of the plus sign; it will have diametrically opposite meanings when
referring to viral or to bacterial genetic characters.

The physiological basis underlying the rapid lysis, or r, mutant character devolves from the phenomenon of *lysis inhibition* (180), which
has been discussed in Chapter 4. If T2-infected bacteria are infected
secondarily with T2 virus particles after intracellular growth of the primary phage is well under way, then lysis of the infected cells is very

much delayed. Rapid lysis T2r mutants differ from the T2r^+ wild type in that they do not manifest lysis inhibition. Bacteria primarily infected with an r mutant phage lyse at the normal time, whether or not there occurs a secondary infection with further phage particles prior to the end of the latent period, even when the superinfecting phages are of the normal, lysis-inhibiting, or r^+ wild type (180). Bacteria infected primarily with r^+ wild type phages, however, will manifest lysis inhibition, even when superinfected secondarily with r mutant types (602). The difference between r^+ wild type and rapid lysis r mutant phages must, therefore, reside in the sequence of reactions leading to disintegration of the host cell that their intracellular growth sets in train. Only in the case of the r^+ wild type can that sequence be temporarily arrested, or reversed, by secondary infection at late stages of the latent period, thus postponing the moment of ultimate lysis. The difference in plaque morphology between wild r^+ and r mutant types is then readily accounted for in terms of lysis inhibition. During the growth of the wild type plaque, the density of phage progeny descending from the original parent virus seeded on the agar plate increases in the domain of the plaque, so that at late stages of its development all bacteria primarily infected by some member of the growing r^+ phage colony will also be secondarily infected, and hence lysis-inhibited. Thus the turbid halo of the r^+ wild type plaque represents a peripheral area of the bacterial lawn where there remain many unlysed bacteria which, though replete with progeny viruses, cannot lyse because of the lysis inhibition established in the terminal phases of plaque development. But since there is no such lysis inhibition during the development of a plaque initiated by an r mutant virus, phage multiplication and bacterial lysis continue as long as the physiological conditions on the nutrient agar surface permit growth, generating in the bacterial lawn a large, clear hole with a sharp edge.

We must now bring into focus the twin concepts **phenotype** and **genotype,** which are as important in phage genetics as in classical genetics, since virus particles, just as higher organisms, do not invariably manifest all the characters which they harbor in their hereditary makeup. The phenotype (from $\phi\alpha\iota\nu\epsilon\iota\nu$, to show) of a phage refers to the directly observable state of the virus particle in regard to some particular character under consideration. Thus a phage particle is of rapid lysis (r) phenotype if, on plating, it produces an r type plaque, or if upon infection of a bacterium with this phage no lysis inhibition occurs; the particle is of wild (r^+) phenotype if it produces an r^+ plaque or if lysis inhibition *does* occur. The phenotype is not invariant and may depend on the exact experimental conditions under which it is tested. For instance, certain r mutants of T2 or T4 form wild type r^+ plaques when plated on strain BB rather than on the more generally used strain B of *E. coli* (466); or r^+ plaques formed by wild type T2 phages on strain B are converted into typical r plaques if the assay plate is sprayed with chloroform after incubation. The phenotype of a phage can, as we shall see presently, also depend on the *history* of the particle, for instance, on the conditions under which the virus was grown.

The genotype of the phage refers to the hereditary constitution that the particle has inherited from its progenitor and which it, in turn, passes on to its own progeny. To determine the genotype of a phage, it is necessary to examine, not its own phenotype, but that of its progeny. Thus if two virus particles growing under conditions as nearly identical as possible give rise to progeny of dissimilar phenotype, then a difference in genotype must exist between the two viruses in question. For instance, two phages are of different genotype even though both form typical r^+ plaques on a plate seeded with strain BB if, after isolating the progeny phage present in each plaque and replating them on plates seeded with the indicator strain B, the progeny of one phage form typical r mutant plaques while the progeny of the other phage form typical r^+ wild type plaques. Differences in genotype among members of a single phage line or **clone,** descended from a common ancestor, arise by a sudden change in informational content of the hereditary substance or **mutation** of some individual virus. This change in genotype is permanent and is passed on to all offspring of the mutant individual.

One further term to be encountered frequently in the following chapters should be defined here, namely, **genome.** In classical genetics, genome connotes the set of chromosomes of an organism, and hence the sum total of its genes. This term has been assimilated into phage genetics, where "phage genome" similarly represents the complement of all the hereditary factors of the virus.

Host Range Mutants

As has been shown in earlier chapters, phage-sensitive bacteria can sport mutants which have become resistant to infection by a particular virus type. It was also pointed out that such phage-resistant bacterial mutants owe their resistance to structural modifications of the cell surface which prevent the stereospecific attachment of the adsorption organs on the phage tail to the phage receptors in the bacterial envelope, so that phage adsorption—and, a fortiori, injection of the phage DNA into the interior of the host cell—can no longer take place. But why, if bacteria can mutate to phage resistance, are there still left in nature phage-sensitive bacterial strains? Why have sensitive strains not been replaced long ago by resistant forms through natural selection? Or why have bacterial viruses not yet been deprived of all suitable host organisms and thus vanished altogether? The answer to these questions, as to all evolutionary problems, is not immediately obvious, but one reason for the continued persistence of phage-sensitive bacterial strains is that the bacteriophage can, as discovered at the dawn of phage genetics, sport **host range** mutants (433). Such host range mutant phages are able to overcome the resistance of phage-resistant mutant bacteria because the structure of the adsorption organs of the mutant phage differs in some subtle way from that of the wild type phage. This structural difference once more permits the necessary stereospecific fit with the phage receptors in the envelope of the phage-resistant mutant bacterium, in spite of the modification of the cell surface that thwarts attachment of the wild type phage. In most of the instances studied, such phage mutations *extend* the phage host range, so that the mutant virus can adsorb to and infect more bacterial strains than the wild type; some host range mutations occur, however, in which the gain in adsorbability to a bacterial strain resistant to the wild type phage is paid for by a concomitant loss of adsorbability to a strain receptive to the wild type phage. With the appearance of host range mutants, however, the phage has by no means put an end to the struggle for existence, since the bacterial strain resistant to the wild type phage and sensitive to the host range mutant phage can sport further bacterial mutants which are resistant to infection by *both* wild type *and* host range mutant phages. At this point the virus, not to be outdone, can respond to the appearance of a superresistant bacterial strain by sporting a super-host range mutant. The coexistence in nature of bacteria and bacterial viruses is thus sustained by a delicate mutational equilibrium that saves both protagonists from total extinction.

Phage geneticists, following the convention established in 1936 by Burnet and McKie (120), designate a phage-resistant bacterial mutant by placing a diagonal or solidus after the symbol of the wild type bacterium and then writing the symbol of the phage type to which the mutant is resistant. (The letter "T" is always omitted in describing bacterial mutants resistant to any of the T series of coliphages.) Thus, B/2 designates a mutant of *E. coli*, strain B resistant to phage T2. (Bacterial geneticists, however, adopted a different notation for phage resistance; they designate resistance and sensitivity to a phage by superscript r and s affixed to the symbol representing the phage. Thus in bacterial genetics, the mutant strain B/2 goes under the name of B,T2^r.) Bacterial mutants are frequently isolated that have acquired resistance to more than one phage type in a single mutational step. An example is the mutant of strain B resistant to both T1 and T5; this mutant bears the designation B/1,5. Another example is the mutant B/3,4,7 which, as mentioned in Chapter 5, owes its multiple resistance to T3, T4, and T7 to a profound alteration in the lipopolysaccharide of the bacterial cell wall.

Bacterial mutants resistant to more than one phage type can also be obtained by *successive* isolation steps; first a mutant cell resistant to one phage type is selected and then among the descendants of this mutant a cell is selected that is also resistant to a second phage type. For example, a mutant of strain B resistant to both T4 and T2 can be constructed by first isolating the T4-resistant mutant B/4 and then selecting among B/4 cells the T2-resistant double mutant B/4/2. (The multiple bars interposed between the symbols representing host and virus strains usually indicate the number and sequence of successive selective steps that occurred in the history of the mutant bacterium.)

In practice, a T2-resistant B/2 strain is isolated by plating some 10^8 cells of strain B in the presence of about 10^5 T2 phage particles. The multiplication of the phages on this plate produces 10^5 plaques, so that after incubation the entire surface of this plate will consist of nothing *but* plaques, or show **confluent lysis.** All the phage-sensitive bacteria on the plate will have been destroyed. However, on such a confluent lysis plate there will generally remain a few bacterial colonies, which can be picked and restreaked through several passages on fresh nutrient agar to free the cells from any contaminating T2 particles carried over from the original confluent lysis plate. A bacterial strain isolated in this way will usually (though, alas, not always!) turn out to be the desired T2-resistant B/2 mutant. If now a plate seeded with about 10^7 B/2 bacteria is inoculated with several hundred wild type T2 particles, no plaques whatsoever will appear, since the viruses are unable to multiply on the indicator bacteria presented to them. However, if instead of several hundred, several *million* T2 particles are inoculated onto the B/2-seeded plate, then a few plaques *will* usually show up. The phage present in one of these rare plaques formed on B/2 may then be picked and isolated. Now, upon replating these phages on plates seeded either with strain B/2 or with strain B, it will be found that the number of plaques formed on B/2 is more or less equal to that formed on strain B; that is, the original plaque picked contained a clone of host range mutant phage able to grow as well on the T2-resistant B/2 strain as on the normal host, strain B. Such host range mutants are described by the symbol h: T2h is a mutant of phage T2 that can infect and grow on strain B/2 resistant to the T2h^+ wild type (285).

   In genetic experiments on phage it is frequently necessary to determine the relative proportion of two genotypes in a mixed population of virus particles. In the case of r and r^+ types, this can be done by simply scoring the number of r and r^+ plaques that are formed upon plating the phage mixture on strain B. The relative proportion of h and h^+ types in a phage mixture can be estimated by two platings, one on strain B and the other on strain B/2. The number of plaques that appear on strain B/2 indicates the number of h types and the difference in the plaque count on strain B and on strain B/2 indicates the number of h^+ wild types. Fortunately, the technique of **mixed indicators,** invented by Delbrück (163) in 1945, permits assay of the relative proportion of h and h^+ types in a *single* plating of the phage suspension. In this technique the phages are inoculated onto a plate seeded with a mixture of roughly equal parts of both B and B/2 indicator strains; all h phage genotypes initially present on the plate will produce normal plaques, since they infect, grow on, and lyse equally well both bacterial indicator strains on this plate; all h^+ wild types, however, will produce *turbid* plaques, since of the two indicator strains they can only lyse bacteria of strain B. In the area covered by each T2h^+ plaque growing on strain B, there will remain intact all the T2h^+-resistant bacteria of strain B/2, which thus prevent the development of a clear plaque and give rise to a turbid plaque (Fig. 8-2).

   In the past fifteen years, many other mutant types of phages T2 and T4, besides rapid lysis and host range mutants, have been identified; a brief summary of the characteristics of some of these mutants is presented in Table 8-I. It is evident from this list that a wide range of properties of the phage can be affected by genetic variation, suggesting that bacterial viruses are the carriers of a complex hereditary apparatus whose informational content must be very high compared to that which could be contained in a simple "trigger" device that acts only on the function of the genetic structures of the host bacterium.

Not only is it possible to isolate phages carrying a single mutant char-

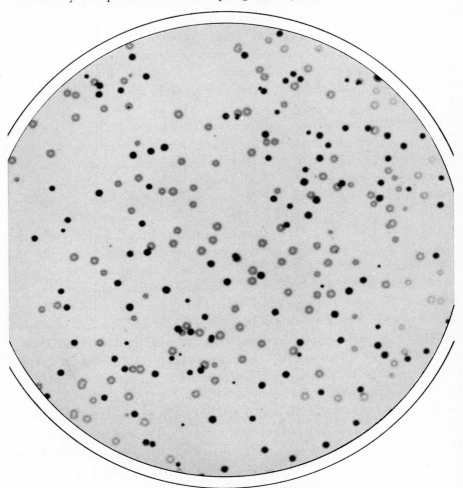

Fig. 8-2.   Plaques formed by a mixture of T2h^+ wild type and T2h mutant phages on a plate seeded with B + B/2 *mixed indicators*. The wild type forms turbid plaques and the *h* mutant forms clear plaques.

acter, but by two successive selective steps **multiple mutants** can also be obtained, which carry in their genetic structures several mutant characters different from the wild type (285). For instance, starting with wild type T2 phage one can first select an h mutant by plating a high concentration of wild type virus on strain B/2 and then select among the host range mutant population an individual that produces an r plaque. Such a phage has the constitution T2hr, and thus differs in two of its characters from the T2h^+r^+ wild type. By means of the technique of plating on B + B/2 mixed indicators, it is possible to recognize on a

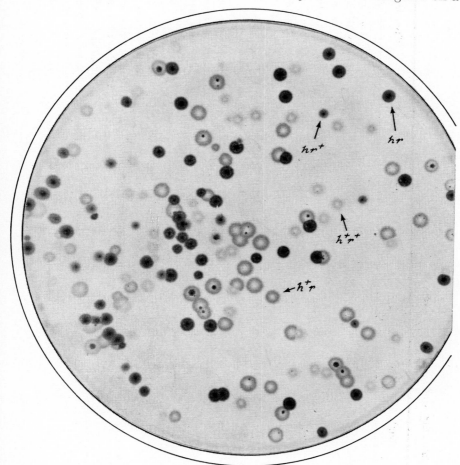

Fig. 8-3. The four types of plaques formed by T2h^+r^+, T2h^+r, T2hr^+, and T2hr on B + B/2 mixed indicators.

TABLE 8-I

Some Mutant Types of the T-even Phages

Name	Symbol	Reference	Phenotype	Physiological Basis of Phenotype
Rapid lysis	r	(284, 285)	forms plaques with sharp edges; infected bacteria not subject to lysis inhibition	not yet definitely known; mutation probably affects synthesis or functional regulation of phage enzymes concerned with sealing reactions of host cell envelope
Minute	m	(310)	forms very small plaques	slow growth or low burst size; latter probably reflects inefficient maturation of phage precursor materials, or precocious lysis
Host range	h	(285, 433)	adsorbs to and forms clear plaques on bacteria resistant to the h^+ wild type	stereospecific modification of polypeptides of adsorption organs, particularly of tail fibers and/or base plate
Host range	ht	(43)	adsorbs slowly to and forms turbid plaques on bacteria resistant to the h^+ wild type; additive effect of several ht mutations in same genome simulates h phenotype	
Turbid	tu	(185)	forms turbid plaques on strain B	not yet known
Cofactor-requiring	c	(11, 166, 90)	requires an organic cofactor, principally tryptophan, for adsorption to host cell	interaction of tail fibers and tail sheath prevents fixation of virus to bacterial receptors; cofactor frees tail fibers from tail sheath
Star	s	(43, 466, 619)	forms sectored or irregularly shaped plaques that contain other genotypes in addition to the original s mutant	mutant grows poorly under conditions of plating; secondary mutations occurring during growth of plaque suppress mutant phenotype, leading to overgrowth of primary mutant clone by secondary mutants

Ultraviolet sensitivity	u	(610)	reduces ultraviolet sensitivity to one-half that of u^+ type	see Chapter 11
Acriflavin resistance	ac	(197)	can form plaques on agar containing acriflavin concentrations lethal to ac^+ wild type	not yet known
Osmotic shock	os	(93)	survives rapid dilution from 3 M NaCl into distilled water	alteration in structure of head protein increases permeability of head membrane
Lysozyme	e	(616)	does not produce lysozyme halo around plaque; bacteria infected with some e genotypes do not lyse	abnormal lysozyme synthesis
Amber	am	(202)	able to grow only on strain K12, but not on strain B	see Chapter 15
Temperature-sensitive	ts	(198)	able to grow only at 25°C but not at 42°C	synthesis of abnormal phage enzymes or structural proteins that cannot function at the higher temperature

single plate (Fig. 8-3) each of the four genotypes (the wild type, the double mutant, and the two single mutants) according to the following scheme:

Genotype	Plaque Type on B + B/2
$T2h^+r^+$	turbid r^+
$T2h^+r$	turbid r
$T2hr^+$	clear r^+
$T2hr$	clear r

Both r and h mutations are *reversible*, in that among many thousands of phage particles of the r mutant type a few r^+ reverse mutants are found, which again breed true as the original wild type. Similarly, among many thousands of h mutants, a few h^+ wild types can be found which have permanently and hereditarily lost their ability to infect strain B/2. In these reverse mutants another sudden change in the hereditary substance has taken place that once more restores to the virus the genetic information carried by its wild ancestor. These mutational interrelations may thus be depicted graphically in the following way:

$$hr^+ \rightleftharpoons h^+r^+ \rightleftharpoons h^+r \rightleftharpoons hr$$

Mutation of the Vegetative Phage

An important fact for understanding the mechanism by which mutant phages arise is that the intact, infective virus particles do not mutate at all: suspensions of T2 wild type phage can be stored for days, weeks, or years without any detectable increase in the number of h or r mutants (285, 433). In other words, the extracellular, infective phage sports no hereditary mutants. Instead, it is only during the vegetative multiplication of the phage in the host cell that new mutants appear on the scene. If, for instance, a culture of *E. coli* is infected with a phage inoculum of 10^6 T2r^+ particles per milliliter and phage multiplication is allowed to proceed through several growth cycles until all the bacteria in the culture have been lysed and the phage titer has risen to a final level of

10^{10} particles per milliliter, then it is found that the proportion of r mutants among the whole phage population rises with each growth cycle, from an initial level of about 10^{-4} r mutants per r^{+} wild type to a final level of about 10^{-3} r mutants per r^{+} wild type. It can be inferred, therefore, that phage mutants arise as **copy errors** during the intracellular replication of the viral genetic substance. That is, the process which copies the hereditary information of the parent virus in the infected cell and generates the genetic substance with which the progeny viruses are to be endowed is necessarily one of very high fidelity; occasionally an error *does* occur in the replication process, however, which engenders a change in informational content, or mutation, in one of the vegetative replicas. The mutant replica of the genetic patrimony later matures into an intact, infective progeny particle, which, in its turn, infects another bacterial cell. In the course of this infection, it is the mutant information that is now replicated faithfully to produce a burst of mutant phage progeny.

We may envisage that there is a fixed chance M per replication act that a particular copy error is made, such as that which converts the r^{+} wild type to the r mutant type, and that once made, the copy error is permanently propagated thereafter among a clone of mutant viruses descended from the original mutant genome. It follows from these considerations that the more replication acts there are, the more opportunity there is for copy errors, and the greater should be the proportion of any rare mutant type in a phage population. Restating this inference analytically, we may write that the rate of increase of the number μ of phage mutants with an increasing total number p of phages in the culture is

$$d\mu/dp = M + \mu/p, \qquad (8\text{-}1)$$

provided that $\mu \ll p$ (so any diminution of μ by *reverse* mutations to the wild type can be neglected). In this relation, the terms on the right, M and μ/p, express increases in μ due to new mutations and multiplication of existing mutants, respectively. Integrating Equation ($8\text{-}1$) after substitution of π, the proportion of mutants in the population, for its equivalent μ/p, we obtain

$$\pi - \pi_0 = M \ln (p/p_0), \qquad (8\text{-}2)$$

where π_0 and p_0 are the proportion of mutants and total number of phages in the culture at the start of the experiment, and π is the proportion of mutants after the total number of phages has risen to p. The chance M per replication act of the mutation $r^+ \longrightarrow r$, or the **mutation frequency,** can then be estimated by use of Equation (8-2) from the increase in proportion of r mutants in the example cited; that is,

$$M = \frac{\pi - \pi_0}{\ln (p/p_0)} = \frac{0.001 - 0.0001}{\ln (10^{10}/10^6)} = 10^{-4} \ r \text{ mutations per replication.}$$

Evidently, according to Equation (8-2) the mutation frequency cannot be deduced from only a single determination of the proportion of mutant virus in a phage population, since at least *two* determinations of the mutant proportion at different stages of growth are required to this end. Nevertheless, the proportion of mutants present in phage stocks grown from inocula containing so few virus particles that it is unlikely that any mutants were already among them ($\pi_0 = 0$), is often used by phage geneticists as a rough estimate of the mutation frequency. The proportion of mutants present in a phage stock grown in this way is called the **mutation index** (51). According to Equation (8-2) the ratio of the mutation index to the logarithm of the ratio of final to initial phage titers is equal to the mutation frequency. Measurements of this mutation index are subject to very great fluctuations, however, since the final proportion of mutants in any phage stock depends very much on the exact moment during the growth of the stock at which the *first* mutation occurs (445). Hence only the average, or preferably, median, value of the mutation index of many replicate phage stocks is a reasonable approximation to the true mutation frequency.

It should be noted that different types of mutations occur in very different frequencies, the mutation T2$r^+ \longrightarrow$ T2r being one of the most frequent that is known. In contrast, the mutation T2$h^+ \longrightarrow$ T2h occurs in only 10^{-8} replication events (284), while the reverse mutation T2$h \longrightarrow$ T2h^+ is very much more probable, its frequency being 10^{-4} mutations per replication (615). A discussion of the reasons underlying the wide range in observed mutation frequencies must, however, be deferred until a later chapter.

Mechanism of Reproduction of the Viral Genome

In 1951, Luria (437) made use of the occurrence of r mutations during intracellular multiplication of vegetative T2 phage to probe the general nature of the process by which the hereditary material of the infecting virus is reproduced. Until that time it had been possible to consider at least three rather different mechanisms by which the single parental phage genome introduced into the bacterium at the outset of the infection might manage to generate the several hundred copies of itself which later appear in intact, infective progeny phage. One of these three possible mechanisms was **geometric** reproduction, under which the necessary number of replicas accrue by successive rounds of self-duplication of all the genetic elements present: the parental genome is replicated in the first round to produce two genomes, each of which is replicated in the second round to produce four genomes, each of which is replicated in the third round to produce eight genomes, and so on, until several hundred replicas have been produced by seven to nine such rounds. This is the mechanism which should obtain if the phage DNA, carrier of the genetic factors of the mature virus, is actually replicated according to the proposal of Watson and Crick described in the preceding chapter. A second of the three possible mechanisms was reproduction by **follow-the-leader,** under which the replica genomes arise by successive replications of only the last element to be formed: the parental genome is duplicated only once, to produce a replica which is then duplicated only once, to produce its own replica, which is then duplicated once to produce *its* own replica, and so on, until the requisite number of replicas has been generated by several hundred such independent duplication acts. Finally, the third of the three possible mechanisms was reproduction by **stamping machine,** under which the replica genomes are formed by successive duplication of only the *initial* element: the parental genome supplies the "die" for a "press" which manufactures the requisite replicas by several hundred independent "stamping" acts. This is the mechanism which should obtain if contrary to the proposal of Watson and Crick replication of the phage DNA is not direct, but indirect, involving the transfer of the genetic information from the parental DNA to some other structure which acts as the template for the construction of *all* the replica polynucleotides in the infected cell.

Now, the occurrence of occasional copy errors, or mutations, would have different statistical consequences under each of the three mechanisms, as shown in Fig. 8-4. Under *geometric replication*, each mutation would at once perpetuate itself and generate a clone of mutant genomes in the infected cell. The final size of each such mutant clone would evidently be the greater the more numerous the replication cycles that had taken place from the moment of the copy error until lysis of the infected cell—that is, the *earlier* in intracellular growth the mutation occurred. But the chance that *any* copy error occurs at any stage is

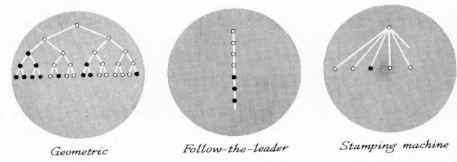

Geometric   Follow-the-leader   Stamping machine

Fig. 8-4.   Three possible mechanisms of reproduction of the viral genome. Open circles represent normal viral genomes and solid circles represent mutant genomes. [From Luria, *Ann. Missouri Botan. Garden*, **32**:235 (1945).]

evidently the greater the *more* replicating phage genomes are already present—that is, the later the stage of intracellular growth. Departing from these considerations, Luria reckoned that if the probability per individual replication act of making a given copy error is M, then under geometric replication the frequency Y_μ of clones comprising μ or more mutants among p replicas of the parent genome should be

$$Y_\mu = \frac{2Mp}{\mu}. \tag{8-3}$$

In other words, under geometric replication the chance that a mutant clone of a certain size appears ought to be inversely proportional to that size.

Under *follow-the-leader* replication, occasional copy errors would likewise generate clones of mutant genomes, but here clones of all sizes should appear with equal probability, at least up to clone sizes no larger than the burst size. For if the chance M per replication act of making a given copy error is constant, then there would be just as many errors made at the first replication act (producing a maximum mutant clone size) as at the last replication act (producing a minimum clone of only a single mutant). Here we may write

$$Y_\mu = M(p - \mu). \tag{8-4}$$

Finally, under *stamping machine* replication, an occasional copy error would generate only a single mutant genome, instead of a mutant clone; a second, independent copy error would have to occur before another mutant genome could arise in the same infected cell. Thus here the number of mutants would be distributed at random over the infected cells, and we may write

$$Y_\mu = \frac{(Mp)^\mu}{\mu}.$$

(8-5)

These three predicted frequency distributions of the number of mutants per infected cell are shown graphically in Fig. 8-5.

Fig. 8-5. The frequency distribution of clones of T2*r* mutants found in the giant quasi-single-burst experiment. [From Luria (437).] The ordinate represents the number Y_μ of plates that contain μ or more *r* mutant plaques, which are shown on the abscissa (both plotted on a logarithmic scale). The solid lines present the distributions to be expected for each of the three alternative mechanisms of replication of the viral genome. Line a: geometric replication, plotted according to Equation (8-3); line b: "follow-the-leader" replication, plotted according to Equation (8-4); line c: "stamping machine" replication, plotted according to Equation (8-5).

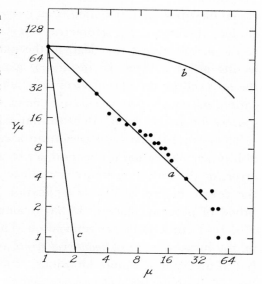

In order to distinguish experimentally between these alternative replication mechanisms, Luria assumed the Herculean task of discovering the actual distribution of the number of mutants per cell by means of a quasi-single-burst experiment. He infected bacteria with single T2*r*+ wild type phage particles and placed small aliquots of the culture into very many individual tubes, so that each tube received a few infected bacteria. The whole set of tubes was then incubated until lysis of the infected bacteria, the entire content of each tube plated on strain B indicator bacteria, and the plates scored for the appearance of *r*-type mutant plaques. Luria examined 2,874 such plates containing the grand total of 1,850,000 plaques, representing the progeny issued from 23,000 infected cells; each tube, therefore, contained the phage yield of an average of 23,000/2874, or about 8 infected bacteria. The result of this experiment was that 90 of the 2874 plates showed some r mutant plaques, whereas the remainder of the plates showed only r^+ wild type plaques. Hence the mutation $r^+ \longrightarrow r$ had occurred in 90 of the 23,000 infected cells. Altogether, 700 r mutant plaques appeared, whose distribution over the 90 plates is shown in Fig. 8-5. It can be seen that the actual distribution of the number of r mutants liberated per infected cell certainly does not fit the random distribution predicted by the *stamping machine*, nor does it fit the expectations of *follow-the-leader* replication. The data are seen to be in reasonable agreement, however, with the clonal distribution anticipated from *geometric* replication. It may be concluded, therefore, that geometric replication corresponds most closely to the actual events that lead to the manifold reproduction of the infecting genome. That is, the initial genetic information brought into the host cell by the parent virus does not possess the monopoly of replication, inasmuch as its vegetative copies also appear to act as information sources for further replications in that cell.

These single-burst data permit an accurate estimate of M, the probability per individual replication act of occurrence of the $r^+ \longrightarrow r$ copy error, or the mutation frequency. Since the error occurred 90 times in the course of the 1,850,000 replication acts that produced the entire brood of progeny phages, M has evidently the value $90/1,850,000 = 5 \times 10^{-5}$ r mutations per replication. This determination of M is based on the measurement of *mutational events* and is thus a much more direct, but also very much more laborious, estimate than that based on Equation (8-2), involving *mutant proportions*.

The foregoing derivation of the frequency distribution of Equation (8-3) was actually based on an idealized conception of phage growth that considered each phage genome the formal equivalent of a bacterium. This simplification allowed use of the same statistical relations as those with which Luria and Delbrück (445) had previously demonstrated the spontaneous origin of bacterial mutants. However, as we saw in the preceding chapters, the intracellular multiplication of phage certainly does not resemble the binary fission of bacterial cells, but proceeds in a noninfective state in the *vegetative pool*, from which components are later withdrawn for maturation into the structurally intact infective units. The final yield of infective phage in Luria's giant single-burst experiment did not, therefore, constitute the total viral sib descended from parent individuals after various growth cycles, but represented a complicated sample of phage genomes withdrawn for maturation from the vegetative pool of infected cells at various stages of the latent period. The analytical formulation of the frequency distribution Y_μ for the case of phage genomes replicated geometrically in a vegetative pool is rather more involved than Equation (8-3). This problem was solved by Steinberg and Stahl (590), who showed that, provided reasonable assumptions are made concerning the steady state number of vegetative phage genomes in the pool and the length of time spent by the average phage genome in the pool prior to its maturation, a frequency distribution can be derived that predicts not only the observed values of Y_μ for values of $\mu < 16$ but also the more rapid decrease in the frequency of mutant clones for which $\mu > 16$.

Mixed Infection

Neither burst size nor latent period of phage-infected bacterium depends on the multiplicity of infection (see Chapter 4), even though one might have thought that a bacterium infected with two or more virus particles should require less time for the growth cycle, or yield more virus particles after a fixed period of growth, than a bacterium infected only with a single phage. This fact caused Luria and Delbrück (115) to suspect that of the numerous phage particles that may be adsorbed to the surface of a single host bacterium, perhaps no more than one can actually cause infection or be the true progenitor of the progeny phages that ultimately issue from the cell. In order to explain this postulated exclusion of all but one of the adsorbed phages from initiation of intracellular phage growth, the idea of a "key enzyme," present in the host bacterium in limited amount and essential for virus reproduction, was proposed; according to this notion, competition for the key enzyme would allow only one of several phage particles to establish the infection. The key enzyme hypothesis had to be abandoned in 1945, however, when Delbrück and Bailey (167), as well as Hershey (284, 285), found that more than one infecting phage *can*, after all, successfully grow in a single bacterial cell. These observations pertained to **mixed-infection** experiments, in which each bacterium was infected with several particles of two closely related but genetically different types and in which both types of progeny virus demonstrably issued from one and the same cell.

In one set of such mixed-infection experiments, bacteria were infected with an average of 3 particles each per cell of T4r and T4r^+ phages and the phage yields of individual infected bacteria were examined by the single-burst technique. The result of this experiment was that the progeny of more than 92% of infected cells included both r and r^+ genotypes. In these mixed yields of individual infected bacteria, the relative proportion of the two parental phage genotypes varied over wide limits, some bursts containing many more r than r^+, some equal numbers of r and r^+, and others containing many more r^+ than r progeny. But the *average* number of the two genotypes per burst was more or less equal. If bacteria were infected with *unequal* numbers of the two parent types, however—for example, with a multiplicity of infection of 2r and 4r^+ particles per cell—then unequal numbers of the two genotypes were also found in the progeny burst, the genotype ratio $r:r^+$ in the output being 2:4, or equal to that of the input.

The joint growth of both r and r^+ phages in a single bacterium can also be demonstrated without recourse to single bursts, by plating the mixedly infected bacteria directly on plates seeded with strain B indicator bacteria, since infective centers that liberate both r and r^+ progeny upon lysis on the plate form **mottled plaques** that are unlike either r or r^+ plaques in appearance (Fig. 8-1). The peculiar morphology of the mottled plaque results from the joint growth of both r and r^+ phages in the same focus of infection; in some areas of the plaque more r^+ than r phages are present, producing a turbid zone characteristic of lysis inhibition, while in other areas more r than r^+ phages are present, producing the clear zone characteristic of rapid lysis. Almost all the bacteria infected with both r and r^+ parent phages give rise to mottled plaques when plated directly before burst.

Although more than one parental virus was thus found to be capable of participating in intracellular phage growth, it seemed likely that there is some *upper limit* to the number of virus particles that is able to do so. An attempt to estimate this maximum number was undertaken by Dulbecco (189), who infected bacteria simultaneously with an average of one T2r mutant per cell and with progressively increasing multiplicities, m, of T2r^+ phages and then scored the fraction of infective centers which failed to yield both r and r^+ genotypes among their progeny. To clarify the intent of this experiment, let us suppose that participation in growth in a single cell is limited to p_x phage particles chosen at random from the single r and the $m\ r^+$ particles adsorbed simultaneously to each cell. Then, so long as the total number, $m + 1$, of phages adsorbed per bacterium does not exceed p_x, all parental phages can participate and both r and r^+ progeny appear in the yield of every mixedly infected cell. But as soon as $m + 1 > p_x$, some of the adsorbed phages will necessarily be excluded from intra-cellular growth. The participating group of p_x phages can be chosen in $(m + 1)!/p_x!(m + 1 - p_x)!$ different ways from the total complement of $m + 1$ phages, of which $m!/p_x!(m - p_x)!$ ways will not include the single r phage. Hence in Dulbecco's experiment, the fraction g_0 of all infected bacteria from which the lone r minority type will be excluded is given by

$$g_0 = \frac{m!/p_x!(m - p_x)!}{(m + 1)!/p_x!(m + 1 - p_x)!} = \frac{m + 1 - p_x}{m + 1}. \qquad (8\text{-}6)$$

Thus, according to Equation $(8\text{-}6)$, an ever-increasing fraction of the infective centers no longer yields any r progeny as the multiplicity of infection m of the r^+ majority type is raised to higher and higher levels.

The outcome of Dulbecco's experiment showed that as long as the input m of r^+ phages per cell did not exceed 6–10, both r and r^+ progeny types issued from nearly all of the infective centers; however, as the r^+ input was increased beyond that value, more and more infective centers failed to yield any r phages among their progeny. The quantitative results could be interpreted according to Equation $(8\text{-}6)$ to mean that $p_x = 10$; that is, as many as 10 phages can participate in intracellular growth in one bacterium. [Equation $(8\text{-}6)$ actually presents a rather oversimplified analysis, since it is not practically possible to infect every bacterium with *exactly* one r and exactly $m\ r^+$ phage particles. Dulbecco, therefore, compared his experimental results with a more sophisticated analytical formulation that takes cognizance of the random distribution of both kinds of parental phage particles over the mixedly infected cells.]

More recently, it has been possible to show by experiments similar in principle to that of Dulbecco but employing another technique—more sensitive than the mottled plaque—for detecting the appearance of the minority genotype from the mixedly infected cell that the upper limit,

p_x, of participating particles is at least two or three times greater than the 10 phages per cell first estimated. It is by no means certain, furthermore, that even this higher figure reflects a real ceiling on intracellular participation, instead of side effects such as lysis-from-without or superinfection breakdown produced by the very high multiplicities of infection necessarily employed in the search for the upper limit of p_x. In any case, it may be concluded that the genetic substance of very many, rather than only one parental virus can take part in the reproductive events ensuing in one and the same host cell.

Partial Exclusion

In Delbrück and Bailey's (167) experiment, designed to investigate whether more than one parental phage can grow in a single cell, bacteria were mixedly infected with T2 and T4 phages. Here, the mixed yielders among the infected bacteria can be scored directly by plating the infective centers before lysis on plates seeded with B/2 + B/4 mixed indicators. On such plates, infective centers that yield both T2 and T4 among their progeny should produce *clear* plaques, whereas infective centers that yield either only T2 or only T4 progeny should produce *turbid* plaques, since both phage genotypes must be present in an infective focus if all the indicator bacteria in the domain of the plaque are to be lysed. The result of this experiment was that 90% of the bacteria mixedly infected with equal numbers of T2 and T4 particles produced clear plaques on the mixed indicators, demonstrating that two or more particles of these closely related phage types are able to grow together in one bacterium. However, after joint growth of T2 and T4 in the same cell, the genotype output is *not* equal to the genotype input: in the phage yield issuing from bacteria mixedly infected with equal numbers of T2 and T4 parental phages, there are about three to ten times more individuals whose host range genotype is T4 (phages that form clear plaques on B + B/2 mixed indicators and turbid plaques on B + B/4) than individuals whose host range genotype is T2 (phages that form clear plaques on B + B/4 and turbid plaques on B + B/2). Later investigations suggested that T4 might derive its predominance over T2 in mixed infection from the higher glucose content in its DNA; as was described in Chapter 3, 100% of the hydroxymethyl cytosine (HMC) residues of the T4 DNA are glucosylated, but only 75% of such residues are glucosylated in T2. Now the minority of T2 genotypes which do issue after joint growth with T4 turn out to be as highly glucosylated as T4, and pass on to their own progeny the property of greater glucosylation. The T2 progeny in the mixed yield have, therefore, been modified hereditarily and are designated as $\overline{T2}$. However, the fully glucosylated $\overline{T2}$ is still at a disadvantage in joint growth with T4, but it predominates, just like T4, in joint growth over its own wild type T2 ancestor (573, 617).

It has not yet been explained why phages with more highly glucosylated DNA should have an advantage in intracellular growth over their less highly glucosylated bedfellows. In fact, this exclusion seems rather puzzling within the framework of the notions on the mechanism of DNA replication outlined in Chapter 7, as does, indeed, the very presence of glucosylated HMC residues in the T-even phage DNA. The glucose, which is grafted onto the HMC residues of the intact progeny DNA polynucleotide according to the specificities of the glucosylating enzymes induced by the virus in the infected cell (372, 408), remains attached to the viral DNA in future growth cycles. This follows from transfer experiments with T2 phage labeled uniformly with radiocarbon C^{14} in all of its constituents; these experiments have shown that the parental glucose is passed on to the progeny virus along with all other components of the parental DNA (136). It is not unlikely that the eventual comprehension of the real function of glucosylated HMC will reveal an important, perhaps as yet unsuspected, insight into the physiology of the viral DNA.

Phenotypic Mixing

It was mentioned in Chapter 6 that Novick and Szilard (497) discovered **phenotypic mixing** by re-examining the anomalous plaque assay behavior of the phages issuing from bacteria mixedly infected with T2 and T4 phages, which had been first noticed by Delbrück and Bailey (167). The anomaly is that the number of progeny individuals of such mixed bursts forming *clear* plaques on B + B/4 mixed indicators is very much greater than the number forming *any* plaques on plates seeded only with strain B/4, even though these numbers should, in principle, both be equal to the number of progeny particles of T2 host range genotype.

Novick and Szilard, it will be recalled, resolved this anomaly by showing that among the progeny of joint growth of T2 and T4 phages there are present many individuals which, though of T2 host range *genotype*, are of T4 *phenotype*. Such hybrid particles produce clear plaques on B + B/4 mixed indicators because they can infect and carry out one cycle of growth on strain B bacteria to generate progeny of T2 host range phenotype that are able to infect, grow on, and lyse both B and B/4 bacteria on the plate. These same hybrid particles, however, will not form any plaques whatsoever on plates seeded with only strain B/4, because (being of T4 host range phenotype) they are unable to adsorb to the only type of bacterium presented to them and thus cannot manage to make that first growth cycle which would yield the progeny of T2 host range phenotype capable of lysing the indicator strain. Joint growth of two genetically different types of virus in one and the same cell may thus result in progeny phages that carry the genotype of one and the phenotype of the other of the two parents.

Phenotypic mixing of the T2 and T4 host range character was studied in more quantitative detail by Streisinger (612), who utilized a fully glucosylated $\overline{T2}$ strain to minimize complications due to the unequal yield phenomenon discussed in the preceding paragraphs. His experiment showed that the association between phenotype and genotype among progeny of mixed infections seems to be no greater than *random*, since phenotypically mixed individuals appear as frequently as those of matching host range phenotype and genotype. Streisinger found, furthermore, that not only host range but also antigenic character—in particular, the structure of the neutralizing antigens—is subject to phenotypic mixing; among the progeny of bacteria infected mixedly with T2 and T4 parents, individuals show up that can be neutralized only by T2-specific antibodies but whose progeny are neutralized only by T4-specific antibodies.

The existence of phenotypic mixing can be readily accounted for in terms of the physiology of phage reproduction discussed in the preceding chapters. It was seen there that synthesis of the phage DNA, carrier of the genotype, proceeds separately from and independently of, the synthesis of phage precursor protein, carrier of (among others) host range and serological phenotype. Thus, in a bacterium mixedly infected with both T2 and T4 phages, molecules of phage precursor DNA carrying the hereditary information of the host range of the one parent may at the time of maturation become encapsulated as readily by phage precursor protein molecules endowed with the tail structure of the other parent as by its own homologous phage precursor protein. When such phenotypically mixed phage particles infect bacteria in a further growth cycle, the heterologous protein is left behind outside the cell, while inside the cell the injected viral DNA now replicates and induces the synthesis of only homologous phage precursor protein, to produce a crop of progeny that are no longer phenotypically mixed. In complete accord with these ideas, phenotypic mixing has thus far been observed only for properties of the phage where the phenotype depends in some way on the character of the protein of the mature virus. Phenotypic mixing is also encountered among the progeny of joint growth of wild type phage and the T2h host range mutant (308), the T4c cofactor-dependent mutant (90), and certain heat-resistant mutants (615). But no phenotypic mixing occurs of phage properties which depend only on some aspect of vegetative phage development, such as the rapid-lysis r character.

Further Reading

Adams, M. H., *Bacteriophages* (2). Chapter IX provides a discussion of the factors that govern the host range of bacteriophages. Chapters XVI and XVII deal with mutation and mixed infection.

Luria, S. E., "The frequency distribution of spontaneous bacteriophage mutants as evidence for the exponential rate of phage reproduction" (437).

Delbrück, M. and Luria, S. E., "Interference between two bacterial viruses acting upon the same host, and mechanism of virus growth" (168). A description of "mutual exclusion" or of the inability of two unrelated phages to grow within the same bacterium.

Hershey, A. D. "Inheritance in bacteriophage" (287). An account of the accomplishments of the first five or six years of phage genetics.

Srb, A. M. and Owen, R. D., *General Genetics* (581). An excellent introductory text to classical genetics.

CHAPTER 9

Genetic Recombination

The Map—The Visconti-Delbrück Theory—The Circular Map—Copy Choice—Heterozygotes—Negative Interference—Breakage and Reunion

THAT MORE than one virus can grow in the same cell was demonstrated by experiments that involved mixed infections of bacteria with two phage types differing from each other in only one genetic character. When, in these very same experiments, Delbrück and Bailey (167) and Hershey (285) undertook mixed infections with virus particles that differed from each other in not one but *two* genetic characters, a most important discovery was made: joint growth of two bacteriophages in the same cell results in the formation of **recombinant** viruses that carry in their genome some of the genetic characters of one and some of the genetic characters of the other of the two viral parents. Thus, Delbrück and Bailey infected bacteria with both the T4r^+ wild type and the T2r mutant and found among the phage progeny of this infection not only the two parental genotypes but also some T4r and T2r^+ individuals, new genotypes that had not been present in the phage inoculum. Similarly, Hershey carried out mixed infections with h and r mutants of T2 and found among the progeny some h^+r^+ wild type and hr double mutant phages, in addition to the two parental types. Here the h^+r^+ wild type recombinant phage that appeared among the progeny derived its host range character from the h^+r parent and its rapid lysis character from the hr^+ parent, whereas the hr double mutant recombinant phage received its host range character from the hr^+ and its character of rapid lysis from the h^+r parent. Bacterial viruses, therefore, can engage in *genetic recombination*, an activity once considered the prerogative of higher forms that have progressed from vegetative to sexual modes of reproduction. Evidently, the propensity for genetic re-

202

combination can be of the greatest importance for the survival of a species, since novel—and possibly "fitter"—genotypes may thus appear by combination of mutant characters already existing in different individuals of the interbreeding population. In contrast, vegetatively reproducing species, in which no individual ever receives its hereditary factors from more than a single parent, can bring forth novel genotypes only by slow accumulation of successive mutations in a single line of descent. Hence bacterial viruses also possess that potential for continuous reshuffling of the genetic substance of natural populations through which an immense variety of individuals is presented to the ever-changing environment for trial in the evolutionary struggle for existence.

The Map

The first detailed study of genetic recombination in phage was carried out by Hershey and Rotman (309, 310), who isolated numerous r mutants of phage T2, assigning consecutive numbers, such as $r1$, $r2$, $r3$, to individual r mutants of independent origin, and also a "minute" mutant m that forms a very small plaque. Each of these mutants was then grown in mixed infection with, or **crossed** to, the host range mutant T2h, and the progeny phages were examined for the presence of the two possible recombinant genotypes hr and h^+r^+, or hm and h^+m^+. The results of crosses of h against the mutants $r1$, $r7$, and $r13$ are presented in Table 9-I, from which the following conclusions can be drawn.

1. The two recombinant genotypes appear in all three of these crosses, and in each case the percentage of the total progeny represented by the hr recombinant is equal to that represented by the h^+r^+ recombinant; therefore, *complementary recombinant types are formed with equal frequency.*

2. The total frequency of recombinant types produced is very different depending on which r mutant is crossed to the h phage; only 1.7% of all the progeny of the cross $h \times r13$ are recombinants, whereas 12.3% of all the progeny of $h \times r7$ and 24% of all the progeny of $h \times r1$ are recombinants.

These observations were interpreted by Hershey and Rotman in the terms of classical genetics. The hereditary material of bacteriophages,

T A B L E 9 - I

*Recombinant Frequencies in T2h × T2r Crosses**

PROCEDURE: A growing culture of 2 × 10⁷ *E. coli* per milliliter was infected with an input average of 5 T2*h* and 5 T2*r* phages per cell. After allowing 5 minutes for adsorption, the infected culture was diluted 10⁴-fold into nutrient broth and incubated for 60 minutes. The progeny phage yield produced was plated for plaque assay on agar seeded with strain B and strain B/2 mixed indicators, on which all four genotypes can be separately scored.

Cross		% of Genotype in Population			
		h^+r^+	hr^+	h^+r	hr
$h × r1$	input	0	53	47	0
	yield	12	42	34	12
$h × r7$	input	0	49	51	0
	yield	5.9	56	32	6.4
$h × r13$	input	0	49	51	0
	yield	0.74	59	39	0.94

* From Hershey and Rotman (310).

they supposed, consists of linear arrays of **genes,** each gene carrying the hereditary information for some character of the virus, analogous to the genes in the chromosomes of higher forms. Different phage mutants then harbor different mutant genes, so that each mutant character is situated in a particular place or **locus** on such a linear structure of linked genes. The genomes of the two mutant viruses, *h* and *r*, coexisting in the mixedly infected bacterium can, therefore, be represented as

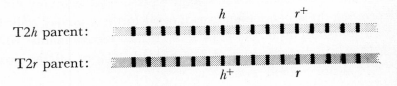

T2*h* parent:

T2*r* parent:

In one of the parents the host range gene locus is of the mutant *h* type and the rapid lysis gene locus is of the wild *r⁺* type, while the corresponding, homologous loci in the other parent are of the wild h^+ and mutant r types. In accord with classical genetic nomenclature, h and h^+, or r and r^+, are said to be **alleles** or alternative configurations of the same gene locus in different individuals. But, in the mixedly infected bacterial cell, the two coexisting phage genomes may proceed to *exchange* homologous parts with each other, as by breakage of the two linear structures at exactly corresponding points between host range and rapid lysis loci, followed by crosswise rejoining of the fragments:

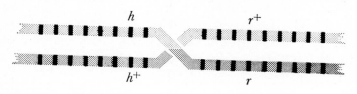

Such **crossover** of genetic material anywhere between the two mutant loci will then generate the two recombinant hr and h^+r^+ genomes that have derived their host range gene from one and their rapid lysis gene from the other of the two parents.

Since the chance event of an exchange can occur at any point along the two parental genetic linkage structures, it follows that the *probability* that a crossover will actually take place *between* two given genetic loci depends on the distance of the two gene loci from each other, or their **linkage.** The closer the linkage of two loci, the less probable is it that a crossover will chance to occur at an intermediate point, and hence the lower the frequency of phage progeny recombinant for the loci in question. In contrast, the greater the distance between the two gene loci, the greater is the chance of a crossover at an intermediate point, and hence the higher the probability of recombinant progeny. The fact that the three r mutants of Table 9-I produce different yields of recombinants in crosses to the h mutant then implies that in the genome of the T2 phage there is more than one gene concerned with the rapid lysis character and that the mutations carried by T2r1, T2r7, and T2r13 are situated at entirely different loci. Of the three loci, r13 must be the locus that is most closely linked and r1 the locus that is least closely linked to the host range locus h. (In phage genetics, as in classical genetics, a gene locus is represented by the symbol of the mutant genotype occurring at that locus, so the host range gene locus is represented by the letter h and the various rapid lysis genes by the symbols r1, r2, and so on.)

These considerations allow one to construct a *genetic map* of the relative situation of the known viral genes on the "chromosome" of the phage. Four conceivable arrangements of the genes *h*, *r*13, *r*7, and *r*1 satisfy the condition that *r*13 is closest to *h* and *r*1 most distant from *h*:

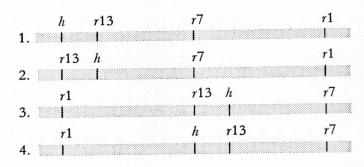

Further crosses are necessary before it can be decided which of these four alternatives corresponds most closely to the truth. If either map (1) or (4) were correct, the *r*13 locus would be more closely linked to the *r*7 locus than the *h* locus is linked to *r*7, whereas if map (2) or (3) were correct, *r*13 would be more distant from *r*7 than is *h*. Thus, in a cross of *r*13 × *r*7, the frequency of crossovers between these two loci should be *lower* under alternatives (1) and (4) and *higher* under alternatives (2) and (3) than the frequency of crossovers between *h* and *r*7. If one carries out the cross *r*13 × *r*7, one finds that there appear r^+ wild type genotypes among the progeny. This confirms, first of all, the inference that the mutations *r*13 and *r*7 are situated at different gene loci, or are *nonallelic*, since these r^+ individuals can have arisen only by the crossover

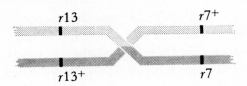

that brought together the wild $r13^+$ and $r7^+$ genes into the same phage genome.

The proportion of these r^+ wild type recombinants, furthermore, is *less* than the proportion of either *hr* of h^+r^+ recombinants produced in the cross *h* × *r*7, showing, secondly, that *r*13 is closer to *r*7 than is *h*, and thus eliminating alternatives (2) and (3). The exchange event that produces the r^+ wild type also generates the *double mutant r13r7*, but since the phenotype of the double r mutant is exactly the same as that of single r mutants—that is, production of an r-type plaque—the double mutant cannot be easily recognized among the progeny.

In genetic terminology, the r mutation is said to be **epistatic** to r^+: as soon as one of the several rapid lysis r gene loci of the phage genome is in the r mutant state, the phenotype of the phage is r. Conversely, a phage is of r^+ phenotype only if *all* of the rapid lysis loci of its genome are in the r^+ wild state. No r^+ recombinants are, of course, produced in the "crosses" $r7 \times r7$, or $r13 \times r13$, since it is impossible to construct a phage genome carrying only r^+ loci by any recombinational event between two genomes carrying an r mutation at exactly corresponding or allelic loci. This allows one to identify the double mutant $r13r7$, inasmuch as this double mutant, in contrast to a single mutant, produces no r^+ recombinants in crosses to either $r7$ or $r13$.

It should be possible to decide between the remaining alternatives (1) and (4) by carrying out the cross $r7 \times r1$, since the frequency of r^+ wild type recombinants produced in this cross ought to be lower under alternative (1) and higher under alternative (4) than the frequency of hr or h^+r^+ recombinants from the cross $h \times r1$. However, the frequency of r^+ wild type recombinants produced in the cross $r7 \times r1$ is about 15%, or more or less the same as the frequency of either the hr or the h^+r^+ recombinant produced in the cross $h \times r1$. Hershey and Rotman interpreted this observation to mean that the $r1$ locus is neither closer to h than to $r7$ [alternative (4)] nor closer to $r7$ than to h [alternative (1)], but that, instead, $r1$ is *unlinked* to either one of these loci and is situated on an entirely separate linkage group. In other words, it was proposed that the T2 phage carries more than one "chromosome." The frequency of 15% for one recombinant species (or 30% for both complementary recombinants) would thus represent the maximum probability of genetic recombination, or that of exchange of unlinked genetic loci carried on different "chromosomes." On the basis of these various crosses, the first linkage map of T2 phage was constructed, which, as shown in Fig. 9-1, envisages the genome of T2 as consisting of three linkage groups. A cross of phages carrying any two unlinked mutant genes situated on different linkage groups of this map would generate wild type recombinants with a frequency of 15%, while crosses between phages carrying linked mutant genes would produce fewer wild type recombinants, the exact frequency depending on the linkage of the loci in question. In subsequent years, as more and more mutant loci of T2 and T4 were discovered and mapped by crosses with previously identified

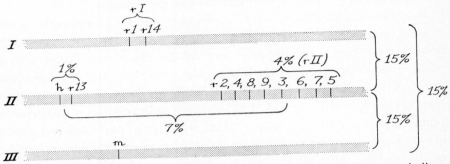

Fig. 9-1. The first linkage map of mutations in phage T2. The percentages indicate relative yield of wild type recombinants produced in equal-input, two-factor crosses. [From Hershey and Rotman (310).]

genes, it became clear that all the genetic loci of these viruses *are* linked to one another; that is, the viral genome is but a single genetic linkage group, or "chromosome" (43, 466, 613), as shown in Fig. 9-2.

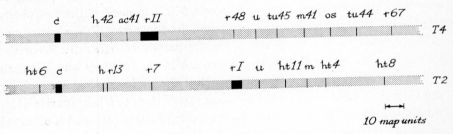

Fig. 9-2. The unified genetic maps of T2 and T4. (See Table 8-I for the meaning of the mutant symbols shown.) [Modified from Brenner (91).]

The distances on these maps are expressed in **map units,** one map unit being the distance that separates two genetic loci x and y for which, in a standard phage cross $T2x^+y \times T2xy^+$, the recombinants $T2xy$ and $T2x^+y^+$ appear among the progeny at a frequency of 1%. But how, in view of this definition, is it possible that this map shows genetic loci separated by *several hundred* map units, when in crosses between any two phage mutants the *maximum* observed frequency for wild type and double mutant recombinants is only 30%? The answer to this riddle will become apparent in the following paragraphs, where the real meaning of recombinant frequencies and their relation to the linkage map will be considered. The discussions will also resolve the apparent paradox that on the map of Fig. 9-2 the $r1$ locus is situated closer to $r7$ than to h—implying that alternative (1) is really the correct one—even though no more wild type recombinants are produced in the cross $r1 \times h$ than in the cross $r1 \times r7$.

The Visconti-Delbrück Theory

Thus far we have viewed a phage cross as an exchange of genetic material between the genomes of the two infecting parental viruses and have pretended that a mixed infection is more or less analogous to the mating of two organisms. Further study of genetic recombination in phage revealed, however, that a phage cross cannot represent merely the exchange of hereditary factors between two parent viruses but that, instead, recombination must involve repeated genetic interactions among the intracellular population of vegetative phage genomes descended from the infecting parents.

1. *Joint appearance of parents and recombinants.* If one examines by means of the single-burst technique the genotypes of phage progeny liberated by *individual* bacteria infected with two phages differing in several of their genetic characters, then one finds that both parental as well as recombinant genotypes issue from a single cell (310). This indicates that the genetic exchange cannot be restricted to the stage of growth preceding replication of the infecting genomes, since there should issue from each infected cell either only the parental or only the recombinant genotypes if no recombinational events occurred after the appearance of replica genomes.

2. *Formation of triparental recombinant.* It is possible to perform a **triparental cross,** in which bacteria are infected simultaneously with three parent viruses that differ from one another in three of their genetic characters, as in the cross $xy^+z^+ \times x^+yz^+ \times x^+y^+z$. From such triply infected cells there issues the triparental recombinant xyz, a genotype that has obtained one genetically marked locus from each of the three parents (300). This indicates that there are repeated recombinational events in the infected cell, since at least two successive genetic exchanges are required for production of the triparental

recombinant—the first between two of the parents and the second between the third parent and the biparental recombinant.

3. *Low yield of minority parent.* If a cross is performed in which an *unequal* input of two parental genotypes is introduced, say by infection of bacteria with 10 phages per cell of type x^+y^+ (majority parent) and 1 phage per cell of type xy (minority parent), then it is found that among the progeny the recombinants of type x^+y or xy^+ are much more frequent than the minority parent (185, 650). But, as will be shown presently, no matter how distantly linked the two genetic markers x and y, any one act of genetic exchange involving the two parents xy and x^+y^+ can yield recombinants x^+y and xy^+ with probability no greater than 0.5. Hence the observed *excess* of recombinants over minority parental genotypes among the progeny indicates that the minority parent must participate in more than one act of genetic exchange with the majority parent; that is, there occur repeated recombinational events in the infected cell.

4. *Drift toward genetic equilibrium.* If one examines the proportion of recombinants among the intracellular infective progeny present at various times after the end of the eclipse period of mixedly infected bacteria, one finds that this proportion increases the longer that phage growth has been allowed to proceed (182, 300, 424) (Fig. 9-3).

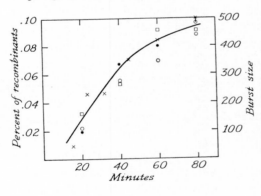

Fig. 9-3. Drift toward genetic equilibrium in a phage cross. *E. coli* growing in broth are infected with an average multiplicity of about five particles each of T2h^+r^+ and T2hr13 parent phages. Lysis of different samples of the infected culture is induced at the time indicated on the abscissa; both total yield of progeny phages per cell and percentage of progeny of hr^+ and h^+r recombinant genotype are scored. The circles and squares refer to recombinant frequencies and the crosses to burst size. [From Levinthal and Visconti (424).]

This indicates that genetic recombination is neither an exclusively initial event which has to precede, nor an exclusively terminal event which has to follow, the replication of the viral genomes. Instead, it may be inferred that there occur repetitive acts of genetic exchange concurrently with the replication of the vegetative phage, so that a *drift toward genetic equilibrium* is manifest among the intracellular population of viral genomes.

Departing from these observations, Visconti and Delbrück (650) in 1953 formulated a theory of genetic recombination in bacteriophages capable of accounting quantitatively for the recombinant frequencies produced under various experimental conditions. This theory, in conformity with the then known mechanism of intracellular phage growth, envisaged that upon infection of the host bacterium the viral genome multiplies in a noninfective vegetative form and generates a pool of viral precursor genomes; that after termination of the eclipse period, the viral precursor genomes are withdrawn at random from this pool for irreversible maturation as structurally intact, infective progeny to be released upon lysis of the infected cell; that until lysis the rate of maturation, or withdrawal of genomes from the pool, is equal to the rate of genome replication in the pool, so that the size of the vegetative pool attains a constant, steady-state value; and that intracellular mature progeny particles do not replicate and no longer participate in any genetic events. The Visconti-Delbrück theory envisaged, furthermore, that in this viral precursor pool there occur repeated, pairwise *matings* of complete vegetative phage genomes, each mating leading to an exchange of genetic material by one or more crossovers between the two mated individuals. These matings occur randomly with respect to time (rather than synchronously) and randomly with respect to partner (so that genetically identical as well as genetically different individuals engage in conjugal acts). Upon conclusion of the mating—which may or may not have produced a phage genome recombinant for the genetic loci under study—the pair of "exconjugant" phages separate and once more return to the pool to further replicate or mate with other partners, until finally withdrawn from the pool upon maturation as intact progeny viruses.

From the vantage point of the Visconti-Delbrück theory, the number of progeny viruses recombinant for two genetic markers introduced into a phage cross is thus seen to depend not only on the linkage of the mutant loci in question but also on the number of mating events which have occurred in the vegetative pool by the time that lysis of the infected bacterium has brought to term the intracellular growth processes. Since linkage of genetic loci cannot, therefore, be simply equated to recombinant frequencies, we now define a "true" linkage, *d*, of two genetic loci as *the average number of crossovers that take place at points between these loci in each mating of two vegetative phages in the mating pool:* the greater the distance that separates the loci on the phage "chromosome," the greater the average number of such crossovers per mating. However, an *observable* recombination of genetic markers at the two loci will result only if the number of crossovers at points between the loci in any one mating is *odd*, for if the number of crossovers happens to be even, then no recombination would be manifest, since the original configuration of the two markers is preserved; for example, the following figure illustrates the result of two crossovers.

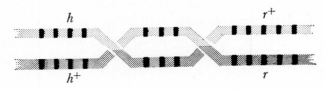

It then follows that the probability *p* of recombination per mating—that is, the probability of an odd number of crossovers between two markers—is related to their "true" linkage, *d*, by the odd terms of the Poisson formula,

$$p = \left(\frac{d}{1!} + \frac{d^3}{3!} + \frac{d^5}{5!} + \cdots \right) e^{-d} = 0.5 \,(1 - e^{-2d}). \qquad (9\text{-}1)$$

This expression, first derived by Haldane (261) in 1917, implies that for large values of *d* (for very distantly linked loci), *p* approaches the limit 0.5. In other words, if there occur a large number of crossovers per mating between two genetic loci, half of the mating events will terminate with an odd and half will terminate with an even number of crossovers. For small values of *d*, characteristic of very closely linked loci, Equation (9-1) simplifies to *p* = *d*; that is, if the average number of crossovers per mating between the two loci is very much less than one, almost all crossovers that occur will be single exchanges. Finally, if the two loci are alleles (*d* = 0), then *p* = 0; that is, there is no chance whatsoever that a recombinant is produced for two genetic markers that occupy exactly the same locus on the phage "chromosome."

The apparent paradox encountered in the construction of the phage genetic map—that no more wild type recombinants are produced in the cross $r1 \times h$ than in the cross $r1 \times r7$, even though the $r7$ locus is more closely linked to the $r1$ locus than the h locus—can now be explained. It would appear that the distance d that separates the $r7$ locus from $r1$ is so great, or the linkage of these two loci so weak, that the probability p per mating of recombination between these loci is already close to the maximum value of 0.5. Hence even though the distance that separates the loci $r1$ and h may still be very much greater than the distance between $r1$ and $r7$, the probability per mating of recombination between $r1$ and h cannot be greater than the maximum value of 0.5. In other words, approximately equal frequencies of recombinant progeny are to be expected in all crosses involving very distantly linked genetic loci.

Let us now consider a bacterium that is infected with an *equal multiplicity* of two parental phage genotypes, carrying genetic markers at two loci x and y for which the probability of recombination per mating is p_{xy}. If in the mating pool of this infected bacterium a fraction R_{xy} of all phages are recombinant for these two markers, then an increment dm in the number of mating events experienced by the average phage particle in this pool will generate a new fraction

$$\tfrac{1}{2}(1 - R_{xy})^2 p_{xy}\, dm$$

of phages recombinant for the two markers through matings of individuals of the opposite parental genotypes. (The factor $\tfrac{1}{2}$ expresses the fact that only half the matings of phages of parental genotype will involve individuals of the *opposite* type.) At the same time, a fraction

$$\tfrac{1}{2}R_{xy}^2 p_{xy}\, dm$$

of already existing recombinants will again disappear and reconstitute parental genotypes by matings involving recombinants of the complementary genotype. The *net* increment in recombinants is therefore

$$dR_{xy} = \tfrac{1}{2}(1 - R_{xy})^2 p_{xy}\, dm - \tfrac{1}{2}R_{xy}^2 p_{xy}\, dm. \qquad (9\text{-}2)$$

This differential equation is readily solved as

$$R_{xy} = \tfrac{1}{2}(1 - e^{-p_{xy}m}), \qquad (9\text{-}3)$$

an expression which relates the frequency of phages recombinant for the two markers x and y to the number of matings m in the line of ancestry of the average phage particle (or **rounds of mating**) and to the probability of recombination per mating p—and thus via Equation $(9\text{-}1)$ to the "true" linkage d of the two markers in question. It follows from Equation (9-3) that the frequency of recombinants increases with the number of rounds of mating and approaches the limit 0.5 for very large values of m. In other words, at **genetic equilibrium** in a two-factor, equal-input cross, half of the phages are recombinant and half are parental genotypes.

For the description of crosses involving *unequal inputs* of the two parental genotypes, the coefficient of the first term of Equation (9-2) must be modified to take account of the unequal probability of homologous and heterologous matings of minority and majority parents in the pool. In this case, the solution of the differential equation becomes

$$R_{xy} = 2w(1 - w)(1 - e^{-p_{xy}m}), \tag{9-3'}$$

where w is the relative frequency of the majority parent in the input. For $w = 0.5$, the *equal-input* cross, under which the recombinant frequency R_{xy} is maximal for any given p_{xy} and m, Equation (9-$3'$) reduces to Equation (9-3).

Of the parameters appearing in Equations (9-3) and (9-$3'$), only w and the recombinant frequency R_{xy} can be measured directly; it is not possible to calculate the number of rounds of mating m or the probability of recombination per mating p_{xy} from the results of a two-factor cross involving the loci x and y, but only the value of the product $p_{xy}m$. Two methods are available, however, for determining the number of rounds of mating m. One of these methods takes advantage of the fact that p, the probability of recombination per mating, approaches 0.5 as a limit as the distance d between two loci becomes very large. Hence, by measuring the frequency of recombinants produced in crosses of phages marked by mutations at two loci known to be very distantly linked and assuming that here $p = 0.5$, one can solve Equation (9-3) for m. For instance, the equal-input cross T2h × T2r1 shown in Table 9-I reveals that the two recombinant types h^+r^+ and hr each appear at the frequency 12%, corresponding to a total recombinant frequency $R_{hr1} = 0.24$. Since the genetic distance between h and r1 can be presumed to be so great that p_{hr1} is near the maximum value of 0.5, it follows from Equation (9-3) that

$$0.24 = \tfrac{1}{2}(1 - e^{-0.5m}),$$

or

$$m = 1.3.$$

That is, in this cross there appear to have occurred 1.3 rounds of mating in the line of ancestry of the average progeny phage genome.

The number of rounds of mating, m, determined in this way is applicable to the analysis of other crosses of T2 phages carried out under similar physiological conditions, irrespective of the linkage of the genetic loci whose recombination is being studied. Hence we can now estimate the values of p_{hr7} and p_{hr13} from the recombinant frequencies of Table 9-I. Thus

$$R_{hr7} = 0.123 = \tfrac{1}{2}(1 - e^{-1.3p_{hr7}}),$$

or

$$p_{hr7} = 0.22,$$

and

$$R_{hr13} = 0.017 = \tfrac{1}{2}(1 - e^{-1.3p_{hr13}}),$$

or

$$p_{hr13} = 0.027.$$

The "true" linkages, d_{hr7} and d_{hr13}, can now be obtained from Equation (9-1):

$$0.22 = 0.5(1 - e^{-2d_{hr7}}),$$

or

$$d_{hr7} = 0.29,$$

and

$$0.027 = 0.5(1 - e^{-2d_{hr13}}),$$

or

$$d_{hr13} = 0.028.$$

Thus it can be concluded that between the h locus and $r7$ or $r13$ loci there occur, respectively, an average of 0.27 and 0.028 crossovers per mating.

The second method of determining m has recourse to the analysis of a three-factor cross—a mixed infection with two phages differing at three, rather than two, of their genetic loci, such as $x^+y^+z^+ \times xyz$. If the order of the loci on the phage chromosome is $x - y - z$ and if the probability per mating of recombination between each of these loci is p_{xz}, p_{yz}, and p_{xy}, then it follows that

$$p_{xz} = p_{xy} + p_{yz} - 2p_{xy}p_{yz}. \tag{9-4}$$

In other words, the probability per mating that an odd number of crossovers will take place between the loci $x - z$ is the sum of the probabilities per mating of an odd number of crossovers between $x - y$ and between $y - z$, minus the probability that an odd number of crossovers will occur between *both* $x - y$ and $y - z$ (in which case the number of crossovers between $x - z$ would be even). If we examine the progeny of such a three-factor cross and score the proportion of progeny recombinant for the loci x and y, y and z, and x and z, then Equation (9-3) predicts that the frequency of each of these recombinant classes should be

$$R_{xy} = \tfrac{1}{2}(1 - e^{-p_{xy}m}), \tag{9-5}$$

$$R_{yz} = \tfrac{1}{2}(1 - e^{-p_{yz}m}), \tag{9-6}$$

$$R_{xz} = \tfrac{1}{2}(1 - e^{-p_{xz}m}). \tag{9-7}$$

Hence, after substituting the experimentally determined values of R_{xy}, R_{yz}, and R_{xz} into these relations, one may solve the four simultaneous Equations (9-4), (9-5), (9-6), and (9-7) for the four unknown parameters p_{xy}, p_{yz}, p_{xz}, and m.

The analysis of recombinant frequencies of three-factor crosses, particularly of crosses involving *unequal* input of the two parental genotypes, yields a much more reliable determination of the number of rounds of mating than the simple two-factor calculation of the first method. In this way, Visconti and Delbrück (650) estimated that in the line of ancestry of the T2 phage particles liberated at the time of normal lysis there occurred *five* rather than only 1.3 rounds of mating. If a similar genetic analysis is carried out on the first progeny to make their intracellular appearance after the end of the eclipse, it is found that these phages have experienced only one or two rounds of mating, whereas the last progeny to mature under conditions of lysis inhibition look back to as many as six to eight rounds of mating in their line of descent (424). In fact, a comparison of the kinetics of phage DNA synthesis and mating in T2- or T4-infected bacteria reveals that rounds of mating in the vegetative phage pool keep more or less in step with rounds of replication, or that acts of mating are as frequent as acts of replication.

We may now reconsider the meaning of the *map unit*, in terms of which distances between genetic loci of the phage are generally given, instead of (as might more properly be done) in terms of their "true linkage" d. Since the map unit is that distance that separates two loci x and y for which in a standard phage cross ($m = 5$) recombinants appear in frequency 1% ($R_{xy} = 0.01$) among the progeny, it follows from Equations (9-1) and (9-3) that the "true linkage" of two such loci is

$$d_{xy} = 0.5 \ln \left[1 + \frac{2 \ln (1 - 2R_{xy})}{m} \right]$$

$$= 0.5 \ln \left[1 + \frac{2 \ln (1 - 0.02)}{5} \right] = 0.004.$$

That is, in the genetic distance represented by one map unit there occurs an average of 0.004 crossovers per mating in the vegetative phage pool; or, within 250 map units, there occurs an average of one crossover per mating.

The Circular Map

As shown in Fig. 9-2, the two genetic loci $h42$ and $r67$ are situated at opposite ends of the map of the T4 phage genome, and the $ac41$ locus is situated between these two very distant loci at a point much closer to $h42$ than to $r67$. When Streisinger, Edgar, and Denhardt (614) carried out the three-factor cross T4$h42ac^+r^+$ × T4$h^+ac41r67$ involving these three loci and examined the recombinant genotypes among the first phage progeny to mature at the end of the eclipse period (in whose line of ancestry at most one or two rounds of mating had taken place), they encountered an unexpected result. On the basis of the relative linkage of the three loci shown in the map of Fig. 9-2, it would have been anticipated that among the $h42ac41$ recombinants of this three-factor cross, equal numbers should bear $r67^+$ and $r67$ alleles, since the distance between $ac41$ and $r67$ is so great that the probability of recombination between $ac41$ and $r67$ in the one mating that produced the recombination between $h42$ and $ac41$ is virtually near the maximum of 0.5. But instead of the anticipated equidistribution of the two parental alleles of the $r67$ locus among $h42ac41$ recombinants, it was found that 66% of $h42ac41$ recombinants carried the $r67^+$ allele (that is, were of the $h42ac41r67^+$ genotype). This result shows that the $r67$ locus not only fails to segregate independently of the two remote $h42$ and $ac41$ loci but appears to be linked more closely to its distal $h42$ locus than to its proximal $ac41$ locus, in evident contradiction with the crossover frequencies to be expected from the map of Fig. 9-2. The only way to resolve this paradox is to conclude that the linkage map of T4 is *circular*, having neither beginning nor end. Only in this way could *r*67 be at the same time both more and less closely linked to *h*42 than to *ac*41.

The proposal that the T4 viral genetic map corresponds to a closed line would have probably been greeted with considerable skepticism had not Jacob and Wollman (340, 341), some three years earlier, already conditioned the reflexes of phage geneticists to the idea of circular genetic maps through the discovery that the *E. coli* chromosome behaves as a circular linkage structure. After all, if the host genome is circular, why not also that of its virus? In fact, it seemed tempting to generalize from these two instances that a circular map is actually typical of the topology of genomes constituted of molecular DNA. If so, the circularity of the map might be the expression of some important feature of the structure and function of the hereditary polynucleotide, whose elucidation, like that of heterozygosis and negative interference, would bring a more profound comprehension of the genetic process.

Soon after the three-factor cross that first revealed the circularity of the map was carried out, two sets of novel phage mutants became available whose genetic loci were found to occur in sufficient density in all sectors of the map that the circularity of the phage genome could be directly established by point-to-point linkage measurements around the circumference of the circle. The first class of these mutants, **amber or am,** was developed by Epstein (202); amber mutants of T4 cannot grow on *E. coli*, strain B, the "normal" host of the T4*am*$^+$ wild type, but they are able to grow on other *E. coli* strains, particularly on certain derivative strains of K12. Study of the physiology of growth of these mutants in the *nonpermissive* strain B host showed that different *am* mutants appear to be blocked at different stages of the ontogenetic sequence of phage development (588). For instance, detailed enzymological examination of the "early protein" synthesized by two particular T4*am* mutants showed that one of these mutants fails to induce formation of deoxycytidylate hydroxymethylase, and the other fails to induce the phage-specific DNA polymerase (enzymes of Nos. 1 and 3 of the metabolic panorama of Fig. 7-3) in bacteria of strain B, although competent to elicit these same enzymes in the *permissive* bacteria of strain K12 (680). Though it has not yet been clarified why an *am* mutant should not be able to give rise to some particular enzyme in one kind of host cell and be able to do so in another, it seems probable that the biochemical basis of this phenomenon is to be explained in terms similar to those used to account for the "ambivalence" of certain rII mutants, which will be considered in Chapter 15. In any case, Epstein accumulated a large collection of *am* mutants which, upon mapping their mutant sites by crossing them against each other and against other previously triangulated genetic markers of T4, could be arranged in the circular array shown in Fig. 9-4.

The second class of mutants that filled in the T4 linkage map comprises the **temperature-sensitive,** or **ts,** mutants developed by Edgar and his collaborators (198). Whereas wild type T4 is able to form plaques with the same efficiency of plating on agar incubated at 42°C as at 25°C, *ts* mutants do not form any plaques at the higher temperature of incubation. This temperature sensitivity of the mutants does not, in the majority of cases at least, represent a greater susceptibility of the infective virus particle to inactivation by heat (such *heat-sensitive* and *heat-resistant* phage mutants do exist, but in most cases the relevant temperature of inactivation is higher than 42°C). Instead, the phenotype of *ts* mutants devolves from their inability to carry out at the higher temperature some essential function of intracellular growth. Study of the growth of *ts* mutants at 42°C showed that at the inhibitory temperature different *ts* mutants, like different *am* mutants in the nonpermissive host, fail at different stages of the reaction sequence of phage development. The explanation of the behavior of the *ts* mutants of T4 is no doubt the same as that of the temperature-sensitive *Neurospora* mutants studied in 1951 by Horowitz and Leupold (318) for the very same purpose of filling in unknown regions of a genetic map: each mutant gene gives rise to some particular altered enzyme protein, whose chemical structure differs from that of the enzyme synthesized by the corresponding wild type gene in being unable to function at the higher temperature, though still capable of functioning sufficiently well at the lower temperature. Edgar et al. accumulated and subsequently mapped a large collection of *ts* mutants and found that these mutants, just like the *am* mutants, could be arranged on the circular map of Fig. 9-4. As can be seen in that figure, between the sets of *ts* and *am* mutants a direct and measured linkage has been established for all points on this map. Hence the circumference of the circle, and thus the total length of the viral genome, is now known: estimated in this way, the T4 chromosome appears to extend over some 700 map units.

A general survey of the nature of the defective physiology of intra-

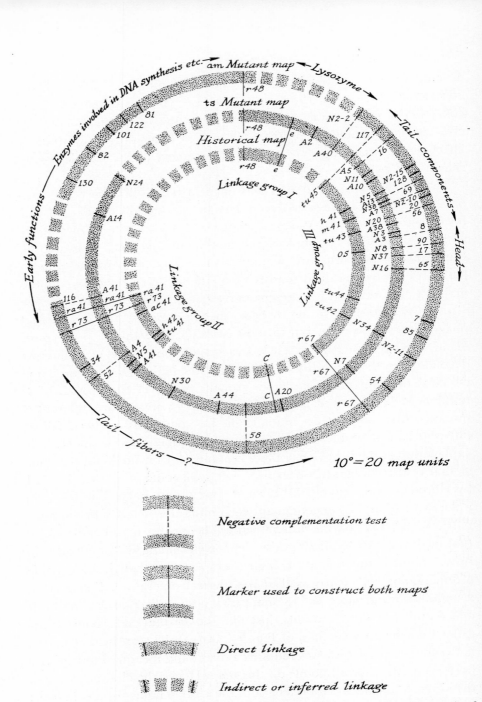

Fig. 9-4. The circular genetic map of T4, based on a comparative linkage analysis of the "historical" map of Fig. 9-2 and numerous amber (*am*) and temperature-sensitive (*ts*) mutants. The physiological functions or phage constituents affected by mutations in various sectors of the map are indicated on the periphery of the circle. [From Edgar and Epstein (198, 202).]

cellular phage growth manifested by each member of the set of *am* mutants in the nonpermissive host and of *ts* mutants at the high inhibitory temperature showed that the biosynthetic potency of each mutant allows its assignment to one of several well-defined classes. This survey includes (a) measurement of the amount of phage DNA synthesized; (b) measurement of the optical density of the infected culture for ascertaining its eventual lysis; (c) serological examination of either spontaneous or artificially induced lysates for the presence of SBP (see Chapter 6), representing the tail fiber antigens; and (d) electron-optical examination of the lysates for the presence or absence of characteristic structural components of the phage. It was thus found that one class of mutants is unable to initiate synthesis of viral DNA; the abortive infective centers constituted by bacteria infected with mutants of this class do not lyse and do not contain any of the head or tail precursor proteins of the intact virus. Other classes of mutants, while able to initiate the synthesis of viral DNA and cause lysis of the infected cell, yield no structurally complete progeny phages in their lysates but only different kinds of incomplete phage constituents. One of this second kind of mutant class, for instance, yields only hollow phage heads and SBP antigens, but no intact phage tail assemblies; another class yields intact tail assemblies and SBP antigens, but no visible heads; and yet another class yields intact heads with attached tails, but devoid of tail fibers and SBP antigens.

The results of these characterizations have been summarized on the periphery of the map of Fig. 9-4; it is evident there that *am* and *ts* mutants whose physiological block concerns the same viral function lie in the same general area of the map. Furthermore, it can be seen that the location of these various mutants coincides with that of other, previously known mutant genotypes whose phenotype is known to concern the same phage function or constituent as the particular physiological defect of the *am* or *ts* mutants. For instance, the map sector assigned to the tail fiber *am* or *ts* mutants includes the *h* host range locus and the *c* adsorption cofactor locus, both concerned with the properties of the tail fibers; the *am* or *ts* phage head mutant sector includes the *os* osmotic shock resistance locus that affects the structure of the phage head; finally, the sector assigned to the *am* or *ts* lysozyme mutants covers the *e* locus, where other lysozyme mutants had been previously mapped.

A rather striking feature of the T4 map is that the disposition of genetic loci appears to be correlated with the *time* of intracellular growth at which the product of the gene locus makes its appearance or starts to function. Thus the loci connected with early functions, such as the *r*II region (to be considered in the next chapter) and the genes concerned with the "early protein" of phage DNA metabolism map in the arc of the circle between 8 o'clock and noon, whereas all the other genes connected with late function or structural proteins of the phage are found in the remainder of the circle. The possible significance of this spatial distribution of phage genes and of the fact that mutants blocked in an early function also fail to carry out the later functions will be considered in the final paragraphs of Chapter 15.

Copy Choice

The Visconti-Delbrück theory supposed that the genetic exchange which takes place upon each mating between two vegetative phages is analogous to crossing-over in chromosomal recombination in higher organisms: point-to-point apposition, or **synapsis,** of two parental chromosomes, followed by breakage and crosswise reunion of homologous parts. This point of view engenders the prediction that every such elementary recombination event generates *both* complementary recombinants in one and the same act; for example, in the cross $T2hr \times T2h^+r^+$, every crossover that produces the recombinant h^+r cannot help but produce also the recombinant hr^+. As was seen in the results of Table 9-I, the complementary recombinants do appear in equal yields in a mass lysate representing the phage progeny of thousands or millions of mixedly infected bacteria, in agreement with this hypothesis. However, when Hershey and Rotman (310) examined by means of the single-burst technique the relative proportions of two complementary recombinants in the yield of *individual infected cells* in crosses of the type $T2hr \times T2h^+r^+$ or $T2hr^+ \times T2h^+r$, they obtained the results shown in Fig. 9-5. These data reveal that there is little, if any, correlation between the frequency of complementary recombinant types among the issue of a single bacterium infected with both parental phage genotypes; there are many cells which liberate a very high proportion of one of the recombinants together with a very low proportion of its complementary genotype. These findings suggested that the production of complementary recombinants is *not* correlated—that is, contrary to the anticipations of

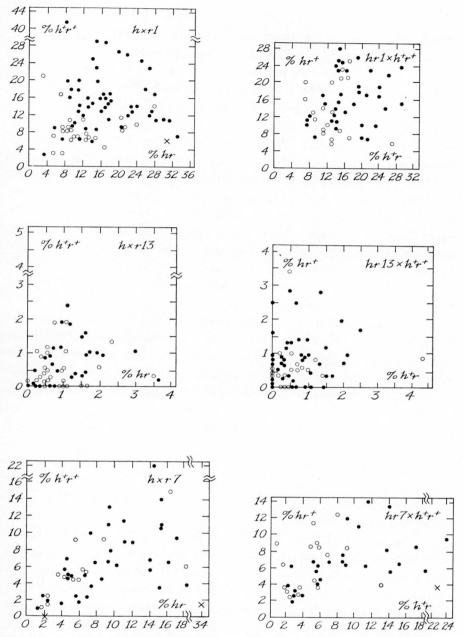

Fig. 9-5. Correlation between proportionate yields of the two complementary recombinants indicated on ordinate and on abscissa in single bursts of bacteria infected with the two parental types indicated in each panel. Each point represents the yield of one bacterium. The open circles indicate bursts with disproportionate yields of the two parental genotypes. [From Hershey and Rotman (310).]

genetic exchange by breakage and crosswise reunion of homologous parts, the elementary recombination event generates only one, and not both, of the two recombinants.

Visconti and Delbrück, who were not unaware of the data of Fig. 9-5 at the time of formulation of their theory, sought to explain the lack of correlation between complementary recombinants in single bursts by proposing that even though both recombinants *are* produced in a single mating act, subsequent random replication and random withdrawal from the mating pool of the recombinants brings about serious departures from equality in the frequency of the two genotypes among the infective progeny of any one cell. In later years, however, Bresch (102) could show convincingly in crosses with phage T1, which is more suitable than T2 for this particular purpose, that complementary recombinants cannot arise in a single recombinational event, and that two separate and independent acts of genetic exchange are required to produce the two crossover genotypes. But in spite of apparently incorporating an erroneous assumption, the mathematical relations of the Visconti-Delbrück theory nevertheless give an adequate description of recombinant frequencies produced in phage crosses. As later, more generalized formulations (104, 589) of this problem show, these relations can be derived quite independently of any specific assumptions concerning the elementary recombinational event and are equally valid whether both or only one of the two recombinant types are produced by each mating event.

Prompted by their findings, and following a suggestion by A. H. Sturtevant, Hershey and Rotman proposed that genetic recombination in phage may not, after all, derive from the physical exchange of preformed genetic structures. Instead, they proposed that recombination occurs as an event incidental to the replication of the genetic material, so that the recombinant is a newly synthesized piece of genetic material which happens to have arisen at the time of the mating act. A number of such recombination mechanisms have been suggested in the meantime —Belling (46) had already proposed a similar process for chromosomal recombination in higher organisms in 1933—and these schemes have become known under a variety of names, particularly as **partial replicas** (286) and **copy choice.** It is the latter name, invented by Lederberg (403), which has found the most general favor. In terms of the copy-choice doctrine, a mating represents the coming together of two parental genomes, at the moment when one happens to be serving as a template for the synthesis of a replica. After part of the genetic information of the first parental genome has already been copied into the replica structure, the copy process suddenly switches to the other of the mated parental genomes and begins to incorporate the genetic information of the second parent into the growing de novo genome. As illustrated in Fig. 9-6, a single recombinant phage "chromosome" thus arises which carries some of the genetic factors of one and some of the genetic factors of the other of the two mated parents. A further, and an entirely independent, recombination act is required to produce the complementary recombinant type, which would in no way be correlated with the formation of its complement, though occurring with equal

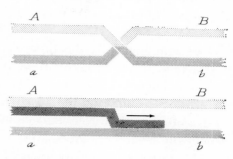

Fig. 9-6. Two mechanisms of genetic recombination. *A* and *B* represent two genetic loci and *a* and *b* their alleles. *Upper figure: breakage and reunion.* The two mated parental genomes break between *A* and *B* and between *a* and *b*, and heterologous pieces rejoin. *Lower figure: copy choice.* Replication (in the direction of the arrow) generates a new daughter genome, using first one and then the other of the two mated parental genomes as template. A copy-choice switch occurs between *A* and *B*. [From Delbrück and Stent (169).]

frequency. If there is a fixed probability per length of phage "chromosome" of a copy-choice switch during a mating of vegetative phage, then the chance of producing a replica genome recombinant for two genetic markers still depends on the distance d between the two loci, just as expressed by Equation (9-1).

Heterozygotes

We shall now consider another phenomenon associated with genetic recombination in phage that, like the independent origin of complementary recombinants, appeared to favor the copy-choice doctrine. The preceding discussion of phage genetics has assumed implicitly that the T2 phage in both its extracellular, infective state and intracellular, vegetative state carries only a single copy of its hereditary information. This assumption, however, is not correct, since there exist phage particles which carry *two* copies of at least some of their genetic loci. Such particles were discovered in 1951 when Hershey and Chase (300) noticed that about 2% of the progeny issuing from T2r × T2r⁺ mixed infection form neither pure r nor pure r^+ type plaques, but instead give rise to *mottled* plaques. As was seen in Chapter 8, such mottled plaques arise upon joint growth of r and r^+ phages in the same focus of infection on the agar plate. At the time of their discovery, the most plausible explanation of the origin of these mottled plaques formed by progeny of mixed infections was that they are produced by *clumps* of r and r^+ particles emerging from the mixedly infected bacterial cell. It is possible to demonstrate, however, that clumps cannot be the true cause of the genetically heterogeneous plaques encountered among the phage progeny. Upon treatment of the phage lysate with heat, with various forms of radiations, or with antiphage serum, the infective centers causing mottled plaques are inactivated at the same rate as the normal r and r^+ phage progeny in the same population. But if the mottled plaque formers represent clumps of one r and one r^+ phage, then after an inactivation treatment which permits the survival of a small fraction s of the initial phage population, only s^2 of the initial number of mottled plaques should survive. That is, if mottled plaques were caused by phage clumps, then they should disappear much more rapidly with inactivation treatments than ordinary plaques.

The mottled plaques are, therefore, initiated by *single* phages that must harbor both r mutant and r^+ wild alleles in their genome and that must segregate upon further growth to produce the two r and r^+ phage genotypes among their progeny. Such phage particles are called **heterozygotes,** a term that has been borrowed from classical genetics, where it denotes organisms that harbor two different alleles of some particular gene among a diploid set of chromosomes. Further studies showed that about 2% of the progeny of any $r × r^+$ cross are r/r^+ heterozygotes, regardless of which one of various r mutants is grown jointly with the r^+ wild type. It could be shown also that a similar fraction of the progeny of an $h × h^+$ cross are heterozygous for the host range character, although the plaques initiated by h/h^+ heterozygotes are difficult to recognize at sight and are better scored by randomly picking plaques formed on strain B and then replating an aliquot of each phage clone on B + B/2 mixed indicators.

An important property of phage heterozygotes came to light when the mottled plaques formed by the r/r^+ heterozygotes produced in an

$hr \times h^+r^+$ two-factor cross were picked and tested for the presence of h and h^+ markers: *the heterozygosity concerns only a very limited region of the phage genome.* In the case of $hr \times h^+r^+$ crosses involving r mutations (such as $r1$), at loci distantly linked to the host range h locus on the phage linkage map, only 3% of the r/r^+ heterozygotes are also heterozygous at the h locus. The frequency of double heterozygotes is thus more or less that expected if occurrences of heterozygosity at each gene locus are statistically independent. In other words, the great majority of those few phage particles that are heterozygous at one locus carry only a single allele at most of the other loci of their genome. This provides further proof that the mottled plaques cannot derive from clumps of several phage particles, since mottled plaques initiated by clumps of hr and h^+r^+ phages should also contain h and h^+ genotypes. In the case of $hr \times h^+r^+$ crosses in which the r mutation is situated at a locus closely linked to h, a very much greater fraction of the r/r^+ heterozygotes produced is also heterozygous at the h locus: among the progeny of the cross $hr13 \times h^+r^+$, 59% of all r/r^+ heterozygotes are also h/h^+ heterozygotes. One may infer, therefore, that the average length of the limited region of the phage genome in which phage heterozygotes carry alleles obtained from more than one parent phage is of the order of the chromosomal distance h to $r13$.

The state of heterozygosity is not permanent, since heterozygous phage particles do not appear to reproduce themselves as heterozygotes, as the following two observations show. First, the frequency of heterozygotes in a phage cross does not increase in the course of intracellular phage growth, in contrast to the frequency of recombinants which, as we have already seen, does rise steadily as the intracellular population of vegetative phages drifts toward genetic equilibrium. No matter when a cell mixedly infected with r and r^+ phages is artificially lysed, the fraction of mottled plaque formers among the phage progeny is always nearly 2%. But if heterozygotes did multiply as heterozygotes in the vegetative phage pool, then their relative frequency should likewise increase continuously. Second, the extracellular, infective heterozygotes do not reproduce as heterozygotes, but instead *segregate* upon infection of the host cell into simple r and r^+ genotypes. Thus when a T2 population containing heterozygotes is passed in single infection through another cycle of growth, then the frequency of heterozygotes among the progeny generation is much lower than among the parental generation. Only about 2% of 2% of the progeny are heterozygotes, a frequency no higher than that expected from the formation of de novo heterozygotes in the 2% of the infected bacteria which happen to be infected with a heterozygote of the parental generation, and correspond, therefore, to cells mixedly infected with r and r^+ genotypes.

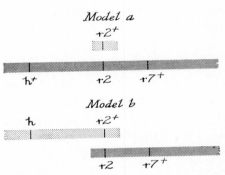

Fig. 9-7. Two possible models for the structure of an $r2/r2^+$ heterozygote generated by the cross of T2$hr2^+r7$ × T2h^+r2r7^+. The genomes of the two parents are represented by different shadings.

In 1953 Levinthal (417) further analyzed the genetic structure of heterozygotes. As shown in Fig. 9-7, heterozygous phages might possess both parental alleles at some locus of their genome because they carry either (a) one complete chromosome derived from one parent and a short chromosomal fragment derived from the other parent, or (b) two long chromosomal fragments, one from each of the parents, which *overlap* slightly to constitute the limited region of heterozygosity. In order to decide between these two alternatives, the three-factor cross $hr2^+r7$ × h^+r2r7^+ was carried out and the phage genotypes present in every mottled plaque formed by the phage progeny were examined. The two models of heterozygote structure lead to different expectations concerning the distribution of parental alleles to be encountered in the mottled plaques of this experiment. Under model (a), one would anticipate that almost all of the few progeny that form mottled plaques because they are r/r^+ heterozygotes at the inner locus $r2$ carry the markers h^+ and $r7^+$ at the outside loci, since such heterozygotes should possess the $h^+ - r2 - r7^+$ parental chromosome and an added short fragment carrying the $r2^+$ allele of the other parent. Under model (b), however, one would anticipate that $r2/r2^+$ heterozygotes should be recombinant for the outside loci—that is, carry the h marker from the parent that supplied the $r2^+$ allele and the $r7^+$ marker from the parent that supplied the $r2$ allele. Levinthal's results were in excellent agreement with the predictions of the overlap model (b), and in complete disagreement with the predictions of model (a): most of the phage progeny heterozygous for the middle marker were indeed recombinant for the outside markers.

This finding, subsequently confirmed also for heterozygotes of phage T1 (638), greatly strengthened the notion already advanced by Hershey and Chase that phage heterozygotes are not some sort of genetic freaks but are intimately connected with the elementary event of genetic recombination in the vegetative phage pool. They had realized that heterozygotes might, in fact, represent the transient mating structures formed in the elementary recombination act: "The . . . heterozygotes . . . segregate to yield one recombinant per heterozygote. The recombinants that are produced in [phage] crosses also have to be assumed to come from structures yielding one recombinant, to explain the independent . . . distributions of sister recombinants among single cell yields of virus." Levinthal now proposed, as one variant of the copy-choice recombination theory, that if synthesis of a replica genome along one of two mated parental chromosomes proceeds from right to left and along the other parental chromosome from left to right, then a region of limited overlap might be generated at the gene locus at which the two *partial replicas* encounter one another. Joint maturation into a single infective phage particle of such overlapping partial replicas would then generate the heterozygote genotype in accordance with model (b). Because the heterozygote might have two "faces" for replication—an "upper," on which one of the two heterozygous alleles, and a "lower," on which the other of the two alleles can be copied into the recombinant replica produced upon replication of the overlap structure—the heterozygote does not reproduce as a heterozygote but only gives rise to simple, nonheterozygous segregants. In support of these notions it could be shown that the frequency of heterozygotes and the estimated average length of the heterozygous region is sufficiently great for heterozygotes to be the source of all the recombinants that appear in any phage cross. The facts are compatible with the idea that a region of genetic overlap is always formed at some intermediate point whenever a recombination act occurs between two genetic loci in a mating event. Levinthal later reformulated the model shown in Fig. 9-7 in terms of the molecular structure of DNA, in an attempt to show that the occurrence of copy-choice recombination during semiconservative replication of the viral DNA could give rise to partial

heteroduplex progeny genomes that carry heterozygous alleles on opposite polynucleotide strands of the DNA double helix (419).

Negative Interference

It would have been a bad mistake in the early 1950's to think that with the invention of the Visconti-Delbrück theory, with the promulgation of the copy-choice doctrine, and with the recognition of the importance of heterozygotes, the details of the mechanism of genetic exchange in phage were now more or less understood. On the contrary, the facts, experimental procedures, and theories on phage recombination that were now developed became so involved that this province of formal phage genetics turned into a highly esoteric discipline, a Cabala incomprehensible to all but a few workers [see (295)]. Probably the most important complication to appear, and the one that most obviously demanded an explanation before it could be pretended that genetic recombination was understood, was the discovery by Chase and Doermann (132) of the clustering of recombinational events.

It had long been known in classical genetics that there exists a negative correlation for multiple crossovers in neighboring regions of a chromosome: if a crossover takes place between two linked loci x and y, then the chance is reduced from that obtaining otherwise that there will occur also a crossover between y and a third locus z, distal to x. This negative correlation between adjacent crossovers was called *interference* (261). Visconti and Delbrück discovered, however, that in phage crosses there exists a slight *positive* correlation for multiple crossovers, a phenomenon which, as the obvious converse of interference, was named **negative interference**. The explanation of negative interference is, in fact, inherent in the Visconti-Delbrück theory: if, as envisaged in that theory, genetic exchange ensues in random matings of entire vegetative phage genomes, then any phage genome in which a recombination act has taken place between the loci x and y is sure to have undergone a mating with a phage of opposite genotype. The chance, therefore, that in this particular phage genome an exchange has also occurred between the loci y and z is greater than the corresponding chance for the *average* genome of the vegetative pool, which may not have ever participated in the requisite heterologous mating.

However, as soon as techniques became available for studying genetic recombination between very closely linked genetic sites in the T4 phage genome (to be described in Chapter 10), Chase and Doermann (132) encountered another kind of negative interference, which, because of its magnitude, they called *high negative interference;* this represents an effect associated with the elementary recombination act, rather than with the population dynamics of the vegetative phage pool. In one of their experiments Chase and Doermann crossed the r mutant genotypes T4r168$r^+$$r$147 × T4$r^+$$r145r^+$ and then examined the frequency of T4r^+ wild type recombinants among the progeny. This wild type recombinant can evidently arise only by means of a *double* crossover:

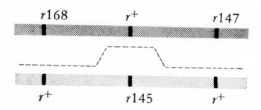

One crossover occurs between the loci r168 and r145 and the other occurs between r145 and r147. Hence the chance per mating of forming the r^+ recombinant ought to be equal to the product of the probabilities of each of the two necessary crossovers, or $p_{xy}p_{yz}$. For these three very closely linked markers, the values of $p_{xy} = 1.4 \times 10^{-3}$ and $p_{yz} = 4.1 \times 10^{-3}$ crossovers per mating had been established in the two-factor crosses T4r168 × T4r145 and T4r145 × T4r147, and hence the expected chance of generating the r^+ double recombinant ought to be $1.4 \times 10^{-3} \times 4.1 \times 10^{-3} = 5.7 \times 10^{-6}$ per mating. But Chase and Doermann found that here the double crossover generating the r^+ recombinant actually occurs at the frequency 1.8×10^{-4}, or 30 times more often than expected. This very considerable excess of double crossovers over the number anticipated from the product of the frequencies of single crossovers constitutes high negative interference. The degree of high negative interference observed in a multifactor cross diminishes rapidly with the distance of the genetic loci between which multiple exchanges are examined and becomes negligible in crosses involving loci for which the probability of crossover is greater than 10^{-2} per mating.

The existence of high negative interference, which has also been encountered in recombination between closely linked genes in such "higher" organisms as fungi (509), reveals that in one mating individual genetic exchanges are not really distributed randomly over the length of the phage chromosome, but appear to be clustered in small "switch areas." The true linkage, d, of two distantly linked genetic loci is therefore not, as stated earlier, the average number of *crossovers* but rather the average number of "switch areas" per mating that occur between the two loci in question.

On the basis of a study of the segregation pattern of T4 heterozygotes carrying complementary alleles of several very closely linked r mutations, Edgar (196) proposed that the multiple exchanges responsible for high negative interference probably do not occur at the time of mating but reflect an event connected with the later segregation of the heterozygote whose formation at the time of mating, according to the proposal of Levinthal, is responsible for the crossover between distantly linked loci of the phage chromosome. This view also derives support from the fact that the average heterozygous region in the phage is of roughly the same length as the region within which high negative interference is observed. But Edgar's later "critical test" (587) of his own idea showed that it, as well as a number of other conceivable alternatives, leads to paradoxes that cannot be resolved without additional assumptions.

It cannot be said, therefore, that at the present time the elementary mechanism of genetic exchange in phage is understood in depth; nevertheless, it seems likely that enlightenment will come, once the nature and structure of the heterozygotes and the meaning of high negative interference have been fathomed.

Breakage and Reunion

Besides accounting for the formation of only one of the two complementary recombinants in a single act of genetic exchange, the copy-choice doctrine of genetic recombination entails another, rather more basic feature that distinguishes it from recombination by breakage and reunion. Under copy choice, the parental genomes whose mating allows formation of the newly synthesized recombinant genome, should remain *intact*, whereas recombination by breakage and reunion should destroy the physical integrity of the parental genomes (see Fig. 9-6). Hence if recombination in the vegetative phage pool really proceeded by copy choice, the number of genomes of parental genotype could never fall below that initially present at the outset of infection, regardless of how many rounds of mating might occur. Recombinants, furthermore, being necessarily composed of newly synthesized DNA, should not contain any of the DNA atoms of the parent phages that entered the cross. But if repeated rounds of recombination by breakage and reunion *do* occur in the vegetative phage pool, then it would be possible that repeated matings bring the number of parental genotypes below the input. Repeated recombination by breakage and reunion, furthermore, would result in further and further dispersal of the atoms of the parental DNA among the recombinants produced.

It was seen in Chapter 7 that in its transfer the DNA of the parent T-even phage *is* dispersed over its progeny particles. It should not now seem far-fetched that this dispersal of the viral DNA complement might be the physical manifestation of genetic exchange by breakage and reunion, since the process that unites DNA fragments of different physiological "age" into the head of a single progeny virus particle could also bring together DNA molecules of different parental origin for the genesis of genetic recombinants. This possibility was first tested by means of an experiment (296, 303) in which bacteria were infected with one P^{32}-labeled T2*h* and ten nonlabeled T2*h*$^+$ particles each; measurements were then made of the fraction of transferred label that resided in progeny endowed with T2*h* host range genotype (that is, adsorbable to B/2 bacteria after "unscrambling" the phenotypic mixing by single-infection passage of the progeny through one cycle of growth in strain B). This experiment showed that only 35% of the transferred parental P^{32} stayed true to the T2*h* genotype, 65% of the parental label having "crossed over" to nonadsorbable progeny of T2*h*$^+$ genotype. Hence, part of the parental DNA molecule evidently reappears in progeny phages carrying a genetic marker different from that with which it entered the host cell.

The supposition that the dispersal of the DNA of the parental phage reflects the dispersal of its genome could also be substantiated by infecting *E. coli* with an average of one highly P^{32}-labeled T2*hr*7$^+$*r*1*m*$^+$ and ten nonlabeled T2*h*$^+$*r*7*r*1$^+$*m* particles per cell. Less than one-third of the infective centers of this unequal-input cross, involving four very distantly linked genetic markers (see Fig. 9-2), yielded any progeny individuals of the minority parental genotype. Those rare *hr*7$^+$*r*1*m*$^+$

progeny particles that did appear were not subject to inactivation by
P³² decay; that is, they did not contain an appreciable fraction of the
P³²-labeled minority parental DNA molecule (538). Thus it could be
concluded that the parental T2 chromosome rarely, if ever, emerges
intact from the vegetative phage pool.

Though these results suggested, contrary to the expectations of the
copy-choice doctrine, that recombination in T-even phages is connected
with dispersal of the parental DNA complement, more compelling evidence regarding the role of breakage and reunion of DNA in genetic
exchange was adduced by Meselson and Weigjle (477) and by Kellenberger, Zichichi, and Weigjle (363), who worked with phage λ active
on *E. coli*. Phage λ, whose particle weight and DNA complement is only
about half that of the T-even strains (see Fig. 3-5, Tables 3-I, 3-III),
will be of great importance in the later discussions of Chapters 12, 13,
and 14. The general features of the growth cycle and genetics of phage
λ are rather similar to those of the T-even phages, including the transfer
of about half the atoms of the parental λ phage DNA to the progeny.
But one important difference between λ and the T-even phages is that
the frequency of genetic exchange in λ is very much less than in the
T-even strains. When the results of crosses of genetically marked λ phages
are analyzed in terms of the Visconti-Delbrück theory, it becomes evident that by the end of the normal latent period only 0.5 to 1 round of
mating has occurred in the line of ancestry of the average λ progeny
virus (334, 350, 692), instead of the 5 rounds of mating experienced by
T-even phage. Thus among the progeny of a λ cross there are many
individuals without any mating experience whatsoever. In order to
examine the connection between
the distribution of the transferred
parental DNA and genetic recombination in phage λ, Weigle and

Fig. 9-8. A primitive genetic map of
phage λ, showing the percent recombination between four widely separated markers. An explanation of the meaning of the
mutant symbols can be found in the legend
to Fig. 12-7.

Meselson infected *E. coli* growing in
an ordinary "light" medium with
"heavy" C¹³N¹⁵-labeled λc⁺mi⁺ wild
type and "light" C¹²N¹⁴-labeled
λcmi double mutant phages. (The
locations of *c* and *mi*, which for the
purpose of this discussion can be considered plaque type mutations, are
shown on the genetic map of phage λ in Fig. 9-8.) The progeny of this

cross, which included about 1.5% c^+mi and cmi^+ recombinants, were then subjected to density gradient equilibrium sedimentation in concentrated CsCl solution and the titer of the various phage genotypes present at all levels in the density gradient assayed. The result of this experiment is presented in Fig. 9-9, from which the following conclusions can be drawn.

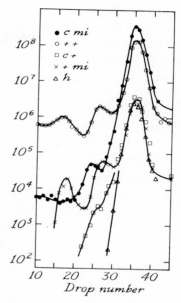

1. The distribution of the originally "heavy" c^+mi^+ parental genotype exhibits three modes: one main component at the lowest density, representing fully "light" progeny particles composed of DNA and protein synthesized de novo in the "light" growth medium, and two minor components at densities corresponding to phage particles possessing one-quarter and one-half of the parental heavy isotopes, respectively. These two minor components represent phage particles whose protein is entirely "light" and whose DNA is either half-parental, half-new (semiconserved), or entirely parental (conserved). The conserved DNA complements have probably not replicated at all, whereas the hybrid DNA complements were no doubt generated by the semiconservative Watson-Crick replication process in the vegetative phage pool. It can be concluded, therefore, that the DNA complement of phage λ, unlike that of the T-even phages, is not widely dispersed over many progeny phages but appears to remain largely intact as a single, semiconserved replicating structure.

Fig. 9-9. Genetic recombination by breakage and reunion in phage λ. Density-gradient centrifugation in concentrated cesium chloride solution of the phage progeny of a cross between "heavy" $C^{13}N^{15}$-labeled λc^+mi^+ wild type and "light" $C^{12}N^{14}$-labeled λcmi, on bacteria growing in $C^{12}N^{14}$-labeled "light" medium. The ordinate shows the titer of progeny phages of parental and recombinant genotypes in drops collected through the bottom of the centrifuge tube after sedimentation equilibrium. The λh phages are added to the centrifugation mixture as a density reference object. [From Meselson and Weigle (477).]

2. The distribution of the originally "light" cmi parental genotype is very different from that of the parental wild type, being present

mostly in the fully "light" band, though a definite skewness of the distribution toward higher densities is manifest.

3. The distribution of the c^+mi recombinant resembles that of the c^+mi^+ wild type parent, in that the recombinant is found in essentially the same three modes as the wild type, whereas the distribution of the reciprocal cmi^+ recombinant, like that of the cmi parent, shows but a single mode.

The presence of c^+mi recombinants in the two "heavy" bands of phages containing conserved and semiconserved parental wild type DNA shows that they contain some of the parental isotope. This demonstrates unequivocally that discrete amounts of original parental DNA appear in recombinant phages, suggesting that "recombination occurs by breakage of parental chromosomes followed by the reconstruction of genetically complete chromosomes from the fragments" (477). The fact that the complementary cmi^+ recombinant is practically free of heavy isotope (though containing the mi^+ marker of the c^+mi^+ parent) can be readily explained on the basis of the relative situation of the c and mi loci of the genetic map of λ. Since, as can be seen in Fig. 9-8, mi is very nearly at the end of the λ chromosome, the cmi^+ recombinant chromosome would obtain no more than a very small segment of the "heavy" DNA of the c^+mi^+ wild type parent in a single exchange. (This explanation presupposes, of course, that the genetic map of λ, unlike that of T4, *has* an end and is not circular.)

The extensive dispersal of the parental DNA complement and the high frequency of genetic exchange of T-even phages, on the one hand, and the general conservation of the integrity of the parental DNA complement and the low frequency of genetic exchange of λ phage, on the other, are thus in excellent accord with the notion that breakage and reunion is involved in phage recombination. But though their findings led Meselson and Weigle to make some new molecular proposals for the exchange process, it would seem that at present the elementary recombination act is still shrouded in mystery.

Further Reading

Adams, M. H., *Bacteriophages* (2). Chapter XVIII (pp. 331–351) provides a discussion of genetic recombination in phage.

Hershey, A. D. and Rotman, R., "Genetic recombination between host range and plaque-type mutants of bacteriophage in single bacterial cells" (310). The first detailed investigation of genetic recombination in phage. A treasure trove of information.

Hershey, A. D. and Chase, M., "Genetic recombination and heterozygosis in bacteriophage" (300). The discovery of phage heterozygotes.

Bresch, C., "Recombination in bacteriophage" (103). A review of phage genetics, with particular emphasis on T1, a phage which has not been given the attention it deserves in the present chapter.

Hershey, A. D., "The production of recombinants in phage crosses" (295). An erudite analysis of the bewildering state of the study of genetic recombination in 1958. Not for the novice.

Brenner, S., "Physiological aspects of bacteriophage genetics" (91). A review.

CHAPTER 10

Genetic Fine Structure and the Molecular Basis of Mutation

The Unit of Recombination—The Unit of Mutation—Shortcut Mapping—The Functional Unit—Topography of Genetic Fine Structure—Mutagenesis—Induced Mutation (in vivo)—Induced Mutation (in vitro)—Induced Reverse Mutation—Mutational Heterozygotes

THE DEVELOPMENT of the concept of the gene as the basic element of the hereditary substance was one of the main fruits of the first four decades of genetic research, the "classical" age inaugurated by the rediscovery of Mendel's work at the turn of this century. During this period, "gene" gradually came to represent the unit of genetic material passed on from parent to offspring that can be recognized operationally through its ability to *mutate* to alternative states, *recombine* with other, similar units, and *function* in the endowment of the organism with some particular character. And it is in this "classical" sense that here too the term "gene" has been employed in our preceding discussion of bacteriophage genetics. For example, the host range gene of phage T2 first came to our notice with the discovery of *h* mutants of the phage, capable of infecting the bacterial strain B/2 resistant to the h^+ wild type virus. The host range gene is evidently that unit of the viral genome which undergoes the permanent alteration in informational content responsible for the extended host range of the phage particle. But we also identified this host range gene with a definite site of the genetic map of the virus, since wild type recombinants that carry the host range gene of one parent and the rapid lysis gene of the other parent appear among the progeny of crosses of the host range mutant with various rapid lysis *r* mutants. Finally, we inferred that there exists a function of the host

238

range gene, since evidently it is not the gene itself that is *directly* responsible for the host range character. This function becomes manifest in bacteria infected jointly with *h* and *h*$^+$ genotypes from which issue *phenotypically mixed* hybrid phages that carry the wild *h*$^+$ genotype (DNA into which the *h*$^+$ information has been inscribed), but possess the *h* mutant phenotype; that is, they are endowed with the phage tail protein whose synthesis in the infected cell represents the function of the host range gene of the *h* parent. From the "classical" point of view, these three aspects—mutation, recombination, and function—are thus the attribute of one and the same hereditary unit: the gene. But as later studies of phage genetics, now to be recounted, have revealed, there is really no such thing as the classical gene, the postulated element that is at one and the same time the unit of mutation, recombination, and function. Indeed, according to Pontecorvo (509), "the theory of the gene, though still indispensable in everyday genetics, is no longer of heuristic value at levels of further refinement, especially when it comes to the enquiry of what genetic materials are and how they work." In spite of this development, the term "gene" has by no means disappeared from the vocabulary of modern phage geneticists, and will also be still encountered in the following pages. There seems to be no general agreement on the precise meaning with which "gene" is now to be used, but in our use henceforth it will connote a segment of the phage genome in which there reside one or more units of function related to one and the same phenotypic character.

The Unit of Recombination

In 1955, Benzer (51, 52) began a series of investigations on *r* mutants of phage T4 that showed up the inadequacy of the classical notion of the gene for understanding the *fine structure* of the viral genome and reformed modern thought on the nature of the units of heredity. Benzer's point of departure was the finding—in itself of only mild interest—that all *r* mutants of T2 and T4 whose map positions cluster in the *r*II region of the T-even phage genome (see Figs. 9-2 and 9-8) possess another phenotypic character in addition to their typical *r* plaque morphology. Such *r*II mutants cannot grow at all on a *lysogenic E. coli* strain that carries the λ *prophage* (see Chapter 12), a strain on which the *r*$^+$ wild type can grow perfectly well. In further discussions of the genetics of

T-even phages, we shall follow Benzer's convention of referring to this lysogenic *E. coli* strain that does not allow growth of *r*II mutants as *strain K*. But it will be necessary to call strain K by its full name, K12(λ), when lysogeny and transduction are to be considered in later chapters. The *r*II mutants adsorb to, infect, and even initiate the synthesis of phage DNA and other products of viral metabolism in strain K host cells, but *r*II-infected K bacteria neither produce infective progeny phages nor do they eventually lyse (236, 493). It was realized by Benzer that this growth defect of *r*II mutants could serve as a powerful selective agent for detecting the presence of a very small proportion of r^+ genotypes within a large population of *r*II mutants, since on agar plates seeded with strain K all of the r^+ but none of the *r*II individuals can form plaques. In particular, it is possible in this way to score *selectively* for very rare r^+ recombinant individuals that arise in crosses between two very closely linked *r*II mutants. In fact, the limit of resolution of this method should allow one to find r^+ recombinants in frequency as low as 0.0001%, a level so low that, if the nonselective method of simply hunting for r^+ plaque types on *E. coli*, strain B were to be employed, 10^6 progeny *r* plaques would have to be inspected for every r^+ recombinant found.

Benzer proceeded to isolate some 60 *r* mutants located in the *r*II region of the T4 phage genome and to cross them again to each other two-by-two in order to map their mutational sites within a single genetic locus. The frequencies of r^+ recombinants produced in these very numerous crosses allowed Benzer to arrange all his mutants in a linear order and thus to construct the **fine-structure genetic map** shown in Fig. 10-1. Among this first set of 60 mutants, Benzer encountered some pairs that produced no r^+ recombinants whatever when crossed to one another. Such mutant pairs must represent recurrences of a mutation at precisely the same site of the viral genome; they must be exact *alleles*. As can be seen in Fig. 10-1, it happened that the *lowest* frequency with which r^+ recombinants were formed in any cross between two different *r*II mutants that produced *any* r^+ recombinants at all was 0.01%. No *r*II mutations were found which had occurred at two nonidentical genetic sites so closely linked that in their cross r^+ recombinants arose in the hundredfold frequency range from 0.01% to 0.0001%, within which r^+ recombinants would have still been readily detectable. Thus Benzer discovered

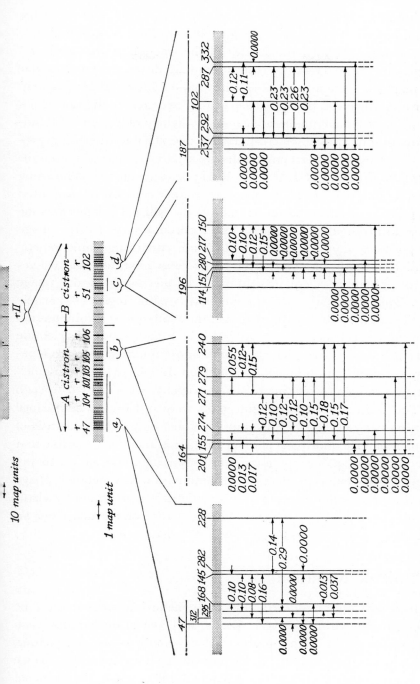

Fig. 10-1. The first fine-structure genetic map of the rII region of T4, based on the frequency of r^+ recombinants produced in pairwise crosses between a set of 60 rII mutants of independent origin. Successive levels on this figure correspond to progressively greater magnifications of the viral genome. On the lowest level, numbered vertical lines represent individual rII mutants, and the decimals indicate the percent r^+ recombinants found in crosses between two mutants connected by an arrow. The horizontal bars shown on the middle and lowest level represent the genetic extent of long-span mutations, or deletions. [From Benzer (51).]

the minimum nonzero distance between two genetic sites still separable by recombination; he had "run the genetic map into the ground."

It is possible to form a rough idea of the fraction of the whole T4 phage genome represented by this minimum distance. The circular genetic map of T4 extends, as we saw in Chapter 9, over about 700 map units, or a distance 700 times that separating two genetic sites for which complementary recombinants appear in frequency of 1% in a "standard," equal-input two-factor cross. Hence two rII mutations that produce 0.01% r^+ wild type recombinants are separated by 0.02 map units or about $0.02/700 = 3 \times 10^{-5}$ of the total phage genome. The meaning of this minimum, nonzero recombination distance can now be translated into chemical terms if it is assumed that (a) the entire T4 phage genome is inscribed into the double-helical DNA macromolecule, (b) the phage neither possesses any "nongenetic" DNA nor carries the same genetic information in more than one sector of the DNA molecule, and (c) genetic recombination is equally probable at all points of the phage genome. Then, since the DNA complement of a single T4 particle contains about 2×10^5 nucleotide pairs, the minimum recombinational distance can be reckoned as $3 \times 10^{-5} \times 2 \times 10^5$, or about 6 nucleotide pairs. That is to say, two phage mutants whose mutated sites are separated by no more than 6 nucleotide pairs on the phage "chromosome" are able to produce recombinant phage progeny when crossed to each other. This estimate of 6 nucleotide pairs may still be too high, since the failure of any of the three assumptions could only reduce the ratio of the number of nucleotide pairs per map unit. It is, therefore, possible that a single nucleotide pair is the minimum recombination distance. In any case, one can conclude that genetic recombination in vegetative phage growth is a process that can separate genetic sites represented by virtually contiguous nucleotides on the viral DNA macromolecule. *Hence the unit of genetic recombination is the individual nucleotide.*

The Unit of Mutation

We have already considered how the genetic information must be inscribed into the viral DNA as a specific sequence of nucleotides, each containing one of the four purines and pyrimidines—*adenine, guanine, thymine,* and *cytosine* (or HMC, in the case of the T-even phages). Since a mutation represents a permanent change in information, the chemical meaning of mutation must correspond to a change in nucleotide sequence, or to a replacement of one purine and pyrimidine base pair by another in the DNA macromolecule. Inasmuch as bacteriophage mutations appear to be errors that occur during vegetative multiplication of the phage genome, it seems eminently plausible that these mutations represent the introduction of an incorrect nucleotide at the moment of replication of the phage DNA. For instance, one might imagine that when growth of the polynucleotide replica along the parental template reaches a point at which the insertion of the adenine nucleotide is called for, the guanine nucleotide is erroneously introduced into the de novo polynucleotide chain. Such errors are, of course, very infrequent, so that the incorrectly inserted guanine perpetuates itself in future replications, making the mutation permanent, or stable. And of course the substitution of guanine for adenine in one of the two complementary polynucleotide chains of the DNA double helix engenders at the next replication cycle the corresponding replacement of thymine by hydroxymethylcytosine at the homologous site in the other polynucleotide chain. Though improbable, it is nevertheless possible that at some future replication act the guanine residue present at the mutated site of the mutant DNA might be replaced by adenine through another copy error; then the original, nonmutant state of the DNA would be restored. In that case, a *reverse* mutation would take place and the genetic information extant prior to the original forward mutation would be recovered.

The smallest mutational unit should thus be the individual nucleotide in the viral DNA, and alteration of a single nucleotide (and of that of its homologous partner on the complementary strand of the double helix) should correspond to a **point mutation.** Such a point mutation, if it really represents the alteration of only a single nucleotide pair in the DNA molecule, also should occupy no more than a single point on the genetic map. Every point mutant in the rII region ought to yield r^+ recombinants in crosses against at least one of two other nonallelic rII test mutants previously shown to yield r^+ recombinants in crosses to each other. Most of the rII mutants isolated by Benzer, and all those represented by vertical lines on the map of Fig. 10-1, do indeed satisfy this criterion for a point mutant. Furthermore, most of these rII mutants sport r^+ wild type reverse mutants during their growth, although the frequency with which they do so varies within very wide limits. Thus the **reversion index** (the mutation index, as defined in Chapter 7, for the reverse mutation $rII \longrightarrow r^+$) was found to be as high as 10^{-2} revertants per phage for some rII mutants of the set and as low as 10^{-7} revertants per phage for others. The probability of reverse mutation no doubt depends on the particular molecular event required for restoring the original wild type configuration to the viral DNA polynucleotides; for instance, the restoration of adenine to an rII mutant site from which it had been displaced by guanine in the forward mutation might be either very much more or very much less probable than an analogous restoration of HMC to a site from which it had been displaced by thymine.

It can be seen from the results presented in Fig. 10-1 that some of the rII mutants isolated by Benzer do not, however, behave as point mutants: they fail to yield r^+ recombinants in crosses to each of two or more rII mutants previously identified as nonallelic point mutants. Such mutants, furthermore, sport no r^+ revertants. This second class of mutants, therefore, appears to involve the simultaneous mutational alteration of several genetic sites. The extent of the mutation of such a long-span mutant can be ascertained by crossing it to the set of previously mapped point mutants in the rII region and observing which point mutants do not yield r^+ recombinants in the cross—that is, are "covered" by the mutation. The genetic sites occupied by some of Benzer's long-span mutants are shown in Fig. 10-1. It can be seen that these mutations vary considerably in length, some cover only a small sector of the map, whereas others extend over the entire rII region and are incapable of yielding r^+ recombinants in crosses to any other rII mutant.

Nomura and Benzer (494) were able to show that these long-span mutations are, in fact, *deletions*, rather than segmental inversions or "nonsense" alterations of the viral genome. Their proof that part of the genetic material is missing employed the long-span mutation $r1695$ and two point mutants, $r168$ and $r924$, which lie on opposite sides of $r1695$ without being covered by it (Fig. 10-2). By crossing each point mutant to the long-span mutant, Nomura and Benzer first constructed the two *double* mutants $r168r1695$ and $r1695r924$ and then carried out the two crosses (a) $r168 \times r924$ and (b) $r168r1695 \times r1695r924$. If, as shown in the figure, $r1695$ is an inversion or "nonsense" segment, then the distance between the two outside loci $r168$ and $r924$ would be unaffected by the presence of $r1695$, and the frequency of crossovers between $r168$ and $r924$ should be the same in cross (a) as in cross (b). But if $r1695$ is really a deletion, then the absence of the genetic segment would diminish the distance between the outside loci, or strengthen their linkage, and fewer crossovers between *r*168 and *r*924 should occur in cross (b) than in cross (a). The experiment showed that 3.6% of the progeny of cross (a) and only 0.7% of the progeny of cross (b) were recombinant for the two outside markers *r*168 and *r*924. Hence the interposition of *r*1695 between

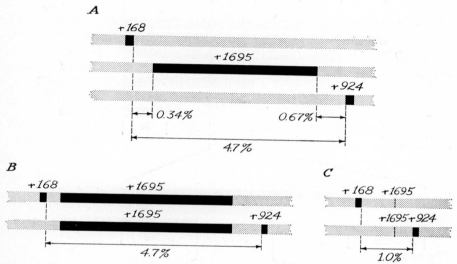

Fig. 10-2. The *r*II mutants used in the demonstration that long-span *r*II mutations are deletions. **A.** Frequencies of *r*⁺ recombinants observed in crosses involving the long-span mutant *r*1695 and the two point mutants *r*168 and *r*924 whose mutational sites lie just beyond its bounds. **B.** Genetic structure of the two recombinants *r*168*r*1695 and *r*1695*r*924, if *r*1695 is an inversion or a stretch of "nonsense." **C.** Genetic structure of these same two recombinants, if *r*1695 is a deletion. The recombinants whose frequencies are to be measured in the cross *r*168*r*1695 × *r*1695*r*924 are *r*1695 and *r*168*r*1695*r*924. [From Nomura and Benzer (494).]

*r*168 and *r*924 caused a shrinkage of the phage chromosome by 2.9 map units. Thus the mutation *r*1695 is indeed a deletion of a polynucleotide segment corresponding to some 800 nucleotide pairs of the viral DNA molecule. It is small wonder that the deletion mutants do not sport *r*⁺ revertants, for from where could the lost DNA segment be restored?

We can conclude, therefore, that *the unit of mutation in the phage genome is of variable length, ranging from the alteration of a single nucleotide in the case of point mutations to the long-span alterations covering hundreds or thousands of nucleotides in the case of deletions.*

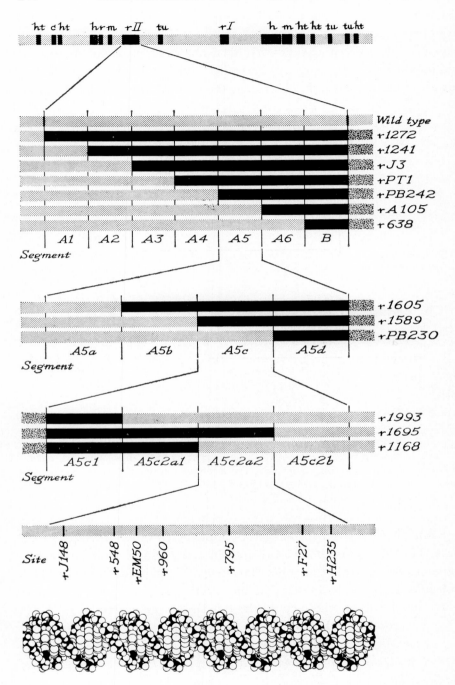

Shortcut Mapping

Deletion mutants were put to good use by Benzer for establishing the detailed map of the rII region in a way that made it unnecessary to cross every mutant of the collection to every other mutant; without this trick, the millions of phage crosses otherwise required would have rendered the construction of this map an impossibly laborious task. Benzer divided the rII region of the T4 phage genome into *segments* (in the manner shown in Fig. 10-3), each segment being defined by the length of the map covered by one particular deletion but not by another. It was then a simple task to make a preliminary placement of each mutant to be mapped into its appropriate segment by establishing the deletions with which the mutant does and does not produce wild type recombinants in crosses. Benzer also rationalized the experimental technique for this segmental classification, so that hundreds of crosses can be carried out in a single day. In this simplified procedure, a small volume of a growing culture of *E. coli* strain B at a density of about 2×10^8 cells per milliliter is infected with one drop each of a high titer stock of the rII mutant to be tested and of a similar stock of the rII reference deletion mutant. After allowing a few minutes for adsorption of the phage particles to their strain B host cells, a droplet of the infected culture is spread by means of a sterile paper strip on an agar plate previously seeded with bacteria of strain K. If the unknown and reference mutants recombine to produce r^+ wild type recombinants in the strain B bacteria to which they are jointly adsorbed, then these r^+ progeny can in turn infect and lyse the strain K indicator bacteria on the agar plate. But if the unknown rII mutant is "covered" by the reference deletion, then no r^+ recom-

Fig. 10-3.   Segmental subdivision of the rII region by means of deletions. *First level:* the whole T4 genetic linkage map. *Second level:* seven deletions define seven segments of the rII region. *Third level:* three deletions define four subsegments of the A5 segment. *Fourth level:* three deletions define four subsubsegments of the A5c subsegment. *Fifth level:* tentative order and spacing established by pairwise crosses of seven point mutants in the A5c2a2 subsubsegment. The site of each of these point mutants probably corresponds to a single base pair in the viral DNA, drawn on the bottom level approximately to the same scale as the genetic map. [From Benzer, *Scientific American*, **206**, No. 1: 70 (1962).]

binants are produced in the first cycle of mixed growth in strain B, and no lysis of the strain K indicator bacteria can ensue on the agar plate.

The result of such a classification of eight different *r*II mutants— according to the segments defined by the reference deletion mutants of Fig. 10-3—is shown in Fig. 10-4. Consider, for instance, the mutant

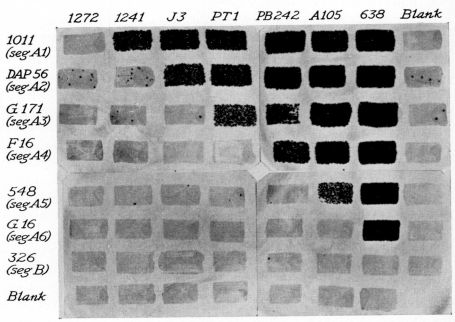

Fig. 10-4. Shortcut mapping of *r*II mutants by spot test crosses against standard deletions. The photograph is a composite of four plates. Horizontal rows correspond to test mutants to be mapped; vertical rows correspond to reference deletions used in the crosses. The results show each of the test mutations to be located in a different segment. A blank signifies that the proportion of *r*⁺ recombinants is less than about 0.001% of the progeny. Plaques appearing in the blanks are due to *r*⁺ revertants present in the *r*II mutant stocks. [From Benzer (55).]

*r*548. Evidently the K bacteria are lysed only in those spots in which the crosses of the mutant against the reference deletions *r*A105 and *r*638 are plated; all the other reference deletions must, therefore, cover *r*548, whose site can be assigned to the segment A5. By introducing the use of additional deletion mutants having suitable starting and ending points, Benzer further dissected the *r*II mutant region of the T4 chromosome into 47 segments, as shown in Fig. 10-5. According to this scheme, an

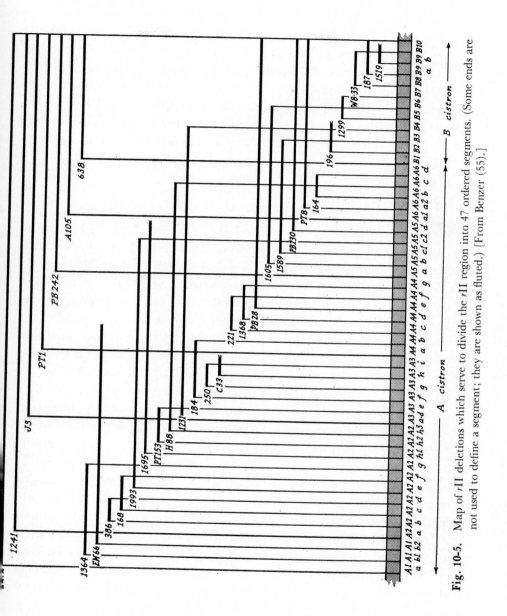

Fig. 10-5. Map of *r*II deletions which serve to divide the *r*II region into 47 ordered segments. (Some ends are not used to define a segment; they are shown as fluted.) [From Benzer (55).]

unknown *r*II mutant is first tested against the seven standard deletion mutants that define the seven main segments; once its main segment is known, the mutant is crossed against an appropriate secondary set of reference deletions in a second series of spot tests. Thus, in only two steps, any point mutation can be mapped into one of the 47 segments. It is fair to say that without this astute exploitation of deletion mutants for rapid mapping, our knowledge of the genetic fine structure of the phage genome would still be very rudimentary; progress would have been hamstrung by the geometric increase in the number of crosses required for the mapping of an arithmetically increasing number of mutants available for study.

The Unit of Function

We are now ready to consider the last of the three basic aspects of the late gene—namely, its role as the unit of function of the hereditary substance. The lesson taught by biochemical genetics, which flowered in the decade prior to the bloom of phage genetics, was that the expression of each gene is effected through synthesis of an enzyme, so that the information which the gene contains must concern the construction of a protein molecule capable of carrying out some particular function. The whole phenotype of a cell would thus be the end product of a network of anabolic and catabolic reactions catalyzed by the ensemble of enzymes, whose synthesis is in turn directed by the genes of its hereditary substance. Protein molecules are composed of one or more polypeptide chains containing some tens or hundreds of *amino acid* residues linked together through peptide bonds. These amino acids are of twenty kinds, the "standard" set of Table 10-I, and though not every protein molecule contains necessarily every member of the set, the same twenty kinds of amino acids are present in proteins from all sources—animals, plants, or microbes (149). The specific function and properties of protein molecules are derived, in the first instance, from their particular three-dimensional structure; and it was first a tenet of the theoreticians and later became an experimental fact (23) that the exact spatial conformation of proteins is determined by the exact order in which the twenty different kinds of amino acids are copolymerized into the polypeptide chains of the macromolecule. Thus, the information carried in the genetic unit of function, and hence the "meaning" of the particular purine-pyrimidine base se-

TABLE 10-I

The "Standard" Set of Twenty Amino Acids

Name	Abbreviation	Formula
Alanine	Ala	$CH_3-CH-COOH$ $\quad\quad\vert$ $\quad\quad NH_2$
Arginine	Arg	$NH_2-C-NH-(CH_2)_3-CH-COOH$ $\quad\quad\Vert\quad\quad\quad\quad\quad\quad\vert$ $\quad\quad NH\quad\quad\quad\quad\quad\quad NH_2$
Asparagine	Asp—NH$_2$	$H_2N-C-CH_2-CH-COOH$ $\quad\quad\Vert\quad\quad\quad\vert$ $\quad\quad O\quad\quad\quad NH_2$
Aspartic Acid	Asp	$HOOC-CH_2-CH-COOH$ $\quad\quad\quad\quad\quad\vert$ $\quad\quad\quad\quad\quad NH_2$
Cysteine	Cy—SH	$HS-CH_2-CH-COOH$ $\quad\quad\quad\quad\vert$ $\quad\quad\quad\quad NH_2$
Glutamic Acid	Glu	$HOOC-(CH_2)_2-CH-COOH$ $\quad\quad\quad\quad\quad\quad\vert$ $\quad\quad\quad\quad\quad\quad NH_2$
Glutamine	Glu—NH$_2$	$H_2N-CO-(CH_2)_2-CH-COOH$ $\quad\quad\quad\quad\quad\quad\quad\vert$ $\quad\quad\quad\quad\quad\quad\quad NH_2$
Glycine	Gly	CH_2-COOH $\vert$ NH_2
Histidine	His	$\quad\quad-CH_2-CH-COOH$ $N\diagdown NH\quad\quad\vert$ $\quad\quad\quad\quad NH_2$
Isoleucine	Ileu	$CH_3-CH_2-CH-CH-COOH$ $\quad\quad\quad\quad\vert\quad\vert$ $\quad\quad\quad\quad CH_3\ NH_2$
Leucine	Leu	$CH_3-CH-CH_2-CH-COOH$ $\quad\quad\vert\quad\quad\quad\vert$ $\quad\quad CH_3\quad\quad NH_2$
Lysine	Lys	$H_2N-(CH_2)_4-CH-COOH$ $\quad\quad\quad\quad\quad\vert$ $\quad\quad\quad\quad\quad NH_2$
Methionine	Met	$CH_3-S-CH_2-CH_2-CH-COOH$ $\quad\quad\quad\quad\quad\quad\quad\vert$ $\quad\quad\quad\quad\quad\quad\quad NH_2$
Phenylalanine	Phe	$CH_2-CH-COOH$ $\quad\quad\vert$ $\quad\quad NH_2$

T A B L E 1 0 - I (Continued)

The "Standard" Set of Twenty Amino Acids

Name	Abbreviation	Formula
Proline	Pro	(ring)—COOH, N, H
Serine	Ser	CH_2—CH—COOH, OH NH_2
Threonine	Thr	CH_3—CH—CH—COOH, OH NH_2
Tryptophan	Try	(indole ring)—CH_2—CH—COOH, N, H, NH_2
Tyrosine	Tyr	HO—(ring)—CH_2—CH—COOH, NH_2
Valine	Val	CH_3—CH—CH—COOH, CH_3 NH_2

quence of the DNA polynucleotides constituting the gene, would in fact represent the specification of the **amino acid sequence** of a polypeptide. This notion leads one directly to the belief that there must exist a *code* that relates purine-pyrimidine base sequence in polynucleotides to amino acid sequence in polypeptides. Some simple considerations quickly reveal the minimum complexity of this code, since for each residue in the polypeptide chain information must be provided as to just which of the twenty "standard" amino acids is to be present there. Certainly there cannot exist a one-to-one correspondence between purine and pyrimidine base pairs in the DNA double helix and amino acids in the polypeptide, because the four complementary base pairs

$$\begin{array}{cccc} A & T & C & G \\ \| & \| & \| & \| \\ T & A & G & C \end{array}$$

taken one at a time could specify only one out of four, and not one out of twenty, kinds of amino acids. Nor would it suffice that *two* adjacent base pairs of the DNA double helix specify one amino acid residue in the polypeptide, since in that case only $4 \times 4 = 16$ kinds of amino acids could be coded by the four kinds of base pairs. Hence the code must involve the specification of one amino acid residue by at least three successive base pairs in the DNA double helix. Four kinds of base pairs taken three at a time could specify more than enough ($4 \times 4 \times 4 = 64$) different kinds of amino acids. The nature of this code will be discussed in much greater detail in Chapter 15.

Mutation—that is, substitution of one purine and pyrimidine base pair for another—at a particular genetic site then results in a mutant phenotype because it engenders a change in the specification of the kind of amino acid at the corresponding site of the polypeptide. This change, in turn, results in an altered spatial configuration, and hence function, of the protein molecule coded by the gene. This mutant protein might function either more or less efficiently than the normal wild type protein, or it might be nonexistent if the mutational change in the purine and pyrimidine base pair produced "nonsense" incomprehensible to the cellular decoding device that ultimately translates the information from polynucleotide to polypeptide (see Chapter 15). (It is, in fact, very likely that because of their undoubtedly very extensively modified polynucleotide sequence most *deletion* mutants produce no protein at all homologous to that specified by the same gene in its nonmutated, or wild type state.) The probable genetic extent of the unit of function can now be estimated from first principles. Since the average or typical polypeptide chain found in enzymes and other proteins is composed of about 300 amino acid residues (the actual number of residues spans an approximately tenfold range about this mean), a minimum length of DNA of about 1000 nucleotide pairs is necessary for harboring the requisite sequence information if a triplet of successive nucleotide pairs specifies each amino acid residue. The genetic unit of function must, therefore, correspond to a segment of the hereditary substance greater by several hundredfold than what, in the preceding sections, we have already inferred to be the minimum units of recombination and mutation.

Benzer was able to design experiments that elucidated also the unit of function of the *r*II gene of the T4 phage genome, by addressing himself to the question whether the *r*II mutants of his collection belong to more than a single unit of function. The mere fact that two *r* mutants manifest the same phenotype under some set of experimental conditions does not automatically guarantee that their mutational alterations pertain to the same functional unit. For instance, we have already noted that the *r* plaque type on strain B is produced by mutations situated at such widely separated sites of the T4 genome that they could hardly belong to one and the same functional unit. And thus the failure of different *r*II mutants to grow on strain K also need not necessarily reflect one and the same functional defect in their hereditary material. In order to examine whether or not two different *r*II mutants belong to the same functional unit, Benzer adapted to bacterial viruses the "cis-trans" or **complementation test** (Fig. 10-6), previously developed with "higher" organisms (425, 508) for the very purpose of probing the nature of the functional unit of the gene. The point of departure of Benzer's test was the finding that *in a strain K bacterium infected jointly with *r*II mutant and *r*+ wild type phages, both genotypes can grow normally*. The normal *r*II gene of the wild type parent is, therefore, able to supply the function necessary for growth in strain K not only for itself but also for the defective *r*II mutant. Or, in the language of genetics, in mixed infection in strain K the *r*+ wild type phenotype is *dominant* over that of the *r*II mutant. In the complementation test a bacterium of strain K is infected with the pair of *r*II mutants in order to examine whether the two mutants, each unable to grow alone in strain K, are able to *cooperate* in the mixedly infected cell to produce a crop of infective progeny. If the mutant pair is able to cooperate in this way, then it may be concluded that the two different mutations have not affected the same functional unit of the viral genome. The failure of one mutant to grow in strain K (its *r*II phenotype) must mean that it cannot carry out one particular function, or elicit the synthesis of one particular protein necessary for growth in the infected K cell, whereas the *r*II phenotype of the other mutant must mean that *it* cannot carry out some *other* necessary function appertaining to a different functional unit of the genome. The two mutants are able to reproduce in joint growth because each supplies that essential function in which the other is deficient. (It goes without saying that either one of these hypothetical functions of the *r*II region can be essential only for growth in cells of strain K, and not in cells of strain B, in which *r*II mutants can grow perfectly well.) But if the two mutants are *unable* to cooperate in successful growth in bacteria of strain K, then it may be

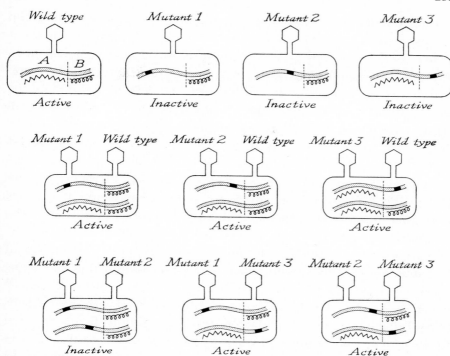

Fig. 10-6. The cis-trans, or complementation, test of rII mutants in *E. coli,* strain K. *Top level:* A and B cistrons are intact in the wild type r⁺ phage genome, so that both A cistron and B cistron polypeptides (shown here as sawtooth and spiral lines respectively) are formed. Mutants 1 and 2 bear defects at two different sites of their A cistron and can form only the B cistron polypeptide; mutant 3 bears a defect in its B cistron and can form only the A cistron polypeptide. Since the presence of both polypeptides is required for growth in bacteria of strain K, all three mutants are inactive on this strain. *Middle level:* In mixed infection with any of the three defective mutants, the wild type can supply both A cistron and B cistron polypeptides, and hence growth proceeds. *Bottom level:* Since neither mutant 1 nor mutant 2 can form the A cistron polypeptide, no growth proceeds in their mixed infection. In mixed infection of mutant 1 or mutant 2 with mutant 3, however, the former supply the B cistron polypeptide, while the latter supplies the A cistron polypeptide; hence growth proceeds. [Modified from Benzer, *Scientific American* **206,** No. 1: 70 (1962).]

concluded that both mutations have occurred at genetic sites belonging to the same functional unit of the viral genome. In that case the rII phenotype of both mutants is caused by a deficiency in exactly the same function, which neither mutant can supply to the other in joint growth.

On the basis of this test, Benzer found that rII point mutants fall into *two* functional groups, A and B; all mutants belonging to one group complement any member of the other group in the production of infective progeny in joint growth in strain K but do not complement in this way any member of their own group. It turned out, furthermore, that the two groups A and B could be assigned definite positions on the genetic fine-structure map of the T4 phage: as shown in Fig. 10-1, all *r*II mutants whose mutational sites are located to the left of the vertical line belong to group A, and all those located to the right belong to group B. Similar complementation tests carried out with deletion mutants show that these obey the same rules. Mutants carrying deletions that map entirely within one group do not complement any mutants of that group but do complement all mutants of the other group; and deletion mutants whose deletion extends across the boundary separating the two groups do not, save for an interesting exception (57), complement any mutants of either group. The two mutant groups thus signal the existence of two units of function within the *r*II region of the phage genome; each functional unit is presumably concerned with the synthesis of a specific polypeptide essential for growth in strain K. Benzer referred to the genetic unit of function revealed by grace of the cis-trans test as the **cistron,** a term whose adoption marks an important advance in the dialectics of heredity.

The approximate length of the cistrons A and B can be inferred from the recombination frequencies of mutant loci identified at their extreme ends; these frequencies indicate that the distance between the two most distant loci of cistron A is about 6 map units, and of cistron B about 4 map units. Using the assumptions concerning the total extent of the T4 genetic map and the DNA content of the virus previously employed for the estimate of the minimum unit of genetic recombination, one reckons that cistron A corresponds to a sequence of $(6/700) \times 2 \times 10^5$ or about 1700 and cistron B to $(4/700) \times 2 \times 10^5$ or about 1100 nucleotide pairs of the viral DNA double helix, in surprisingly good accord with the rough a priori estimate of the length of the functional unit inferred from first principles.

Topography of Genetic Fine Structure

The establishment of the fine-structure map of the *r*II region of the T4 genome thus brought into prospect at last the bridging of the gap between chemistry and genetics, since it had now become possible to follow genetic events at the level of the DNA nucleotide. Benzer, therefore, lost no time in training his methods on the process of mutation, which could now be studied with a much higher degree of sophistication than had been possible in the classical days when the units of recombination, mutation, and function were still all rolled into the old gene. First, Benzer addressed himself to the question of the *topography* of the *r*II region, that is, whether there are any local differences between various parts of the structure. In particular, he investigated whether all genetic sites are equally mutable, in which case mutations would occur everywhere at random, and the topography would be monotonous. But if there exist sites of particularly high or particularly low mutability, then interesting topographical features ought to be manifest. For this purpose, Benzer (52, 55) proceeded to map some thousands of independently isolated *r*II point mutants, first locating each mutant in its appropriate segment by crosses against the standard set of deletions. Mutants falling into the same segment were then crossed pairwise to determine whether they represented mutations at different sites of the segment or independent recurrences of a mutation at one and the same site. In this way a topographic map for the entire *r*II region of the T4 genome was constructed (Fig. 10-7). This map, on which each occurrence of a mutation is indicated by a little square, shows over 300 distinct sites at which independent mutations have been found. (Within each segment, the sites have been drawn in an arbitrary order.) A glance at this map makes it immediately obvious that the distribution of mutants over these sites is far from random. The most striking feature of this topographical map is the two "hot spots," one in segment A6c of cistron A and the other in segment B4 of cistron B, at each of which mutation has recurred hundreds of times. At the other extreme, there are many sites at which only a single mutational occurrence has so far been found.

It may be concluded, therefore, that different sites of the phage genome experience the forward mutation $r^+ \longrightarrow r$ with greatly different probabilities; once different sites have mutated, furthermore, the likelihood of their reverse mutation is likewise subject to great differences. No doubt these differences in forward and reverse mutation rates reflect the nature of the particular nucleotide pairs at and around each genetic site before and after the mutational event, some base pair combinations being more prone to copy errors than others. Looking back now, with

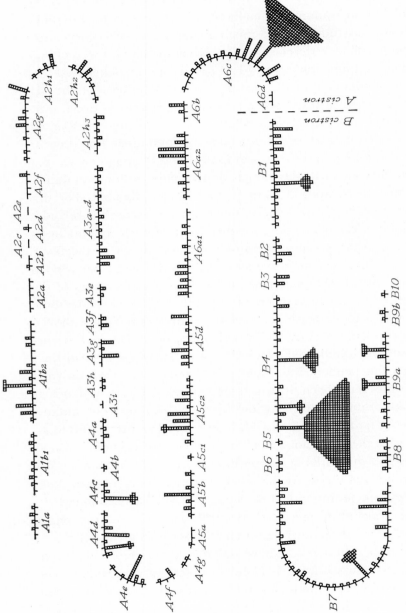

Fig. 10-7. Topographic map of the rII region for spontaneous mutations. Each square represents one occurrence observed at the indicated site. Sites with no occurrences indicated are known to exist from induced mutations, and from a few selected spontaneous ones. The arrangement of sites within each segment is arbitrary. Each mutant arose independently in a plaque either of the standard T4r⁺ wild type or, in somewhat less than half the cases, of r⁺ revertants of various rII mutants. The data for mutants isolated from standard wild type and from revertants are pooled in this figure. [From Benzer (55).]

the wisdom of hindsight, on earlier studies of forward and reverse muta-tion rates of "classical" genes, one realizes that such determinations were but crude summations over a very heterogeneous set of events at differ-ent fine-structure sites. These studies could have hardly yielded much insight into the basic molecular processes responsible for the permanent alteration of the hereditary substance.

Mutagenesis

In their first paper on the mechanism of DNA replication, Watson and Crick (659) also proposed, for good measure, a molecular explana-tion for the occurrence of mutations. It will be recalled that under the Watson and Crick replication scheme the two complementary poly-nucleotide strands of the parental DNA molecule separate. Each pa-rental strand then serves as the template for the ordered synthesis of a new complementary polynucleotide chain through the formation of spe-cific hydrogen bonds between purine and pyrimidine bases of the paren-tal polynucleotide and the mononucleotide building blocks available for polymerization in the intracellular metabolic pools. The formation of the specific Watson-Crick hydrogen bonds between adenine and thy-mine and between guanine and cytosine (or HMC), however, requires that these bases be in the particular **tautomeric** forms shown in Fig. 3-9. But, in fact, in an aqueous medium each base exists in a state of equi-librium between various tautomeric forms, of which those shown in Fig. 3-9 are merely the most probable. In some other, less probable form of each base, the shift of a crucial hydrogen atom makes possible the formation of specific hydrogen bonds to a base different from that of the normal complementary base-pairing scheme. For instance, the rare *imino* form of adenine and the rare *enol* form of thymine shown in Fig. 10-8 allow "illegitimate" complementary bonding of these bases to cytosine and guanine, instead of the "legitimate" base pairing to thymine and adenine, respectively. Watson and Crick thought it possible, therefore, that mutations derive from the rare circumstance that a purine or pyrimidine base attached to either the parental polynucleotide chain or to the free nucleotide building block to be incorporated into the replica chain happens to be in its rare tautomeric form at the very moment that it participates in the replication act. In this way, an "illegitimate" base pairing would result in the introduction of an incorrect nucleotide into the growing replica polynucleotide; there would thus be a permanent change in nucleotide sequence, or a mutation. This mutation could be reversed only by another infrequent accident in which, just

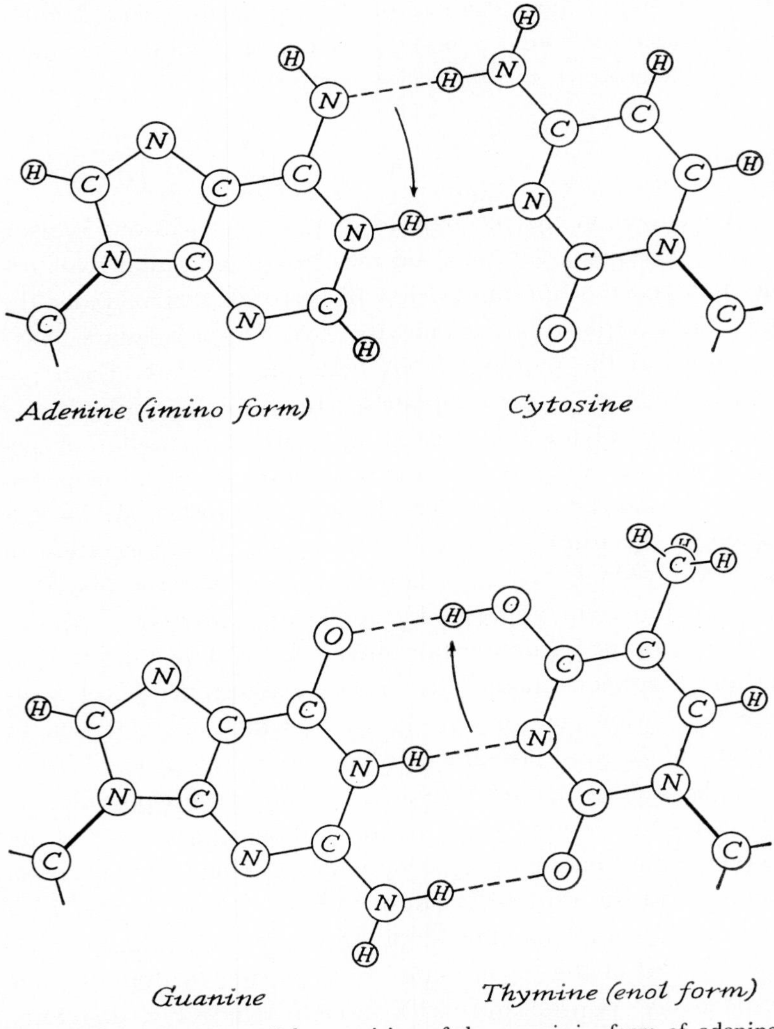

Adenine (imino form)   *Cytosine*

Guanine   *Thymine (enol form)*

Fig. 10-8.   "Illegitimate" base pairing of the rare *imino* form of adenine with cytosine, and of the rare *enol* form of thymine with guanine.

when at some future time the mutated site is about to act as a template, one of the two bases involved in the replication act happens to be in that rare tautomeric form which restores the original nucleotide to its rightful position in the polynucleotide chain by another "illegitimate" base pairing. Although, as we shall soon see, this proposal of Watson and Crick probably does not correctly describe the manner in which most spontaneous T4rII mutants arise, it nevertheless provided the basis of our present understanding of the mutation process.

Induced Mutation (in vivo)

Since the discovery thirty-five years ago by H. J. Muller and by L. J. Stadler that X-rays and ultraviolet light can *induce* mutations, or raise the frequency of mutant genotypes above the background of spontaneous mutants, many physical agents and chemical substances have been found to act as **mutagens** on the genetic material of living cells. The study of mutagenesis in bacterial viruses was, however, rather slow in getting under way, probably because it soon appeared that irradiation of phage particles, or their treatment with any of the other then usual mutagens, produces few or no mutants. Only when mutagens were finally applied to *phage-infected bacteria*, rather than to the extracellular virus particles, did significant increases in mutant frequencies become manifest. Thus it was observed in 1949 that irradiation of T2-infected bacteria at late stages of intracellular phage growth does result in a 10- to 30-fold increase in the frequency of *h* host range mutants among the phage progeny issuing from the surviving infective centers (395); not long thereafter, treatment of phage-infected bacteria with nitrogen mustard (570), streptomycin (204), and proflavine (170) was also found to induce mutations in the viral genome. But it was not until 1955—when Litman and Pardee (427) discovered that addition of the thymine analogue 5-bromouracil to the culture medium of T2-infected bacteria results in the appearance of a very greatly increased proportion of all sorts of phage mutants—that there seemed much hope for arriving at an understanding of the molecular basis of the mutation process through the use of mutagens.

5-bromouracil

Under the conditions in which it acts as a mutagen, bromouracil is incorporated into the phage DNA in place of thymine (194). The introduction of bromouracil residues into the DNA polynucleotides in place of thymine cannot, however, in itself represent a mutation, since upon removal of the mutagen from the growth medium (as upon assaying on

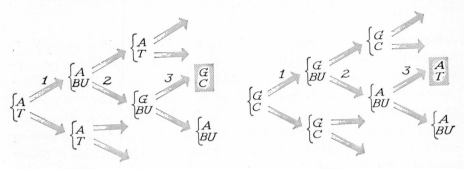

Template transition   *Substrate transition*

Fig. 10-9. Two mechanisms of bromouracil-induced mutagenesis in replicating DNA. *Template transitions:* 1. Bromouracil (BU) in its keto form is incorporated into a growing replica strand in place of T by pairing with A of the template strand. 2. At some subsequent replication cycle, the BU happens to be in its rare enol form and directs the illegitimate incorporation of G into the growing replica strand. 3. At the next replication cycle, the falsely incorporated G directs the incorporation of C into the growing replica strand, leading to the permanent replacement of the original A-T pair by a G-C pair at the mutant site. Here, the actual mutagenic step 2 *can* proceed in the absence of BU from the growth medium. *Substrate transitions:* 1. BU in its rare enol form is incorporated into a growing replica strand in place of C, by illegitimate pairing with G in the template strand. 2. At the next replication cycle, the falsely incorporated BU, now once more in its keto form, directs the incorporation of A into the growing replica strand. 3. Sometime later, after removal of BU from the growth medium, BU is replaced by its natural analog T, leading to the replacement of the original G-C base pair by an A-T pair at the mutant site. Here, the actual mutagenic step 1 *cannot* proceed on the absence of BU from the growth medium.

ordinary nutrient agar plates the bromouracil-labeled phage stock) bromouracil residues in the parental phage DNA are once more replaced by thymine residues in the replica chains. Hence the substitution of thymine by bromouracil entails no permanent change in nucleotide sequence or informational content of the viral DNA. Rather, the mutagenic action of bromouracil must derive from its propensity to raise the probability of copy errors that result in permanent replacement of one purine and pyrimidine base pair by another. How does bromouracil raise this probability? The most frequent tautomer of bromouracil, like that of thymine, is its *keto* form, so that bromouracil generally forms its specific base-pairing hydrogen bonds with adenine. But the presence of the bromine atom at the 5-position of the pyrimidine ring causes bromouracil to be in the rarer *enol* form, which is suitable for an "illegitimate" base pair with guanine, a much greater fraction of the time than thymine (Fig. 10-8). Thus bromouracil should be able to increase the frequency of copy errors in two different ways: (a) by promoting *template* transitions, in which residues of bromouracil already incorporated into DNA (in place of thymine) make more probable incorrect insertions of guanine (in place of adenine) into the replica chain growing on the bromouracil-labeled parental template strand, and (b) by promoting *substrate* transitions, in which bromouracil residues attached to free nucleotide building blocks make more probable erroneous insertions of bromouracil (and, hence, ultimately of thymine) in place of cytosine into de novo polynucleotides. The mutational event corresponds in the first case to the replacement of an adenine-thymine base pair by guanine-cytosine, and in the second case to the replacement of a guanine-cytosine base pair by adenine-thymine (Fig. 10-9). It is possible to show experimentally that bromouracil does exert its mutagenic action on the T-even phage genome in these two different ways: one class of mutations, the template transitions, is found to occur upon replication of bromouracil-substituted phage DNA in the absence of any bromouracil in the culture medium, whereas another class of mutations, the substrate transitions, occurs only while bromouracil is present in the culture medium (510, 623).

Spontaneous mutation, according to Benzer (54), is a "chronic disease whose cause in the case of any one mutant is unknown." Does bromouracil merely render this same disease acute? In order to make their diagnosis, Benzer and Freese (60) isolated many bromouracil-induced *r*II mutants of independent origin and then constructed a fine-structure topographic map of this collection, just as the map of spontaneous mutants had already been established. If the mutagenic effect of bromouracil represented a general, nonspecific stimulation of the process of spontaneous mutation, then the topography of the bromouracil-induced mutants should have resembled closely that of the spontaneous mutants. The result of Benzer and Freese's analysis was, however, that the bromouracil-induced mutants revealed a topography of the rII region entirely different from that inferred from the distribution of spontaneous mutants. In particular, the two prominent "hot spots" of spontaneous mutants were completely missing from the bromouracil mutant map, whereas "hot spots" of bromouracil mutants were manifest at several genetic sites at which none, or very few, of the spontaneous mutants had been previously identified.

These differences between the topographic maps of spontaneous and bromouracil-induced mutants show that bromouracil exerts a *specific* mutagenic effect on the T4 genome, and not a general enhancement of spontaneous mutation. Since the total frequency of bromouracil-induced rII mutants is several hundredfold higher than the frequency of spontaneous rII mutants, it can be inferred that at the bromouracil hot spots at which spontaneous rII mutants appeared, the presence of the mutagen raises the probability of copy error per replication by a factor of about 10^4. Conversely, it follows that bromouracil has little or no effect in promoting copy errors at the sites where the spontaneous hot spots are located. As in the case of spontaneous mutants, the occurrence of bromouracil-induced mutations is distributed very unevenly over all the sites of the rII region. Hence it follows that the probability that bromouracil causes its specific transition at a given genetic site cannot depend solely on which of the four types of purine or pyrimidine bases is present but must also in some way depend on the chemical nature of the *neighborhood* of the nucleotide in question in the polynucleotide chain.

This inference was further strengthened when similar topographic maps were constructed also for T4rII mutants induced by exposure of T4r^+-infected *E. coli* to the acridine dye proflavine (95) or to the purine base analogue 2-aminopurine (223).

Proflavine   2-Aminopurine

The mutagenic action of 2-aminopurine, like that of bromouracil, appears to derive from its propensity to be incorporated into the viral DNA and thus for promoting both template and substrate transitions; the probable mutagenic action of acridines shall be considered at a later time. The topographical distributions of rII mutants induced by these two mutagens were found to be very different both from one another as well as from the distributions of either spontaneous or bromouracil-induced mutants. It may be concluded, therefore, that also proflavine and 2-aminopurine are specific mutagens, capable of promoting certain molecular transitions at a restricted number of nucleotide sites of the phage genome.

Induced Mutation (in vitro)

The study of the molecular basis of mutation was put on a more secure footing when, at last, a class of chemical mutagens became available that produces its genetic effects by direct action on the DNA of the extracellular, free phage particle. Now it became possible to examine the permanent mutagenic chemical modifications caused in the viral polynucleotides.

The first such chemicals found to be highly mutagenic for extracellular T-even phages were the alkylating agents *ethyl methane sulfonate*, or EMS, and *ethyl ethane sulfonate*, or EES (431, 432).

$$CH_3SO_3CH_2CH_3$$
ethyl methane sulfonate
(EMS)

$$CH_3CH_2SO_3CH_2CH_3$$
ethyl ethane sulfonate
(EES)

These agents appear to react with the phage DNA by ethylating the 7-position of the purine ring of guanine or adenine. This reaction is then followed by hydrolysis of the purine-deoxyribose bond and thus by an eventual loss of the whole purine base from the polynucleotide chain (42, 398). Upon replication of the viral DNA containing such an ethyla-tion-induced gap in one of its strands at a site at which there had pre-viously resided one of the purines, either the correct complementary pyrimidine or an incorrect purine or pyrimidine may be inserted at the homologous site in the growing complementary de novo strand. If the correct pyrimidine happens to be inserted, the original genetic informa-tion has been restored; but if an incorrect base happens to be inserted, a permanent change in base sequence results—that is, a mutation occurs. This proposal for the mutagenic mechanism of EMS is supported by the pattern of *delayed* appearance of T4r mutants in bacteria infected with EMS-treated T4 phages (252).

Another highly effective in vitro mutagen for bacteriophages is *nitrous acid*, HNO_2 (221, 627, 648), which had first been found to cause mutations in the genetic *ribo*nucleic acid of the tobacco mosaic virus (241). Incubation of suspensions of T2 and T4 bacteriophages at 25°C with 0.05 *M* nitrous acid at *p*H 4.0 inactivates the phage population with a half-life of 10 minutes; among the survivors, an ever-increasing proportion of diverse mutants, including *r*II mutants, is found. The kinetics of appearance of these mutants suggest that they result from the interaction of a single molecule of nitrous acid with the phage DNA. Direct chemical study of the reaction of nitrous acid with model nucleotide substances and intact nucleic acid molecules shows that the most probable reactions are the conversions by oxidative deamination of cytosine to uracil (or, in the case of the T-even phage DNA, of HMC to 5-hydroxymethyluracil), of adenine to hypoxanthine, and of guanine to xanthine (Fig. 10-10) (550, 552). It is obvious that the conversion of HMC to hydroxymethyluracil at any site of the parental phage DNA would almost certainly entrain the incorporation of adenine, instead of the rightful guanine, into the first replica polynucleotide chain at the site complementary to that which had experienced the in vitro conversion, since the hydrogen bonding facilities of hydroxymethyluracil are identical to those of thymine. In the next replication cycle of the phage DNA, the adenine at the mutated site would attract a thymine into *its* complementary polynucleotide, and the replacement of the HMC-guanine base pair by a thymine-adenine base pair would be the ultimate issue of this in vitro deamination of HMC in the viral DNA. It is more difficult to predict the behavior in further replication cycles of the hypoxanthine and xanthine residues produced by the reaction of nitrous acid with adenine and guanine, since the hydrogen bonding facilities of hypoxanthine and xanthine are unlike those of either adenine or guanine. But if hypoxanthine and xanthine pair with cytosine (or HMC) at the time of DNA replication, as they well might, then the deamination of adenine, in analogy with the deamination of cytosine, would ultimately result in the replacement of the adenine-thymine base pair by a guanine-HMC base pair at the mutated genetic site, whereas the deamination of guanine would not be mutagenic at all (221, 647).

From the chemical point of view, the most specific in vitro mutagen

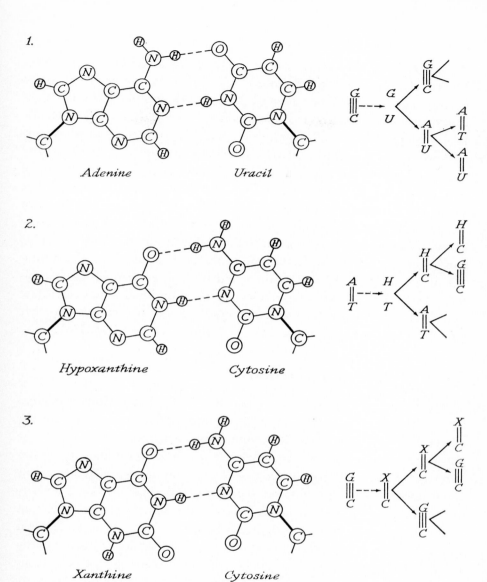

Fig. 10-10. The chemical basis of the mutagenicity of nitrous acid. 1. The 6-amino group of cytosine in a G-C base pair is deaminated to yield uracil; upon replication of the HNO$_2$-treated DNA, uracil pairs with adenine, ultimately leading to the permanent replacement of the G-C pair by an A-T pair. 2. The 6-amino group of adenine in an A-T base pair is deaminated to yield hypoxanthine; upon replication of the HNO$_2$-treated DNA, hypoxanthine pairs with cytosine, ultimately leading to the permanent replacement of the A-T pair by a G-C pair. 3. The 2-amino group of guanine in a G-C base pair is deaminated to yield xanthine; upon replication of the HNO$_2$-treated DNA, xanthine still pairs with cytosine, thus entailing no permanent change in base pair configuration. [From Freese (224).]

presently available appears to be *hydroxylamine*, NH_2OH (225, 226). Hydroxylamine reacts preferentially with HMC, and converts it to the corresponding uracil derivative (106, 551). Hence phage mutants induced by hydroxylamine treatment can be supposed to derive from the replacement of an HMC-guanine base pair by a thymine-adenine pair.

Benzer (55) ascertained also the distribution on the fine-structure topographic map of a set of T4rII mutants induced by treatment of T4r^+ wild type phages with EMS or nitrous acid. Here, he found that while the distribution of the mutants induced by these two in vitro mutagens bears little resemblance to the topographic maps of either the spontaneous mutants or the mutants induced by the three in vivo mutagens—bromouracil, 2-aminopurine, and proflavine—the mutational spectra of EMS and nitrous acid do look very much alike. This would suggest that the same nucleotide neighborhood factors facilitate action of these two rather different kinds of specific reagents in their putative conversion of purines and pyrimidines of the viral DNA.

Induced Reverse Mutation

The variety of topographic maps thus shows that various mutagens affect preferentially a very restricted number of molecular sites in the phage DNA, encouraging the notion that each mutagen causes some specific change. But this very variety renders it difficult to utilize topography for either confirming or disproving various schemes of the molecular basis of the mutational act, such as those we have already considered. For unless one can ascertain the nature of the molecular singularity that exists at the particular kinds of DNA sites at which each mutagen appears to act preferentially, it is not possible to draw many conclusions from the noncongruence of mutational spectra of various mutagens. A considerable advance in the understanding of the molecular action of the ever-increasing number of mutagens found to be effective in inducing mutations in phage was, however, achieved when closer examination was made of the efficacy of these mutagens in inducing, not the forward mutation to the rII mutant state, but the **reverse mutation,** or *reversion* from the rII to the r^+ wild state. These studies were initiated by Benzer and Freese (60) and greatly expanded by Freese (222, 224), some of whose results are summarized in Table 10-II. Several hundred rII mutants have been listed in this table according

TABLE 10-II

Induced Reverse Mutation of a Set of Spontaneously Reverting T4rII Mutants*

Mutagen Used for Induction of $r^+ \rightarrow r$II (forward mutation)	No. of rII Mutants Tested	% of rII Mutants Found Inducible to Revert to r^+ by Base Analogue Mutagens
Aminopurine	98	98
Bromouracil	64	95
Hydroxylamine	36	94
Nitrous acid	47	87
Ethyl ethane sulfonate	47	70
Proflavine	55	2
Spontaneous	110	14

* From Freese (224).

to their origin, which is either spontaneous or induction by different in vivo or in vitro mutagens. These mutants, all of which are point mutants that revert spontaneously, were grown in the presence of either bromouracil or 2-aminopurine, the two *base analogue mutagens*, and the resulting reversion index of r^+ revertants was compared with the spontaneous r^+ reversion index. For some of these mutants, the reversion index in the presence of the base analogue mutagens was essentially the same as the spontaneous reversion index; the reverse mutation of such mutants evidently cannot be induced by these mutagens. For other mutants, the reversion index was tens, hundreds, or thousands of times greater in the presence of the mutagen than in its absence; such mutants are considered to be "inducible to revert." The data of Table 10-II show that the origin of a T4rII mutant has a strong influence on its inducibility to revert: practically all the mutants originally induced from the T4r^+ wild type by bromouracil, 2-aminopurine, hydroxylamine, and nitrous acid, and most of the EES-induced mutants, can be induced to revert by the two base analogue mutagens; but practically none of the proflavine-induced mutants and only about 10% of the spontaneous mutants respond to the base analogue mutagens in regard to their reversion rate to the r^+ state.

This dichotomy of mutant types suggested to Freese (222, 224) that there must exist two basically different sorts of chemical alterations of the viral DNA responsible for *r*II point mutations: mutations of the *first kind* that arise by the action of base analogue mutagens (and of EES, nitrous acid, and hydroxylamine) and that are revertible by base analogue mutagens, and mutations of the *second kind* that arise by the action of proflavine (and, rarely, of EES), and that are not revertible by base analogue mutagens. Only about 10% of spontaneous *r*II mutants carry mutations of the first kind, whereas the remainder of spontaneous *r*II mutants carry mutations of the second kind.

From what has already been said concerning the way in which bromouracil, 2-aminopurine, nitrous acid, and hydroxylamine are likely to exert their mutagenic effect, it seems most plausible that mutations of the first kind correspond to that alteration which results in the replacement of one pyrimidine by another pyrimidine, or of one purine by another purine, at some site of the DNA polynucleotide chain. Such changes are now called **transitions.** They can be represented by the schema

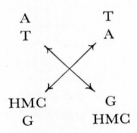

It is easy to understand why base analogue mutagens induce both forward and reverse mutations of the first kind. Bromouracil, for instance, once incorporated into the viral polynucleotide chains in place of thymine, greatly raises the probability of the template transition that incorrectly attracts guanine instead of adenine into the replica chain by illegitimate base pairing at the time of replication. But bromouracil can also induce the reverse mutation that once more replaces the mutant guanine-HMC pair by the original adenine-thymine pair, by greatly raising the probability of the substrate transition of incorrectly incorporating bromouracil (and hence, ultimately thymine) into the growing replica chain by illegitimate base pairing with the guanine at the mutant site. The original Watson-Crick proposal for the occurrence of spontaneous mutations by tautomerism of purine and pyrimidine bases thus probably describes correctly the origin of that 10% of spontaneous mutants that carry mutations of the first kind, and also accounts for the spontaneous reversion to the r^+ wild type of rII mutations of the first kind (albeit at a rate considerably lower than in the presence of base analogue mutagens).

The molecular explanation of mutations of the second kind is not as obvious as that of mutations of the first kind. Freese (222) proposed that mutations of the second kind represent **transversions,** in which a pyrimidine has been replaced by a purine, or a purine by a pyrimidine, in the DNA polynucleotide chain, according to the schema

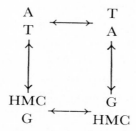

For instance, a copy error that resulted in the substitution of thymine for adenine, and hence ultimately of the pair thymine-adenine for the pair adenine-thymine, would constitute a transversion. One of the consequences of Freese's proposal is that at each site of the viral DNA two different mutations of the second kind should be possible, since two transversions, one to adenine and the other to guanine, can occur at every pyrimidine, and two transversions, one to thymine and the other to HMC, can occur at every purine residue.

It has been taken for granted in these discussions that the r^+ revertants sported by various rII mutants all owe their wild phenotype (their ability to grow on strain K) to a genuine act of reverse mutation in which the "incorrect" purine-pyrimidine base pair extant at the mutant site of the viral DNA has been replaced by the "correct" base pair of the wild type genome. Such "true" reversions are, however, not the only way in which individuals might arise that exhibit the wild phenotype. Instead of a restoration of the mutant site to its original, wild type state, it is also possible that there occurs a **suppressor mutation** at another genetic site which "suppresses" the mutant phenotype. Such suppressor mutations, whose interaction with the original mutant locus to restore the wild phenotype can have a variety of entirely different physiological explanations, are well known in the genetics of "higher" organisms and bacteria (700) and occur also in bacteriophage (466). If suppressors also occur among rII mutants of T4, then the inducibility to revert of a particular mutagen might not at all reflect the necessary chemical change at the mutant site itself. Instead it might reflect quite another chemical change at a specific suppressor site whose "forward" mutation suppresses the rII phenotype of the mutant under study and restores to it the r^+ wild type. Benzer and Freese were not unaware of this possibility and attempted to establish in various ways that the r^+ revertants found in their studies really represent "true" reversions and not suppressor mutations. Unfortunately, it is possible to prove conclusively only the presence of a suppressor mutation, but not its absence. Nevertheless, it seems likely that most r^+ revertants sported by rII mutants of the *first kind* really derive from "true" reversions of the mutant site.

But as shall be seen in Chapter 15, many r^+ revertants sported by rII mutants whose origin is a mutation of the *second kind* are not, in fact, true revertants but suppressed *double mutants* that owe their ability to grow on strain K to a juxtaposition of two mutations, the original and its suppressor, in the rII region of the T4 genome. This fact lends strong support to the proposal of Brenner, Barnett, Crick, and Orgel (94) that mutations of the second kind represent *insertions* or *deletions* of single nucleotide residues into or from the DNA polynucleotide chain, rather than the transversions imagined by Freese. This idea is based in part on the fact that no mutations of the second kind are found in those regions of the phage genome in which the information for a structural component of the mature virus particle appears to be coded, as for instance in the *h* host range locus of T2 which controls the synthesis of the phage tail fibers. It can be argued that any additions to or subtractions from the nucleotide sequence of any cistron would so completely upset the decoding process that *no* protein—or a radically *altered*, completely useless mutant protein—would be the product of the mutant cistron. Hence, all mutations of the second kind in cistrons of structural virus proteins would be invariably *lethal*, since no infective, structurally intact mutant particles carrying such a mutation could ever arise. The idea that acridines promote nucleotide deletions or insertions also derives support from the probable interaction of proflavine, the acridine mutagen for mutations of the second kind, with the viral DNA. Acridine molecules appear to intercalate or slide in between adjacent base pairs of the double helix and thus distort the macromolecule in a way that might

well render more probable the accidental insertion of an extra nucleotide, or the omission of a required nucleotide, from the growing DNA
replica chain (412). Nevertheless, even if mutations of the second kind
are really short insertions or deletions, it would not be excluded that the
postulated transversions also occur; if transversions do occur, however,
then they would probably be included among mutations of the first kind,
and thus be inducible as well as revertible by base analogue mutagens.

Mutational Heterozygotes

If the elementary mutational event corresponds to the introduction of
an incorrect nucleotide at some site of the growing replica polynucleotide chain, and if the DNA of the vegetative phage replicates through
the *semiconservative* mechanism of Watson and Crick, then it is possible
to predict a feature of the nascent viral mutant genomes that could
hardly have been anticipated before the molecular basis of these events
had been understood. Let us suppose that during the growth of one
of the replica chains a copy error occurs—for example, that a thymine
residue in the parental strand makes one of the rare illegitimate pairings
with guanine, instead of the legitimate pairing with adenine. The double
helical DNA molecule resulting from this mutagenic replication act
would then carry the mutant information in its de novo strand, whereas,
the old, unaltered parental strand would still carry the original, nonmutant message (Fig. 10-11). At the next replication cycle the complementary strands of this nascent mutant molecule would separate again,
with each strand acting as the template for the synthesis of its complementary polynucleotide chain. This would now result in the appearance
of one DNA double helix that carries the mutant information in *both* of
its strands and one DNA double helix that is entirely nonmutant. The
nascent mutant DNA molecule thus formally resembles a *heterozygote* in
that it carries two alleles, one mutant and the other nonmutant, at one
of its genetic sites, and in that it *segregates* into mutant and nonmutant
genomes in a later replication cycle. One could expect, therefore, that
during intracellular phage growth some phage precursor DNA molecules
that harbor a copy error mutation of the last replication cycle are withdrawn from the vegetative pool for encapsulation into structurally intact,
infective virus particles. Such particles would be *mutational heterozygotes*.

It could be expected, therefore, that some of the r mutants that arise during the growth of T4r^+ wild type phages should produce *mottled plaques* when plated on *E. coli* strain B, if their DNA complement included a *heteroduplex* molecule containing one polynucleotide strand still endowed with the r^+ rapid lysis cistron and one carrying the corresponding r mutant cistron. It is difficult to demonstrate the existence of such r/r^+ mutational heterozygotes among spontaneous r mutants because the overwhelming majority of r mutant particles present in any ordinary population of T4r^+ phages carry mutations that occurred in the distant past of the growth history of the stock; thus even if all mutants of the stock were once genetically heterozygous, they would have had ample time to segregate into mutant and nonmutant types. It was possible, however, to show that most, if not all, bromouracil-induced r^+ reverse mutants of a T4r mutant of the first (base analogue-induced) kind do initially arise as genetically heterozygous rII/r^+ genomes that only later segregate into homozygous r^+ revertants (510). For this purpose, bromouracil mutagen was added to bacteria infected with the T4rII mutant just before the end of the eclipse period of intracellular phage growth, and the first infective progeny particles that appeared intracellularly just after the end of the eclipse period were released by artificial lysis of the cells. This program of

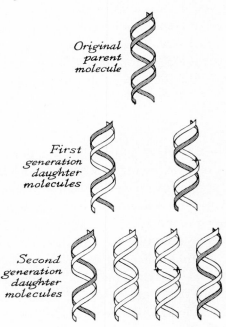

Original parent molecule

First generation daughter molecules

Second generation daughter molecules

Fig. 10-11. Genesis of mutational heterozygotes in semiconservative replication of the phage DNA. A copy error causes the introduction of an incorrect purine or pyrimidine base (marked by an "x") into the de novo polynucleotide chain of one of the two first-generation daughter DNA molecules. This produces a "heterozygous" DNA double helix that carries the original, nonmutant base sequence in one of its strands and the new mutant base sequence in the other of its strands. At the next replication cycle all strands of the first-generation daughter DNA molecules separate, and each strand acts as template for the synthesis of its complement. This produces one fully mutant and three nonmutant structures among the second-generation daughter DNA molecules.

mutagenesis insured that any r^+ reverse mutants induced and withdrawn from the phage DNA precursor pool during the short exposure of the culture to the mutagen must have arisen only during the very last replication cycle. The copy error responsible for restoring to the viral DNA the genetic information of the r^+ wild state occurred, therefore, so late that no further replication (and hence segregation into homozygous mutant structures) could have occurred. The result of this experiment was that more than 80% of all r^+ revertants induced by a brief exposure to bromouracil are indeed mutational heterozygotes, carrying both the original rII as well as the reverse-mutated r^+ allele. Hence, just as demanded by the mechanism of Watson and Crick, and contrary to the expectation of other conceivable DNA replication mechanisms that predict a *conservative* distribution of the substance of the parental DNA molecule, copy errors in the synthesis of replica polynucleotides do appear to generate a heteroduplex which, in one of its halves, still preserves intact the hereditary message of its progenitor.

Mutational heterozygotes seem to appear also after treatment of extracellular phage particles with nitrous acid; a high proportion of nitrous acid-induced r mutants in T2r^+ and T4r^+ stocks are found in mottled plaques containing both mutant and wild type phages (627, 648). These mottled plaques could derive from virus particles carrying DNA molecules that contain a deaminated purine or pyrimidine in one of the two polynucleotide strands. For instance, a heterozygous r mutant might harbor in one DNA strand a hydroxymethyluracil residue generated by deamination of HMC at some site of a rapid lysis cistron and retain at the homologous site in the other, complementary strand the old guanine residue originally paired with the "wild type" HMC destroyed by the nitrous acid treatment. After its injection into the host cell, the heteroduplex DNA molecule replicates to generate approximately equal proportions of r mutant and r^+ wild type genomes, containing respectively the base pairs thymine-adenine and cytosine-guanine at the genetic site in question.

The existence of mutational heterozygotes demonstrates that *both* complementary strands of the DNA of the infective virus transmit the information they harbor to the DNA molecule of the progeny generation. This inference, which we earlier implicitly took for granted, was by no means certain a priori.

Further Reading

Benzer, S., "Fine structure of a genetic region in bacteriophage" (51); Benzer, S., "The elementary units of heredity" (52); Benzer, S. and Freese, E., "Induction of specific mutations with 5-bromouracil" (60); Benzer, S., "On the topography of genetic fine structure" (55). All of Benzer's writings on the genetic fine structure in phage are models of clarity and should be read for an appreciation of his work. The first two papers describe the methodology and theory of fine-structure analysis, and the last two papers deal with the topography of the map.

Benzer, S., "On the topology of the genetic fine structure" (53). Another important contribution of Benzer not even mentioned in this chapter. By use of a large set of deletion mutants, Benzer demonstrated in an entirely novel way that the *topology* of the map of T4rII mutant sites corresponds to a *linear* array. A clever and rigorous proof of a proposition that had been more or less taken for granted in phage genetics.

Streisinger, G. and Franklin, N. C., "Mutation and recombination at the host range genetic region of phage T2" (615). An illustration of how, once appropriate selective methods for detecting rare recombinants have been worked out, Benzer's fine-structure analysis can be applied to other genetic loci of the phage.

Freese, E., *The molecular mechanism of mutations* (224). A summary presented before the Vth International Congress of Biochemistry.

CHAPTER 11

Radiobiology

Ultraviolet Light—Photoreactivation—Genetic Control of UV Sensitivity—Crossreactivation (or Marker Rescue)—Functional Survival—Multiplicity Reactivation—Effect of UV on Genetic Recombination—Radiophosphorus Decay—X-Rays—Radiosensitivity of the Vegetative Phage

AS EARLY AS 1922, not long after their discovery, it was found that infectivity of bacterial viruses can be destroyed by irradiation (24, 244). Since that time, the effects on the virus particles of radiations from nearly every sector of the electromagnetic spectrum have been the subject of intensive study. Indeed, it can fairly be said that it is with bacteriophages that radiobiological methods have found one of their more profitable applications. But much of this work has a peculiar relation to the rest of bacterial virology. As Stahl (583) has put it, ". . . the primary aim in employing radiation in the study of phage is to elucidate the *normal* state of affairs. However, almost all experiments involving the irradiation of phage have raised far more questions than they have answered. This has resulted in the situation that there now exists a 'radiobiology of bacteriophage,' a collection of observations and hypotheses arising *from* irradiation experiments, leading no one knows where, but selfishly demanding an explanation."

The accumulated body of data relevant to the interaction of radiations with bacterial viruses is so extensive that all but its most cursory review must remain beyond the scope of our discussion. The effects of only two kinds of radiobiological agents will be mainly considered here: ultraviolet light and decay of incorporated radiophosphorus, P^{32}. As shall be seen, ultraviolet light and P^{32} decay are relatively specific in their action, in that their noxious effects can be traced with reasonable

certainty to lesions in the viral DNA. The lethal molecular modifications of the viral DNA produced by ultraviolet light and by P^{32} decay
are, however, of a very different nature, and entail different physiological consequences. The effects of X-rays, which appear to be rather
less specific in their action than either ultraviolet light or P^{32} decay, will
also find brief mention.

Ultraviolet light

Ordinary germicidal lamps are nowadays the most commonly used
source of ultraviolet light (UV) in phage experimentation. The maxi-

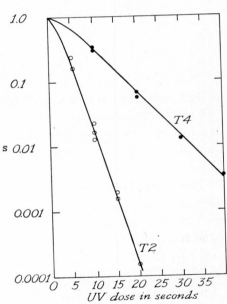

mum output of radiant energy of
these lamps occurs at the wavelength of 2536 Å, corresponding
to an emission of quanta whose
energy is 4.9 electron volts. Figure
11-1 shows the result of an experiment in which populations of T2
and T4 bacteriophages were
placed under a germicidal lamp
and the surviving fraction of infective centers was assayed after
various times of illumination. It
can be seen in this figure that the
logarithm of the surviving fraction s of both phage strains decreases linearly with the time of
irradiation, except for a slight initial "shoulder" that causes the
survival curve to extrapolate to
an intercept with the ordinate at
a value 1.6 times higher than the
initial titer. Ignoring for the moment this slight initial acceleration in the rate of UV inactivation, it may be concluded that

Fig. 11-1. Inactivation of bacteriophages
T2 and T4 by UV light. The ordinate shows
the surviving fraction, s, of the phage populations after their exposure to UV light of
wavelength 2537 Å for the number of sec-
onds shown on the abscissa. Irradiation and
plaque assays are carried out under yellow,
nonphotoreactivating light. [From Harm
(265).]

UV inactivation of T2 and T4 phages proceeds according to simple
exponential kinetics. This suggests, as the following considerations show,

that the absorption of a single quantum of UV light suffices to kill a T-even virus particle.

The kinetics of inactivation of UV-irradiated bacteriophages can be interpreted in terms of the **target theory**, under which the virus particles are thought of as "targets" for the radiation. Some molecular component of a virus particle interposed in a quantum beam absorbs all or part of the energy of a UV quantum and as a consequence is raised to a higher energetic or excited state. If this excitation results in some permanent chemical modification, the particle is said to have sustained a "hit." Hits that "kill"—modifications that destroy the reproductive potential of the phage—are called **lethal hits.** If a single hit suffices to abolish the capacity of the virus to give rise to infective progeny, and if each virus particle of a population of bacteriophages being irradiated with a flux of q quanta/cm²/sec absorbs ϕ cm² of these quanta, of which absorptions a fraction QY produces a lethal hit, then the average phage particle has sustained $\phi \cdot QY \cdot q \cdot t$ lethal hits after t sec of irradiation. The surviving fraction s of the phage population that has sustained *no* lethal hits by this time is given by the zero term of the Poisson law:

$$s = e^{-\phi \cdot QY \cdot q \cdot t}$$

or

$$\log s = -(1/2.3)(\phi \cdot QY \cdot q \cdot t). \qquad (11\text{-}1)$$

In this relation, the factor $\phi \cdot QY$ represents the *UV sensitivity* of the virus and the factor $q \cdot t$ the *UV dose*.

Although the observed inactivation kinetics of the T-even phages suggest that the absorption of a single UV quantum *suffices* for inactivation, further study of the *quantum yield QY* of the reaction shows that only a very small fraction of the absorbed quanta actually destroys the ability of the virus to produce a plaque on the assay plate. As the calculation of Table 11-I shows, the probability is only 3.3×10^{-4} that any UV quantum absorbed by a T2 particle engenders a lethal hit.

It is possible to ascertain which of the two major components of the phage, protein or DNA, actually absorbs the lethal UV quanta. For this purpose, phage populations are irradiated with *monochromatic UV* of various known wavelengths, and at each wavelength the rate of phage inactivation is determined per unit of radiant energy emitted by the monochromatic source. The first to work out such an **action spectrum** was Gates (240), who found in 1934 that, in the UV range 2300–2970 Å, the wavelength 2600 Å is maximally effective in administering lethal

TABLE 11-I

The Quantum Yield of UV Inactivation of T2*

It follows from Equation *(11-1)* that when $s = e^{-1}$, or when the irradiated population has been given one lethal hit,

$$QY = \frac{1}{\phi qt}.$$

An incident dose qt of 3.5×10^{14} quanta/cm^2 of wavelength 2650 Å delivers one hit to T2. At 2650 Å the absorbancy ϕ of T2, as determined by UV spectrophotometry of highly purified phage particles in accurately known concentration, is 8.6×10^{-12} cm^2 per particle. Hence

$$QY = \frac{1}{8.6 \times 10^{-12} \times 3.5 \times 10^{14}}$$

$$= 3.3 \times 10^{-4} \text{ hits per quantum absorbed.}$$

* From Zelle and Hollaender (704).

hits to staphylococcus phage. An action spectrum for the UV inactivation of T2 phage, plotted together with the UV *absorption spectra* of a

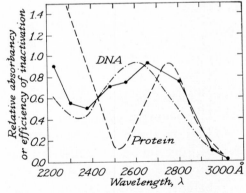

Fig. 11-2. The action spectrum of UV inactivation of bacteriophage T2. Suspensions of T2 phage in phosphate buffer are irradiated with monochromatic UV light of nine different wavelengths from a quartz crystal monochromator. The intensity of the radiant energy, or the number of UV quanta q per cm^2/sec, incident on the phage suspensions at each wavelength, was measured by a thermopile. The fraction of each phage type surviving a given UV dose is determined by plaque assay. These measurements allow an estimate of the radiation dose qt in number of quanta/cm^2 required to deliver one hit to the phage population (that is, to reduce the fraction of survivors to e^{-1}) for various wavelengths λ. The ordinate shows the *relative* efficiency of inactivation, in terms of the ratio of the dose required for one hit at 2650 Å to the dose required for one hit at the wavelength λ shown on the abscissa (points connected by solid lines). The broken lines show the UV absorption spectrum of DNA and of a typical protein. [From Zelle and Hollaender (704).]

DNA and a protein similar in composition to the DNA and protein of T2, is shown in Fig. 11-2. It is apparent that the action spectrum of inactivation resembles quite closely the absorption spectrum of the

DNA but is rather different from the absorption spectrum of the protein. The resemblance of the inactivation action spectrum and the DNA absorption spectrum indicates that the UV quanta that produce lethal hits are absorbed by the DNA; that is, the viral DNA rather than the viral protein is the "target" of the radiation.

The absorption of UV by DNA is known to produce a variety of chemical modifications in the purine and pyrimidine residues of the

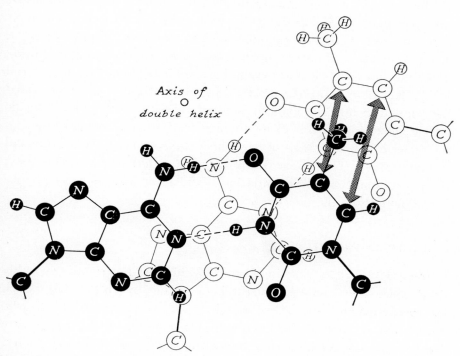

Fig. 11-3. The thymine-thymine dimer photoproduct of UV irradiation of DNA. *Upper figure:* Presumed chemical structure of the dimer. [From Wacker (652a).] *Lower figure:* A dimer formed between contiguous thymine residues of two successive adenine-thymine base pairs in the DNA. The UV-induced bonds that weld successive levels of the double helix are shown as heavy arrows.

irradiated polynucleotide chains. One of these modifications, the **dimerization** of two adjacent thymine residues belonging to nucleotides on the same DNA polynucleotide chain (74, 652a, 653) is shown in Fig. 11-3. It seems very likely that it is this thymine-thymine dimer that is, in fact, the lesion predominantly responsible for the death of UV-irradiated phage particles. This kind of lethal UV lesion does not destroy the overall structural integrity of the viral DNA double helix, a fact that is of importance for understanding the physiological and genetic behavior of UV-irradiated phages.

We may now consider some of the properties of the "dead" UV-irradiated phages. That such phages are no longer able to reproduce themselves indefinitely, or give rise to a plaque on the assay plate, need not necessarily mean that there is not *some* life left in them. Indeed, UV-inactivated T-even phages may still adsorb to sensitive bacteria, may still inject their "dead" DNA molecules, and may still kill their host cells, even though they produce no infective progeny particles (444). The UV-inactivated viruses, furthermore, may still cause the dissolution of the host nuclei (449) and may still arrest further synthesis of bacterial DNA, RNA, and protein (143). Most importantly, UV-inactivated T-even phages may still elicit the synthesis of many of the phage-specific "early" enzymes (178, 372) mentioned in Chapter 7, though they can no longer initiate synthesis of new phage DNA or of phage head or tail proteins (654). The phage DNA carrying a lethal UV lesion may, therefore, be still capable of initiating considerable phage-specific physiological activity in the infected host cell.

Photoreactivation

Some T2 particles carrying lethal UV hits are not even irrevocably dead, since they can be brought back to life by visible light. Such **photoreactivation** was discovered in 1950 by Dulbecco (190), who found that if bacteria infected with UV-inactivated T2 phages are exposed to a strong light source (such as a fluorescent lamp), then a considerable proportion of the "dead" virus particles are reactivated and produce infective progeny. Photoreactivation occurs only by illumination of phage-infected bacteria, and not by illumination of free virus particles, since reactivation derives from the erasure of UV lesions in the viral DNA by an enzyme system (246) present in the bacterial cell.

This autochthonous bacterial enzyme system seems to be "activated" by the visible light to give rise to a product that restores to their natural state the modified purine or pyrimidine residues (in particular the thymine-thymine dimers) of the irradiated phage DNA (85, 86). After the UV lesions of the viral DNA have been erased in this way, normal intracellular phage growth commences and leads to the production of infective progeny viruses (411).

Not every UV-induced photochemical lesion in the T2 DNA is photo-restorable, however. If the UV inactivation of a T2 phage population is measured with and without photoreactivation, by incubating one set of assay plates in strong light and another set in the dark, two survival curves are obtained: the one representing assays made in the light has only 0.4 the negative slope of the one representing assays made in the dark. That is, evidently 0.6 of the UV lesions that are lethal in the dark can be erased upon incubation in the light; the other 0.4 can not. The fraction of lethal lesions that is photorestorable is called the **photo-reactivable sector** of the phage, which, in the case of T2, is thus 0.6.

Genetic Control of UV Sensitivity

Comparison of the slopes of the two UV survival curves of Fig. 11-2 shows that the UV sensitivity of phage T4 is only about half that of its close relative T2. Since the average T4 particle absorbs the same fraction of incident UV quanta as the average T2 particle—that is, since the absorbancy ϕ of Equation (11-1) is the same for both strains—it follows that the quantum yield QY, or the chance that an absorbed UV quantum generates a lethal hit, must be twice as great for T2 as for T4. This difference in the efficiency of UV killing reflects the presence of a "UV sensitivity" locus in the T-even phage genome (610). The u allele of this locus carried by the T4 wild type reduces by half the number of lethal hits sustained by a corresponding phage genome harboring the u^+ allele carried by the T2 wild type. The u locus behaves as a single hereditary factor in genetic crosses and is situated in the T-even linkage map at the position indicated in Fig. 9-2. Two principal alternatives were at first envisaged for the manner in which the u allele might reduce the UV sensitivity of the T-even phages. (a) Possession of the u allele reduces the *intrinsic* sensitivity of the phage DNA to induction of lethal photochemical lesions, so that after exposure to an equivalent dose of

UV a phage of *u* genotype carries one-half the number of noxious modifications of its DNA bases that a phage of the complementary *u*⁺ genotype carries. (b) Possession of the *u* allele, while leaving the intrinsic UV sensitivity of the phage DNA unaffected, promotes or allows repair of some of the noxious modifications after injection of the irradiated phage DNA into the host cell.

The second of these two alternatives must correspond more closely to the real situation (265). In mixed infection of *u* and *u*⁺ phages the *u* allele is *dominant:* the UV sensitivity of a phage of the more sensitive *u*⁺ genotype is reduced by half, as long as its survival is measured on bacteria infected simultaneously also with a phage of *u* genotype. The most plausible explanation of this finding is that the intracellular presence of the *u* gene promotes either synthesis or function in the infected cell of some substance that can repair UV lesions carried by the infecting phage DNA, whether of *u* or of *u*⁺ genotype. Furthermore, these very UV lesions that are erased under the influence of the *u* gene must be of the same kind that are also restored by photoreactivation, since the photoreactivable sector of phages carrying the *u* allele is only 0.2, compared to the photoreactivable sector of 0.6 of *u*⁺ genotypes (190). That is to say, even though the rate of UV inactivation of T2 is twice that of T4 when survival is measured in the *dark*, T2 and T4 show very similar rates of inactivation when survival is measured in the *light* under conditions of maximum photoreactivation. We may thus imagine that the photoreactivating visible light stimulates to greater activity the intrabacterial enzyme system that in the dark is also stimulated by the *u* gene. This system restores some of the modified bases on the irradiated viral DNA to their initial state. Lethal UV hits can, therefore, represent only that fraction of lesions which, for one reason or another, is not erased after infection by the bacterial restoration system. The spontaneous erasure of lesions might also explain the slight "shoulders" in the T-even UV survival curves of Fig. 11-2, since an initial increase in the rate of UV inactivation of T2 and T4 would be observed if, as is not altogether unlikely, the fraction of UV-induced lesions "spontaneously" restored after infection is greater when the viral DNA carries but a few lesions than when the viral DNA has already sustained very many lesions. This rather ad hoc explanation derives some support, however, from the observation that the UV inactivation of T2 and T4 after maximum photoreactivation does appear to follow true single-hit kinetics without any initial "shoulder."

Crossreactivation (or Marker Rescue)

But even those lethal UV hits that fail to be erased by the physiological restoration reactions just discussed are not necessarily lethal to the whole genome of the irradiated phage, as is shown by the **crossreactivation** of genetic markers of irradiated phages (438): if a bacterium is infected jointly with "dead" UV-irradiated and with active phages that differ from each other in one or more of their genetic loci, then genetic markers of the inactive irradiated parents may appear among the progeny of the mixed infection. Figure 11-4 presents results of an experiment showing the occurrence of crossreactivation; in this experiment, aliquots of a population of T4r^+ wild type phages were irradiated with various doses of UV and an average of 0.5 particles per bacterium were allowed to adsorb to *E. coli*, strain B. At the same time, the bacteria were also infected with an average of 3 unirradiated, fully viable T4rII mutant phages per cell. These infective centers were then diluted and allowed to lyse under the conditions of single burst, and the phage yields of the individual bursts were plated for plaque assay. Any plate showing an r^+ wild type plaque must

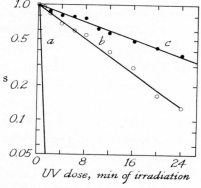

Fig. 11-4. Rescue of the r^+ marker of UV-irradiated T4r^+ by crossreactivation with fully viable T4r. The ordinate shows the surviving fraction, s, of the irradiated T4r^+ after an exposure to UV for the time indicated on the abscissa. Curve A. Survival of the irradiated phages as plaque formers, being a measure of the total radiation damage, or lethal hits, delivered. Curve B. Crossreactivation of the r^+ marker, being the fraction of bacteria infected jointly with irradiated r^+ and nonirradiated r parents that yield at least one viable r^+ progeny genotype. Curve C. Survival of the bacterial killing ability of the irradiated phages (determined by a method similar to that outlined in Table IV-3). [From Doermann, Chase, and Stahl (184).]

have received the yield of an infected bacterium that liberated at least one active progeny particle bearing the r^+ marker of the irradiated parent. It can be seen in Fig. 11-4 that UV irradiation abolishes survival of the r^+ locus of the T4 phages in mixed infection with viable T4rII very much more slowly than it abolishes the infectivity of the whole T4r^+ virus particle; after the UV irradiation had inactivated the plaque-forming ability of all but 2% of the phages, nearly every one of the irradiated wild type phages could still act as coprogenitor of at least one r^+ progeny virus. The data of Fig. 11-4 show also that those lethal hits which do finally eliminate the r^+ marker from the yield do not do so by destroying the whole virus altogether, since UV irradiation can be seen to suppress the ability of the virus to kill its bacterial host even more slowly than the crossreactivability of the genetic locus.

In seeking to comprehend the mechanism of crossreactivation, one may ask whether reactivation is an all-or-none phenomenon that, when it does occur, reactivates the *entire* genome of the irradiated virus, or whether crossreactivation is a fractional process that rescues some *parts* but not others of the moribund genome. The answer to this question is provided by experiments in which several genetic markers are introduced into the crossreactivation experiments, and single bursts of bacteria infected jointly with UV-inactivated phages and with active phages of complementary genotype are examined. If, on the one hand, crossreactivation were an all-or-none process, bacteria liberating *any* marker of the UV-irradiated parent ought to liberate *all* the other markers of the UV-irradiated parent as well. If, on the other hand, crossreactivation rescued only parts of the genome of the irradiated virus, the phage progeny of many individual bursts should then bear only some, but not all, of the genetic markers of the irradiated parent. Such single-burst experiments were carried out by Doermann and his collaborators (183, 184), who infected bacteria mixedly with UV-irradiated T4 wild type and the active T4*mrtu* triple mutant, and then scored for the appearance of the m^+, r^+, and tu^+ wild type markers among the single-burst progeny. In one set of these experiments the three mutant markers were closely linked; in another set the three markers were only distantly linked. The results of these experiments show that one marker of the irradiated parent may be completely absent from the burst while another is represented in several progeny particles. Missing markers can be considered to have been "knocked out" individually by the UV, and reactivation cannot be an all-or-none process. Furthermore, closely linked markers are knocked out in a correlated manner, whereas distantly linked markers are knocked out independently of each other. Finally, the average number of progeny phages bearing crossreactivated markers in single bursts of mixedly infected bacteria yielding *any* markers of the irradiated parent represents only a small fraction of the mixed yield. It can be concluded therefore that the genome of the irradiated parent is at a disadvantage vis-à-vis the unirradiated parent in the course of intracellular phage growth.

These results have led to the idea that, though lethal UV lesions destroy only that small part of the phage genome that is represented by the phage DNA in the immediate vicinity of the UV-modified pyrimidine base, each such lesion prevents the autonomous reproduction of the whole phage genome. However, if an irradiated phage DNA happens to enter a bacterium simultaneously infected also with a fully viable, unirradiated phage genome which can supply the necessary physiological functions required for the synthesis of phage progeny substance, then genetic loci residing in "healthy," lesion-free regions of the irradiated DNA can be rescued from the moribund genome by genetic recombination with the replicating genome of the viable bedfellow. Since replication of the genetic loci of the irradiated parent begins only after their rescue by recombination and since rescue is likely to occur only after considerable replication of the unirradiated parent has already taken place, the burst size of the rescued markers can be expected to be very low.

Functional Survival

The inability of rII mutants to grow on strain K can be used to determine the UV sensitivity of not only the genetic but also the *functional* survival of the viral genome (383). The design of this experiment is similar to that of the cis-trans test (p. 254). Bacteria of *strain K* are infected simultaneously with nonviable, UV-irradiated T4rII^+ wild type phage and with unirradiated, fully viable T4rII mutant phage. The $rII^+ \times rII$ infected K bacteria are plated on agar seeded with strain B bacteria and the total number of plaques is scored. Any plaque formed under these conditions must derive from an infected K bacterium in which the rII^+ locus of the irradiated wild type genome provided the function necessary for growth on this host cell of the unirradiated but hereditarily functionally defective rII mutant. Conversely, the failure of any K bacterium infected with both *r*II⁺ and *r*II phages to produce a plaque on the assay plate must derive from a UV lesion in the *r*II⁺ wild type parent that prevents function of that one of its two *r*II cistrons which is homologous to the cistron in which the mutational defect carried by the particular *r*II mutant is situated.

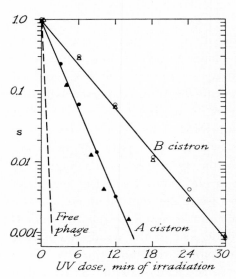

The results of a typical functional survival experiment are presented in Fig. 11-5. Here, UV-irradiated *r*II⁺ phages were allowed to infect strain K cells jointly with one of four different *r*II mutants. Two of these mutants carried their mutation in the A cistron and two in the B cistron. The results demonstrate that the function of the *r*II region is much less UV-sensitive than the infectivity of the virus; nearly all of the *r*II⁺ × *r*II infected K bacteria still produce plaques after exposure of the *r*II⁺ parent to a UV dose that left only 1% of the individuals viable. But higher doses of UV can be seen to destroy the function of the *r*II⁺ locus, the rate of inactivation evidently depending on which *r*II mutant is used for the test of functional survival. The relative slopes of these survival curves indicate that the capacity of the *r*II⁺ wild

Fig. 11-5. Functional survival of the *r*II locus of UV-irradiated T4*r*II⁺ wild type in mixed infection on *E. coli*, strain K, with fully viable T4*r*II mutants whose mutational sites are situated in either the A cistron or the B cistron of the *r*II region. The ordinate shows the fraction of strain K bacteria infected jointly with irradiated *r*⁺ and nonirradiated *r*II parents that yield any progeny after an exposure of T4*r*⁺ to UV for the time shown on the abscissa. [From Krieg (383).]

type to complement *r*II mutants bearing a mutational defect in their A cistron is destroyed at 0.1 times the rate of loss of infectivity and that the ability to complement B cistron mutants is destroyed at 0.05 times the rate of loss of infectivity. It can be concluded, therefore, that, so far as survival of their function is concerned, *r*IIA and *r*IIB cistrons of the wild type phage genome represent UV "targets" that are one-tenth and one-twentieth, respectively, of the "target" represented by whole phage.

That the A cistron should represent a bigger UV target than the B cistron agrees with the longer genetic map size which has been estimated for the A cistron from recombination frequencies of rII mutant loci situated at the extreme ends of both cistrons (see pp. 240–242). But the relative UV target size of the rII region is very much greater than its share of the total phage genome. As was estimated in Chapter 10, each of the two rII cistrons represents less than 1% of the total extent of the T-even genetic map. A possible resolution of this discrepancy between relative target size of functional survival and genetic extent is to suppose that a UV lesion can suppress the function of a viral cistron even though the lesion lies beyond the physical domain of the cistron. That is, the UV target of cistronic function can be imagined to represent not the cistron itself but a much greater genetic envelope that has to be free of UV lesions if the cistron it encloses is to function.

Approximate determinations of the UV sensitivity of other functions of the T-even genome—such as the capacity for synthesis of the internal protein (488) and of some of the phage-induced enzymes listed in Fig. 7-3 (178)—have also been undertaken. For this purpose strain B bacteria were infected with UV-irradiated T-even phages and the overall rate of synthesis of the gene product in question was assayed directly in the infected culture. This work showed that cultures infected with populations of UV-irradiated phages of which only a small fraction of the individuals remains viable can still form the phage-specific proteins at a nearly normal rate. But cultures infected with even more highly UV-irradiated phages form the virus-specific proteins at a reduced rate. From the dependence of the rate of formation of these viral gene products on the UV dose delivered to the infecting phage, approximate target sizes of genetic function can be estimated. These target sizes are similar in magnitude to those estimated for the two cistrons of the rII region.

Multiplicity Reactivation

Not only can genetic loci of UV-irradiated phages be rescued by joint growth with unirradiated phage particles, but two UV-inactivated phage particles, neither one able to reproduce itself alone, can still cooperate to produce infective progeny if they happen to infect the same bacterium (434). This phenomenon is called **multiplicity reactivation.**

Figure 11-6 presents the results of a typical multiplicity reactivation experiment; in this experiment T2 phages were irradiated with various doses of UV and bacteria were infected with samples of the irradiated phage stocks at an average of 3.5 particles per cell before being plated on sensitive indicator bacteria for infective center counts. It can be seen in this figure that the surviving fraction of infective centers that yields at least one infective progeny virus particle falls off much more slowly with UV irradiation than the fraction of bacteria that is evidently infected with "survivors" of the UV treatment. That is to say, in many of these multiply infected cells, "dead" UV-killed phages reactivated each other to produce infective offspring.

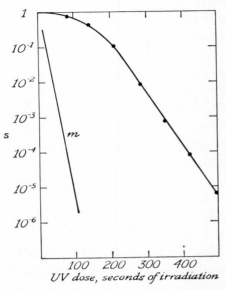

Fig. 11-6. Multiplicity reactivation of UV-irradiated T2. The experimental points show the fraction of bacteria infected with an average of four T2 phages per cell surviving as infective centers after an exposure of the infecting virus particles to UV for the time shown on the abscissa The solid line labeled m shows the survival of the infecting virus particles as plaque formers in single infection. [From Dulbecco (191).]

From the first, Luria interpreted multiplicity reactivation as a sort of genetic exchange. In particular, Luria assumed that the viral genome consists of a number of different "subunits," each of which multiplies independently of the others in the phage-infected bacterium, and that the progeny virus particles are later assembled as a complete subunit set from intracellular replicas of the parental subunits. Each lethal UV hit would kill the phage by inactivating, or preventing the replication of, one and only one of these subunits. These assumptions then led to the prediction that provided a bacterium is infected with two "dead" phage particles which have not sustained lethal UV hits in a pair of *homologous* subunits, one complete functional and replicating set of phage subunits can always be assembled by pooling the undamaged subunits of the two parents. The quantitative relations concerning the dependence of the extent of multiplicity reactivation on UV dose and multiplicity of infection by the irradiated phages implied in this theory were derived by Luria and Dulbecco (447), who found that the predicted relations appeared to be in reasonable agreement with experimental results. Thus supported, the doctrine of independently replicating phage subunits held sway for two or three years. But not long thereafter Dulbecco (191) carried out a so-called "critical test" of multiplicity reactivation, and his results appeared to be in flagrant disagreement with Luria's independently replicating subunits. Thus, throwing the baby out with the bath, the idea of multiplicity reactivation by genetic exchange of undamaged parts was again abandoned, even by Luria (438). Nevertheless, Luria's subunit theory marked an important step in the radiobiology of phage, since it presented for the first time the notion that the various parts of the irradiated phage genome need not necessarily stand or fall together.

The studies on the mechanism of crossreactivation (pp. 285–287) showed that Luria's basic idea of genetic exchange between undamaged parts of the genome of "dead" phage particles was probably correct after all. In multiplicity reactivation, viable phage genomes do seem to arise by recombination between those parts of the parental DNA molecules in which there are no UV lesions. However, in order for multiplicity reactivation to be possible it is not enough that the complement of irradiated phage particles present within the same cell possess between them at least one functional allele of every gene that can be rescued by recombination; it is also essential that between them the phages can still carry out in the infected cell all "early" functions that are necessary before rescue by genetic recombination can proceed. Those genetic regions of the phage in which a UV hit inactivates the expression of a *function* that is a necessary prelude to genetic rescue are called "vulnerable centers" (36): the reactivating irradiated phages must possess between them one set of surviving vulnerable centers. It has been estimated that in phage T4 there are three such vulnerable centers, which make up about 40% of the total UV "target" of the virus. By introducing the parameter of vulnerable centers into Luria and Dulbecco's analytical formulations of the multiplicity reactivation phenomenon, a modified theory can be derived that is in excellent agreement with observed data (264).

Effect of UV on Genetic Recombination

The notion that UV-inactivated phage particles exchange undamaged parts of their genome finds strong support from the stimulatory effect of UV irradiation on the very process of genetic recombination. As was first discovered by Jacob and Wollman (335), the frequency of recombinants issuing from crosses of λ phages can be greatly increased if the two parental genotypes are UV-irradiated. This effect exists also with the T-even strains, as the following experiment (298) shows: two mutant stocks, T2r4 and T2r7, bearing two moderately closely linked r mutations in the rII gene, were given an average of about 6 lethal UV hits per phage and allowed to infect bacteria at a multiplicity of 4 particles per cell. Almost all of these infective centers liberated infective progeny phage because an ensemble of 8 T2 particles, each having received 6 lethal UV hits, is capable of producing very efficient multiplicity reactivation. The result of this experiment was that the fraction of r^+ wild type recombinants among the progeny was 8%, but in exactly analogous crosses involving unirradiated parent phages, the fraction of progeny recombinant for the same two markers never exceeds 2%. Thus the presence of UV lesions on the DNA of the infecting phage parents produces a fourfold stimulation of the genetic recombination process.

It is not difficult to explain this effect in terms of the mechanism of phage recombination outlined in Chapter 9. Under the Visconti-Delbrück theory, the "true linkage" d of two genetic sites refers to the average number of crossovers between them per mating during the replication of *normal* phage genomes. We may now envisage that replication of a vegetative phage genome derived from a UV-irradiated parent DNA can proceed along those parts of the genome that bear no UV lesions; as soon as the replication process reaches a lesion, replication stops and does not resume until, as in the postulated crossreactivation mechanism, replication can continue along the undamaged homologous part of a genome furnished by another UV-irradiated phage present in the same cell. It is thus apparent that if irradiation has placed a UV lesion between two particular sites on the phage linkage map, the chance has been greatly raised that an exchange, or recombination, will occur between these two loci at the time the irradiated genome is replicated. Or, in genetic terms, the presence of UV lesions stretches the phage linkage map by raising the crossover probability per mating.

Radiophosphorus Decay

Inactivation Kinetics

Another method of radiobiological inactivation of bacterial viruses was discovered in 1951 by Hershey, Kamen, Kennedy, and Gest (306), who found that the infectivity of T2 and T4 bacteriophages is lost upon decay of radiophosphorus P^{32} atoms incorporated in the viral DNA. In these experiments, bacteria growing in a medium of very high specific P^{32} activity were infected with phage, so that the progeny phage particles produced in these cultures likewise contained a high level of the radioisotope among the phosphorus atoms of their DNA polynucleotides. When such populations of labeled phages were stored in the refrigerator and their survival assayed daily, it was observed that as the radioactive atoms decayed, a progressively decreasing fraction of the phage population retained the ability to reproduce itself. This loss of

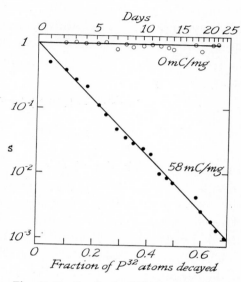

Fig. 11-7. Survival of P^{32}-labeled and non-labeled stocks of T2 bacteriophage stored at 4°C, as a function of the fraction of the P^{32} atoms that have decayed by the day of the plaque assay. The specific P^{32} activity of the labeled T2 stock is 58 millicuries/mg of total phosphorus. [Replotted from data of Hershey Kamen, Kennedy, and Gest (298).]

infective titer occurred even in highly dilute suspensions of labeled phage, indicating that the inactivation of any particular phage particle was not produced by the radiation emitted by external radioisotope contained in other phages or in the medium, but was produced by the disintegration of its own internal P^{32} atoms.

Figure 11-7 presents the survival of a stock of heavily P^{32}-labeled T2 phages, as well as that of a nonradioactive T2 control population, stored at 4°C and assayed periodically over several weeks. It is seen that while the nonradioactive phages are stable under the conditions of storage, the heavily P^{32}-labeled population is markedly unstable—the logarithm of the number of surviving individuals decreases linearly with the number of P^{32} atoms that have decayed up to the time of assay. The inactivation by P^{32} decay thus also follows the single-hit target theory kinetics of Equation (*11-1*), except that in P^{32} decay the radiation dose term qt refers to the total number of P^{32} atoms decayed per virus by the time of assay and the radiosensitivity term ϕQY to the fraction of such decays which are lethal to the virus. Equation (*11-1*) can be rewritten in terms of parameters more suitable for inactivation by radioactive decay, namely

$$\log s = -1.48 \times 10^{-6}\alpha A_0 Z(1 - e^{-\delta t}), \qquad (11\text{-}2)$$

where α is the efficiency of killing or the probability of generating a lethal hit per P^{32} disintegration, A_0 the specific radioactivity of the medium in which the phages were grown, Z the total number of phosphorus atoms per phage particle, δ the fractional decay of P^{32} per day, and t the number of days that decay has been allowed to proceed. This equation correctly states that a plot of $\log s$ against $(1 - e^{-\delta t})$, the fraction of P^{32} atoms decayed by the tth day, is a straight line.

The slope of the survival curve of P^{32}-labeled phages is thus a function of the parameters A_0, Z, and α. The values of A_0 and Z can be determined directly by radiochemical analysis of the labeled phages; thus α, the efficiency of killing per P^{32} disintegration, can be estimated from the slope of the survival curve. Hershey et al. inferred from their data that this efficiency of killing is approximately 0.1, or that about one out of every ten P^{32} disintegrations kills the T2 or T4 particle in which it occurs. These studies were subsequently extended to a variety of other phage strains that differ from the T-even phages and from one another in size, chemical composition, and phosphorus content, and it was found that the efficiency of killing per P^{32} disintegration is in the neighborhood of 0.1 in all these strains (597). The efficiency of killing varies, however, with the temperature at with P^{32} decay is allowed to take place; α rises from a low of 0.04 at -196°C to a high of 0.3 at $+65$°C, the intermediate value of 0.1 pertaining only to the efficiency of killing at $+4$°C.

Mechanism of Lethal Action

Every P³² disintegration generates a "hard" β electron that leaves a trail of ions along its track. Hence it might be thought that the inactivation of P³²-labeled phages derives from the noxious effects of these

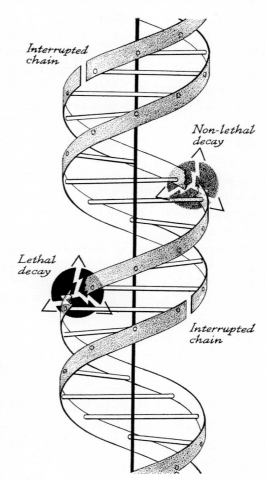

Fig. 11-8. Mechanism of lethal action of decay of incorporated P³² atoms in terms of the double helical structure of DNA. Nonlethal decays are thought to cause an interruption of only one of the two intertwined deoxyribose-phosphate chains; lethal decays are thought to cut both chains. [From Stent and Fuerst (597).]

ionizations attending the passage of the β electron on its way out of the virus particle. Reconstruction experiments, in which nonradioactive phages were bombarded by β electrons emitted by P³² atoms *outside* the virus particles showed, however, that the brief passage of β electrons of internal origin cannot be the principal cause of death of radioactive viruses. Instead, it can be concluded that a short-range consequence of the radioactive disintegration—the transmutation $P^{32} \longrightarrow S^{32}$ or the *recoil* sustained by the decaying atomic nucleus—must be responsible for loss of infectivity. This lethal effect of P^{32} decay can be understood in terms of the Watson-Crick structure of DNA, shown schematically in Fig. 11-8. Since the P^{32} atoms are located in the phosphate diester bonds responsible for the continuity of the polynucleotide chains, and since such diester bonds could hardly survive radioactive transmutation, it seems inevitable that every P^{32} disintegration breaks a polynucleotide chain. Breakage of a *single* polynucleotide chain need not necessarily lead to the disruption of the double helical DNA macromolecule, however, since the hydrogen bonds between purine and pyrimidine residues of opposite chains still hold the two complementary sister strands together. The majority of P^{32} decays are therefore *not* lethal, because the DNA molecule can preserve its structural and functional integrity despite occasional interruptions of the two complementary polynucleotide chains, and an event secondary to the disruption of the diester bonds must attend that minor fraction α of lethal disintegrations. That lethal event appears to be a *complete cut of the double helix*, which could ensue whenever the recoil of the disintegration nucleus in one polynucleotide chain has sufficient energy, and is suitably oriented, to break also the other chain. This explanation of inactivation by P^{32} decay thus identified the lethal "hits" as those that cut in two (or depolymerize) DNA, a view that has found confirmation from direct molecular weight determinations and from the biological behavior of the radioactive macromolecules at various stages of decay (599, 629).

Reactivation

The rate of decay inactivation of P^{32}-labeled T-even phages does not depend on the presence of either allele of the *u* locus: T2 and T4 phages carrying the same number of P^{32} atoms in their DNA die at the same rate. Furthermore, phages inactivated by P^{32} decay are not photoreactivable. Neither of these facts should be particularly surprising, since it could hardly have been expected that the bacterial enzyme that restores UV-modified pyrimidines to their normal state is also competent to solder together polynucleotide chains cut by lethal radioactive disintegrations. But genetic markers of P^{32} decay-inactivated phages *can* be crossreactivated by joint growth with active phages. Thus, lethal P^{32} disintegrations, like lethal UV lesions, do not destroy in a single blow the whole of the genetic structures of the virus particle (582, 592). Crossreactivation of genetic markers of decay-inactivated phages also appears to represent a process of rescue by genetic recombination of gene loci of the moribund genome, since the probability of jointly crossre- activating two genetic markers increases with the degree of their genetic linkage. In one aspect, however, rescue of genetic markers of P^{32} decay- inactivated phages differs from that of UV-inactivated phages: the individual burst sizes of crossreactivated markers of P^{32} decay-inactivated phages are nearly normal, indicating that if a genetic locus belonging to an inactivated genome is rescued at all, it is not at a serious disadvan- tage in the competition of intracellular growth with its allele introduced into the infected cell by the active parent. The much greater yield per cell of markers crossreactivated from P^{32} decay-inactivated phages over that from UV-inactivated phages can be readily understood in terms of the mechanism of action of the two lethal agents. Since UV- induced modifications of pyrimidine residues preserve the structural continuity of the irradiated DNA macromolecule, loci of a phage genome carrying lethal UV lesions all remain together and none of them is replicated in the mixedly infected cell until rescue by recombination has taken place. The molecular scissions caused by lethal P^{32} disintegrations, however, physically sever different genetic regions from each other and thus might allow the immediate vegetative replication of genetic loci residing in undamaged parts of the DNA, prior to their recombination into viable progeny structures.

X-Rays

The wavelength of radiations emitted by ordinary X-ray tubes is in the range of 0.1 to 10 Å, corresponding to quantum energies in the range of about 10^5 to 10^3 electron volts, or several orders of magnitude greater than the quantum energy of UV light. In contrast to the selective absorption of UV quanta, which depends on the particular chemical combinations of the atoms of the irradiated matter, the absorption of X-ray quanta is nonselective, in that it depends only on the atomic number of the absorbing atoms. Upon X-irradiation of a bacterial virus suspension, the incident quanta are absorbed mostly by the suspending medium. These primary absorptions result in the pro- duction of highly energetic secondary electrons that travel through the irradiated medium and cause further energetic events in their wake until the total energy of the absorbed quantum has been dissipated. About half the energy of each primary X-ray quantum absorbed is ultimately dissipated in *ionizations* (in which an electron is completely removed from its atom) and half in *excitations* (in which an electron is raised to a higher energy level while remaining in the orbit of its atom). The radiation dose delivered by an X-ray tube is, therefore, not expressed in terms of the total energy *incident* on the irradiated *surface*, but rather in terms of the energy absorbed by the irradiated *volume*. The energy unit employed for the measurement of X-ray dose is the *roentgen*, which corresponds to an absorption of 0.1083 ergs by 1 cm³ of air.

The lethal action of X-rays thus does not derive from the immediate absorption of the primary radiant quanta by the phage particles themselves but from subsequent interactions with secondary products generated by the absorbed radiation in the suspending medium. Two general types of X-ray inactivation, *indirect* and *direct*, can be experimentally distinguished. Indirect inactivation arises from lethal modifications of the vital structures of the phages by their reaction with toxic chemicals produced in the irradiated medium (5, 448, 657). Indirect inactivation can be largely suppressed by addition to the suspending medium of protective substances which react with the toxic agents as soon as they are formed and thus spare the phage particles. Direct inactivation arises from effects of X-irradiation which cannot be eliminated by addition of any protective substances to the medium. Direct inactivation is probably the consequence of ionizations or excitations produced within the physical domain of the virus by the passage of secondary electrons (441). Here we shall consider only experiments carried out under conditions in which only the *direct* inactivation has come into play.

Direct inactivation by X-rays also proceeds according to the single-hit kinetics of the target theory described by Equation (*11-1*), in that the logarithm of the surviving fraction *s* of the phage population decreases linearly with the X-ray dose. It follows that each hit is the ultimate consequence of the absorption of a single X-ray quantum, even though the inactivated virus particle may not actually have interacted directly with that quantum, but only with one or more of its secondary products. Equation (*11-1*) can be rewritten in terms of parameters more suitable for X-rays, namely

$$\log s = -(1/2.3)(V_s D), \qquad (11\text{-}3)$$

where D is the total X-ray dose in roentgens and V_s the "sensitive volume" in hits/roentgen. (V_s has the units of volume, since roentgen has the units of energy/volume.) The parameter V_s incorporates the compound probability that one of the aggregate of ionizations and excitations produced per roentgen occurs within the domain of a given virus particle and that this occurrence results in a lethal hit. The slope of an X-ray survival curve plotted according to Equation (11-3) is thus equal to V_s, or to the X-ray sensitivity of the irradiated phage strain.

As in the case of UV light and P^{32} decay, the site of the lethal action of the direct effects of X-rays appears to be the viral DNA. This may be inferred from the fact that immediately after the injection of the phage DNA into the interior of the infected cell, the X-ray sensitivity of the infective center is similar to that of the free phage (394, 675). Furthermore, as comparison of the X-ray sensitivities of various phage strains listed in Table 11-II shows, the more DNA a phage particle harbors,

TABLE 11-II

The X-Ray Sensitivity of Various Bacteriophages *

Phage	DNA Content (g/particle $\times 10^{16}$)	X-Ray Sensitivity (hits/roentgen $\times 10^5$)	Intrinsic X-Ray Sensitivity (hits/roentgen/g of DNA $\times 10^{-11}$)
T-even	2.3	2.5	1.1
T5	1.8	2.8	1.6
T1	0.7	1.1	1.6
T3	0.9	1.1	1.2
T7	0.6	1.0	1.7
λ	1.2	0.9	1.3
P22	0.7	0.9	0.8

* Modified from Stent (594).

the greater is its sensitive volume V_s—that is, the higher its radiosensitivity.

The manner in which X-rays destroy the activity of the viral DNA is not yet clearly understood. But it is known that X-rays and other ionizing radiations do break down DNA molecules into fragments of progressively smaller molecular weight, at doses comparable to those involved in the direct inactivation of bacteriophages. In contrast, UV light does not produce any breakage of DNA even at doses very much higher than those necessary for phage inactivation. Hence it is not unlikely that the lethal effect of X-irradiation, like that of P^{32} decay, derives at least in part from cutting viral DNA molecules. As is the case for P^{32} disintegration, furthermore, for every X-ray hit that has resulted in a complete scission of the DNA *double* helix, there have also been induced many more breakages of only one of the two polynucleotide chains (4, 703). These scissions of the polynucleotide chains induced by X-rays are no doubt due to the more highly energetic *ionizations* of DNA atoms caused by the passage of secondary electrons. But since about half of the radiant energy of X-rays is dissipated also in less energetic *excitations*, similar to those caused by absorption of UV quanta, it is to be expected that X-rays also cause another class of lethal modifications in the viral DNA that does not involve polynucleotide scissions.

Much of the very extensive body of experimental results pertaining to the properties of X-ray-inactivated bacterial viruses (399, 441, 656a) can be explained from the viewpoint that the lethal effects of X-rays are heterogeneous: some of the hits cause damage involving the cutting of the viral DNA polynucleotide chains, as P^{32} does, and some cause chemical modifications of purine, pyrimidine, or deoxyribose residues that leave intact the overall structural integrity of the DNA double helix, as UV does.

Radiosensitivity of the Vegetative Phage

In 1947, Luria and Latarjet (451) designed an experiment for following the radiosensitivity, not of the free, extracellular virus, but of the intracellular vegetative phage at various stages of the latent period. For this purpose, bacteria were infected with single particles of T2, and phage development was permitted to proceed for various times within the host cell before the infected complexes were exposed to various doses of UV light and assayed for the surviving fraction of irradiated complexes still able to produce at least one infective progeny particle. Luria and Latarjet anticipated that this experiment would provide a method for measuring the extent to which the infecting parental phage particle had already multiplied within the infected cell at any time, or for counting the number of vegetative phages present at any instant. A phage-infected bacterial cell already containing several vegetative phages should survive as an infective center so long as UV irradiation has left at least one vegetative phage intact, since the surviving phage should be able to initiate the synthesis of more replicas of itself. More precisely, when n duplicates of the parental phage have made their intracellular appearance, the fraction s_n of the infected bacteria still registering as infective centers after a UV dose qt—which, according to Equation $(11\text{-}1)$ would have left a fraction s of free, infective phages still active—should be

$$s_n = 1 - (1 - s)^n. \qquad (11\text{-}4)$$

A plot according to Equation $(11\text{-}4)$ of log s_n against the UV dose qt results in a family of "multiple-hit" survival curves whose final slopes for all values of n approach the rate of UV inactivation of the free, infective phage and whose *multiplicities* (the antilogs of the intercepts of the extrapolation of the asymptotes to zero UV dose) are equal to the number of existing duplicates n (Fig. 11-9).

The experimental results showed that the UV sensitivity of the T2-infected bacteria at the outset of intracellular growth is similar to that of the free, resting T2 phage. Contrary to expectation, however, the UV inactivation curves of the infected complexes in which phage development has been allowed to progress for various times do not follow the family of "multiple-hit" curves described by Equation $(11\text{-}4)$ but result rather in a family of straight lines of decreasing slopes; this indicates that the *intrinsic* UV *sensitivity* of the vegetative T2 phages becomes enormously reduced during the initial stages of the eclipse period. This may be seen in Fig. 11-9, where the result of a typical Luria-Latarjet experiment, carried out by use of an improved experimental design (49), is presented. This method, therefore, cannot be used for straightforward counting of the number of vegetative T2 phages present within infected cells, since some aspect of vegetative phage multiplication other than the appearance of a progressively greater number of intracellular units identical in radiosensitivity to the infecting T2 phage particle must primarily be responsible for the overall UV sensitivity pattern during the eclipse period.

An experiment similar in principle to Luria and Latarjet's was later carried out to study the sensitivity of T2-infected bacteria to inactivation

Fig. 11-9. Radiosensitivity of the vegetative phage. **A.** Theoretical survival curves for infected bacteria containing n replicas of the infecting phage, plotted according to Equation (11-4). **B.** Survival curves of T2-infected bacteria irradiated with UV at different times during the latent period. Each curve is marked with the time in minutes after onset of intracellular phage growth at which the sample was removed from the culture and irradiated. Average multiplicity of infection: 2×10^{-3} phages/cell. [From Benzer (49).] **C.** Survival as infective centers: of a T2 phage stock labeled with P^{32} at the specific activity of 260 millicuries/mg of phosphorus; of equally P^{32}-labeled infected bacteria in which this phage stock has been allowed to grow for the number of minutes indicated on each curve before being frozen and stored in liquid nitrogen; and of the T2 progeny phage finally issuing from the infected cells. Multiplicity of infection: 1 phage/cell. [From Stent (593).]

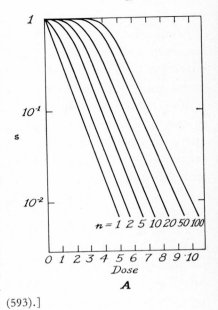

A

by decay of incorporated P^{32} atoms at various stages of intracellular phage development (593). Heavily P^{32}-labeled *E. coli* bacteria growing in heavily P^{32}-labeled medium were infected with equally heavily P^{32}-labeled T2 phages, and phage development was allowed to proceed for various times before the infected complexes were frozen and stored at $-196°C$ to allow radioactive decay to proceed at well-defined stages of the eclipse period. From time to time, samples of the various infective centers were thawed and assayed for survival of their ability to generate at least one infective progeny particle. Here it was anticipated that a multiple-hit survival pattern like that described by Equation *(11-4)* would surely be found, since the decay of the incorporated P^{32} atoms ought to inactivate the radioactive parental DNA and all of its radioactive replicas formed prior to radioactive decay—that is, destroy the genetic substance and self-duplicating matter of the phage. The result of this experiment is also presented in Fig. 11-9, where it can be seen that, once more contrary to expectation, a family of curves essentially similar to that of the UV resistance is obtained: the T2-infected bacteria become highly refractory to inactivation by radioactive decay at later

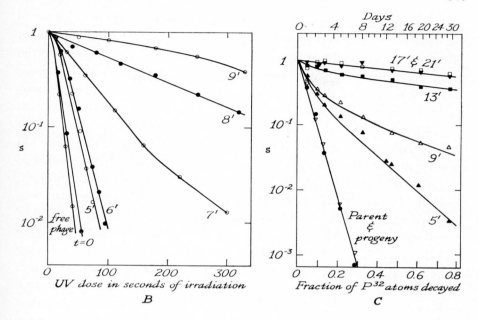

B

C

stages of the eclipse period.

How can one explain the development of this great reduction in intrinsic UV- and P^{32}-decay sensitivity of the vegetative bacteriophage at the outset of its intracellular development? It is conceivable that a mechanism akin to *multiplicity reactivation* becomes possible once replicas of the parental DNA have made their appearance; as long as UV irradiation or P^{32} decay has not destroyed exact allelic loci in already duplicated units, some process of genetic exchange or cooperation could always restore one working copy of the entire DNA and thus lead to the production of infective progeny. The opportunity for such reactivation would lead to inactivation kinetics rather different from those described by Equation (*11-4*). To be sure, a family of downward concave inactivation curves should still be anticipated as more and more DNA replicas make their appearance in the course of the eclipse period, but the downward bend of these curves might become so gradual that at the inactivation doses employed in the experiments shown in Fig. 11-9 straight-line survival curves would be simulated. It is, however, also conceivable that multiplicity reactivation is *not* the explanation of this phenomenon, particularly since a considerable reduction in radiosensitivity appears to *precede* the onset of replication of the viral DNA (511). A number of alternative theories have, therefore, been proposed to account for the great difference in intrinsic radiosensitivity of infective and vegetative phage, but none of these theories has so far found very much experimental support (397, 511, 593, 594, 598, 620).

Even though the Luria-Latarjet experiment failed to achieve the purpose for which it was invented—and instead posed a puzzle on whose solution some phage workers seem to have expended a good deal of vain effort—it nevertheless turned out to be an excellent empirical tool for following the progress of intracellular phage growth. For instance, this method allows one to determine whether multiplication of T2 phage can get underway in the presence of some particular metabolic inhibitor: one infects a bacterial culture in the presence of the inhibitor to be tested, incubates the infected culture for various times, and then irradiates the infective centers. The radiosensitivity of the infective centers becomes reduced during the incubation if and only if phage development can occur in the presence of the inhibitor. It was shown in just this way that synthesis of the "early protein" discussed in Chapter 7 is necessary for onset of intracellular phage growth, since bacteria infected with T2 phage in the presence of the chloramphenicol develop very little reduction in their intrinsic sensitivity to UV or P^{32} decay; the low radiosensitivity of the vegetative phage is attained only after protein synthesis has been allowed to resume upon removal of the antibiotic from the infected culture (511, 637). This method also allows a demonstration that *r*II mutants of T-even phages infecting *E. coli*, strain K (on which they are unable to give rise to infective progeny), do manage to complete at least the early stages of intracellular virus growth, since these mutants do attain the low intrinsic radiosensitivity characteristic of the vegetative phage (236). (It is possible to measure the radiosensitivity of *r*II mutants in K bacteria by adding divalent ions to the agar of the assay plate. These ions permit "transmission" of the mutants on the differential host.) This result shows that the "block" that prevents *r*II mutants from producing infective progeny in K bacteria must occur at a late stage in the intracellular reproductive process. Finally, the Luria-Latarjet method has even been adapted successfully for the study of the early events in the intracellular growth of plant and animal viruses (531, 568, 569).

Further Reading

Adams, M. H., *Bacteriophages* (2). Chapter VI and pp. 357–363 of Chapter XVIII provide many other details on the radiobiology of phage.

Luria, S. E. and Dulbecco, R., "Genetic recombinations leading to production of active bacteriophage from ultraviolet inactivated bacteriophage particles" (447). A detailed analysis of multiplicity reactivation.

Dulbecco, R., "Experiments on photoreactivation of bacteriophages inactivated with ultraviolet irradiation" (190).

Stent, G. S. and Fuerst, C. R., "Inactivation of bacteriophages by decay of incorporated radioactive phosphorus" (598).

Benzer, S., "Resistance to ultraviolet light as an index to the reproduction of bacteriophage" (49). A restudy of the Luria-Latarjet experiment.

Luria, S. E., "Radiation and viruses" (441); Stahl, F. W., "Radiobiology of bacteriophage" (583). Two excellent, and in many ways complementary, reviews on phage radiobiology.

Stent, G. S. and Fuerst, C. R., "Genetic and physiological effects of the decay of incorporated radioactive phosphorus in bacterial viruses and bacteria" (599). A specialized review.

CHAPTER 12

Lysogeny

Lysogenic Bacteria—The Prophage—Induction—Temperance and Virulence—Curing—Immunity—Nature of the Prophage—Zygotic Induction and the Repressor—Specificity of Prophage Location—Genetic Control of Lysogenization—Chromosomal Attachment of Prophage—Defective Prophages—Conversion—Episomes

Lysogenic Bacteria

So far, bacteriophages have been regarded as bacteriocidal agents that invade bacteria, take over and monopolize the synthetic capacities of the host for their own ends, and multiply to yield an issue of several hundred progeny viruses within each infected cell; intracellular growth of the virus parasite kills the infected bacterium, since the host cell is lysed to allow escape of the nascent phage progeny into the world outside. This view demands that survival of bacteriophages is wholly dependent on the concomitant death of sensitive host bacteria. But such a morbid bite-the-hand-that-feeds existence of bacteriophages is by no means their only way of life, inasmuch as bacteriophages can also be *perpetuated as part of the bacterial hereditary apparatus* during normal growth of the host cell. This "symbiotic" relation between bacteria and their viruses will now be our concern.

That in nature bacteriophages should be living in association with bacteria is no more surprising than any other natural togetherness of parasite and host; hence the discovery in 1921 by Bordet and Ciuca (84) and by Gildemeister (243) that strains of *E. coli* isolated from nature often contain bacteriophages or are **lysogenic** (capable of producing bacterial lysis), appeared perfectly reasonable. Though Gildemeister (245) tried to prove that his strain of *E. coli* maintained its "lysogenic power" in the absence of any free phage, d'Hérelle declared that lysogenic bacterial strains are contaminated with phage and can readily be made rid of their virus by appropriate purification procedures. But Bail (34) and Bordet (79) soon demonstrated that lysogeny cannot be explained all that easily, since they found that after repeated serial isolation of single colonies of lysogenic *E. coli* strains each successive bacterial clone was still lysogenic. Bail concluded therefore that phage production is an attribute, not of the culture as a whole, but of every bacterium of the lysogenic strain. At the same time, Bordet's collaborator McKinley (467) showed that these lysogenic strains preserve their capacity to produce phage when cultivated in the presence of an antiphage serum that should neutralize the infectivity of any and all contaminating phage particles. Hence, lysogenic bacteria appeared to maintain their capacity for phage production in the absence of any free, extracellular virus particles. These facts led Bordet (79) to propose that "the faculty to reproduce bacteriophage is inscribed into the very hereditary weft of the microbe." This statement sounds much more apt today than the meaning that Bordet probably intended by it at the time, since he considered bacterial heredity to be merely the maintenance through successive cell divisions of an ensemble of physiological processes and bacteriophagy only a pathological exaggeration of these normal physiological functions. The first to attack the problem of how this capacity to produce phage is actually propagated *within* lysogenic bacteria were Burnet and McKie (119), who in 1929 induced lysis of a lysogenic culture of *Salmonella enteritidis* with an extrinsic phage unrelated to the "carried" phage; in this way they found that only 0.1% of the lysogenic bacteria liberated any intracellular phage. Since the majority of the lysogenic cells were thus shown to contain *no* infective virus, Burnet and McKie proposed that lysogenic bacteria perpetuate the power to produce infectious phage as a noninfective *Anlage* of the phage that multiplies in step with the cell. Production of infectious phage, according to Burnet and McKie, ensues only upon "activation" of the *Anlage*.

In 1931, *Escherichia* and *Salmonella* temporarily gave way to *Bacillus megaterium* as main objects for the study of lysogeny, when den Dooren de Jong (186) discovered that the sporogenic strain 899 of *B. megaterium* is lysogenic and carries a phage to which a nonsporogenic, nonlysogenic derivative of strain 899, the **mutilat** strain, is sensitive. Den Dooren de Jong found that spores of strain 899 can be heated to 100°C without loss of their capacity to give rise to lysogenic bacterial clones upon subsequent germination. He concluded, therefore, that the maintenance of lysogeny in the spores cannot be due to the presence of phage, which ought to have been killed by the heat treatment. This argument was not entirely convincing, however, since the heat resistance of the spores is due in large part to their dehydrated state; and hence the putative intrasporal phage could also be more heat-resistant than the homologous free phage if the intrasporal phage were as dehydrated as the spore itself. But a few years later, the elder Wollmans (688) proved the absence of phage from most of the cells of the lysogenic strain 899, by demonstrating that lysozyme-induced lysis of the gram-positive *B. megaterium* liberates no infective phage. The Wollmans then proposed that in the life cycle of the phage there occurs an alternation between infective and noninfective phases, that the noninfective phase is perpetuated in lysogenic bacteria as part of the hereditary structures of the cell, and that infective viruses are produced by, or from, the noninfective phase (689).

How are the infective virus particles liberated from the lysogenic cells in which they are produced? Northrop (496) addressed himself to this question in 1938 by studying the production of phage in growing cultures of the lysogenic *B. megaterium*. Northrop found that the concentration of infective phage in the culture increases at the same logarithmic rate as the number of bacteria themselves and as the concentration of the enzyme gelatinase secreted into the culture medium by the growing cells. He inferred from these observations that the phage, like the enzyme, is *secreted* by growing lysogenic bacteria, rather than liberated by the lysis of dying cells. This inference was not valid, of course; Northrop's experiment would have given precisely the same result whether phages are liberated by secretion or by lysis, since, as Burnet and McKie (119) had already shown, only a minority of the cells of the culture are, in any case, concerned with the production of phage at any moment.

When, with the rise of Delbrück's school of phage workers in the 1940's, the United States became the "Holy Land of Bacteriophage" (453), lysogeny fell into disrepute and was no longer considered worthy of the attention of the American avant-garde. Since none of the T strains of coli phage on which efforts were now concentrated manifest the lysogenic state and since the entire previous literature on lysogeny was

either ignored or viewed with some suspicion, d'Hérelle's attitude came
to prevail that the sort of intracellular "symbiosis" between phage and
bacterium envisaged by Bordet, Bail, Burnet, and the Wollmans
probably does not exist. Instead, it was proposed that any long-term
association between phage and host could be explained simply as
"pseudolysogeny." Pseudolysogenic bacteria can adsorb the phage they
carry but are resistant to infection. Every cell in a culture of such bacteria
was thought to carry extracellular free phage on its surface, and the
multiplication of the phage during growth of the culture could be
provided for by infection of occasional phage-sensitive bacterial variants
that appear in the pseudolysogenic population (164). Since d'Hérelle
had already demonstrated the occurrence of pseudolysogenic "carrier"
strains and since the mistaken assertion that lysogenic bacteria secrete
their phage without cellular lysis was taken as the conceptual *sine qua non*
of "true" lysogeny, lysogeny had been temporarily defined out of
existence.

The Prophage

After World War II, André Lwoff resumed the work on the lysogenic
B. megaterium begun by his late colleagues, the elder Wollmans, who had
been arrested at the Pasteur Institute in 1943 and disappeared in one of
the Nazi extermination camps. Lwoff thought that how the phage is
liberated by lysogenic bacteria is of little importance for the definition
of lysogeny, and insisted that the really significant aspect of lysogeny,
and the one most urgently in need of indubitable proof, was the maintenance of the capacity to produce phage in the absence of extracellular
virus. This did not mean, however, that the mode of liberation of the
phage was not also worthy of some attention. Lwoff, therefore, posed
himself these questions (455):

1. Can the faculty for producing bacteriophages really be perpetuated without intervention of exogenous bacteriophages?
2. How do lysogenic bacteria liberate the bacteriophages which they produce?
3. If the production of bacteriophages appertains to only a certain proportion of the
   bacteria, then what factors induce the production of bacteriophages in a population
   of potentially lysogenic bacteria?

To Lwoff it seemed "evident a priori" that the study of mass cultures
of lysogenic bacteria, as it had been previously practiced, could furnish

only partial and not definitive answers to these questions and that only observations carried out on *individual* bacteria, or on microcultures containing a small number of individuals, could lead to unambiguous conclusions. Lwoff and Gutmann (455), therefore, proceeded to cultivate an individual cell of *B. megaterium* in a microdrop and watched its division under the microscope. Immediately after the division, one of the two daughter cells was withdrawn from the microdrop by means of a micromanipulator and plated on agar to determine whether a colony of lysogenic descendant bacteria would be produced. As soon as the cell that remained in the culture fluid had once more divided, one of the two new daughter cells was withdrawn and plated on agar, and the process of withdrawal and plating of one of the cells generated by each division was repeated for a total of 19 divisions. In the same experiment, samples of the culture medium were also withdrawn from the microdrop at various times and assayed on the nonlysogenic, phage-sensitive *mutilat* strain for the presence of any free phage. The result of this experiment was that every colony derived from the cells in the microdrop was lysogenic, and none of the samples of the culture fluid contained any infective phage. Lysogeny was thus demonstrated to persist for at least 19 successive divisions *in the absence of any free phage*. The maintenance of lysogeny could not have been due to the presence of reversibly adsorbed phage particles, since the *B. megaterium* cell inoculated into the microdrop at the outset of this experiment would have had to hold the impossibly large number of 2^{19} phage particles on its surface, if after 19 divisions each daughter cell was still to be endowed with one of these original virus particles. The total absence of any infective phage in the culture fluid of this experiment showed, moreover, that lysogenic bacteria do not continuously secrete phage during their growth.

In other, analogous microscopic studies of the division of individual bacteria, Lwoff and Gutmann occasionally observed what appeared to be the spontaneous lysis of the cell in the microdrop. Whenever the culture fluid was assayed for the presence of free phage after such an event, some hundred phages were found to be present in the drop. It could thus be inferred with some confidence that *lysogenic bacteria liberate their phage by lysis*, each lysing cell yielding a burst of many virus particles. These findings allowed Lwoff to describe lysogeny in the terms in which the phenomenon is now understood: each bacterium of a lysogenic strain harbors and maintains a noninfective structure, the **prophage,** which endows the cell with the ability to give rise to infective phage without intervention of exogenous phage particles. In a small fraction of a population of growing lysogenic bacteria the prophage becomes *induced* to produce a crop of infective phage, prophage induction leading to death and ultimate lysis of the cell.

Induction

Having thus disposed of the first two of the three questions that Lwoff had set for himself, he and his pupils Siminovitch and Kjeldgaard (458, 459) turned their attention to the third. They had reason to believe that induction of the prophage is under control of factors external to the lysogenic cell and began, therefore, a search for agents or conditions that would raise the small fraction of lysogenic bacteria which were producing phage spontaneously. After trying without avail a great variety of chemical and physical treatments, they finally found that irradiation of a growing culture of *B. megaterium* with small doses of ultraviolet light induces phage production in the quasi-totality of the population of lysogenic cells. The result of an analogous experiment carried out with a lysogenic strain of *E. coli* is presented in Fig. 12-1. It can be seen that for the first 70 minutes after UV irradiation, the lysogenic bacteria grow in size, as indicated by the continued increase in turbidity of the culture, and that lysis of nearly all the bacteria suddenly ensues after that time, as indicated by a

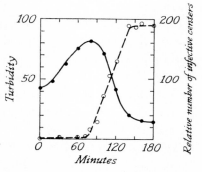

Fig. 12-1. Induction of the prophage of lysogenic *E. coli*, strain K12(λ), by UV light. A culture of exponentially growing bacteria is exposed to an optimal dose of UV that induces vegetative phage development in more than 90% of the population. The irradiated suspension is then incubated in broth. The turbidity in arbitrary units (plotted here as filled circles) and the titer of infective centers, or ratio of the number of plaque-forming units to the number of irradiated bacteria (plotted here as open circles), of the culture are determined after the number of minutes shown on the abscissa have elapsed since its irradiation. [From Jacob and Fuerst (328a).]

rapid loss of turbidity, or clearing, of the culture. It can be seen, furthermore, that plaque assays made throughout this period show that there are very few free, infective virus particles in the culture until the onset of bacterial lysis. Thereafter the number of free phages increases rapidly, until a final infectivity plateau has been attained that represents an average yield of nearly 200 phages per lysogenic cell in the irradiated culture. There is little doubt, therefore, that the phages are liberated by lysis of the induced lysogenic cells. It thus appeared not only that the lysogenic bacterium passes on the faculty for producing phage to all of its descendants, a few of whom might at some future time lyse and liberate infective virus particles, but also that *every* bacterium of the culture can be induced at will to commence at once production of infective phage without the intervention of any exogenous, free virus particles. Later experiments showed that induction of the prophage can be effected also by treatment of the lysogenic bacteria with hydrogen peroxide (456), X-rays (396), or nitrogen mustard (322). All of these inducing agents share the property of being mutagens and carcinogens, a coincidence that was at first believed to have some theoretical significance, but that probably reflects only a common propensity for producing toxic modifications in polynucleotides.

The events that ensue in the lysogenic cell after induction of its prophage are entirely analogous to those of the vegetative phase of phage development following *infection* of a sensitive bacterium with an exogenous free phage particle. There first occurs an eclipse during which no infective phage can be detected in the cell but during which the substance of the progeny, both their genetic DNA as well as their proteinaceous structural components, is synthesized; later, about halfway through the latent period, these various phage precursors begin to combine to constitute mature, infective progeny viruses. These progeny, which can also be released prematurely by artificial lysis of the cells, appear in the culture medium after spontaneous lysis at the end of a latent period (332).

Temperance and Virulence

Both Bail (34) and Bordet (79) had found that a fraction of non-lysogenic bacteria infected with phage carried by a lysogenic strain do not lyse, but instead survive the infection to give rise to clones of lysogenic bacteria that henceforth carry the infecting phage as prophage. "Artificial" lysogenic strains were thus created, which, according to

Lwoff (453), represented "the first example of a specific hereditary property being conferred to an organism by a specific extrinsic particle." Infection of a nonlysogenic bacterium with a phage may, therefore, result in two very different *responses*.

1. The *lytic response*, in the course of which the infecting phage enters the vegetative phase, multiplies, forms mature progeny virus particles, and ultimately lyses the host cell at the end of the latent period. This is, of course, the sequence of events which was the subject of the preceding Chapters 4, 5, 6, and 7.

2. The *lysogenic response*, in the course of which the infecting phage does not multiply and is, instead, "reduced" to the prophage state, allowing the host cell to survive as a lysogenic bacterium.

All bacterial viruses worthy of the name bacteriophage (excluding of course the few exceptions to be considered later that "prove the rule") are capable of giving the first of these responses, since a phage that *never* lyses any bacteria is not a "devourer of bacteria," and hence rather difficult to observe. Only **temperate** phages, however, are capable of giving the lysogenic response, in contradistinction to the so-called **virulent** phages which do not give the lysogenic response and are never found in lysogenic bacteria in prophage guise (330). This classification, though presently still in general use, is not entirely satisfactory; whereas one can be sure that a phage strain is "temperate" once a bacterium carrying its prophage has been found, it is more difficult to be certain that a phage strain is "virulent," since failure to observe its lysogenic response might indicate only that it has not been presented to a suitable strain of bacteria under a suitable set of experimental conditions. For the chance that infection with a temperate phage actually leads to the lysogenic rather than the lytic response depends on various physiological and genetic factors appertaining to both phage and host cell (71, 87, 426). The group of virulent phages, furthermore, is a motley ensemble, since phages may fail to give the lysogenic response for fundamentally very different reasons. For instance, the T-even coliphages seem to be a most rabid kind of virulent phage which, since they destroy the genetic and biosynthetic capacity of their host at the outset of their intracellular development, are certain to kill the cell and nip in the bud any prospective clone of lysogenic bacteria carrying their prophage. But other kinds of virulent phages are only one-step mutants of temperate phages that, were it not for some slight physiologico-genetic aberration, could give the lysogenic response. The "virulence" of these mutants seems to have little in common with that of the T-even phages.

A simple, though not completely reliable, distinction between temperate and virulent phages can be made on the basis of their plaque

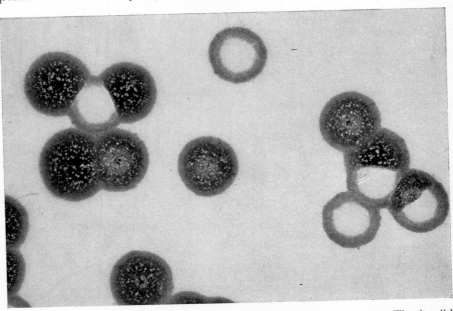

Fig. 12-2.   Plaques formed by bacteriophage λ and two of its mutants. The λ wild type produces turbid plaques; one of the clear-plaque mutants allows no bacterial growth in the center of its plaque, while the other clear-plaque mutant does. [From Weigle (673).]

morphology: on plates seeded with sensitive bacteria temperate phages usually produce plaques with turbid centers in which bacteria have grown that were lysogenized rather than lysed by the phage clone of the plaque. In fact, one of the easiest ways of obtaining an artificial lysogenic strain carrying some particular prophage is to isolate bacteria from the center of a plaque formed by that phage on a nonlysogenic indicator strain. Virulent phages, in contrast, usually produce *clear* plaques under the same conditions, since the only growth that can occur within the domain of a virulent phage plaque is that of the rare phage-resistant bacterial mutants sported by the sensitive indicator strain (Fig. 12-2).

Curing

Lysogeny is usually a very stable property of a bacterial strain, as stable as any other of its hereditary characters. Thus in most populations of lysogenic cells only a very small percentage of individuals appear to have lost their prophage—that is, have been *cured* of their lysogeny. Nevertheless, nonlysogenic derivatives of erstwhile lysogenic bacteria *can* be isolated; one of the first documented examples of curing is den Dooren de Jong's (186) previously mentioned isolation of the nonlysogenic *mutilat* variant of *B. megaterium*. In fact, there occurs an accumulation of such spontaneously cured, nonlysogenic variants of *B. megaterium* upon repeated passage of the culture in a calcium-free synthetic medium (135). It is difficult to make a precise determination of the frequency of curing in a growing culture of lysogenic bacteria, but Bertani (69) has estimated that in the case of a lysogenic strain of *E. coli* the spontaneous rate of prophage loss is only of the order of 10^{-5} cured cells per cell generation. It is relatively easy to isolate cured derivatives of lysogenic strains by screening the colonies formed by surviving cells of heavily UV-irradiated lysogenic cultures; a high proportion of such colonies do not contain any phage, and represent clones of nonlysogenic, cured cells (401).

Immunity

Ever since their discovery, it has been known that lysogenic bacteria are **immune** to infection by phage particles of the same type as their prophage. Such immunity is almost a logical necessity for the very existence of lysogeny, since any culture of lysogenic bacteria *sensitive* to infection and lysis by the temperate phage it carries would soon be destroyed by a chain reaction of successive viral growth cycles initiated by the first infective phage particle that appeared in the culture upon spontaneous prophage induction of one of the lysogenic cells. Lysogenic immunity does not prevent the fixation of the temperate virus particles to the bacterial surface, since lysogenic strains generally adsorb their homologous phages. *Immunity* is, therefore, to be distinguished from phage *resistance* which, as already discussed in connection with the life cycle of virulent phages in earlier chapters, bacteria can acquire through hereditary modifications of their cell envelope that block phage adsorption.

What happens when a temperate phage infects an immune bacterial cell? The bacterium continues to grow and divide as though no infection had occurred, while the genetic material of the infecting phage, though injected into the cell, does not multiply; the phage genome remains singular and is passed on to one of the two daughter cells in successive bacterial divisions (68, 325). Immunity thus prevents the infecting temperate phage from entering the vegetative state. Immunity, furthermore, is highly specific and extends only to infecting phages of a type identical, or very closely related, to that carried as prophage; a cell lysogenic for one phage strain is usually sensitive to infection by all other phage strains to which the corresponding nonlysogenic bacterium is sensitive. It is the prophage itself that must be responsible for the specific immunity of the lysogenic cell, because after loss of the prophage the nonlysogenic, cured derivative is fully sensitive to the temperate phage type formerly carried.

We shall defer the attempt to gain a deeper understanding of these

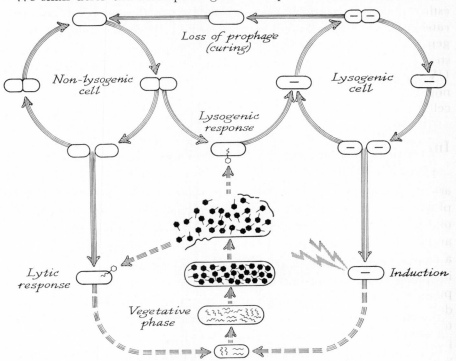

Fig. 12-3.   General view of lysogeny. [From Lwoff (453).]

facts until the latter part of this chapter, and now merely summarize them in Fig. 12-3, where Lwoff's diagrammatic representation, the Device of Lysogeny, has been reproduced.

Nature of the Prophage

What kind of organelle is the prophage that perpetuates in lysogenic bacteria the faculty to produce phage in the absence of extrinsic phage?

Not only does it not possess the infectivity of the intact, free phage, but it does not even carry any of the antigenic proteins of the mature virus particle, since noninduced lysogenic *B. megaterium* cells do not contain any materials that can react specifically with the antibodies of an antiserum directed against the homologous infective temperate phages carried by the strain (479). But inasmuch as the prophage must contain the genome of the virus, it seems most probable that the prophage, like the noninfective vegetative phage of the lytic response, comprises the phage DNA. This supposition has found

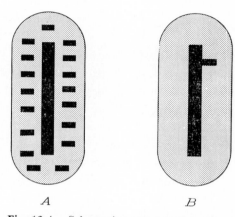

A   *B*

Fig. 12-4. Schematic representation of two alternative hypotheses on the relation of the prophage to the lysogenic bacterial cell. **A.** The prophage is constituted of many cytoplasmic particles. **B** The prophage is incorporated into the bacterial chromosome. [From Jacob (325).]

support from the observation that the sensitivity of the prophage to inactivation by decay of incorporated P^{32} atoms is the same as that of the homologous free phage, suggesting that both represent DNA "targets" of equal size (600).

In considering the relation of the prophage to the bacterial cell, two general alternative hypotheses can be entertained (Fig. 12-4).

1. The prophage is a "cytoplasmic" bacterial particle whose rate of reproduction is adjusted to that of the host cell. It is distributed *at random* to the two daughter cells at each bacterial division. Since in lysogenic cultures the frequency of cells that have been spontaneously "cured" of their lysogenicity, or lost their prophage, is very low, it

would then be necessary that the average lysogenic bacterium carry not just one, but *many* prophage particles. For if the average number of randomly distributed prophages per cell just prior to the moment of division is $2m$, it would follow from the Poisson distribution that the fraction of daughter cells receiving by chance no prophage at all is

$$p_0 = e^{-m}. \tag{12-1}$$

Since, according to Bertani's estimate, only 10^{-5} lysogenic bacteria per division experience spontaneous curing, one can reckon from Equation (*12-1*) that prior to its division the average lysogenic bacterium would have to contain more than 20 prophage particles.

2. The prophage is directly associated and replicates in synchrony with some bacterial structure that is distributed *regularly* rather than randomly over both daughter cells at the time of division. In that case the rarity of spontaneous curing would be compatible with a *small* number of prophages per lysogenic cell, since the regularity of the distribution mechanism would automatically assure that each daughter cell gets its prophage. The structure which most readily fulfills the requirement of regular distribution over daughter cells at division is, of course, the bacterial chromosome. If the chromosome were the site of the prophage, a few prophages per cell would suffice to assure the permanence of the lysogenic character.

These alternatives were first adumbrated around 1950, when "cytoplasmic inheritance" happened to be a fashionable topic that offered promise of new insights into some genetic phenomena hard to explain solely in "classical," nuclear terms. The first of these two hypotheses was, therefore, favored initially in the anticipation that the prophage would prove to be another member of the growing ranks of cytoplasmic particles endowed with genetic continuity. But as in the succeeding years most examples of "cytoplasmic inheritance" just faded away or turned out to be something else after all, so also the prophage failed to support the doctrine of the cytoplasm as a genetic continuum.

It soon appeared from the results of experiments in which lysogenic bacteria were *superinfected with mutants* of the temperate phage carried as prophage that, contrary to the requirements of randomly distributed "cytoplasmic" particles, there are probably only a very few prophages per lysogenic cell. First, though the lysogenic cell is in principle immune to the superinfecting homologous phage, the superinfecting phage *can* develop vegetatively together with the carried phage once the prophage of the superinfected cell has become induced. In such a cell, joint growth of exogenous and endogenous phage produces an equal yield of super-infecting and carried genotypes if the multiplicity of infection of exog-enous phage is about equal to the number of nuclei in the bacterium. This suggests that there is only about one prophage per nucleus (66, 332). Second, even though bacteria can be readily lysogenized successively with several *unrelated* temperate phages, it is much more difficult to es-tablish a clone of lysogenic cells that carry the prophages of two different genotypes of the *same* strain of temperate phage. The superinfecting phage is either excluded altogether from becoming prophage, or, if it does succeed in being reduced to prophage, the superinfecting phage usually displaces or substitutes for the previously established prophage (67). There appears, therefore, to exist an *incompatibility* between homo-logous prophages, as though a given type of prophage "saturates" a very limited number of bacterial sites. The cytoplasmic particle hypothesis was thus already rendered rather unlikely, although the results of these superinfection experiments did not bring any compelling proof of the chromosomal situation of the prophage.

It became possible to study the relation of prophage and bacterial chromosome in a much more unambiguous manner after Esther Lederberg (401) found in 1951 that *E. coli*, strain K12, the very strain in which J. Lederberg and E. L. Tatum (404) had previously discovered conjugation and genetic recombination, is, in fact, lysogenic and carries a temperate phage, which she called λ (Fig. 12-5). The lysogeny of K12 became manifest after a number of its nonlysogenic derivatives had been accidentally isolated. On these nonlysogenic derivatives, samples of the culture fluid of the parent K12 strain produce plaques of phage λ. According to the convention now in use (67), under which lysogenic bacteria are designated by the name of the bacterial strain followed in parentheses by the symbols representing the phage strain carried as pro-phage, the Lederbergs' lysogenic strain of *E. coli* was henceforth referred to as K12(λ). This is the strain with which we have already become familiar under the name K in preceding chapters, in connection with the genetics of the *r*II locus of the T-even phages.

The discovery of lysogenic (λ⁺) and nonlysogenic (λ⁻) lines in the sexually fertile strain of *E. coli* thus opened the way for bacterial crosses

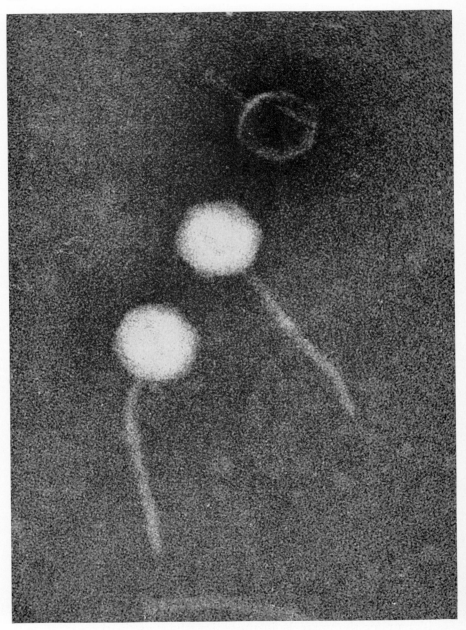

Fig. 12-5.   Portrait of bacteriophage λ. [Unpublished electron micrograph provided by
E. Kellenberger, University of Geneva.]

in which the distribution of the lysogenic character among recombinant bacteria produced could be followed. The first such crosses (219, 402, 690) were carried out at a time when the nature of the bacterial conjugation process was still incompletely understood and when the frequency of bacterial recombinants was only of the order of 10^{-6} per cell. Nevertheless, these first experiments already showed that, in one respect, at least, the λ prophage does appear to behave as a chromosomal hereditary determinant, in that the prophage *segregates* among the recombinants, some of the hybrid genotypes being lysogenic and others nonlysogenic. The pattern of this segregation further showed that λ lysogeny is *linked* to the Gal locus responsible for the fermentation of galactose: most of the recombinant bacteria had derived their Gal and λ characters from the same parental strain. However, in contrast to the behavior expected from a chromosomal determinant, the λ prophage showed an *asymmetrical* distribution in reciprocal crosses between lysogenic and nonlysogenic bacteria (25, 690): whereas the nonlysogenic ($λ^-$) character of an F^+ donor parent appeared in the recombinants of crosses to a lysogenic ($λ^+$)F^- recipient, the lysogenic ($λ^+$) character of an F^+ donor parent was almost never found among recombinants of crosses to nonlysogenic ($λ^-$)F^- recipients.

Once "high-frequency" (Hfr) fertility mutants of F^+ donor lines of K12 had been isolated (129, 269)—and it had been recognized by Wollman and Jacob (693, 695) that an Hfr bacterium transfers its chromosome in an oriented manner to the conjugal F^- cell, beginning with a definite point of *origin*—genetic loci of the Hfr chromosome could be mapped by measuring their times of entry into the zygote. In this way, it was shown by crossing a nonlysogenic Hfr ($λ^-$) to a lysogenic F^- ($λ^+$) that the $λ^-$ character enters the zygote after the Gal locus and before the Try locus, and segregates among the recombinants like any other marker (337, 691). Furthermore, a cross in which both Hfr and F^- were lysogenic but carried different genetically marked λ prophages showed that the Hfr prophage genotype enters the zygote and segregates among the recombinants exactly as the $λ^-$ character of the preceding cross. It could be concluded from these results that the prophage occupies a site on the *E. coli* chromosome between Gal and Try loci, as shown on the circular genetic map of *E. coli* of Fig. 12-6, and that the characters ($λ^+$) and ($λ^-$) are to be considered as alternative states of the same chromosomal locus.

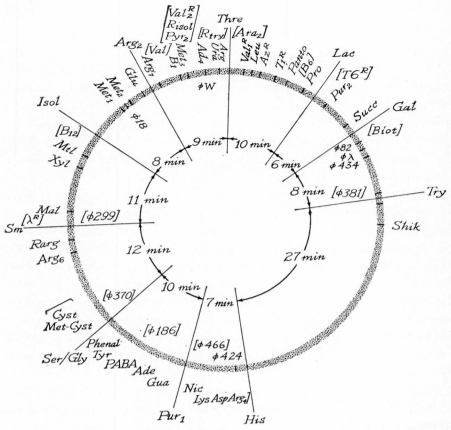

Fig. 12-6. Schematic representation of the genetic map of *E. coli*, strain K12. The outer circle represents the order of the characters (not their absolute distances). The arrows represent the time intervals of penetration between pairs of markers corresponding to the radial lines.

Symbols correspond to synthesis of threonine (Thre), leucine (Leu), pantothenate (Panto), proline (Pro), purines (Pur), biotin (Biot), pyrimidines (Pyr), tryptophan (Try), shikimic acid (Shik), histidine (His), arginine (Arg), lysine (Lys), nicotinamide (Nic), guanine (Gua), adenine (Ade), para-aminobenzoic acid (PABA), tyrosine (Tyr), phenylalanine (Phe), glycine (Gly), serine (Ser), cysteine (Cyst), methionine (Met), vitamin B_{12} (B_{12}), isoleucine (Isol), thiamine (B_1), valine (Val); to fermentation of arabinose (Ara), lactose (Lac), galactose (Gal), maltose (Mal), xylose (Xyl), mannitol (Mtl); requirement for succinate (Succ), aspartate (Asp), glutamate (Glu); resistance to streptomycin (Sm), to valine (Val^r), sodium azide (Az^r), phages T1 (T1^r), T6 (T6^r), λ (λ^r); repression for arginine (R_{arg}), isoleucine (R_{isol}), tryptophan (R_{try}); location of the prophage (represented by the Greek letter ϕ) of the phage strains 82, λ, 434, 381, 21, 424, 466, 186, 370, 299, 18, and W. Symbols in brackets indicate that the location of the marker with respect to neighboring markers has not been exactly determined. [From Jacob and Wollman (342).]

Zygotic Induction and the Repressor

The distribution of lysogeny among the recombinants is very abnormal, however, when the Hfr parent is lysogenic and the F⁻ parent is nonlysogenic. In this case, the prophage is almost never inherited by the recombinants, whose frequency is very much lower than and whose genetic character is very different from that found in crosses of the types $Hfr(\lambda^-) \times F^-(\lambda^+)$ or $Hfr(\lambda^+) \times F^-(\lambda^+)$. Jacob and Wollman (333, 694) could show that these abnormalities are the consequence of a phenomenon which they called **zygotic induction**: whenever a chromosomal segment of the lysogenic Hfr carrying the λ prophage is introduced into the nonlysogenic F⁻ recipient, the prophage becomes induced, enters the vegetative state, and causes the growth of one to two hundred infective λ virus particles, which are finally liberated upon lysis of the zygote. In such crosses, most zygotes into which the Hfr had introduced the chromosomal segment carrying the prophage are lost, and only those genetic markers of the donor which are transferred earlier than the prophage, or are proximal to the origin, can be expected to appear among the recombinants. No zygotic induction occurs, however, when the F⁻ is lysogenic, whether the Hfr parent is lysogenic or not, and no anomalous segregation of parental markers is observed among the issue of such crosses. Hence the presence of the λ prophage renders the F⁻ recipient immune not only against superinfection by the homologous free λ phage but also against vegetative development of a homologous chromosomal λ prophage introduced into it from an Hfr donor parent.

Since it is evidently the *cytoplasm of the F⁻ cell* that determines whether or not induction of the zygote occurs, it may be concluded that the immunity of lysogenic bacteria is due to a **cytoplasmic factor,** or to what Bertani (69) called an "immunity substance." This factor not only prevents vegetative multiplication of an exogenous phage genome introduced into the lysogenic cell but, even more importantly, also holds the endogenous prophage itself in check and thus makes possible the very maintenance of the lysogenic condition (327, 328). According to Jacob and Monod (331), this cytoplasmic factor is a **repressor,** itself formed under the influence of the prophage. This immunity repressor specifically inhibits the synthesis of one or more of the "early" proteins (see Chapter 7) whose presence in the infected cell is essential for the initiation of vegetative phage growth. *Induction* of prophage development, either spontaneous or radiation-induced, is then to be understood as a transient reduction in the intracellular concentration of the repressor to a level sufficiently low for synthesis of the "early" proteins to occur and for vegetative phage multiplication to be irreversibly initiated. It is by destroying or inhibiting the function of the immunity repressor that agents such as UV light and peroxide probably exert their inducing action.

It follows from these notions that every introduction of a temperate phage genome into a nonlysogenic bacterium, whether by infection or by conjugation, "results in a 'race' between the synthesis of the specific repressor and that of the 'early' proteins required for vegetative phage multiplication. The fate of the host cell, survival with lysogenization or lysis as a result of phage multiplication, depends upon whether the synthesis of the repressor or that of the protein is favored. Changes in the cultural conditions favoring the synthesis of the repressor, such as infection at low temperature, or in the presence of chloramphenicol, would favor lysogenization, and *vice versa*" (331). The synthesis of its own self-repressor is thus the very essence of the temperance of temperate phages.

Specificity of Prophage Location

The existence of a single specific chromosomal locus for the λ prophage readily explains the difficulty of producing a lysogenic bacterium carrying simultaneously the prophages of several genetically marked strains of the same temperate phage, since the genomes of superinfecting, homologous, free virus particles find their prophage sites already occupied. By the same token, the facility with which bacterial strains can be produced that carry the prophages of several *unrelated* temperate phage strains suggests that such unrelated prophages occupy different chromosomal sites, for whose occupation they do not compete. In order to examine this point, Jacob and Wollman (337, 339) lysogenized Hfr and F⁻ bacteria with 14 different, unrelated temperate phage strains and mapped the locations of their prophages by conjugation experiments, in which either only the donor or only the recipient cells carried the prophage in question. In this way, the definite locations on the *E. coli* chromosome shown in the map of Fig. 12-6 could be assigned to the prophages of 13 of the 14 phage strains studied. The supposition of "one prophage, one locus" was thus confirmed, and the chromosome was shown to possess several prophage regions in which the genetic material of different phage strains can be maintained as part of the bacterial genome. However, it did not prove possible to identify the prophage site of one of the 14 temperate phage strains, a fact that shall be of significance in the considerations of the next chapter.

The lysogenic response ensuing upon infection of a nonlysogenic sensitive cell by a temperate phage thus leads to the attachment of the viral genome to some specific site on the chromosome of the host cell. This attachment does not, however, appear to represent a direct physical incorporation of the DNA molecule of the infecting phage into the bacterial DNA, since very few of the phosphorus atoms of the infecting phage DNA appear in the prophage to which it gives rise (598). Instead, the prophage seems to derive from a *replica* of the DNA of the infecting virus.

Genetic Control of Lysogenization

The plaques of phage λ, like those of other temperate phages, have turbid centers that are caused by the secondary growth of lysogenized bacteria of the sensitive indicator strain. Mutants of λ can be readily found, however, which make plaques with *clear* rather than turbid centers. These so-called c mutants owe their variant plaque morphology to a hereditary defect in the reactions leading to the reduction of the phage to prophage; the frequency with which c mutants give the lysogenic response is very much less than the corresponding frequency for the c^+ wild type, and hence no secondary growth of lysogenized bacteria takes place in the center of the c mutant plaques (Fig. 12-2). These c mutants were studied by Kaiser (351), who found through genetic crosses of c mutants to other plaque-type mutants of λ that all c mutants cluster in one segment, the so-called c region, of the λ genetic map (Fig. 12-7). The ability of phage λ to lysogenize the sensitive host cell appears, therefore, to be controlled by the c region of its genome; mutational alteration of any site in that c region leads to a blockage of the sequence of events which terminates in the reduction of the infecting viral genome to the prophage state. Since in mixed infection of sensitive bacteria with λc^+ and λc lysogenic clones carrying both c^+ and c prophages can be recovered, it follows that c^+ is dominant over c; hence it is the c^+ gene that gives rise to a cytoplasmic product. This suggests that the c region controls the synthesis of the specific repressor responsible for immunity and that λc mutants carry a hereditary defect for synthesis of an effective immunity repressor. In spite of their inability to synthesize immunity substance, λc mutants are, however, still sensitive to the inhibitory action of the normal repressor elaborated by the λc^+ wild type phage.

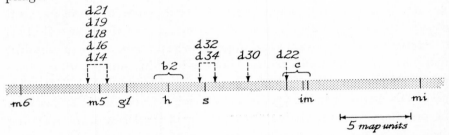

Fig. 12-7. The genetic map of bacteriophage λ. Meaning of mutant symbols: $m5$ and $m6$ = medium-size plaque; $g1$ = large plaque; h = host range mutant; $b2$ = density mutation causing abortive lysogenic response; s = small plaque; c = clear plaque; im = specificity of immunity substance; mi = minute plaque; d = defective prophage mutants. [Linkage data from (342, 350, 352, 364).]

It can be seen in Fig. 12-6 that close to the prophage site of λ phage in the *E. coli* genome there is located the prophage site of another temperate virus, phage 434. These two "neighboring" phage strains do not share a common immunity specificity, since infecting λ phages multiply on and lyse K12(434) bacteria, and infecting 434 phages similarly multiply on and lyse K12(λ) bacteria. However, λ and 434 will grow together in nonlysogenic K12 bacteria and will even undergo genetic recombination with one another under these conditions. Kaiser and Jacob (352) took advantage of this fact in order to determine the regions of the phage genome responsible for immunity specificity and prophage location. For this purpose, they crossed various plaque-type mutants of λ against the 434 wild type, then looked for the appearance of recombinant phage progeny of wild type plaque morphology but of λ immunity specificity— progeny able to grow on K12(434) but not on K12(λ). They found in this way that phage 434 can supply the wild allele of every one of these mutant loci to a phage of λ immunity specificity except of those mutant sites that lie in the small *im* segment of the *c* region (Fig. 12-7). That is, whenever a phage carries the *im* segment of the *c* region of λ, it has the immunity specificity of λ, and whenever it carries the *im* segment of the *c* region of 434, it has the immunity specificity of 434. It is the *im* segment, therefore, that appears to govern the specificity of the immunity relations, in regard both to the particular structure of the repressor synthesized by the *c* region as well as to the sensitivity of the phage to the repressive action that prevents initiation of vegetative phage growth.

Kaiser and Jacob also constructed a *hybrid* 434 phage, which had derived all of its genome except the *c* region from λ, by a series of backcrosses of 434 to various λ mutants, and then lysogenized K12 bacteria with this 434Hy phage. Genetic analysis of the lysogenic K12(434Hy) bacteria showed that the 434Hy prophage is located on the *E. coli* chromosome at the typical 434 site and not at the λ site. But subsequent experiments involving a hybrid phage between λ and another of its relatives, strain 21 (whose prophage location is more distant from that of λ than that of strain 434), revealed that though 21Hy manifests the immunity specificity of 21, and thus carries the *im* segment of 21, K12(21Hy) bacteria carry their prophage at the λ prophage site (342). Hence it does not seem true, as had first been inferred from study of the 434Hy prophage, that the *c* region also determines the precise location of its prophage on the chromosome of the host cell.

Indeed, the sector of the λ genetic map that *is* responsible for incorporation of the viral genome into the bacterial chromosome has now been identified. This became possible when G. Kellenberger, Zichichi, and Weigle (364, 705) discovered the mutant λ*b*2, which contains about 18% less DNA per phage than does the wild type—and hence is of lower buoyant density than normal λ. This λ*b*2 mutant cannot multiply in the prophage state, though it is perfectly capable of vegetative growth and reproduction. Upon infection of a sensitive *E. coli* bacterium, λ*b*2 gives either the normal lytic response or an *abortive* lysogenic response. In the abortive lysogenic response, the infected bacterium survives as a lysogenic, immune cell (in which normal phage development can be induced by the usual inducing agents), but at each cell division the abortive lysogen gives rise to a nonlysogenic, λ-sensitive daughter cell that does not harbor either phage or prophage. In the abortively lysogenized cell the phage genome does not form part of the bacterial chromosome but remains as a singular, nonmultiplying structure in the "cytoplasm" of the host. In phage crosses, the *b*2 character (in both its buoyant density as well as abortive lysogenization phenotypes) behaves as a single genetic locus, and can thus be assigned a position of the λ map, as shown in Fig. 12-7. This position is evidently not near the *c* locus, but in the region of *m5–h*. [In regard to its bent for abortive lysogenization, λ*b2* resembles the λ*l* mutant discovered earlier by Jacob and Wollman (334). Probably *b2* and *l* represent mutations in the same gene.]

The most probable explanation of the role of the *b2* region in the lysogenization process is that the viral DNA representing this sector of the λ*b2*+ wild type genome is "homologous" with the host DNA representing the prophage site of the bacterial chromosome. This homology between viral and host DNA allows the recognition necessary for integration of the prophage at its specific chromosomal site. The λ*b2* mutant, however, appears to be missing that very region of its DNA in which virus and host are "homologous." Hence the genome of this deletion mutant cannot find the place at which it is to be integrated as prophage into the bacterial chromosome.

Chromosomal Attachment of Prophage

What is the nature of the link that ties the prophage to its chromosomal site? Is the phage genome *added* to or is it *substituted* for a segment of the chromosome of the nonlysogenic cell? If it is substituted, then there would exist in the chromosome of the nonlysogenic bacterium a set of genetic loci for which the genome of the infecting phage is exchanged in the lysogenic response by means of a process analogous to crossing-over. Jacob and Wollman (341) came to the conclusion that the substitution alternative is very unlikely, since formerly lysogenic bacteria cured by UV irradiation seem to have lost all "memory" of the prophage they once possessed: after curing, none of the genetic loci of the late prophage seem to remain, inasmuch as none ever reappears in any secondary prophage established by relysogenizing the cured strain. Relysogenization of the cured strain furthermore proceeds with the same efficiency and at the same prophage site as the primary lysogenization, so that if in lysogenization the phage genome is really exchanged for an allelic segment of the chromosome of the nonlysogenic cell, it would have to be supposed that these lost nonviral alleles can somehow be recovered in the curing process, a most improbable hypothesis. It seems much more reasonable, therefore, to suppose that there does not exist a region allelic for the whole phage genome in the nonlysogenic cell and that, instead, the prophage is a genetic segment that is added to the nonlysogenic chromosome in the lysogenic response and again removed in toto in curing.

If the prophage is really added to the genetic structures of the host cell, one may inquire into the topology of this addition. (1) Is the prophage *inserted* into the continuity of the bacterial chromosome, possibly by breaking the bacterial DNA at its "prophage locus" and splicing the break with the phage DNA? Under this hypothesis curing would represent removal of the splice. (2) Is the prophage attached to the bacterial chromosome at the prophage locus without being introduced into its continuity? Under this hypothesis curing would represent release of the prophage attachment. (3) Is only *part* of the phage genome, possibly its *b2* region, inserted into the continuity of the bacterial chromosome, as under the first hypothesis, while the remainder of the phage genome remains outside, as under the second hypothesis?

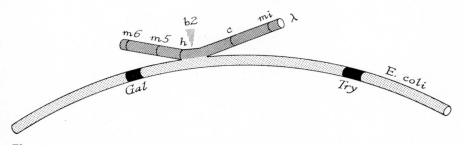

Fig. 12-3. The λ prophage as a "hook" on the bacterial chromosome. (The distance of the markers is not drawn to scale.) [After Jacob and Wollman (341).]

No definitive answers to these questions on the topological relation of the prophage to the bacterial chromosome are as yet available, but Jacob and Wollman (341) found against the notion of insertion of the whole phage into the bacterial chromosome. First, the presence of the prophage 18 does not appear to reduce the linkage of the two closely linked loci Met$_1$ and Met$_2$, between which the prophage 18 can be mapped (Fig. 12-6). This is contrary to the lengthening of the genetic distance expected from an interposition of the whole phage genome between these markers. Second, in bacterial conjugation the transfer of prophage 18 from donor cell to zygote occurs *both before and after* the Met$_1$ locus, as though at least part of the prophage is outside the continuity of the chromosome and overlaps the Met₁ site. Jacob and Wollman therefore favored the idea that the prophage is "hooked" to the bacterial chromosome (Fig. 12-8). In the case of phage λ, the "hook" would probably be the *b2* region of the λ genome, which, as we saw, plays an essential role in the lysogenization process. This model does give a satisfactory account of many of the available facts, but it is difficult to imagine the molecular basis of the "hook."

Campbell (127), in contrast, favored the insertion hypothesis for λ, though he was unable to explain the behavior of prophage 18 from this

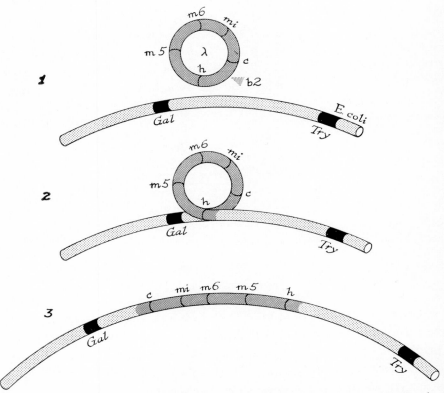

Fig. 12-9. The prophage as an insertion into the bacterial chromosome. 1. The circular vegetative λ phage genome synapses with the λ prophage site of the bacterial chromosome. 2. The phage genome breaks between *h* and *c* in the *b2* region, the bacterial chromosome breaks between Gal and Try, heterologous pieces rejoin. 3. The crossover generates one continuous genetic structure containing the λ genome interposed between the bacterial loci Gal and Try. (The distance of the genetic markers is not drawn to scale.) [After Campbell (127).]

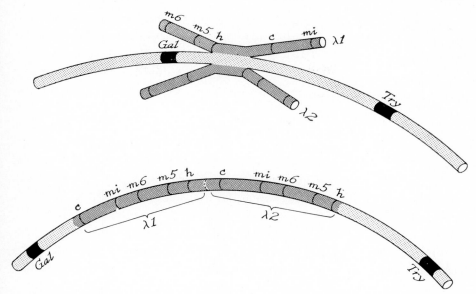

Fig. 12-10.   Genetic structure of a doubly lysogenic strain of *E. coli* carrying two prophages, λ1 and λ2, if the prophage is *hooked* to the chromosome (upper figure), or if the prophage is *inserted* into the chromosome (lower figure).

point of view. Campbell proposed that the λ phage genome, like that of T4, is circular and that at the moment of lysogenization homologous parts of viral and bacterial genome synapse (probably, as one would now think, at the *b*2 region). The phage could then be inserted as a linear structure into the continuity of the chromosome by a crossover within the synapsed regions (Fig. 12-9). This hypothesis has the advantage of being more readily comprehensible in molecular terms than the "hook." But in order to reconcile the supposition that the λ genome is circular with the inference drawn in Chapter 9—that the *mi* locus is at a physical "end" of the λ map—it would be necessary to assume that prior to maturation as an infective λ phage, the circular vegetative genome is always broken between *mi* and *m*6 to generate the linear structure of Fig. 12-7. This further assumption leads to an important prediction of the insertion hypothesis: since in lysogenization the circular vegetative λ genome is broken by a crossover in the *b*2 region and not near *mi*, one would expect the order of some of the genetic markers of the λ prophage to be different from that of the infective phage. But this is just what Calef and Licciardello (124) had already suggested when they inferred the prophage map order *c–mi–h* from bacterial conjugation experiments involving genetically marked λ prophages in donor and recipient cells, instead of the order *h–c–mi* of Fig. 12-7 established for the infective λ phage. Good arguments can thus be adduced both for and against the "hook" and "insertion" hypotheses; at the moment, it would seem prudent to retain an open mind concerning these alternatives.

As already stated, it is difficult to establish a clone of lysogenic cells that carry the prophages of two different genotypes of the same temperate phage strain by superinfecting an immune bacterium already lysogenic for one genotype with phage of a second genotype. But a *polylysogenic* strain does arise readily after simultaneous infection of a nonlysogenic λ-sensitive bacterium with two different λ genotypes (29). Since it can be shown by genetic mapping experiments that the two different λ prophages of such a doubly lysogenic strain are situated at the same bacterial locus, one is led to suppose that in the normal lysogenization of the sensitive cell more than one λ genome is usually "hooked" on to or integrated in tandem into the λ prophage site of the *E. coli* chromosome (Fig. 12-10).

Defective Prophages

Mutations can occur in the temperate phage genome not only during its vegetative growth but also during its lysogenic reproduction as part of the hereditary apparatus of the host cell. Some of these prophage mutations concern the same phenotypes—for example, plaque type or host range variants—as those engendered by mutations of the vegetative phage. But there is one class of phage mutants that can only be studied in the prophage state: the **defectives** whose phenotype is their very inability to give rise to structurally intact, infective virus particles. Defective lysogenic strains have been isolated in various bacterial species, either after infection of sensitive bacteria with temperate phages (321, 457) or after exposure of normal lysogenic bacteria to heavy doses of UV light (26, 336). The characteristic attribute of a defective lysogenic strain is that though very few infective phage particles, or none whatsoever, are found in its culture, the lysogenic character is nevertheless clearly manifest through the specific immunity pattern, which is always that of the original lysogenic strain from which the defective mutant had been derived; for example, a defective lysogenic strain derived from K12(λ) is still immune against infection by exogenous λ phage particles.

Different defective lysogenic strains isolated from the same wild type prophage differ as to the nature of the defect that prevents formation of infective virus particles. We may first consider the strain K12(λd14), isolated by Jacob and Wollman (336) after UV irradiation of the K12(λ) wild type. Strain d14 does not spontaneously release any infective phage particles; nevertheless, upon UV irradiation of the culture, prophage induction appears to take place, since all the bacteria lyse after the normal latent period. Only one in 10^7 of these induced bacteria liberates any normal λ phage particles, whereas the remainder do not yield any infective virus particles at all. But the lysate of the defective strain does contain empty phage heads, phage tails, phage lysozyme, and a variety of antigenic proteins characteristic of the normal λ phage. Thus, once its immunity repressor has been destroyed by an inducing dose of UV, the defective d14 prophage is capable of directing the synthesis of most or all of the phage proteins.

It is possible to ascertain the location of the d14 mutation on the λ linkage map by superinfecting the defective K12(λd14) bacteria immediately after their UV induction with the plaque type mutant λm5c; since irradiation abolishes immunity, the superinfecting phage multiplies in every cell and producess a crop of structurally intact progeny particles. This progeny population is a mixture of infective and noninfective phage; the infective particles carry the normal d^+ allele of the superinfecting λm5c "helper" phage and the noninfective particles carry the d14 allele of the defective prophage. In this way, defective phage genomes can achieve maturation as virus particles, by courtesy of the normal morphogenetic reactions carried out by the "helper" (27). Most of the infective phage produced by such superinfection are of the m5c genotype of the superinfecting phage, but a considerable number of infective recombinants of m5c^+ genotype can also be found. However, there appear hardly any progeny of the other two conceivable infective recombinant types m^+c and m^+c^+. This result implies that the superinfecting "helper" phage can undergo genetic recombination with the defective λm^+c^+d14 prophage and thus replace its own c allele with the c^+ allele of the defective genome. The failure to find many infective recombinants carrying the m^+ allele of the defective prophage must then mean that the genetic site of the d14 defectivity mutation is so closely linked to the $m5$ site (Fig. 12-7), that defectivity goes along with $m5^+$ in most recombinational events. The missing classes of recombinants are, therefore, probably of the defective genotype m^+c^+d14 and m^+cd14, and hence unable to reveal their presence as plaque formers.

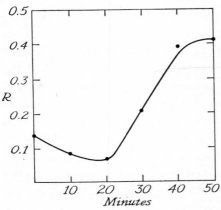

Fig. 12-11. Superinfection of a defective lysogenic strain of *E. coli* at various times after UV induction of its prophage. A culture of K12($\lambda d14$) is exposed to an inducing dose of UV and incubated in nutrient broth. At various times thereafter, samples of the induced culture are superinfected with $\lambda g1c$ at an average multiplicity of 0.2 phages/bacterium. After neutralization with anti-λ serum of any unadsorbed phages of the superinfecting population, the samples are incubated for another 150 minutes, and the resulting lysates plated on indicator bacteria for assay of the genotypes among the phage progeny. The ordinate shows the ratio R of the titer of $g1c^+$ recombinants to the titer of the superinfecting $g1c$ parental types, in samples superinfected at the time after irradiation shown on the abscissa. [From Jacob and Wollman (336).]

Jacob, Fuerst, and Wollman (329) made use of such crosses between superinfecting phage and defective prophage to examine whether after UV induction the defective phage genome enters the vegetative phase and multiplies. For this purpose, the defective lysogenic strain K12($\lambda d14$) was superinfected with mutant helper $\lambda g1c$ phage at various times after UV induction of the $d14$ prophage and the ratio scored of the number of gc^+ recombinants to the number of gc superinfecting parental types that ultimately appeared among the phage progeny upon lysis of the induced culture. As shown in Fig. 12-11, it was found that the more time had elapsed between the moments of UV induction and superinfection of the defective culture, the greater the ratio of recombinant to parental types among the progeny. The data of Fig. 12-11 can mean only that the defective genome begins to multiply some 20 minutes after UV induction and generates in the intracellular mating pool more and more vegetative copies of itself with which the nondefective superinfecting genome can recombine to generate more and more gc^+ recombinants.

It thus follows that the $d14$ mutation has produced a defect that prevents the successful completion of a *late* step in vegetative phage growth, since synthesis of the proteins of phage λ as well as replication of its genome (or its DNA), can still occur. In fact, the defect appears to concern the *maturation* of the virus—to prevent in some way the proper union of the major viral components, DNA and protein, into the structurally intact, infective unit. In this respect, λ phage development in the defective K12(λd14) resembles growth of virulent T2 or T4 phages in the presence of proflavine, under which conditions all major components of the T-even viruses are synthesized without maturation into infective virus particles (Chapter 6). The very few infective λ phage particles that are found in UV-induced cultures of K12(λd14) represent the descendants of rare $d14 \longrightarrow d^+$ *reverse* mutations in the prophage genome.

A number of defective lysogenic strains, such as $d16$, $d18$, $d19$, and $d21$, have been independently isolated from the K12(λ) wild type, that act very similarly to $d14$; upon UV induction of their prophage, both viral genome and viral structural components are formed, only to be liberated as noninfective materials upon lysis of the induced cells at the end of the normal latent period. As shown in Fig. 12-7, all these defectivity mutations, just like $d14$, map at or near the $m5$ locus of the λ phage genome. Other defective lysogenic mutants of K12(λ) have been discovered, however, such as $d22$, $d30$, $d32$, and $d34$, that behave very differently from this first set of defectives. First of all, in this second set of strains the defective genome does *not* multiply after UV induction: the proportion of infective gc^+ recombinants appearing upon superinfection of the UV-induced defective culture with $\lambda g1c$ "helper" phages is independent of the time elapsed between UV irradiation and superinfection, thus resulting in a horizontal curve in an experiment as that of Fig. 12-11. Second, genetic mapping experiments show that the sites of the mutations responsible for defectivity in these strains are located in a different region of the λ phage genome, namely, between the $m5$ locus and the c region (Fig. 12-7). Third, some of these strains synthesize no detectable phage proteins at all upon UV induction of their prophage, whereas others are capable of producing at least some phage antigens, for example tail fibers. This second class of defectivity mutations appears to block an *early* rather than a late step in the vegetative development of the virus. The genome of this second set of defectives is thus unable to multiply vegetatively, though it is evidently capable of normal reproduction in the prophage state. In these defectives it is not the capacity of the viral genome to replicate that has been lost, since replication can proceed as long as the viral genome is an integral part of the bacterial host genome; it is only the capacity for replication as an independent, autonomous unit that has been suppressed. In other words, the defectivity mutation appears to have abolished the expression of the very phage functions that allow the escape of the viral genome from those mechanisms of cellular control that prevent the transition of the prophage to the vegetative state.

Defective lysogenic bacteria offer the remarkable spectacle of the indefinite perpetuation by the host cell of viral genetic material that, because of its hereditary defect, can never develop into infective virus particles. Probably many such defective lysogenic strains exist in nature without their lysogenic character having been recognized. Unless the nondefective ancestor of the defective provirus carried by the strain is known, it is unlikely that the presence of the prophage would be noticed by its chief manifestation—the specific immunity conferred on the defective lysogenic bacterium against superinfection by exogenous homologous temperate phage. Defective prophages may thus be considered to lie in the twilight zone between virus and cellular organelle (327).

Conversion

Besides constituting a potentially lethal factor for the lysogenic bacterium and conferring on it immunity against infection by an extrinsic homologous phage, the prophage may also endow the host cell with other traits. Such phage-mediated acquisition of new traits, whose connection with the prophage is often much less obvious than capacity for phage production or immunity, is called **conversion** (37, 254). An example of conversion has, in fact, already been described in Chapter 10: whereas nonlysogenic strains of K12 support the growth of *r*II mutants of T-even phages, lysogenic K12(λ) strains do not. The presence of the λ prophage thus engenders some change in the physiology or structure of the bacterium that renders function of the two otherwise dispensable *r*II cistrons of the T-even genome essential for successful phage multiplication in the converted host. It seems possible that the λ-mediated conversion of *E. coli* into an unproductive host for *r*II mutants derives from an effect of the λ immunity repressor on the metabolism of components, and hence on the structure, of the cell envelope. If this hypothesis were

correct, it would be the presence of the *im* segment of the *c* region of the
λ genome that is responsible for the conversion of this particular trait.
Several other examples of conversion affecting the ability to support
growth of heterologous phages are known (66, 405), and one of these,
a case of "host-controlled modification," will be examined in some detail
in Chapter 14.

Another instance of conversion was encountered by Japanese workers
(320, 622, 645), who noticed that the presence of certain antigenic structures on the surface of *Salmonella* is the consequence of lysogenization
with particular phage types. One such case, the conversion by phage ϵ^{15}
of *Salmonella anatum* from one antigenic class to another, was analyzed
in some detail by Uetake, Luria, and Burrous (644). This work showed
that a new antigen appears on the surface of *S. anatum* within 15 minutes
of infection of nonlysogenic bacteria with ϵ^{15} phage, whether the infection results in the lytic or in the lysogenic response. Concomitantly with
the appearance of the new antigen, there develop receptors for another
phage, ϵ^{34}, which cannot adsorb to the nonlysogenic strain. The cells
that survive infection with phage ϵ^{15} segregate both lysogenic and nonlysogenic cells among their progeny upon further growth. The lysogenic
segregants permanently retain the new surface antigen, whereas the
nonlysogenic segregants, after temporarily carrying the changed antigenic structure for a few generations, once more regain the primitive
surface configuration of their nonlysogenic ancestor. These results show
that conversion of the bacterial surface is induced by the ϵ^{15} phage
genome in both its vegetative and prophage states.

Probably the most dramatic example of conversion, and indeed one
of the few circumstances under which bacteriophages are known to play
an important role in a matter of practical significance, concerns the
production of diphtheria toxin by *Corynebacterium diphtheriae*. It was discovered by Freeman (220) that toxigenic strains of *C. diphtheriae* can be
isolated after exposure of nontoxigenic strains to temperate diphtheria
phages, there being a one-to-one relation between toxigenicity and
lysogeny among the bacteria that survive infection. Further study of
this phenomenon by Groman (254, 255) and by Barksdale and Pappenheimer (38) showed that the capacity of *Corynebacterium* to produce
diphtheria toxin is conferred by the presence of a specific phage. The
ability of this phage to carry out the conversion from nontoxigenicity
to toxigenicity can be traced to a particular sector of its genome (256).

However, in contrast to the conversion of *Salmonella* surface antigens effected by either vegetative or prophage states of the converting ϵ^{15} phage, here the actual production of toxin occurs only when the prophage of the converted lysogenic *C. diphtheriae* becomes induced and lyses the cell. *Synthesis of diphtheria toxin thus appears to be an adjunct of the vegetative development of the temperate diphtheria phage* (37).

Conversion thus constitutes a way of variation, through which bacteria can acquire new hereditary traits. These changes in genotype derive from *additions* of new genetic information to the bacterial genome, rather than from substitution of new information for old, since the converted traits disappear and the cells again regain the character of their prelysogenic state as soon as the prophage is lost. In this respect, the genetic modifications brought about by conversion differ from those produced by substitutive mechanisms of bacterial variation, such as mutation, transformation, or conjugation. They also differ from those brought about by another kind of phage-mediated transfer of bacterial heredity, which will be the subject of the next chapter.

Episomes

The foregoing considerations have shown that temperate phages such as λ are elements endowed with genetic continuity which, upon being introduced into a nonlysogenic bacterium, can exist in two different, mutually exclusive states: an *autonomous* or vegetative state, in which the viral genome reproduces independently of the host genome, and an *integrated* or prophage state, in which the viral genome forms part of and is reproduced in synchrony with the host genome. The study of bacterial genetics has revealed the existence of at least two other types of genetic elements that, like temperate phages, can enter bacteria as extrinsic agents and then exist in the host cell in either of those two, autonomous or integrated, states. These elements are the *F sex factors*, which are responsible for sexual differentiation into donor and recipient cells (see Chapter 2), and the *colicinogenic factors*, which control the synthesis of proteinaceous bacteriocidal substances, the colicins, active on some strains of *E. coli*. Jacob and Wollman (338, 342) recognized this similarity between temperate phages, sex factors, and colicinogenic factors, the essence of which they distilled into their concept of the **episome.**

An episome, according to Jacob and Wollman, is a genetic element that is *added* to the genome of a cell, and hence may be either present or absent. When absent from the cell, an episome can be acquired only from an external source; it cannot simply appear by mutation, rearrangement, or alteration of the endogenous cellular genome. When present in the cell, an episome alternates between the two mutually exclusive autonomous and integrated states. The phenotypic characters acquired by the cell through possession of an episome are usually dispensable, since episomes are not necessary cellular constituents. Once a bacterium has been "cured" of an episome, the phenotypic character associated with the episome is also irretrievably lost.

One important difference between temperate phages and the sex and colicinogenic factors, however, is that bacteria can acquire the phage episome by *infection*, since the virus particles possess their own infective apparatus, whereas acquisition of the other two episomes is entirely dependent on mechanisms of genetic transfer from donor to recipient cells. Thus the nonviral episomes can be acquired only by bacterial conjugation or by the *transduction* process to be considered in the next chapter. From an evolutionary point of view, therefore, bacterial viruses may be considered as that class of episomes that have developed the hereditary information necessary for synthesis of a proteinaceous soma into which the genetic material can be encapsulated. In this way the viral DNA has evolved into an *infectious* episome that, in the guise of a virus particle, is capable of an extraprotoplasmic existence for the transit from host to host.

Further Reading

Lwoff, A. and Gutmann, A., "Investigations on a lysogenic *Bacillus megaterium*" (455). The single-cell experiments that led to the notion of the prophage; the paper is prefaced by a concise statement of the problems that Lwoff proposed to settle. [Reprinted in English translation in (596).]

Lwoff, A., "Lysogeny" (453). An extensive review by Lwoff of the body of information on lysogeny that accumulated in the three years following the publication of his first paper, as well as of the work of his predecessors.

Weigle, J. J. and Delbrück, M., "Mutual exclusion between an infecting phage and a carried phage" (676). Details on the UV induction of the λ prophage (and on the interference by phage T5 with the growth of λ phage).

Kaiser, A. D. and Jacob, F., "Recombination between related temperate bacterio-phages and the genetic control of immunity and prophage localization" (352).

Jacob, F. and Wollman, E. L., "Genetic aspects of lysogeny" (337); "The relationship between the prophage and the bacterial chromosome in lysogenic bacteria" (341). Two definitive and well-written reviews.

Bertani, G., "Lysogeny" (69). Another review that also treats temperate phage types not mentioned in this chapter.

Adams, M. H., *Bacteriophages* (2). Chapter XX discusses colicins and other bacteriocins, noninfective bacteriocidal agents perpetuated by bacteria that resemble bacterio-phages in some respects. Chapter XXI discusses the use of phages in epidemiological studies. Neither of these subjects has found consideration in this book.

CHAPTER 13

Transduction

The Filtrable Agent—The Transducing Phage—Cotransduction of Linked Markers—Fine-structure Mapping—Abortive Transduction—Specialized Transduction—The Relation of Generalized to Specialized Transduction

SOME FIVE YEARS after Lederberg and Tatum (404) had discovered genetic recombination in *Escherichia*, Lederberg and his student Zinder (709) searched for an analogous sexual process in the bacterial genus, *Salmonella*. They employed the same experimental procedure that had been so successful in revealing the existence of conjugation in *E. coli:* about 10^9 cells each of two mutant strains of *S. typhimurium*—LT-22, unable to synthesize the amino acids phenylalanine, tryptophan, and tyrosine (Phe⁻, Try⁻, Tyr⁻), and LT-2, unable to synthesize the amino acids methionine and histidine (Met⁻, His⁻)—were plated together on an amino acid–free synthetic medium like that described in Table 2-II, containing only inorganic salts and a carbohydrate as a source of carbon and energy. The result of this experiment was that about 10^{-5} of the bacteria plated grew into prototrophic colonies that no longer required any added amino acids for growth. Since none of the bacteria of either auxotrophic strain plated *alone* were able to grow into colonies in this minimal medium in the absence of their required amino acids, the amino acid–independent prototrophs that appear in the mixed plating could not have derived from reverse mutants in which the auxotrophic Phe⁻, Try⁻, Tyr⁻, or Met⁻, His⁻ mutant sites had spontaneously reverted to their prototrophic state. Instead, these prototrophs must have represented *genetic recombinants* that united within the same cell the wild type Phe⁺, Try⁺, Tyr⁺ alleles of LT-2 and the wild type Met⁺, His⁺ alleles of LT-22. In further experiments, Zinder and Lederberg found

341

that other characters can also be exchanged between the two *Salmonella* strains: genetic recombinants arose also during mixed growth of LT-2 with other mutants of LT-22 that were unable to ferment galactose (Gal⁻), or xylose (Xyl⁻), or mannitol (Mtl⁻), or maltose (Mal⁻), or that were resistant to streptomycin (Smʳ). *Salmonella*, like *Escherichia*, is, therefore, capable of engaging in a process of genetic exchange that results in the appearance of recombinants endowed with genetic characters from bacteria of different lines of descent.

The Filtrable Agent

In order to ascertain whether *contact* between *Salmonella* cells of complementary genotype is required for this genetic exchange, Zinder and Lederberg used the "Davis U-tube" (Fig. 13-1), originally designed

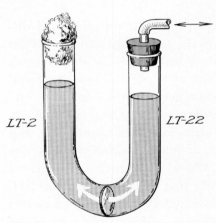

LT-2   *LT-22*

Fig. 13-1. The Davis U-Tube The two arms of the U are separated by a sintered glass filter impervious to bacterial cells but allowing free passage of the growth medium. The two parent strains are inoculated into opposite arms and alternating pressure and suction applied to one end of the U.

for demonstrating the necessity of cell contact in conjugation and recombination in *Escherichia* (153). The two auxotrophic strains LT-2 and LT-22 were inoculated into opposite arms of the U, separated at the bottom by a sintered glass filter impervious to *Salmonella* cells. The two bacterial cultures were then allowed to grow to saturation, while the culture fluid was slowly pushed back and forth from one arm to the other through the filter, by alternating suction and pressure on one end of the U. In this way, the two auxotrophic strains shared the same growth medium without their cells having come into contact. After growth of the two strains in this device for some hours, it was found that prototrophic recombinants no longer requiring any amino acids for growth had, in fact, been produced in the arm containing LT-22. Thus, in contrast to conjugation in *E. coli*, cell contact between complementary genotypes does not seem necessary for the kind of recombination observed here. It appeared, therefore, that genetic exchange in *Salmonella* is mediated by a *filtrable agent* (FA), small enough to pass through the sintered glass pores, that brings hereditary factors from LT-2 donor to LT-22 recipient cells.

It seemed possible at the time that these findings might represent merely another instance of bacterial transformation. The transmission of genetic factors from cell to cell by free bacterial DNA had been known to exist in *Diplococcus pneumoniae* since 1944 (33), and there was no reason to think that it should not also occur in another bacterial genus such as *Salmonella*. Some further tests readily showed, however, that FA cou'd not, in fact, be simply transforming DNA liberated by the LT-2 strain that carries the alleles from LT-2 donor to LT-22 recipient cells through the sintered glass filter. First of all, the activity of FA, unlike that of the pneumococcal "transforming principle," is not destroyed by treatment with the DNA-specific hydrolytic enzyme deoxyribonuclease. Second, though FA passes through pores of sintered glass filters, it *is* retained by filter membranes of average pore diameter less than 100 mμ, a size that should still allow passage of free DNA molecules. Finally, FA sediments in centrifugal fields with a specific velocity far greater than that characteristic of the sedimentation of free DNA molecules.

Closer examination of the two auxotrophic *Salmonella* strains revealed that strain LT-22 is lysogenic, carrying the prophage of a phage now called P22, whereas strain LT-2 is nonlysogenic and sensitive to infection by P22. Since strain LT-2 did not seem to produce its FA spontaneously but only when strain LT-22 was present in the other arm of the U-tube, it seemed a good guess that FA appeared in the culture medium as the consequence of the lysis of some LT-2 bacteria by phage P22. These phages would have originated by spontaneous prophage induction of the lysogenic LT-22(P22) in one arm and then gained access to LT-2 in the other arm through the sintered glass filter. Not only could this guess be readily substantiated, but it transpired that FA *is* phage P22; that is, the genetic factors carried from LT-2 donor cells back through the glass filter to LT-22 recipient cells are either part of, or identical with, the phage particles released after growth of P22 on the sensitive LT-2 cells. It was possible (706) to reach this conclusion from the following correlations between FA and P22:

1. The infectivity of P22 and the genetic competence of FA are protected from inactivation by hydrolytic enzymes, such as deoxyribonuclease and trypsin.
2. The dimension and mass of P22 and FA are indistinguishable.
3. Treatment with anti-P22 serum or with heat inactivates the infectivity of P22 and the genetic competence of FA at the same rate.
4. Phage-resistant strains of *Salmonella* that no longer adsorb phage P22 cannot interact genetically with FA; P22 and FA have the same host range.

Zinder and Lederberg had thus discovered a third mechanism of genetic exchange in bacteria, radically different from either transformation or conjugation, in which a bacterial virus plays the role of a vector of infective heredity. They gave the name **transduction** to this process, whose discovery suddenly placed the natural role of bacterial viruses into an entirely new light. As outlined in the preceding chapter, the existence of lysogeny had already revealed that bacteria need not necessarily be destroyed by their viruses and can maintain a sort of peaceful coexistence with them; now at last the teleological "reason" for the toleration of bacteriophages became comprehensible. For if bacteriophages transduce genetic information from cell to cell, then the evolutionary advantages they offer to their hosts by promoting new combinations of pre-existing mutant characters should more than recompense bacteriadom for occasional havoc wrought by phage-induced wholesale lysis.

The Transducing Phage

Once the role of the temperate phage P22 in transduction had been established, it was unnecessary to carry out further experiments in the U-tube. Instead, the basic experimental procedure of transduction became the following. The donor strain LT-2 is infected with a lysate of phage P22, lytic multiplication of the phage on the sensitive bacteria is allowed, and the progeny phages produced are harvested and freed of any remaining unlysed donor bacteria. A culture of the recipient strain LT-22(P22) is then infected with this phage lysate and the bacteria plated on a selective agar that allows growth of only those genotypes into which some particular character of the LT-2 donor strain has been transduced. [Strain LT-22(P22) is, naturally, *immune* to P22, and hence all of the recipient cells will survive superinfection. If the recipient strain is *sensitive*, such as a variant of LT-22 cured of its P22 prophage, then transduced bacterial clones can descend from only those bacteria in which infection has not resulted in the lytic response. Sensitive bacteria giving the lytic response are of course lost and cannot give rise to transductants.] This procedure allows a quantitative estimate of the frequency with which transduction occurs. The relative efficiency of P22 as FA is evidently the ratio of the number of transduced colonies formed on the selective agar to the number of P22 phage particles with which the recipient LA-22(P22) bacteria had been infected. Such estimates show that *this efficiency is very low:* only about 10^{-5} to 10^{-7} of P22 phages grown on LT-2 can transduce a given character of the donor strain—for example, capacity for amino acid synthesis or sugar fermentation—into the recipient bacteria.

Zinder and Lederberg now addressed themselves to the question of how much of the genome of the LT-2 donor cell is carried by one of these evidently very rare transducing particles. For this purpose, a stock of P22 phage was grown on a prototrophic, streptomycin-sensitive (Try$^+$, Gal$^+$, Xyl$^+$, Sm^s) strain of LT-2, and a multiple mutant (Try$^-$, Gal$^-$, Xyl$^-$, Sm^r) strain LT-22 was infected with this phage lysate. The appearance of Try$^+$, or Gal$^+$, or Xyl$^+$ transductants was then scored on three different media: (1) minimal agar without tryptophan; (2) EMB*-galactose agar; (3) EMB*-xylose agar. Each of these media selects for transduction of only *one* of the donor characters, the other characters remaining *unselected*, inasmuch as the bacterial clone can grow or give a positive color on EMB agar whether or not the other characters have been transduced. The result of this experiment was that roughly equal numbers of transductants appeared on all three types of agar, showing that the chances were about equal that a P22 phage particle carried either the Try$^+$, or the Gal$^+$, or the Xyl$^+$ character of the donor bacterium. When these transductants were then tested for their unselected characters, however, it was found that practically none of the bacteria transduced for a selected character had also at the same time acquired

---

* EMB agar is a nutrient broth medium containing the dyes eosin and methylene blue and the sugar whose fermentation is to be tested. On this medium, a bacterium able to ferment the sugar grows into a darkly colored colony, whereas a nonfermenting bacterium produces a lightly colored colony.

one of the unselected characters of the donor; for example, all the Try⁺ transductants that grew on the minimal agar still had the Gal⁻, Xyl⁻, Smʳ characters of the recipient strain. Since similar results were found also when other fermentation or auxotrophic mutations were employed as selected or unselected characters, it could be inferred that each transducing phage particle carries and brings into the recipient cell only a *small part* of the genome of the donor bacterium on which it had grown. This inference is of course eminently plausible, since the total amount of DNA contained in the nucleus of the *Salmonella* bacterium is about a hundred times greater than the amount of DNA in the head of the P22 phage. It would thus be difficult to imagine that any one virus particle could contain very much more than a few percent of the total DNA, and hence of the genome, of the donor cell.

The following image of the transduction phenomenon was thus developed. As the temperate P22 phage grows in its lytic cycle on the sensitive LT-2 bacterium, a small fragment of the bacterial DNA manages to insinuate itself into the head of a progeny phage at the time that the viral DNA molecules are withdrawn from the vegetative phage pool for maturation into infective virus particles. When, after its release from the donor cell, such an unusual phage particle infects a recipient bacterium, the stowaway bacterial DNA is injected into the cell along with the viral DNA molecules. If this infection does not result in a lytic response and the bacterium survives, then the transduced bacterial DNA has an opportunity to undergo genetic exchange with its homologous alleles on the recipient host chromosome and thus to produce the rare recombinant cell that carries a small part of the genome of the donor cell.

Cotransduction of Linked Markers

Stocker, Zinder, and Lederberg (608) extended the study of transduction in *Salmonella* to genetic characters governing the presence, function, and antigenic structure of the flagella responsible for bacterial motility. This work showed that nonmotile mutants of strain LT-22 that have lost their capacity to form flagella can regain this capacity after infection with phage P22 previously grown on flagellated donor bacteria. Furthermore, bacteria possessing flagella of one particular antigenic structure can be transduced into sporting flagella of a different antigenic structure by infection with P22 phage grown on a donor strain with flagella of the second kind. With this system, the previous finding of transduction of single genetic characters could be confirmed. But there appeared also an exception to the general rule of single marker transduction: two characters, one pertaining to the function and one pertaining to the antigenic structure of flagella, though usually transduced separately, were occasionally *cotransduced* in a single event. This observation suggested that transducing phage particles can sometimes carry a segment of the bacterial chromosome long enough for neighboring genetic loci to travel together from donor to recipient cell. Or, conversely, the occasional cotransduction of the two flagellar characters implied that their genetic loci are closely linked on the *Salmonella* chromosome.

It was obvious that the behavior of linked genetic loci in transduction should be of great significance for understanding how the virus particles actually acquire parts of the donor genome and how these parts are later integrated into the recipient genome. Hence it seemed a pity that transduction had been encountered only in *Salmonella*, then still largely a genetic *terra incognita*, and not in *E. coli* K12, for which a variety of mutant characters were available whose linkage relations on the bacterial chromosome had already been established by conjugational analysis. It was good news, therefore, when both Lennox (410) and Jacob (326) found that the two closely related phage strains P1 and 363 are capable of transducing genetic markers from donor to recipient cells in *E. coli*. [Phage P1 was isolated by Bertani (65a) from the venerable *E. coli* strain with which Bordet (79) twenty-five years earlier had proved the existence of lysogeny, and phage 363 was isolated at the hospital of the Pasteur Institute.] This discovery made it possible to show that none of the genetic characters previously known to be situated at distant loci of the *E. coli* chromosome are ever cotransduced. But it could also be shown now that the two linked genetic loci Thr and Leu (see Fig. 12-6), concerned with the synthesis of the amino acids threonine and leucine, *are* cotransducible with a frequency of about 1%; that is to say, about 1% of Thr$^-$ recipient bacteria into which the Thr$^+$ allele of the donor bacterium has been transduced has also obtained the (unselected) Leu allele of the donor strain. The distance between Thr and Leu is approximately 2% of the total length of the *E. coli* genome; although they act as very closely linked genetic sites in the recombi national events ensuing upon bacterial conjugation, the linkage of these genes is thus just barely demonstrable in transduction.

Lennox and Jacob also utilized their discovery of transduction in *E. coli* for a demonstration that lysogeny, like any other hereditary factor, is transducible. For this purpose, phages of strain P1 or 363 were grown on a K12(λ^-) donor culture that was not lysogenic for phage λ, and then a lysogenic multiple mutant Thr$^-$Lac$^-$Gal$^-$ K12(λ) recipient culture carrying the λ prophage was infected with these phages. All the Thr$^+$ or Lac$^+$ transductants then selected for synthesis of threonine or fermentation of lactose were still found to carry the λ prophage. But among the Gal$^+$ transductants that had arisen in this experiment some 10% no longer carried the λ prophage: the nonlysogenicity of the donor bacterium had been transduced into the lysogenic recipient cell. A complementary experiment, in which a Thr$^+$Lac$^+$Gal$^+$ K12(λ) donor strain carried the λ prophage and the Thr$^-$Lac$^-$Gal$^-$ recipient was nonlysogenic, showed that whereas here none of the Thr$^+$ or Lac$^+$ transductants had become lysogenic, about 10% of the Gal$^+$ transductants had acquired the λ prophage. This result thus confirms the conclusions already reached in the preceding chapter, that lysogeny and nonlysogeny represent alternative states of the bacterial nucleus and that there is a definite site on the *E. coli* chromosome (Fig. 12-6) closely linked to the Gal locus at which the λ prophage resides. It is this locus in its λ^- state that is exchanged for the homologous λ^+ recipient locus when nonlysogenicity is cotransduced with Gal$^+$ from the K12(λ^-) donor, and conversely, it is this locus in its λ^+ state that is exchanged for the λ^- recipient locus when lysogenicity is cotransduced with Gal$^+$ from the K12(λ) donor. We thus reach the surprising conclusion that the bacterial viruses P1 and 363 can carry within their proteinaceous heads the entire genome of the completely unrelated virus λ, as well as a segment of the host cell genome.

Fine-structure Mapping

The linkage of two genetic markers on the bacterial chromosome can thus be inferred from the relative frequency with which they are cotransduced: the greater the frequency of cotransduction, the closer the linkage. This is eminently plausible, for after all, the closer the two markers, the greater should be the chance that they happen to be incorporated into one and the same transducing phage particle. But if one examines cotransduction of genetic markers so closely linked that, if transduced at all, they ought nearly always be carried in the same phage particle, one finds nevertheless that such markers do not invari-

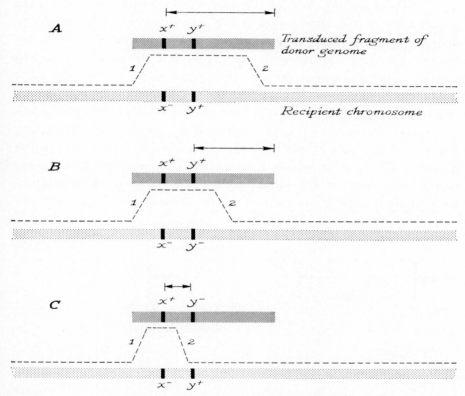

Fig. 13-2. Double crossovers in the neighborhood of two closely linked genetic sites x and y required to generate x^+y^+ transductants. **A.** If the x^+y^+ wild type acts as donor and the x^-y^+ single mutant acts as recipient. **B.** If the x^+y^+ wild type acts as donor and the x^-y^- double mutant acts as recipient. **C.** If the x^+y^- single mutant acts as donor and the x^-y^+ single mutant acts as recipient. The arrow in each panel indicates the length of the genetic segment within which the second crossover must occur.

ably show up together in the same transductant bacterium. This transductional *segregation* of very closely linked markers is, no doubt, a reflection of the process of genetic recombination by which the transduced genetic donor loci become integrated into the genome of the recipient cell. As shown in Fig. 13-2, a double crossover is required for every integration act. It follows, therefore, that two closely linked genetic markers of the donor genome brought into the same recipient cell are integrated together into one and the same recombinant genome, only if *neither one* of the two required crossovers occurs anywhere *between* them. Since the chance that one of the two required exchanges *will* occur between the two markers increases with their distance, it is possible to infer the map distance of very closely linked genetic sites from the frequency of their cotransduction, or to obtain in this way a *fine-structure map* of a small segment of the bacterial chromosome.

M. and Z. Demerec (173, 174, 177) were the first to take advantage of this possibility, and they mapped the chromosomal region of *Salmonella typhimurium* concerned with the synthesis of the amino acid tryptophan. For this purpose they focused their attention on a set of Try⁻ auxotrophic mutants of *Salmonella*, which Brenner (88) had divided into distinct groups according to the exact step in the pathway of tryptophan biosynthesis that each mutant is unable to carry out (Fig. 13-3). Mutants

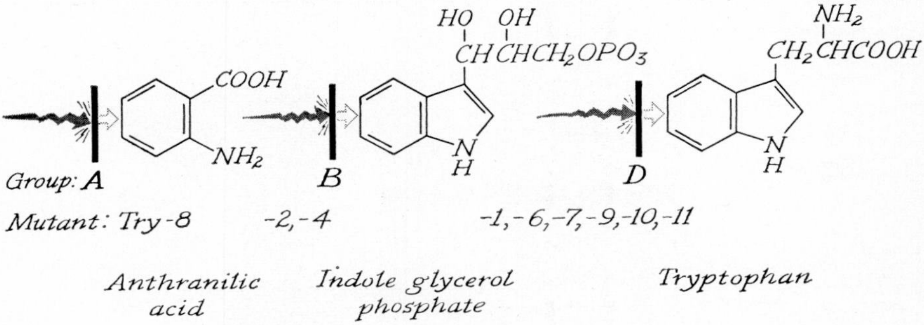

Fig. 13-3. The terminal three steps in the biosynthesis of tryptophan in *Salmonella* and a list of Try⁻ mutants that are blocked at the step under which their numbers are written. Mutants of group A will grow on minimal medium if supplied with anthranilic acid *or* with indole glycerol phosphate *or* with tryptophan. Mutants of group B will grow in minimal medium if supplied with *either* indole glycerol phosphate *or* tryptophan. Mutants of group D will grow on minimal medium *only* if supplied with tryptophan.

of group A are not able to synthesize anthranilic acid; mutants of group B cannot convert anthranilic acid into indole glycerol phosphate; mutants of group D cannot convert indole glycerol phosphate into tryptophan. The Demerec carried out many cross-transduction experiments in which each of the ten Try⁻ auxotrophs acted both as donor and as recipient for Try loci transduced by phage P22. These experiments

also included transductions in which the Try$^+$ prototrophic wild type
Salmonella acted as donor strain and each of the Try$^-$ mutants as
recipient. The results of this study are presented in Table 13-I. It
can be seen, first of all, that the greatest number of transductants

TABLE 13-I

Transductional Fine-structure Mapping of the Try Region of the Salmonella *Chromosome**

Phage P22, grown on the donor Try$^-$ auxotroph, was allowed to infect a culture of
the recipient Try$^-$ auxotroph at a multiplicity of 5 particles per cell. After an adsorption
period of 5–15 minutes, about 2×10^7 bacteria of the infected culture were spread on a
synthetic agar plate containing only a trace of tryptophan. The figures of the table
indicate the total number of Try$^+$ transductant colonies found on 4 plates after incubation for 2 days. The boxes enclose the results of cross-transductions between mutants
belonging to the same group.

Recipi-ent	\multicolumn{9}{c	}{Donor}	Try$^+$ (wild type)
	Try$_{\bar{1}}$	Try$_{\bar{6}}$	Try$_{\bar{7}}$	Try$_{\bar{9}}$	Try$_{\overline{10}}$	Try$_{\overline{11}}$	Try$_{\bar{2}}$	Try$_{\bar{4}}$	Try$_{\bar{8}}$	
Try$_{\bar{1}}$	0	66	203	104	219	208	706	458	418	1264
Try$_{\bar{6}}$	141	0	11	60	21	182	179	234	100	1617
Try$_{\bar{7}}$	21	2	0	10	19	22	537	435	107	717
Try$_{\bar{9}}$	26	8	41	0	101	66	361	247	437	1456
Try$_{\overline{10}}$....	4	2	7	12	0	0	628	602	206	1822
Try$_{\overline{11}}$....	22	1	23	22	0	0	240	315	497	1406
Try$_{\bar{2}}$	542	375	126	320	295	440	0	18	66	3074
Try$_{\bar{4}}$	173	120	44	213	145	235	20	0	85	2257
Try$_{\bar{8}}$	144	123	138	560	345	111	125	44	0	3264

* From M. Demerec and Z. Hartman (177).

(roughly 10^{-5} per phage particle) is found when the Try$^+$ prototroph is
the donor strain. For here Try$^+$ transductants arise by *any* pair of double
crossovers that exchanged the Try$^+$ allele of the donor brought into the
recipient cell by the transducing phage particle for the Try$^-$ allele of
the recipient. The frequency of these Try$^+$ transductants is, therefore, a
measure of the *maximum* efficiency of transduction in this system.
Second, it can be seen that, with the exception of the cross Try$_{\overline{10}} \times$ Try$_{\overline{11}}$,
all cross-transductions of two different Try$^-$ mutants do generate Try$^+$
transductants, albeit in frequency considerably lower than that found
when the Try$^+$ prototroph acted as donor strain.

In order to account for this result, we may consider two Try⁻ mutant strains, Try_x^- and Try_y^-, whose Try⁻ mutations occurred at different sites (x and y) of the Try region of the *Salmonella* genome. Suppose that strain Try_x^- (which carries the x^- and y^+ alleles) is infected with a transducing phage that brings into the recipient cells the Try region of the Try_y^- mutant donor strain (thus bearing the x^+ and y^- alleles of the donor). If the double crossover that integrates the transduced fragment occurs in such a way that there is one crossover on the side of x distal to y and one between x and y, then x^+ and y^+ are brought into the same genome and a prototrophic transductant has been generated (Fig. 13-2). Thus the chance of producing a prototrophic transductant from a "cross" of two auxotrophs decreases with increasingly closer linkage of the sites of their auxotrophic mutations. In case the same auxotroph is used both as donor and as recipient, as in the "selfings" of Table 13-I, there is no chance at all that a crossover occurs between the mutated sites in donor and recipient genomes; hence no transductants can be expected, and none are found. The failure to find transductants in the cross $Try_{10}^- \times Try_{11}^-$ suggests that these mutants carry their auxotrophic mutations at the same site, as allelic recurrences of the same mutation.

After analyzing the relative frequencies of transductants of Table 13-I from this point of view, it can be concluded that the Try⁻ mutants again fall into three groups. Each group that had been recognized as a group on the basis of the biochemical block of its mutants also formed a group on the basis of the transduction tests, since cross-transduction between mutants belonging to the same group produced many fewer transductants than cross-transduction between mutants belonging to different groups. Hence the intellectually satisfactory inference could be drawn that the sites of mutation affecting precisely the same function are in general more closely linked to each other than to the sites of mutations affecting a different function, a conclusion already reached in Chapter 9 from our consideration of the fine structure of the T4rII mutants. But all cross-transductions between this set of auxotrophs produced fewer prototrophic transductants than cross-transductions in which the wild type prototroph acted as donor. Hence it could be inferred that the three groups of genetic sites controlling the sequential three steps in tryptophan biosynthesis are closely linked on the *Salmonella* chromosome. That is to say, cotransduction of any Try⁻ mutant site with the Try$^+$ wild type allele of any other site is much more probable than crossover between the two sites and exchange of only the Try$^+$ allele of the donor for the Try$^-$ allele of the recipient.

By means of further, more complicated three-factor transduction tests involving also the Cys locus (concerned with the synthesis of the amino acid cysteine) near the Try locus, it became possible to assign an *order* to the three groups of Try$^-$ mutant sites on the genetic linkage map; this order, amazingly enough, turned out to be A–B–D! Thus it appeared that not only are the three functionally related loci concerned with the synthesis of tryptophan closely linked on the *Salmonella* chromosome, but their sequential arrangement happens to coincide with the sequence of the biosynthetic reactions catalyzed by the enzymes they control. An analogous congruence of genetic and biochemical sequence in *Salmonella* was established also by P. Hartman for the histidine region (176, 267). In very extensive experiments with 200 His$^-$ mutants it could be shown that four genetic loci concerned with the formation of enzymes in the pathway of histidine biosynthesis are also closely linked in the *Salmonella* genome and arranged in an order that, with one exception, appears to mimic the biosynthetic sequence of histidine.

As will be seen in Chapter 15, it is now understood why functionally related genetic loci are often found to be closely linked. But why the order of these loci on the bacterial chromosome should reflect the sequence of the reactions they control still remains to be explained, an enigma whose solution might provide an important clue to some heretofore unsuspected function of the hereditary substance.

Abortive Transduction

In their experiments on the transduction of flagellar characters, Stocker, Zinder, and Lederberg (607, 608) noticed the frequent appearance of "trails" of microcolonies after inoculating soft agar with non-motile *Salmonella* recipient bacteria infected with P22 transducing phage grown on motile donor cells (Fig. 13-4). Though the continuous displacement of the microcolonies suggested that they represented clones of descendants of flagellated transductants moving through the soft agar, the microcolonies themselves proved on subculture to contain only nonmotile individuals. Stocker et al. explained these paradoxical observations in terms of what they called **abortive transduction:** the

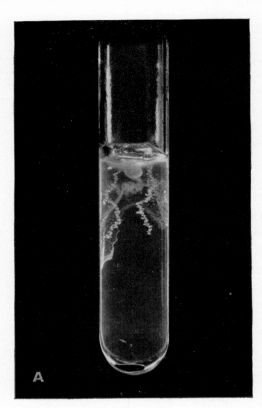

A

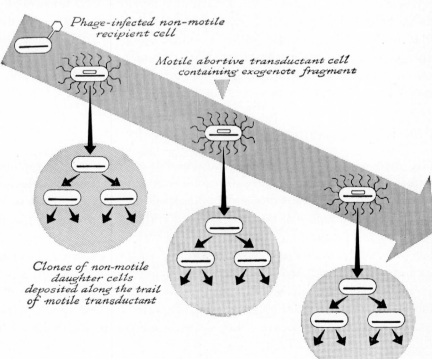

Phage-infected non-motile recipient cell

Motile abortive transductant cell containing exogenote fragment

Clones of non-motile daughter cells deposited along the trail of motile transductant

B

functional allele for flagellation of the donor bacterium is carried into the nonflagellated recipient bacterium by the transducing phage but is neither integrated into the recipient genome nor replicated during subsequent bacterial growth. The transduced segment from the donor bacterium, or **exogenote,** thus remains singular, like the genome of a temperate phage superinfecting an immune lysogenic cell. In spite of not being integrated, the exogenote fragment gives phenotypic expression to the genetic factors it carries into the recipient cell. Inasmuch as the allele for flagellation is dominant over the allele for nonflagellation, the **heterogenote** cell harboring both alleles becomes flagellated and motile. But since only one of the two daughter cells arising at each division of this abortively transduced motile cell can obtain the single copy of the exogenote allele, the other daughter cell necessarily gives rise again to a clone of nonflagellated, nonmotile cells. Thus at any stage after the abortive transduction there is present only one motile transductant cell that moves through the agar and deposits nonmotile descendants along its trail (Fig. 13-4).

Ozeki (499) later found that abortive transduction is not confined to flagellar characters, but occurs also in the transfer of genetic characters concerned with the biosynthesis of growth factors. In his work, Ozeki infected various purine-requiring mutants of the LT-22 strain of *Salmonella* with P22 phage grown on the purine-independent wild type strain and plated the infected bacterial population on purine-free minimal agar. These platings resulted in the appearance of stable purine-independent transductants that form normal colonies. However, in addition to these normal colonies there appeared an even greater number of *minute* colonies. Restreaking of these minute colonies on minimal agar revealed that each contained only one cell capable of

---

Fig. 13-4. Abortive transduction of motility in *Salmonella*. **A.** Trails produced by abortive transductants. A culture of the nonflagellated, and hence non-motile, recipient strain is infected with phage P22 grown on a motile donor strain. The infected bacteria are diluted and a sample planted on the top of a column of very soft agar in a test tube. The abortive transductants become motile and swim into the agar column, depositing nonmotile daughter cells in their wake. These daughter cells grow into macroscopic colonies. This photograph was taken after incubation of the tube for several days. [From Lederberg, *Genetics*, **41**: 845 (1956).] **B.** Diagrammatic explanation of trail formation. [After Stocker (607).]

forming a minute colony; all the rest of the thousands of bacteria of the minute colony could not grow at all in the absence of added purines. It thus appeared that the initiator of each minute colony was an abortively transduced cell that carried a nonreplicating prototrophic allele of the donor bacterium and was, therefore, capable of synthesizing its essential purines. Growth and division of the abortively transduced cell would only result in the production of purine-requiring auxotrophs

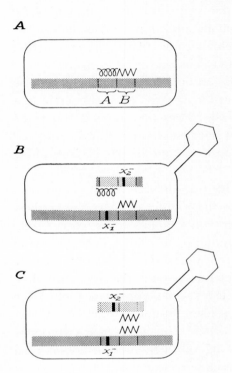

A

B

C

Fig. 13-5. Schematic representation of abortive transduction as a cistron test. **A.** The normal X^+ cell, in whose genome two cistrons, A and B, direct the formation of two specific polypeptides that function in the synthesis of the metabolite X. This bacterium will produce a normal colony on minimal agar, in the absence of any added X. **B** and **C.** Abortive transductants resulting from the transduction of a fragment of the X region of an X_2^- mutant donor cell into an X_1^- mutant recipient cell. **B.** The X_2^- donor mutation is situated in cistron B and the X_1^- recipient mutation in cistron A. Functional A and B cistron polypeptides will be formed in this abortive transductant, which can grow on minimal medium and produce a minute colony of X_1^- daughter cells. **C.** The X_2^- donor mutation is situated in cistron A, as is the X_1^- recipient mutation. No functional A cistron polypeptide will arise in this abortive transductant, which cannot grow on minimal medium to produce any visible colony.

that ceased growing on the minimal agar as soon as the purine supply provided by their abortively transduced progenitor was exhausted.

Abortive transduction provided a means for distinguishing operationally between different functional units (*cistrons*) of the bacterial chromosome, since it made possible a cis-trans test similar to that discussed in Chapter 10 in connection with the physiological genetics of *r*II mutants of phage T4. Two auxotrophic mutations, X_1^- and X_2^-, that engender the same general growth requirement pertain to different functional units, or fall within two different cistrons, A and B, if abortive X^+ transductants appear upon infecting X_1^- recipient bacteria with transducing phage grown on X_2^- donor bacteria. In this case, the heterogenote cell can carry out the necessary biosynthetic reactions, and thus grow into a minute colony on minimal agar, if the A cistron of the exogenote fragment forms an intact functional unit which is not disturbed by the X_2^- mutation, in the B cistron, and if the B cistron of the recipient genome is part of another intact functional unit that is not disturbed by the X_1^- mutation in the A cistron. However, if both X_1^- and X_2^- fall within the *same* cistron, for instance, within A, exogenote and recipient genome cannot complement each other by supplying the function of which the other is incapable, since both are unable to carry out the very same function. In this case the heterogenote cannot grow into a minute colony on minimal agar, and no abortive transductants become manifest (Fig. 13-5). *Stable* prototrophic transductants, in which the exogenote fragment has been integrated and replicated, can of course arise whether or not donor and recipient mutations belong to the same functional group, since, as long as the two mutations are nonallelic, an intact cistron can always be generated by genetic recombination between exogenote and recipient genome.

Ozeki examined from this point of view a set of nonallelic purine-requiring *Salmonella* mutants, which, like the Demerec' set of tryptophan auxotrophs, had been previously assigned to four different groups, both on the basis of their exact growth requirements and their genetic linkage. Ozeki found that whereas every cross-transduction using one of these auxotrophs as donor and another as recipient produced some stable, purine-independent transductants, only those crosses yielded minute colonies of abortive transductants in which donor and recipient belonged to different physiological groups. The four previously identified groups thus indeed correspond to four separate cistrons concerned with purine biosynthesis.

Specialized Transduction

The kind of gene transfer discussed so far in this chapter is called **generalized transduction,** because transducing phages such as P22 in *Salmonella* or P1 in *Escherichia* can transfer a great variety of loci of the bacterial genome from donor to recipient cell at the same, albeit rather low, frequency of 10^{-5} to 10^{-7} transductants per phage. It must not be thought now that the capacity to carry out generalized transduction is a universal, or even common, property of temperate bacteriophages. On the contrary, the capacity for generalized transduction seems to be the exception rather than the rule. It was really fortunate that Zinder and Lederberg happened to select a strain carrying the P22 prophage in their search for genetic exchange in *Salmonella*. And Lennox, as well as Jacob, had to examine many types of temperate phages active on *E. coli* K12 before he found the one that would carry out the desired gene transfer.

Like Lennox and Jacob, the Lederbergs and their student Morse (483, 484) were looking for transduction in *E. coli* K12 and considered the possibility that phage λ might be able to do for *Escherichia* what phage P22 can do for *Salmonella*. They therefore carried out an experiment in which the λ prophage of a culture of prototrophic, wild type K12(λ) was induced with UV light in order to generate a lysate of λ phages. A variety of nonlysogenic mutant cultures of K12 was then infected with these λ phages and plated on various selective agars, in order to test whether any of the wild type alleles of the donor strain had been transduced into the mutant recipients. The results of this survey were mostly negative: none of the donor characters was found to have been transduced by λ phage. There was one important exception, however: in the case in which the nonlysogenic recipient bacteria had been Gal$^-$, about 10^{-6} of the λ-infected Gal$^-$ bacteria had actually acquired the Gal$^+$ character of the wild type donor strain. It was thus found that phage λ *is* capable of some kind of transduction, but only of a **specialized** sort that appertains exclusively to the Gal region in the vicinity of the λ prophage site (Fig. 12-6). Phage λ does not seem capable of generalized transduction of genetic loci from any other part of the bacterial genome.

Upon closer examination of the clones of transduced bacteria which had acquired the Gal$^+$ character of the prototrophic donor cell, it was found, first of all, that all the Gal$^+$ transductants were either actively lysogenic (liberated infective λ phages on induction) or at least immune to infection by exogenous λ, showing that the nonlysogenic K12 Gal$^-$ recipient cell had acquired the λ prophage along with the exogenote Gal$^+$ fragment. Second, it was found that most of these Gal$^+$ transductants were genetically *unstable;* each Gal$^+$ colony contained about 1–10% of individuals that had lost the Gal$^+$ character and were once more of the same Gal$^-$ genotype as their recipient ancestor. The frequent segregation of recipient genotypes by the transductants (estimated to be about 2×10^{-3} per bacterial division), led to the inference that these transductants are actually Gal$^+$/Gal$^-$ *heterogenotes*, in which the Gal$^+$ chromosomal fragment brought in by the transducing λ phage has been *added* to the recipient genome, rather than exchanged for its Gal$^-$

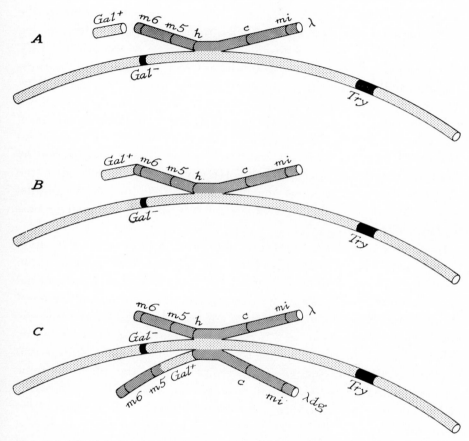

Fig. 13-6. Evolution of the ideas on the genetic structure of Gal$^+$/Gal$^-$ heterogenote transductants, resulting from infection of Gal$^-$ *E. coli* recipients with λ phage progeny issued from a lysogenic, Gal$^+$ donor strain. **A.** An autonomous Gal$^+$ fragment of the donor genome transduced by the λ virus is added to the recipient genome, instead of replacing its Gal$^-$ alleles. **B.** A Gal$^+$ fragment of the donor genome is joined to the λ phage genome, and hence to the prophage. **C.** A Gal$^+$ donor fragment is part of the defective λ phage genome, where it replaces the viral *h* region. The heterogenote transductant is polylysogenic, carrying both defective λdg and normal λ++ prophages.

alleles (Fig. 13-6A). In this case, the Gal⁻ segregants would represent individuals from which the Gal⁺ exogenote fragment has been lost.

But a most remarkable thing was found when the λ prophage of a culture of such lysogenic Gal⁺/Gal⁻ heterogenotes was induced by UV light: the lysate of infective λ phages resulting from this induction possessed an extraordinarily high transducing power, since nearly half of the virus particles now appeared to be capable of transducing the Gal⁺ character into new Gal⁻ recipient cells. Such lysates were called HFT, for high-frequency transduction, in contrast to the original LFT (low-frequency transduction) lysates from which the heterogenote trans-ductants had first been obtained at a frequency of only about 10^{-6} transductants per phage. As is the case for LFT lysates, HFT lysates can transduce only the Gal character, and the transductants produced are mostly unstable lysogenic Gal⁺/Gal⁻ heterogenotes, which yield further HFT lysates upon UV induction. The Gal character carried by the transducing phage particles of the HFT lysate appears to reside in the viral genome, since infective and transducing titers increase in parallel upon lytic growth of the HFT phages on λ-sensitive, nonlysogenic host bacteria (674).

In order to explain these observations, one could imagine that upon UV induction of the prophage of the original K12(λ)Gal⁺ donor strain there is produced in about 10^{-4} to 10^{-6} of the lysogenic cells an unusual phage genome that, prior to leaving its prophage site on the bacterial chromosome, happens to incorporate the neighboring Gal loci into the viral genome and appears as a mature phage particle in the LFT lysate. When such a bastard virus—part phage, part bacterium—infects and lysogenizes the nonlysogenic Gal⁻ recipient cell, the phage genome attaches itself at or near its usual chromosomal site and thus produces a Gal⁺/Gal⁻ heterogenote, in which the Gal⁺ exogenote forms part of the prophage (Fig. 13-6B). From time to time, during the growth and reproduction of the Gal⁺/Gal⁻ heterogenotes, the extra Gal⁺ fragment might become detached from the prophage, an event that would give rise to a Gal⁻ segregant. Alternatively, the Gal⁺ fragment might also undergo genetic exchange with its homologous nearby Gal⁻ alleles on the recipient chromosome, to generate a stable Gal⁺ recombinant bacterium that no longer throws off any Gal⁻ segregants. In any case, upon UV induction of the heterogenote, the prophage, together with its extra fragment, would enter the vegetative state and give rise to a burst of λ progeny phages, all carrying their Gal⁺ loci; that is, it would produce an HFT lysate. When these λ progeny in turn infect sensitive recipient cells, new Gal⁺/Gal⁻ heterogenote transductant lines would be established.

But subsequently, Arber, G. Kellenberger, and Weigle (28, 31), as well as Campbell (125), found that the specialized Gal transduction by λ phage is somewhat more complicated than this simplified image. For if nonlysogenic Gal⁻ recipient bacteria are infected at a *low multiplicity of infection* with the λ phages of an HFT lysate, so that each bacterium that is infected at all is infected with only *one* phage particle, then practically all heterogenote Gal⁺/Gal⁻ transductants produced appear to be *defective* lysogenics; though they liberate no infective λ phages, they are immune to superinfection by exogenous λ particles. Such transductants harbor a defective prophage because just those phage particles in the HFT lysate which carry the Gal⁺ marker of the donor cell are themselves defective, unable to reproduce in single infection and hence unable to form plaques. But the *infective* λ particles of the lysate have no transducing power whatsoever.

These defective transducing particles now go under the name of λ*dg*. Like the other defective λ mutant strains discussed in Chapter 12, the λ*dg* phages of the HFT lysate can multiply vegetatively and give rise to structurally intact progeny viruses, as long as they are together in the same cell with nondefective, normal λ helper phages that can supply the missing synthetic or morphogenetic functions to the defective genome. The λ*dg* phages can, therefore, be crossed to nondefective, genetically marked λ, and the site of the defectivity in the transducing genome located on the λ genetic linkage map. Such crosses showed that the defectivity of the λ*dg* particles, as well as their transducing power, arises from an *exchange* of the Gal region of the bacterium for about one-third to one-fourth of the whole phage genome, so that the defective λ*dg* phages are entirely missing some of their own essential genetic factors (28, 126). The missing viral genes belonged to the *h* region of the λ phage genome, the same region in which, as seen in Fig. 12-7, the most helpless types of defective λ, such as λ*d*32 and λ*d*34, have their defectivity mutant sites. Nondefective or actively lysogenic Gal⁺ transductants are therefore obtained only if the nonlysogenic Gal⁻ bacteria are infected at a high multiplicity of infection with the phages of the HFT lysate, so that every cell that has been infected with a λ*dg* transducing phage has, at the same time, also been infected with a normal, nontransducing λ particle. The probable genetic structure of the actively lysogenic Gal⁺/Gal⁻ heterogenotes, which are evidently *polylysogenic*, carrying both defective λ*dg* and nondefective λ+ + prophages, is shown in Fig. 13-6C. Segregation of Gal⁻ genotypes during the growth of the Gal⁺/Gal⁻

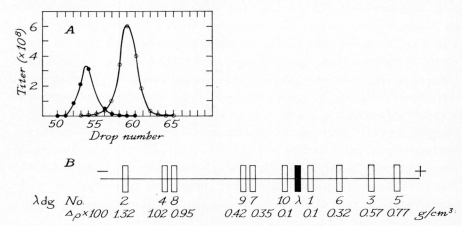

Fig. 13-7. Density differences between normal λ+ + and λ*dg* transducing phages. **A.** Density gradient centrifugation in a concentrated cesium chloride solution of an HFT lysate obtained by UV induction of a Gal⁺/Gal⁻ heterogenote transductant. After sedimentation equilibrium has been reached and the phages have moved into bands corresponding to their density, the centrifuge is stopped and the contents of the centrifugate tube collected drop by drop through a hole in the bottom of the tube. The drops are assayed for their titers of normal plaque-forming λ+ + phages (open circles) and λ*dg* transducing phages (solid circles). An increasing tube number on the abscissa represents decreasing density. It is apparent that the λ*dg* particles of this HFT lysate are more dense than normal λ+ + particles. **B.** Densities of some λ*dg* stocks of independent origin. Each vertical bar represents the band position of one of ten different λ*dg* transducing strains, as well as that of the λ+ + wild type, in a cesium chloride density gradient. The difference between the densities of each strain and of the λ+ + wild type, Δρ, is shown here multiplied by 100. [From Weigle, Meselson, and Paigen (677).]

heterogenote transductants would thus represent the occasional loss of the defective Gal⁺ prophage; and appearance of mature λ*dg* phage particles in HFT lysates upon UV induction of the lysogenic heterogenote would derive from the joint intracellular vegetative development of the defective λ*dg* and normal λ+ + helper prophages.

The incorporation of fragments of host genome into phage genome can also be demonstrated by physicochemical techniques, since the buoyant density of λdg phages differs from that of normal $\lambda + +$ virus particles (677). That is, the genetic events that exchange the Gal region of the bacterial chromosome for the h region of the viral linkage map do not appear to be reciprocal and hence result in defective transducing phages that comprise either more or less DNA than the normal λ genome. Since the viral protein, whose amount per λ phage particle is probably constant, is less dense than the viral DNA, λdg phages carrying either more or less DNA than $\lambda + +$ have a correspondingly greater or lesser weight per unit volume than normal infective phage particles (Fig. 13-7). This difference in buoyant density permits the physical separation of mixtures of defective and normal phage particles and hence the preparation of pure stocks of λdg, free of the infective λ helper phages in whose absence in the host cell the defective genome could not have achieved maturation as an intact virus.

The Relation of Generalized to Specialized Transduction

The discovery that specialized λ transducing particles are defective stimulated analogous experiments designed to test the possible defectivity of the generalized transducing P22 and P1 phages. In previous work on generalized transduction, the transductants recovered after infection of nonlysogenic recipients were usually lysogenic (carried the prophage of the transducing virus), because proper precautions had not been taken to avoid multiple infection of the nonlysogenic recipients by the transducing phage stock. When conditions of true single infection were at last realized, it was found that transducing P22 and P1 likewise carry a functionally or structurally abnormal genome. However, in contrast to the *defective* lysogenic transductants encountered after single infection of K12(λ^-)Gal$^-$ with λdg, nearly all transductants appearing after single infection of nonlysogenic *Salmonella* or *Escherichia* with P22 or P1 transducing phages turned out to be *nonlysogenic*, still sensitive to the phage type that transduced them (1, 586, 707). Lysogenic transductants *can*, of course, be obtained if the recipient bacteria are infected with several P22 or P1 phages per cell. Phage populations liberated by UV induction of such lysogenic transductants, however, do not possess the high transducing power comparable to that of HFT lysates produced by the induction of the Gal^+/Gal^- heterogenote clones encountered after specialized transduction.

The differences between generalized and specialized transduction may now be summarized. In generalized transduction, the transducing phage can transfer *any* genetic character of the donor to the recipient at a frequency of about 10^{-5} to 10^{-7} transductants per phage. The transductants that arise are genetically stable *homogenotes*, from which the allele of the recipient genome replaced by the transduced character has disappeared. The transducing phage particle does not establish itself as a prophage in the transductants, which, provided that multiple infection of the recipient cells has been avoided, are nonlysogenic and phage-sensitive. In specialized transduction, only a very restricted part of the donor genome—namely, that contiguous to the prophage site of the transducing phage—can be transferred to the recipient cell. The transductants that arise are genetically unstable *heterogenotes* that harbor both the donor allele brought in by the defective transducing phage genome and the allele of the recipient bacterium. The transducing phage particle establishes itself as a defective prophage in the transductant, which is a defective lysogen immune to superinfection by exogenous homologous phage. And UV induction of transductants containing also a normal, helper prophage leads to the production of HFT lysates which contain a high proportion of mature, defective transducing particles.

Do these differences really signify that generalized and specialized transduction are entirely different phenomena, or is it possible that both represent but alternative manifestations of the same fundamental process? The much wider range of characters transducible by P1 than by λ can, in fact, be explained: the one temperate phage for which Jacob and Wollman (341) could not find any definite prophage site on the *E. coli* chromosome (see p. 325) was precisely phage 363, the close relative of P1 that is also capable of generalized transduction. One may imagine, therefore, that a phage type can achieve generalized transduction because its prophage, unlike that of λ, does not occupy a permanent specific site on the bacterial chromosome but is, instead, deposited temporarily at many different chromosomal sites. Such a phage would thus have the opportunity to exchange many different segments of the host cell genome for part of its own viral genome in order to generate a defective transducing phage.

But how can one reconcile the differences in the *character* of the transductants that appear as a consequence of the two types of trans-ductions? The answer to this question was provided by Luria, Adams, and Ting (442), who showed by means of a comparative study of transduction in two different bacterial species that the nature of the products of generalized and specialized transduction can also be understood on a unitary basis. In these experiments, the ability to ferment lactose (Lac$^+$) was transduced by phage P1 between strains of *E. coli* K12 and *Shigella dysenteriae*. When P1 phage was grown on a Lac$^+$ donor strain of K12 and then allowed to infect a Lac$^-$ mutant strain of K12, Lac$^+$ transductants appeared in a frequency of 10^{-5} to 10^{-6} per infective P1 particle adsorbed. These Lac$^+$ clones were genetically stable and possessed all the other typical attributes of transductants produced in generalized transduction. When Lac$^-$ *Shigella* recipient bacteria were infected with the same *Escherichia*-grown P1 phage stock, however, Lac$^+$ transductants appeared only in a frequency of 10^{-7} to 10^{-8} per infective P1 particle adsorbed. These transductants, furthermore, were genetically unstable; the Lac$^+$ clones sported frequent Lac$^-$ segregants, and could be shown to carry their Lac$^+$ exogenote fragment as part of a defective P1*dl* prophage. And UV induction of Lac$^+$ *Shigella* transductants that carried also a nondefective, helper P1 prophage, gave rise to HFT lysates that could transduce the Lac$^+$ character with high frequency into Lac$^-$ *Shigella* or *Escherichia* recipients. The Lac$^+$ *Shigella* clones consequently possessed all the typical attributes of transductants produced by *special-ized*, rather than generalized, transduction.

Luria, Adams, and Ting thus found that, depending on the nature of the recipient strain, the self-same population of P1 phages can give rise to transductants of either type, and they explained this in terms of the degree of genetic *homology* of transduced fragment and recipient chromo-some. When *Escherichia* was both donor and recipient, the exogenote and its recipient alleles were entirely homologous (except for the single Lac$^-$ mutant site), so that the double crossovers required for integrating the Lac$^+$ allele of the donor into the transductant genome could occur much more readily than the establishment of the defective P1*dl* genome as prophage on the recipient chromosome. When *Shigella*, phylogenetically distant from the donor *Escherichia*, was the recipient, however, very little homology existed between the exogenote and any corresponding region of the recipient chromosome, so that the probability of occurrence of the genetic exchange necessary for integration of the donor fragment was very much below the chance that the P1*dl* genome lysogenized the Lac⁻ *Shigella* recipient.

The following unified interpretation of transduction was, therefore, proposed. A segment of the chromosome of the donor cell becomes "associated" with the genome of the transducing phage and is incorporated into a maturing virus particle. Once in the recipient bacterium, the transducing element either becomes prophage by lysogenization, along with the phage genome of which it forms part, or it becomes integrated into the bacterial chromosome by genetic exchange, without the rest of the phage genome. The character of the transductants recovered then depends on which of these alternatives is relatively more probable; these probabilities depend, in turn, on the extent of the defectivity of the transducing element as a viral genome, on the opportunities that may exist for expression of those viral functions of which the transducing element is still capable, and on the degree of genetic homology between exogenote and recipient chromosome. Finally, *abortive* transductants may be thought to derive from transducing elements that, because of their defectivity, are unable to multiply and have little capacity for genetic exchange, and hence are *neither* reduced to prophage *nor* integrated into the recipient chromosome.

*   *   *

Bacteria and their viruses thus stand revealed as one general genetic system, as viral genome turned out to be part of bacterial genome in lysogeny and bacterial genome part of viral genome in transduction.

Further Reading

Jacob, F. and Wollman, E. L., *Sexuality and the Genetics of Bacteria* (342). The definitive monograph on conjugation and genetic recombination in *E. coli*. Contains also valuable discussions of lysogeny and transduction.

Zinder, N. D. and Lederberg, J., "Genetic exchange in *Salmonella*" (709). The discovery of transduction.

Ozeki, H., "Abortive transduction in purine-requiring mutants of *Salmonella typhimurium*" (499).

Jacob, F., "Transduction of lysogeny in *Escherichia coli*" (326). One of the proofs of the chromosomal situation of the prophage.

Hartman, P. E., "Transduction: a comparative review" (268). A detailed account of the first four years of work on transduction.

Jacob, F., "Genetic control of viral functions" (327). A semipopular account of the physiological genetics of bacterial viruses.

CHAPTER 14

Comparative Bacterial Virology

Fate of the Host Cell Nucleus—The Capacity—Autarky—Genetic Interaction between Phage and Host—Host-controlled Modification—Minute Phages—An Exception that Disproves the Rule

SINCE THE preceding discussions on the physiology, genetics, and radiobiology of bacterial viruses of Chapters 3 to 11 were concerned almost exclusively with the T-even strains, it was surely presumptuous to have spoken so frequently of *the* bacteriophage, when, in fact, only T2 or T4 could have been properly meant (and when the general applicability to bacterial viruses of this or that inference may be either unsupported by any direct evidence, or, worse yet, even be contradicted by experience). But it was necessary to give this very one-sided account because with no other types of bacteriophages has there been carried out an amount of chemical and biological work comparable to the effort already expended on the T-even strains. Any attempt to present an integral view of bacterial viruses must, therefore, be either blithely one-sided in favor of the T-even strains, or else be constantly interspersed with distractive reminders of the behavior of other, less-known bacteriophage types. But so that some redress might be given to the parochial outlook engendered by this preoccupation with only one phage-host system, we shall now consider a few of those aspects of the T-even strains which set them apart from other bacteriophages. Of course, the considerations of Chapters 12 and 13 have shown already a most important difference between the T-even phages and phage types such as λ or P1 : the T-even strains do not manifest the peaceful genetic coexistence with their bacterial hosts that makes possible lysogeny and transduction. It will now be seen that this exclusion of T-even phages from the prophage state is actually only one of many, at first sight superficially unconnected, consequences of what we will refer to as their **autark** way of life, in contrast to the much greater dependence of temperate phages on physiological functions supplied by their bacterial hosts. In this penultimate chapter, we shall also examine briefly some other phage types that are so different from the T-even strains that, except for the methodology used in their study, they have little in common with any of the kinds of bacterial viruses so far discussed.

Fate of the Host Cell Nucleus

The DNA of bacteria is localized in distinct **chromatin bodies,** their "nuclei" (527). As pointed out in Chapter 2, these bacterial nuclei differ structurally and chemically from the nuclei of higher cells [and hence Kellenberger (355) prefers to call them "nucleoids," a more conservative appellation]. But their behavior does make them the functional equivalent of true nuclei: they harbor the hereditary factors of the cell and are

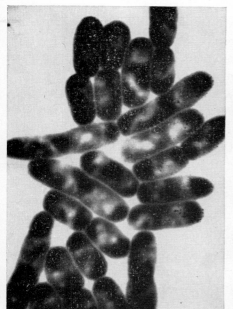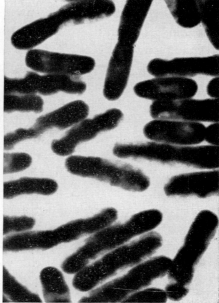

Fig. 14-1. Nuclear breakdown of *E. coli* infected with bacteriophage T2. The preparation is colored with a DNA-specific stain, fixed, and examined in a high-power microscope. *Left panel:* uninfected, growing bacteria with normal nuclei. *Right panel:* bacteria some time after their infection with an average of ten T2 particles per cell, showing breakdown of the cell nucleus and appearance of marginal vacuoles. [From Kellenberger (356).]

in control of its physiological functions. What happens to these bacterial nuclei in the course of intracellular phage growth? This question has been resolved by staining phage-infected bacteria at various times after the onset of phage development and examining the preparations in the microscope. In this way, it was found that within 2 to 3 minutes after infection with T-even phages, the nuclei of *E. coli* bacteria are disrupted into small blocks of chromatin material, which collect at the periphery of the cell. At later stages, toward the end of the eclipse period, the entire infected cell fills up with chromatin, representing, no doubt, the DNA of the phage progeny (157, 449, 489) (Fig. 14-1). The same sequence of events was already seen very clearly in Fig. 6-6 in the electron micrographs of ultrathin sections of T-even infected bacteria prepared at various stages of the intracellular phage growth. This nuclear breakdown is still elicited by infection with UV-inactivated T-even phages (449) but not by empty DNA-free phage "ghosts" (77). Protein synthesis is necessary for starting this breakdown, since nuclei of bacteria infected with T-even phages in the presence of chloramphenicol retain their morphological identity so long as protein synthesis is inhibited by the presence of the antibiotic (355). These facts lead one to infer that the breakdown of the host nucleus results from the action of an "early" phage enzyme (possibly the deoxyribonuclease described in Chapter 7), whose synthesis is induced by the infecting viral DNA at the outset of vegetative phage development (502). The cytologic observation of the phage-induced disruption of the host nucleus is, of course, in harmony with the chemical finding, mentioned in Chapter 6, that during T-even phage growth the major part of the host DNA is degraded to substances of low molecular weight that are subsequently repolymerized into phage-specific polynucleotides and appear as the *bacterial contribution* among the DNA of the progeny viruses.

The cytologic picture found with bacteria infected with T-even phages is, however, very different from that encountered with phages T1, T7, λ, P1, or P22 (354, 449, 555, 679). Here the nuclei of the infected cells *retain* their morphological identity throughout most of the latent period, although some modification of nuclear structure becomes manifest at the last stages of phage growth. That this second group of phages leaves the nucleus of its host intact is also attested by the continued synthesis in the infected cells of bacterial protein (323), and in particular of bacterial enzymes (322, 571), in contrast to T-even infected bacteria, in which, as was seen in Chapter 7, the destruction of the host nucleus by the virus immediately brings to term synthesis of all host proteins. This degradation of the host DNA during intracellular growth of T-even phages is probably also connected with the *genetic exclusion* and *breakdown* of the viral DNA of homologous secondary phages super-infecting a T-even infected cell (see pp. 153–154), since phages of the second group that leave the nucleus intact do not induce genetic exclusion (329, 631), or breakdown (228) of superinfecting phages, or synthesis of a phage-specific deoxyribonuclease (503).

The Capacity

The differential treatment that T-even strains, on the one hand, and phages such as T1, λ, and P22, on the other, accord to the nucleus of their host can now be compared with the degree to which these strains appear to require the *integrity* of that same nucleus for their successful repro-duction.

T2 bacteriophages can still grow on bacteria that have been sterilized by irradiation with UV, that is have lost the ability to give rise to colonies when plated on nutrient agar (14). This can be demonstrated by exposing suspensions of *E. coli* to various doses of UV and infecting these bacteria with T2 phages. A phage which happens to be adsorbed to a bacterium in which the UV irradiation has left intact the **capacity** to reproduce the infecting particle will multiply in that cell, and, if the infected complex is plated on sensitive indicator bacteria before the end of the latent period, it will give rise to one plaque on the assay plate. It is seen in this way that the capacity of *E. coli* to reproduce T2 is very resistant to UV; extremely high doses have to be delivered to the bacteria before an appreciable fraction of the infective centers is lost. For example, a UV dose which still leaves intact the capacity of 1 in 3 of the bacteria permits the (extrapolated) survival of only 1 in 10^{13} of the bacteria as colony formers. The T2 capacity of *E. coli* is not only much more resistant than its colony-forming ability but also more resistant than the survival of the free T2 phages themselves. Similar results can be observed also for the capacity to reproduce other T-even strains (49, 390, 624). The high UV resistance of the bacterial capacity for T2 growth was actually taken for granted implicitly in our discussion of the Luria-Latarjet experiment in Chapter 11. It would have been impossible to study the UV sensitivity of intracellular T2 phage if the capacity of the bacterium, which is of necessity irradiated together with the intracellular phage in that experiment, were *more* radiosensitive than the virus.

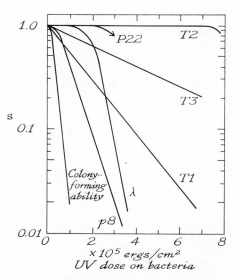

Fig. 14-2. UV-sensitivity of the bacterial capacity to support growth of the coliphages T1, T2, T3, λ, of the *Salmonella* phage P22 and of the *Pyocyanea* phage p8. The ordinate shows the fraction of the population of UV-irradiated bacterial hosts still capable of reproducing the particular phage or of forming a colony, after exposure to the UV dose shown on the abscissa. [From Stent (594).]

The high resistance of the T-even capacity of *E. coli* to UV irradiation might seem, at first sight, somewhat surprising, since already at UV doses which still leave that capacity fully intact, serious metabolic disturbances of the bacterial cells make their appearance. The synthesis of bacterial DNA, for instance, is already suppressed in *E. coli* after exposure to 4×10^4 ergs/cm^2 of UV (365, 654), a dose which, as can be seen in Fig. 14-2, preserves the T2 capacity in all the bacteria. It would thus appear as though the T-even phages are endowed with a reproductive autonomy which allows them to direct the synthesis of infective progeny viruses within host cells that have sustained serious lesions in their UV-sensitive nucleus.

Subsequent experiments revealed that the capacity of the bacterial host for reproduction of other bacteriophage types is much more radiosensitive than its capacity to support the growth of the T-even strains. Benzer and Jacob (61), the first to use the term "capacity" in this connection, observed that the capacity of *Pseudomonas pyocyanea* to reproduce phage p8, although still being more radioresistant than the colony-forming ability of the cells, is more sensitive to UV than the free phages themselves. Similar studies on phages T1, T3, λ, and P22 showed that the capacity of bacteria for the reproduction of these phages is also much more radiosensitive than the capacity for the T-even strains (61, 239. 324, 362, 624). In Fig. 14-2, the results of various capacity studies have been plotted together; evidently there exists a wide variation in the UV sensitivity of the capacity among different phage-host systems. In the case of those coliphages, such as T1, T3, λ, and T-even, which are active on the same bacterial strain, this differential sensitivity can only mean that after having been exposed to a given dose of UV the same bacterial cell can still support the reproduction of one but not of another type of infecting bacteriophage particle. Analogous studies have also been carried out on the relative sensitivity of the capacity to radiations other than UV. These experiments have shown that the capacity for T-even phages is also much more resistant to inactivation by X-rays (391, 529) than the capacity for phage P22 (239) or for the pyocyanea phage p8 (633). Similarly, decay of P^{32} atoms incorporated into the DNA of *E. coli* cells destroys the capacity for growth of λ phages much more rapidly than the capacity for T-even phage growth (598).

In systems where the capacity of the host cells is more UV-sensitive than the infectivity of the phage, it is possible to examine how long after infection the integrity of the host nucleus is actually required for the successful reproduction of the infecting virus. Thus, Benzer and Jacob (61) irradiated with UV at various stages of intracellular phage growth *P. pyocyanea* infected with phage p8 and then assayed for survival of the ability of the irradiated complexes to liberate viable progeny phages. This experiment showed that the capacity retained its high UV sensitivity throughout the greater part of the eclipse period. A decrease in UV sensitivity became manifest only when mature, infective progeny made their intracellular appearance; after this point the infectivity of the complexes was destroyed at the slower rate of inactivation of the free p8 virus. Analogous results were also obtained when the sensitivity to P^{32} decay of the λ capacity of *E. coli* was studied at different stages of intracellular λ growth (598). For this purpose, heavily P^{32}-labeled bacteria were infected with nonradioactive λ particles, and phage development was allowed to proceed for various times before the infected complexes were frozen and stored at $-196°C$. Here it was found that throughout most of the eclipse period P^{32} decay eliminated the ability of the infected complexes to liberate viable progeny phage at the same rate as at the outset of phage development. Only at the end of the eclipse was a stabilization against the inactivation process evident; after this point the infective centers disappeared at the much slower rate of inactivation of the mature, P^{32}-labeled progeny phages now present within the infected cells. The integrity of the host cell nucleus, whose destruction leads to the abortion of reproduction of these phage types, is therefore required not only at the outset of intracellular phage development but throughout those processes which are responsible for the replication of the infecting virus particle.

Autarky

It is apparent, therefore, that the T-even phage strains, whose capacity is very radioresistant, also engender the destruction of the host nucleus, whereas the other phage strains, whose capacity is much more radio-sensitive, leave the nucleus intact during their reproduction. This set of independent observations is internally consistent, for a phage strain could hardly require the integrity of the bacterial nucleus, *if*, as in the case of the T-even phages, the nucleus is destroyed at the outset of infection, or *unless*, as in the case of λ, the nucleus is preserved throughout the eclipse.

We thus arrive at the notion of the **autarky** of the T-even strains: these viruses bring into the host cell sufficient genetic information for the construction of all enzymes and regulatory substances whose synthesis may be required after infection of the bacterium has taken place. The T-even phages can, therefore, dispense with any further synthetic activities by the host DNA, whose very molecules they cannibalize. Other phage types, such as λ, do not possess this degree of self-sufficiency and still depend on continued synthetic activity by the genetic material of the host cell throughout the period of their growth. The destruction of the host nucleus by the T-even phages probably accounts also, at least in part, for their power to *exclude* T1, T7, or λ from joint growth in mixed infection (49, 163, 168, 676), since phage types that require a functional nucleus for their growth could hardly be expected to prosper in a cell in which the presence of a T-even virus has dissolved the bacterial DNA.

Genetic Interaction between Phage and Host

The preservation of the bacterial nucleus during vegetative growth of some phage types makes possible not only physiological but also genetic interactions between virus and host. The existence of such genetic interactions, from which the T-even phages, by virtue of their immediate dissolution of the bacterial nucleus, are of course excluded, was already brought forth in our considerations of transduction, which showed that the exchange of parts of the bacterial chromosome for parts of the genome of temperate viruses gives rise to defective transducing phages. We shall now consider another kind of apparent exchange of genetic factors between host and viral genomes. In this case the degenerate genetic intercourse produces *infective* rather than defective phage genomes, which reveal their presence as new, stable *recombinant* phage genotypes, which can be easily mistaken for phage mutants by the unwary.

A particularly clear case of such recombinants was discovered by Dorothy Fraser (217, 303), who observed that a minor fraction of T3-infected *E. coli*, strain B bacteria growing in nutrient broth fail to lyse at the end of the usual latent period, although lysis of these "persistent" complexes can be induced by dilution into fresh broth. When the genetic properties of the T3 progeny issuing from persistent complexes were examined, it was discovered that as many as 1% of these phages are host range "mutants" (able to grow on the T3-resistant bacterial strain B/3). This is an extraordinarily high mutant frequency when compared with the host range mutant frequency of less than 0.003% among the progeny liberated by the T3-infected bacterial cells lysing at the normal time. The proportion of infected cells which act as persistent complexes depends on the physiological condition of the cells prior to infection; practically all the bacteria can be made to form persistent complexes if starved for 2 hours prior to their infection with T3 and yield a high proportion of host range "mutants" after prolonged incubation in broth followed by dilution-induced lysis. A similar increase in the frequency of host range "mutants" can also be attained by heavy UV irradiation of the bacteria prior to their infection with T3.

Several distinct variant plaque types were recognized by Fraser among the T3 host range mutants produced in this manner. When the genetic structure of these variants was examined, however, it was discovered that each variant differs from the original T3 wild type in three or four genetic loci, since the variants show segregation and recombination in genetic crosses. This seemed difficult to reconcile with a mutational origin of these new host range genotypes, since single mutational events should alter only single genetic loci. An alternative explanation of the origin of these new genotypes seemed preferable—that they had arisen by recombination between infecting phage and genome of the bacterial host cell. Fraser was able to adduce the following evidence for this hypothesis.

1. Some bacterial host strains can be found which differ greatly with respect to the relative frequency with which they bring forth specific T3 variant types, as if different host-cell genomes can lead to different phage-bacterium recombinants.
2. The T3 variants can be "backcrossed" against a given host genotype by isolating a series of successive variants on the same bacterial strain. A T3 strain is thus finally isolated which produces no further variants upon growth on this bacterial strain; it has become "isogenic" with this host. Upon growth on *other* bacterial strains, however, the backcrossed phage strain sports further variants. Two T3 strains, furthermore, which have been made isogenic separately against the same host by independent successive backcrosses, produce no recombinants when crossed with each other; they are also isogenic with each other.

It thus appears that there exist certain physiological conditions of coli bacteria under which the reproduction and/or maturation of progeny of an infecting T3 particle is delayed in favor of a genetic interaction between vegetative bacteriophage and host genome. Some analogous instances of hereditary modifications of phages λ and T1 have been observed that could be interpreted also in terms of a possible genetic exchange between phage and host genome (324, 624, 673).

Host-controlled Modification

Like other viruses, bacteriophages can "adapt" themselves to better proliferation on different kinds of host cells. It was noticed by many of the early phage workers that phage types which at first grow only very poorly on some bacterial strains will grow much better after one or more "passages" on the new hosts. This adaptive capacity of bacteriophages was considered by d'Hérelle (279) as one of the strongest arguments in favor of their "living" nature. It was commonly thought in those days that viruses, and indeed microbes in general, are endowed with a plastic sort of heredity that can respond directly, and hence adapt itself, to the environment—a notion which, according to Luria (435), made microbiology "the last stronghold of Lamarckism." With the rise of phage genetics, however, the idea gained currency that the adaptation of viruses represents the selection of spontaneous, "fitter" phage mutants during repeated passage on the new host and that their hereditary plasticity derives only from the variety of mutant genotypes always present in large viral populations. But just as these more sophisticated genetic notions had finally replaced old-time Lamarckian naïvetés, it was found that there does exist a type of adaptive variation in phage which cannot be accounted for by mutation and selection, and which does appear to take place under direct influence of the host cell. This kind of variation, which is now called **host-controlled modification** (or host-induced modification, or host-controlled variation) was discovered more or less independently and almost simultaneously by Ralston and Krueger (523) with a *Staphylococcus* phage, by Anderson and Felix (8) with a *Salmonella* phage, by Luria and Human (450) with T2, and by Bertani and Weigle (70) with λ and the *Shigella* phage P2.

The instances of host-controlled modifications that have been recognized thus far all concern either a restriction or an extension of the host range of bacteriophages, although other properties of the phage may also be subject to such nonhereditary variations. The following describes a typical example: all but a small minority of the individuals in a stock of a phage P grown on a bacterial strain, A, are unable to grow on a second bacterial strain, B. Hence P phages grown on strain A, designated as P·A, are *restricted* in their host range. Those rare P·A phages that *are* able to grow on strain B give rise in their first cycle of growth on strain B to a population of *unrestricted* phage progeny of type P·B that can now grow with full efficiency on both strains A and B. The few restricted P·A phages that do manage to grow on bacteria of the refractory strain B are not exceptional—for example, mutant—particles. Instead, it is the few productive B bacteria which are exceptional, since their frequency varies with the physiological conditions of growth and can be raised by UV irradiation of the culture before infection. After one cycle of growth of the unrestricted P·B phage on strain A, however, all but a small minority of the phage progeny are once more of the *restricted* P·A type that can grow only on strain A but not on strain B. The dependence of the host range on the bacterial strain in which the phage has undergone its *last reproductive cycle* thus represents an adaptive change that is phenotypic rather than genetic, and is entirely distinct from the mutational extension of viral host range discussed in Chapter 8.

For the sake of simplicity, rather than historical equity, we shall con-
fine our discussions here to the example of host-controlled modification
shown schematically in Fig. 14-3. This example, thanks to the work of

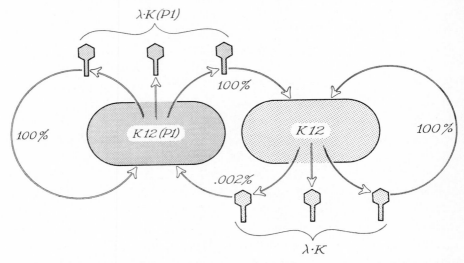

Fig. 14-3. Host-controlled modification of bacteriophage λ in K12(P1). Stipple
pattern in the phages represents phage structures whose specificity is determined by the host cell, similarly stippled, in which the phage was
grown. The percentages indicate the efficiency of plating of a phage on
the type of host indicated by the arrow. [Modified from Bertani and Weigle
(70).]

Arber and Dussoix (30, 195), is the case that is presently best understood.
Our preoccupation with one example must not be taken to mean that the
original discoverers cited earlier had not already progressed quite far in
recognizing the nature of host-controlled modification [a summary of
that stage of the subject can be found in a review by Luria (439)] or that
later workers, particularly Zinder (239, 708), working with phage P22,
and S. Lederberg (405) and Christensen (133, 134, 187), working with
phage T1, did not also contribute substantially to the clarification of this
curious phenomenon.

As shown in Fig. 14-3, most particles in a stock of λ phages grown on
E. coli K12 (designated hereafter as λ·K) are unable to multiply on
lysogenic *E. coli* K12(P1) carrying the P1 prophage (which had already
figured in our considerations of generalized transduction). All of the
progeny of those rare λ particles that do succeed in growing on K12(P1)

[designated hereafter as λ·K(P1)] are able to propagate themselves with full efficiency on both lysogenic K12(P1) as well as nonlysogenic K12. It is thus the presence of the P1 prophage that, at one and the same time, prevents the growth of most of the λ·K phages in the *E. coli* bacterium and modifies those rare λ particles that do succeed in growing into the unrestricted λ·K(P1) form. When a single unrestricted λ·K(P1) phage infects a nonlysogenic K12 bacterium, then there appears about one λ·K(P1) phage per cell still capable of growing on K12(P1) among the 100 to 250 progeny particles liberated by each infective center; all the rest of the progeny phage have been modified to the restricted λ·K type unable to grow on K12(P1) bacteria. This finding suggested that the rare unrestricted λ·K(P1) progeny phages issuing from the nonlysogenic K12 bacteria owe their unrestricted character to some material transfer from their λ·K(P1) parent. The nature of this transferred material could be identified in two different ways. Nonlysogenic K12 bacteria were infected either with highly radioactive P^{32}-labeled or with "heavy" D_2O-labeled unrestricted λ·K(P1) phages; then either the sensitivity to P^{32} decay or the density of the progeny phage populations was examined. The result of this experiment is presented in Fig. 14-4. It may be seen there (a) that whereas the restricted λ·K progeny population was perfectly stable during prolonged storage, the few unrestricted λ·K(P1) individuals among the progeny capable of forming plaques on K12(P1) bacteria were inactivated by radioactive decay at just one-half the rate of inactivation of the P^{32}-labeled λ·K(P1) parent phages, and (b) that whereas the restricted λ·K progeny population was completely "light," the few unrestricted λ·K(P1) individuals among the progeny were "heavy"; they banded in the cesium chloride density gradient at a density corresponding to about one-fourth the deuterium content of the fully deuterated λ·K(P1) parent phages. It may be concluded, therefore, that the transferred material that preserves the K(P1) host specificity during growth of phage λ in nonlysogenic K12 bacteria is none other than the parental phage DNA. Half of that DNA—probably one of the two strands of the semiconservatively replicated parental λ phage DNA moiety—is carried by each of the rare, unrestricted λ·K(P1) progeny phage. [The λ·K(P1) progeny, though harboring half of the parental DNA, contain only one-fourth of the parental deuterium because the parental phage protein, comprising about half of the mass of the virus, is not transferred at all.]

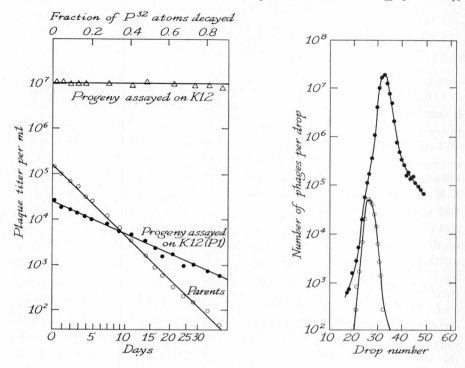

Fig. 14-4. Transfer of the host specificity of unrestricted $\lambda \cdot K(P1)$ phages through one cycle of growth on K12. A culture of nonlysogenic K12 growing in non-radioactive, nondeuterated medium is infected either with highly P^{32}-labeled $\lambda \cdot K(P1)$ phages [grown on highly P^{32}-labeled K12(P1) bacteria] or with fully deuterated $\lambda \cdot K(P1)$ phages [grown on K12(P1) bacteria in a D_2O medium] at a multiplicity of about 0.01 phages per cell. Intracellular phage growth is allowed to proceed for about one hour, at which time the infected bacteria yield an average burst of 80 $\lambda \cdot K$ and 0.5 $\lambda \cdot K(P1)$ phages per cell. *Left panel:* joint transfer of host specificity and sensitivity to decay inactivation from highly P^{32}-labeled $\lambda \cdot K(P1)$ parent phage. Here the progeny phage population as well as a sample of the original P^{32}-labeled parental $\lambda \cdot K(P1)$ stock is stored at 4°C and assayed periodically for plaque count on both the "permissive" strain K12 and the "restrictive" strain K12(P1). *Right panel:* joint transfer of host specificity and deuterium atoms from the fully deuterated $\lambda \cdot K(P1)$ parent phage. Here the progeny phage population is subjected to density gradient centrifugation, as described under Fig. 13-7. The drops collected through the bottom of the centrifuge tube are assayed for their content of unrestricted λ on K12(P1) (open circles) and for their content of total λ on K12 (solid circles). [From Arber and Dussoix (30.)]

What is the nature of the block that prevents the restricted $\lambda \cdot K$ phages from growing on K12(P1) bacteria? Arber and Dussoix could show that $\lambda \cdot K$ phages not only adsorb to K12(P1) bacteria but even inject their DNA into the refractory host cell. Shortly after this injection, however, the $\lambda \cdot K$ DNA is broken down and its constituents are released by the infected cells into the medium. In case the refractory K12(P1) host is infected with *both* $\lambda \cdot K$ and $\lambda \cdot K$(P1) phages, genetic markers of the restricted phage genome can be *rescued* by recombination into the unrestricted genome. Since in such mixed infections breakdown of the $\lambda \cdot K$ phage DNA competes with its recombinational rescue, the chances of survival of markers of the $\lambda \cdot K$ parent are greater when infection with the unrestricted phage precedes infection with the restricted phage than when the two parent genotypes enter the K12(P1) bacterium in the reverse order. Finally, Arber and Dussoix investigated also how $\lambda \cdot K$ phages acquire the $\lambda \cdot K$(P1) character; they infected nonlysogenic K12 bacteria *simultaneously* with restricted $\lambda \cdot K$ and with P1 phages and found not only that the $\lambda \cdot K$ phages can multiply under these conditions but also that a very large proportion of the λ progeny issuing from such mixedly infected complexes are of the unrestricted $\lambda \cdot K$(P1) type. It was concluded, therefore, that the vegetative P1 phage as well as the P1 prophage can produce the modification of the λ phage DNA that assures its subsequent acceptance by lysogenic K12(P1) cells.

This system of host-controlled modification can thus be explained in terms of two apparently separate and distinct functions of the P1 phage genome: P1 causes a modification of the DNA of λ phages growing in its presence; this modification then protects the λ DNA against a break-down mechanism likewise set in train by P1 that destroys ordinary or nonmodified λ DNA. When λ phages carrying P1-modified DNA molecules infect nonlysogenic K12, all the replicas of the parental λ DNA are necessarily of the nonmodified, or breakdown-sensitive type, and hence give rise to restricted λ progeny viruses. The modified parental λ DNA chains always retain their breakdown-resistant character, however, and reappear in unrestricted descendant phages on transfer. The chemical nature of this modification is as yet unknown, though it probably represents a substance whose formation is induced by the P1 genome and becomes attached to the λ phage DNA. In any case, the discovery of such nongenetic modifications of the viral DNA has added another dimension to the concept of "specificity" of the hereditary substance, which in all of our preceding discussions had been assumed to derive exclusively from the permutation of the four purine and pyrimidine bases in the deoxypolynucleotide chain.

Minute Phages

In 1927 Burnet (108) isolated a phage active on *Salmonella*, *Shigella*, and *Escherichia* to which he gave the designation S13. At first this phage did not seem to be particularly unusual, except for the catholicity of its host range, but a few years later, when accurate methods of particle size determination were developed, it transpired that S13 must be a dwarf among bacterial viruses. Schlesinger (545) inferred from the sedimentation velocity and Elford and Andrewes (200) from the ultrafiltration end point (see Fig. 3-3) that the diameter of the S13 particle is only about 20 mμ, compared to the diameter of about 90 mμ of what were later to be called the T-even phages. The volume, and hence mass, of S13 could therefore be estimated to be about two orders of magnitude smaller than that of other bacteriophages. Though for many years after its isolation this *minute* bacteriophage strain did not seem to find much employment in biological experimentation, it did have the honor to be selected as one of the reference objects of radiobiology. It was with S13 that the target theory of radiation inactivation was first tested, particularly that part of the theory which laid claim to providing a new means of size determination of viruses and other small biologically active entities (400). The notion underlying this claim was that since each X-ray ionization occurring within the "target" would surely inactivate it, the "sensitive volume" should be equal to the number of hits [in the sense of Equation *(11-1)*] delivered to the X-ray irradiated target population, divided by the total number of ionizations per unit volume known to be caused by the incident X-ray dose (399). And it was with phage S13 that the target theory had one of its few triumphs, because here indeed the sensitive volume, V_s, reckoned from X-ray sensitivity, turned out to be in good agreement with the particle volume inferred from sedimentation velocity and ultrafiltration end point of the virus.

Strangely enough, it did not seem to bother the champions of the target theory that analogous calculations carried out with phage T2 lead to a sensitive volume ten times smaller than that of the actual physical volume of the T2 virus. For, though the estimated particle volume of S13 was only about 1/100 that of T2, the known X-ray sensitivity of S13 was as high as 1/10 that of T2 (628). Since, as was evident from Table 11-II, there does exist a reasonable proportionality between X-ray sensitivity and content per particle of DNA among all the bigger phage strains, including the T series of coliphages, it should have seemed puzzling that the calculated X-ray sensitive volume should match the actual physical volume only in the case of the tiny S13 virus. This discrepancy became even more evident when it was found that the rate of inactivaticn of S13 by decay of incorporated P^{32} atoms at 4°C is about 1/8 that of T2 phage labeled at the same specific activity of the radioisotope (628). Thus, if the efficiency of killing per P^{32} disintegration were the same in S13 as in all other phage strains previously examined, one would have to conclude that each S13 particle contains about 3×10^{-17} g of DNA, an impossibly large nucleic acid content for the estimated particle volume of S13 of 3×10^{-18} cm^3.

One possible resolution of this quandary was to assume that the intrinsic radiosensitivity of S13 is in no way unusual and that previous estimates of its size were simply in error. These size estimates inferred from filtration end point and sedimentation velocity had, after all, only *assumed* a spherical shape for the virus, for the very good reason that in the mid-1950's the shape of S13 was still unknown. And if S13 were a slender *rod*, it might—though manifesting the same filtration end point— possess a very much greater volume than the postulated sphere of 20 mμ diameter. It should have been a simple matter to settle this vexing question by purifying some S13 phages and examining their shape in the electron microscope, except for two inconveniences. The S13 virus is rather unstable to chemical and physical manipulations; furthermore, if the virus were really a sphere of 20 mμ diameter, it would be just about of the same size, and hence difficult to separate from, the *ribosomes*, the small ribonucleoprotein particles present in the bacterial host cell liberated into the medium together with the phage particles upon lysis of the infected cells (542). But if S13 really were no bigger than the minute volume attributed to it, then it would be necessary to suppose that there is something unusual about its nucleic acid, something that causes its intrinsic radiosensitivity to be ten times greater than that of the DNA of bigger or "normal" bacterial viruses (628).

That there certainly is something unusual about the nucleic acid of minute phages was shown by Sinsheimer in a series of investigations with phage ϕX174. This phage was discovered in 1935 by Sertic and Boulgakov (565), and is undoubtedly a close relative of S13. Phage ϕX174 has the same radiosensitivity as S13 (76, 626), and the two phage strains are antigenically related (though not identical), share a common host range, and can grow together in mixed infection within the same bacterial cell (701). Phage ϕX174, however, has the advantage over S13 in that it is more stable and hence more easily obtained in pure form. Sinsheimer (574) was thus able to purify a stock of ϕX174, taking care to separate the virus particles from contaminating bacterial ribosomes. Physical and chemical measurements on the purified virus particles then revealed that they really *are* as small as had been supposed all along. The weight of ϕX174 is only 1/40 and its DNA content only 1/80 that of T2. The intrinsic sensitivity of ϕX174 to P^{32} decay is, therefore, necessarily ten times greater than that of T2, so that the efficiency of killing in ϕX174 is unity: in ϕX174 every P^{32} disintegration kills. As can be seen in the electron micrographs of Fig. 14-5, the ϕX174 virus is a polyhedral particle of diameter 25 mμ, not only much smaller but also much simpler in morphology than its bigger bacteriophage cousins of our acquaintance.

When Sinsheimer studied the properties of the nucleic acid of ϕX174, he discovered that the single DNA molecule of molecular weight 1.7×10^6 daltons contained by each virus particle does not manifest several of the properties characteristic of ordinary DNA. Unlike ordinary DNA, ϕX174 DNA does not have the usual complementary purine-pyrimidine base composition: 24.6% of its nucleotides contain adenine, 32.8% contain thymine, 24.1% contain guanine, and 18.5% contain cytosine. Adenine and guanine cannot, therefore, be paired with thymine and cytosine in the ϕX174 DNA. Furthermore, unlike the relatively unreactive hydrogen-bonded amino groups of purines and pyrimidines of ordinary DNA, the amino groups of the ϕX174 DNA are readily accessible to chemical reaction; apparently they do not take part in intramolecular hydrogen bonds. Finally, unlike the macromolecules of ordinary DNA, ϕX174 DNA molecules do not behave as rigid rods in solution. From these observations Sinsheimer inferred that the DNA of the ϕX174 virus is not in the double-stranded, Watson-Crick configuration, but is, instead, composed of only a *single* polynucleotide strand

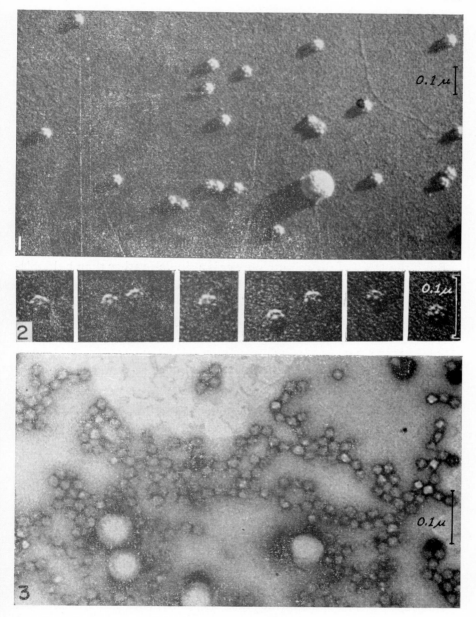

Fig. 14-5. Electron micrographs of bacteriophage ϕX174, utilizing different procedures of specimen preparation. [From Hall, Maclean, and Tessman (263).]

(575). This conclusion now explained the greater radiosensitivity, and in particular, the higher efficiency of killing per P^{32} disintegration, in S13 and ϕX174 phage particles. For it must be obvious from what has been previously said of the mechanism of P^{32} decay inactivation in Chapter 11 that whereas only 10% of the breakages of the polynucleotide chain attending each radioactive disintegration lead to the simultaneous disruption of both strands of the double-stranded DNA molecule, *every* P^{32}-induced break must necessarily cause a complete scission of, and hence be lethal to, a DNA molecule that consists only of a single strand. The additional finding that the sensitivity to P^{32} decay of the minute phages, in contrast to that of the "normal" phages, does not vary with the temperature at which decay proceeds, lends further support to this inference (626). From the radiobiological viewpoint, therefore, the minute phages are exceptions that prove the rule.

But if the DNA of the minute phages is a single-, rather than a double-stranded molecule, then how does its replication proceed in the infected cell? Does the semiconservative Watson-Crick replication process have any relevance here? It became possible to study this problem when it was found (259, 315, 558) that *E. coli* bacteria can be infected with purified native ϕX174 DNA, provided that the bacterial envelope is first rendered sufficiently permeable to allow entrance of the DNA molecules extracted from the virus particles. Thus, if a low concentration of viral DNA is added to a suitably treated bacterial suspension, about 20–30% of the viral DNA molecules penetrate the cells successfully and give rise to infective centers that, at the conclusion of a latent period, yield several hundred normal, structurally intact ϕX174 particles. This experiment furnished, of course, a much less equivocal proof that DNA is the viral germinal substance than Hershey and Chase's (301) then eight-year-old blendor experiment with T2, a proof that should have finally obliged all remaining sceptics to accept the shibboleth of DNA. But more importantly, this experiment made it possible to assay the infectivity of the *intracellular* pool of vegetative phage DNA, by presenting artificial lysates of ϕX174-infected cells to test suspensions of receptive bacteria.

In order to examine the intracellular fate of the viral DNA, Sinsheimer (577, 578) infected *E. coli* bacteria growing in an ordinary (N^{14}-P^{31}) medium with heavy N^{15}-P^{32}-labeled ϕX174 particles and lysed the infected bacteria at various times after infection. He then added non-radioactive, light (N^{14}-P^{31}) carrier DNA extracted from purified ϕX174 phage particles to the lysates and determined the densities of the various

DNA fractions present in the lysate by cesium chloride density gradient equilibrium sedimentation. The results of one of these analyses are presented in Fig. 14-6. It may be seen first of all in the left part of the figure that in a control mixture of the three kinds of DNA that might be expected to be present in these lysates—the heavy N^{15}-P^{32}-labeled viral

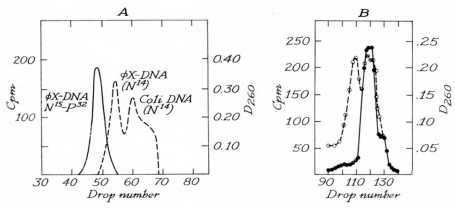

Fig. 14-6. The *replicative* form of the DNA of bacteriophage ϕX174. Cesium chloride density gradient centrifugation of mixtures of N^{15}-P^{32}-labeled and ordinary nonlabeled DNA. Drops are collected through the bottom of the centrifuge tube after sedimentation of the various DNA species into bands and analyzed for their total DNA content by measurement of the optical density to UV light at 260 mμ (stippled lines, right-hand ordinates) and for their content of labeled DNA by measurement of the radioactivity (solid lines, left-hand ordinates). **A.** A mixture of labeled and unlabeled ϕX174 phage DNA and unlabeled *E. coli* DNA. The bands of all three species of DNA are well resolved. **B.** A lysate obtained 14 minutes after infection of a culture of *E. coli* with an average of five N^{15}-P^{32}-labeled ϕX175 particles per cell. Nonlabeled carrier ϕX174 phage DNA, extracted from intact phage particles, has been added to the lysate before centrifugation. (The carrier phage DNA leaves the tube mainly in drop No. 108, whereas the *E. coli* DNA is found in drops Nos. 114–128.) Here the band of the N^{15}-P^{32}-labeled DNA of the infecting ϕX phages is seen to have shifted to a considerably lower density. [From Sinsheimer (577).]

DNA, the ordinary, light (N^{14}) viral DNA, and the light (N^{14}) DNA of the bacterial host cell—all can be clearly resolved as separate bands in the density gradient. Second, it is evident in the right part of the figure that the P^{32}-labeled material extracted from the infected cell no longer bands at the position characteristic of the DNA extractable from the heavy N^{15}-labeled virus. Instead, the N^{15}-P^{32}-labeled DNA is even lighter than the carrier DNA provided by the light (N^{14}) virus, and appears to have very nearly the same density as the bacterial DNA. Since this is precisely the density expected from a double-stranded N^{15}-N^{14} *hybrid* DNA of the purine-pyrimidine base composition of ϕX174, it may be inferred that the heavy single-stranded DNA of the parent virus entered a *double-stranded replicative form* (RF) in the course of vegetative phage growth. [The density of the double-stranded N^{14}-N^{15} hybrid RF is even less than that of the single-stranded N^{14} viral DNA because, for reasons which cannot be entered into here, single-stranded DNA exhibits a greater buoyant density in CsCl solutions than double-stranded, native DNA (475).] Sinsheimer also examined the infectivity of artificial lysates of ϕX174-infected cells to which no carrier DNA had been added and found that the vegetative RF DNA is also infective. This allowed him to test some of the biological properties of the replicative form; most importantly among these properties, Sinsheimer discovered that RF is only 1/10 as radiosensitive as the infective DNA extracted from the mature virus, exactly as would be expected for a double-stranded form from the considerations of the preceding paragraphs.

It is thus possible that the replication of the DNA of these minute phages also proceeds according to the mechanism of Watson and Crick. Upon its entrance into the host cell, the single-stranded viral DNA molecule would first serve as the template for the synthesis of a complementary polynucleotide chain to generate a double-stranded DNA molecule, which would then replicate by successive unwindings and complement additions, in the semiconservative manner. Just prior to maturation of a virus particle, the two strands of the vegetative, or RF, DNA would separate, and only one of the complementary chains would be encapsulated into the viral protein to constitute an infective unit of the progeny generation.

Sinsheimer's discovery that the DNA of the minute phages is single-stranded stimulated study of their genetic behavior. Zahler (701), whose work actually antedated this discovery, isolated numerous plaque type and host range mutants of both S13 and ϕX174 and searched for the existence of genetic recombination in these viruses. Although Zahler could demonstrate that more than one virus particle can grow successfully in the same cell, he was unable to detect any genetic recombination. Of course, since the maximum number of DNA nucleotides separating even the most distant loci on the genome of a minute virus could be only about 1% of the number of nucleotides separating the most distant loci on the T-even genome, a lower recombinant frequency ought, in any case, to be expected for crosses of S13 and ϕX174. But later work showed that if S13 parental phages are given a light dose of UV before being crossed—which, as we have already learned, stimulates recombination in T2 and λ—recombinants *can* be found in frequency of about 10^{-4} per progeny virus (625). Once suitable selective genetic markers were developed, genetic recombination in ϕX174 could be detected without any UV irradiation of the parent phages, at a level between 10^{-4} and 10^{-5} recombinants per progeny virus, so that even the rudiments of a genetic map could be established for this strange virus (504).

An Exception that Disproves the Rule

Phages S13 and ϕX174, though radically different in structure and morphology from the other bacteriophages of our acquaintance, satisfy at least one basic aspect of bacterial virology: their genetic material is DNA, albeit in single-stranded rather than Watson-Crick configuration. But recently a phage type was discovered that does not even meet this last-ditch criterion. This phage, f2, grows only on "male" (Hfr or F$^+$) but not on "female" (F$^-$) strains of *E. coli* K12 (429), probably because the virus particles cannot attach to or penetrate bacterium unless the cell carries in its envelope some secondary male trait induced by the F fertility agent. Electron micrographs reveal that f2 has about the same minute dimensions as ϕX174 and particle weight determinations show that f2, like ϕX174, contains only about 3×10^{-15} mg of nucleic acid per phage. This viral nucleic acid, however, must be *ribonucleic acid* (RNA), since analysis of purified f2 particles reveals that they contain ribose, instead of deoxyribose, and uracil, instead of thymine (430). This minute phage *is*, therefore, almost indistinguishable from the smallest animal and plant viruses. The latent period of f2 growing on *E. coli* is about 30 minutes, and the burst size may reach values as high as 20,000 infective progeny per cell. Although, at first sight surprisingly high, this numerical yield of phage particles is, of course, no greater than the yield of T2 phages per infected cell when reckoned in terms of total viral *mass*. That the nucleic acid of f2 phage is RNA rather than DNA can also be proved indirectly, by adding a mixture of fluorodeoxyuridine and uridine to the culture medium of f2-infected bacteria. In the presence of this mixture, which strongly inhibits synthesis of DNA (but not of RNA) and hence prevents multiplication of normal, DNA containing phases (144, 247, 541), f2 phages can proliferate perfectly well. This fact shows not only that DNA cannot be the germinal substance of the infective f2 virus but suggests also that no intracellular synthesis of DNA is required for replication of the vegetative f2 phage.

*   *   *

This brief comparative appreciation of the distinctive features of some different kinds of bacterial viruses should have demonstrated that, though the T-even strains have served well as experimental objects for understanding the nature of biological self-reproduction, it is not only heuristically imprudent but downright unjustified to make any automatic generalizations about bacterial viruses from the properties of this model system. Instead, as different bacteriophage types are studied in more and more detail, it becomes apparent that the only unifying principle that can be safely asserted is the tautological platitude that all bacterial viruses grow on bacteria as their host cells.

Further Reading

Stent, G. S., "Mating in the reproduction of bacterial viruses" (594). A comparative review of the genetic, physiological, and radiobiological behavior of different types of bacterial viruses, set within the framework of a now discredited theory.

Luria, S. E., "Host-induced modifications of bacterial viruses" (439). A review of the initial stage of development of this subject.

CHAPTER 15

Expression
of the Hereditary Message

General Nature of the Genetic Code—The Messenger—The Adaptor—Synthetic Messengers—Ambivalence—Regulation

IT WAS noted earlier that in 1939 Ellis and Delbrück's (201) one-step growth experiment allowed statement of the fundamental problem of self-reproduction in terms of the events that ensue within the infected bacterium in that half-hour latent period during which the infecting virus manages to reproduce itself a hundred- to a thousandfold. How, then, is matter assimilated from the components of the host cell and culture medium and worked into progeny virus particles according to the specific plan contained in the hereditary structures of the parent phage? The first great clue to this conundrum came in 1952 with Hershey and Chase's (301) discovery that of the two principal constituents of bacterial virus particles, DNA and protein, only the DNA enters the host cell; and that once infection has been accomplished, the bulk of the viral protein appears to be devoid of any further function in the remainder of the intracellular growth processes about to ensue. The basic problem of phage replication could, therefore, be restated in terms of two functions, "autocatalytic" and "heterocatalytic," of the viral DNA complement. (a) How does the DNA manage to replicate itself "autocatalytically" several hundredfold to generate the germinal substance with which the progeny virus are to be endowed? (b) How does the viral DNA manage to induce or preside over "heterocatalytically" the synthesis of the virus-specific enzyme proteins that govern the reactions of vegetative phage growth and of hundreds of copies of the structural protein that the infecting virus had just shed at the gates of the cell?

Within the year of the phrasing of these questions, it became feasible to imagine an answer to the first question in genuine molecular terms. For, as was seen in Chapter 7, the discovery of the double-helical structure of DNA by Watson and Crick in 1953 (660) immediately suggested a mechanism of replication for this molecule: the two complementary polynucleotide strands of the parental DNA molecule separate, and each of the two strands serves as a template for the ordered copolymerization of a complementary de novo polynucleotide chain, through specific hydrogen-bond pairing between purine and pyrimidine bases. It could thus be thought that the DNA of the infecting parental virus undergoes many successive rounds of unwinding and complement addition in order to build up the intrabacterial pool of viral replica DNA molecules identical to the DNA of the parent, in order to provide the hereditary substance for the offspring virus. During the next few years, many counterproposals and "improvements" of the Watson-Crick DNA replication mechanism were offered, and attention was drawn to the supposed difficulties inherent in this scheme (169, 594). But the manner of distribution of the atoms of the parental DNA over its replicas (374, 475), as well as the heterozygous character of nascent phage mutants (510), finally left little doubt that it is by means of the semiconservative replication mechanism of Watson and Crick, or some process at least formally analogous to it, that the "autocatalytic" function of the viral DNA is really expressed.

An understanding in molecular terms of the "heterocatalytic" function of the phage DNA—the way in which it expresses its hereditary message —was somewhat longer in coming. But as we shall now see, the answer to the second, rather more difficult of the two questions, is also very nearly at hand.

General Nature of the Genetic Code

In our earlier considerations in Chapter 10 on the functional unit of the genetic material it was already adumbrated that there must exist a *code* that relates the purine and pyrimidine base sequence in the polynucleotide chain of each viral *cistron* to the amino acid sequence in the polypeptide chain whose structural information the cistron carries. This code, we had noted, could be no simpler than specifying each of the "standard" set of twenty amino acids through a *triplet word* made up of three of the four kinds of nucleotide base pairs. We shall now examine in some more detail the nature of this code that gives meaning to the hereditary message.

The first to put forward a formal scheme for a genetic code was the physicist-cosmologist George Gamow (231). Gamow proposed in 1954 that each particular constellation of four contiguous purine and pyrimidine residues of the DNA double helix—two on one and two on the other of the two complementary polynucleotide chains—generates one of twenty specific kinds of "cavities" in the surface of the DNA macromolecule into which the side chain of one and only one type of amino acid of the "standard" set can fit. In this way, Gamow thought, the DNA can function as the direct template for the ordered copolymerization of the specific polypeptides from their amino acid monomers. When Gamow found that this scheme leads to internal contradictions and his attention was drawn to the fact that proteins are probably not synthesized *directly* on the DNA anyway, he generalized his proposal to take account of the possibility that not the DNA but some other substance is the immediate template of protein synthesis (232). The purely informational essence of Gamow's revised scheme in its most general form can be summarized as follows.

1. Three successive nucleotide base pairs on the DNA polynucleotide chains code for one amino acid. There are, therefore, 4^3 or 64 possible triplet words for the standard set of 20 amino acids.
2. Each nucleotide pair participates in the coding of three amino acids (Fig. 15-1). The code is, therefore, **overlapping.**
3. An amino acid can be represented by more than one kind of nucleotide pair triplet, or word. The code is, therefore, **degenerate.**

Such an overlapping code imposes serious restrictions on the possible sequences of amino acids that could occur in nature. For instance, in any polypeptide an amino acid whose code word is ATT could not be the neighbor of an amino acid whose code word is ACC. If this type of code were actually in use, it should be possible to "break" it through purely cryptographic methods by looking for the occurrence of neighbor restrictions among amino acids found in proteins. A survey by Brenner (89) of protein amino acid sequences known by 1957 revealed, however, that there does not seem to exist any such neighbor restrictions; hence there was no hope of breaking the code in this way. Brenner even demonstrated that the actual structure of proteins appears to rule out all overlapping codes of the type proposed by Gamow.

A

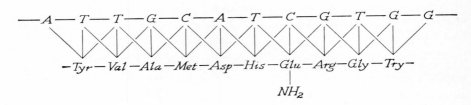

B

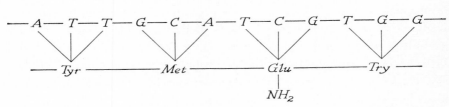

Fig. 15-1. Two general types of codes relating nucleotide sequence in DNA to amino acid sequence in polypeptides. The letters A, G, C, T represent the four purine and pyrimidine bases in one of the two complementary polydeoxynucleotide strands of the DNA and the abbreviations represent the twenty "standard" amino acids in the polypeptide chain whose amino acid sequence is specified by the DNA. In both codes, one amino acid is represented by three successive nucleotides. The assignments made here of any amino acid to a given nucleotide triplet is entirely hypothetical. **A.** An *overlapping* code in which each nucleotide participates in the specification of *three* amino acids. The *coding ratio*, or the ratio of the number of nucleotides in a segment of DNA to the number of amino acids in the polypeptide chain coded by this segment, is 1:1. **B.** A *nonoverlapping* code, in which each nucleotide participates in the specification of one amino acid. Here the coding ratio is 3:1.

Crick, Griffith, and Orgel (151) then devised a nonoverlapping code. Under this code each triplet of nucleotide base pairs in the DNA double helix specifies one amino acid and each base pair participates in the specification of only one amino acid (Fig. 15-1). With such a code, though it relieves one of the worries about neighbor restrictions or cryptographic code-breaking, a new difficulty has to be faced. If the transcription of the template during protein synthesis does not happen to start at the beginning of the polynucleotide chain, how is the "reader" supposed to know which of the triplets to "read"? For example, in the sequence of nucleotides . . . , ATT, GCA, TCG, TGG, . . . shown in Fig. 15-1, where ATT represents one amino acid, GCA another, and so on, how could this message be read correctly if the commas were removed? To resolve this difficulty, Crick, Griffith, and Orgel placed an additional restriction on their code: each code word triplet, such as ATT, GCA, TCG, TGG, can be automatically recognized as a word by means of a *dictionary of sense words*. The set of sense words would have the property that no sense word can be formed by misreading parts of any two adjacent sense triplets. Only sense words of nucleotide triplets correspond to amino acids in the dictionary; all the other triplets—those that could be formed by misreading adjacent sense triplets—do not code for any amino acid at all and are, therefore, *nonsense*. For example, if ATT and GCA are sense words in the dictionary, then TTG, TGC, CAA, and AAT, which might be misread from the fragments ATTGCA and GCAATT, are necessarily nonsense words not to be found in the dictionary. In this way, a *comma-less* code can be generated, which assures correct reading of the message without any necessity for starting the reading at the beginning of the polynucleotide chain or having commas between adjacent sense triplets. Such comma-less codes are not only formally possible but in any such code no more than 20 of the 64 possible triplets can make sense, and hence the remaining 44 triplets are necessarily nonsense. Thus this kind of comma-less code is nondegenerate —only one code word per amino acid—and marvelously explains the apparent excess of possible triplets over the number of amino acid types in the standard set. The restricted nature of the dictionary allows the automatic recognition of the beginning and end of each code word and thus eliminates the need for a comma or spacer symbol.

As it turned out, nature does not seem to avail herself of this clever system of information storage and retrieval, perhaps because it is *too* clever by half! The nondegenerate comma-less code probably lacks evolutionary flexibility; and, to be workable, the whole system, like Athena, would have to have sprung full-blown from Zeus' head. Instead, as Crick, Barnett, Brenner, and Watts-Tobin's (150) experiments with *r*II mutants of T4 phage later showed, the code is very likely of the following nature:

1. As in the previous comma-less code, nonoverlapping nucleotide base pair triplets code for each amino acid residue, and there are no special commas that show how to select the right triplets for reading. But the correct reading of a long nucleotide sequence is assured by beginning the transcription from a fixed starting point, instead of using a dictionary of sense and nonsense triplets. If this starting point is displaced by one nucleotide, then the reading of all triplets is displaced and produces a totally incorrect transcription.

2. As in Gamow's original proposal, the code is degenerate, in that in general one particular kind of amino acid may be represented by more than one particular nucleotide triplet.

These experiments evolved from a study of reverse mutation in T4 phage. In this study it was noticed that most of the spontaneous r^+ wild type revertants sported by the T4rII mutant FC0 do not carry true reversions of the mutated genetic site, but instead represent *double mutants* that carry a suppressor mutation in the vicinity of the original rII mutation. That is, these revertants (whose presence was detected, as usual, by their ability to form plaques on *E. coli*, strain K) are not really wild r^+ genotypes at all, but only "pseudowild" phenotypes in which the juxtaposition of two particular rII mutant sites, FC0 and its suppressor, renders the virus capable of growth on the differential host, strain K. The presence of these suppressor mutations can be demonstrated by crossing such a pseudowild revertant to the authentic T4r^+ wild type phage; from this cross of two phenotypically r^+ parents there issue rII recombinants that form typical r plaques on *E. coli*, strain B and cannot grow at all on strain K. These rII recombinants are of two types: one type carries the original FC0 mutation and the other type carries a new rII mutation, the suppressor to FC0. (No r recombinants would, of course, be produced from a cross of a true r^+ revertant to the T4r^+ wild type.) It is possible to ascertain the location of these rII suppressor mutations to FC0 by means of the fine-structure mapping methods already discussed in Chapter 10, and the sites of 7 different such suppressors to FC0 have been indicated on line B of Fig. 15-2. It can be seen that these suppressors are all close, but not *very* close, to FC0. They cluster at two separate sites on either side of FC0, the distance between the two clusters being about one-tenth the whole length of the B cistron of the rII gene, in whose B1 segment FC0 is situated.

Since each of these suppressors is an *r*II mutant in its own right, it is possible to study also its reverse mutation to the r^+ state, in the same manner as that already used for FC0. It was found in this way that these suppressor mutants, like FC0, do not generally revert to the true r^+ wild type either, but instead again sport suppressed double mutants capable

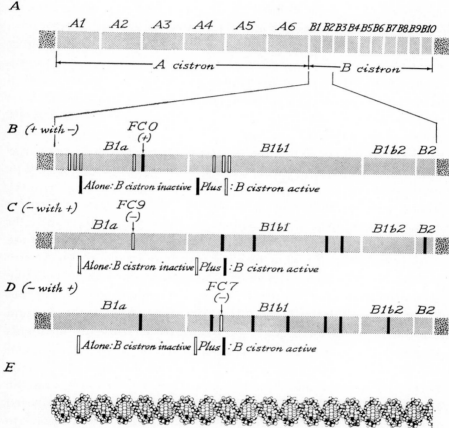

Fig. 15-2. The ensemble of mutually suppressive mutations in the *r*II region of the T4 genome. *Line A:* the two cistrons, A and B, of the *r*II region, shown subdivided into their segments. *Line B:* sites of the mutation FC0 in the B1a subsegment of the B1 segment of the B cistron, and of seven mutations isolated as suppressors to FC0. *Lines C and D:* sites of the two mutations FC9 and FC7, isolated as suppressors to FC0, and of twelve further mutations in B1 and B2 segments isolated as suppressors to the suppressors. *Line E:* the viral DNA drawn to approximately the same scale as the genetic map. The two segments contain about 100 nucleotide base pairs. [From Crick, *Scientific American*, **207**, No. 4: 67 (1962).]

of growing on strain K. Lines C and D of Fig. 15-2 show the locations of a number of rII mutants that were isolated as suppressors to the two suppressors FC9 and FC7. It is evident that these secondary suppressor mutations likewise occur in the general neighborhood of the original FC0 mutant site in the B cistron. Finally, suppressors to the suppressors to the suppressors can be isolated in the same way. Thus Crick et al. isolated altogether a set of some 80 independent rII mutants, including FC0, all of which are suppressors of some mutants in the set and fall within a limited region of the B cistron of the rII gene. The double mutants that carry a mutation and its suppressor (and can thus form plaques on strain K) form, however, a variety of plaque types on *E. coli*, strain B. Some of these plaque types are indistinguishable, or hardly distinguishable, from true r^+, whereas the mutant character of others is easily recognized and rather resembles the r plaque type.

The key to understanding the genetic interaction of this ensemble of suppressor mutations was the fact that FC0 is an rII mutant induced by treatment of a T4r^+-infected bacterium with an acridine dye. Now since acridine dyes, according to the hypothesis (94) mentioned in Chapter 10, may derive their mutagenic action from promoting either the *insertion* or the *deletion* of nucleotides from replicating DNA chains, it can be supposed for the sake of discussion that the mutation of FC0 represents the insertion at the FC0 site of an additional nucleotide into the wild type purine-pyrimidine base sequence. What effect would such an insertion have on the transcription of the polypeptide chain coded by the wild type B cistron if, as set forth in the preceding paragraphs, the nucleotide sequence is really read triplet by triplet, from one end (say the "left" end) of the B cistron to the other? As is evident from Fig. 15-3, the insertion of an extra nucleotide at the FC0 site will obviously cause the reading of *all* the triplets to the "right" of FC0 to be shifted by one nucleotide, and hence be incorrect. In other words, from that point onwards, the amino acid sequence coded by the B cistron polypeptide will be completely altered, and if any protein is formed at all, it will bear little resemblance to that produced by the normal, wild type rII gene. Crick et al. now postulated that a suppressor mutation to FC0, for example FC7, corresponds to the *deletion* of a nucleotide. When the FC7 deletion mutation is present *by itself*, all triplets to the "right" of FC7 will be read incorrectly, and thus the normal rII$^+$ function is absent: FC7 is an rII mutant. But when both FC0 and FC7 mutations are present within the same genome, as in the pseudowild double mutant, then, although the reading of triplet words *between* FC0 and FC7 will still be altered, the correct reading will be restored to the rest of the cistron lying to the right of FC7. And if the *r*II enzyme protein can tolerate some alterations in amino acid sequence in the short region of the B cistron

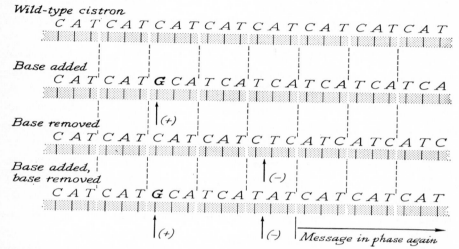

Fig. 15-3. The effect of mutational insertions or deletions of single nucleotides on the genetic message, if the code is comma-less, and transcription of the message proceeds from a fixed point to the right, nucleotide triplet by triplet. The hypothetical "correct" message of the wild type polynucleotide segment shown here is CAT CAT, CAT, ····. Insertion of the nucleotide G distorts the remainder of the message to TCA, TCA, TCA, ····. Deletion of the nucleotide A distorts the remainder of the message to ATC, ATC, ATC, ····. Insertion of G at one site and deletion of A at another restores the correct message CAT, CAT, CAT, ····. [From Crick, *Scientific American*, **207**, No. 4: 70 (1962).]

polypeptide chain coded in the vicinity of FC0 without losing all of its enzymatic function, the protein synthesized by the suppressed double mutant could be of sufficient enzymatic activity to allow successful phage growth in bacteria of strain K. However, the function of this modified enzyme might not be wholly "normal," in which case the double mutant, while capable of growth on strain K, would not necessarily manifest the true r^+ plaque phenotype when plated on strain B.

The following convention can now be established. The mutant FC0, which for the sake of discussion had been supposed to carry an *insertion* of a single nucleotide, is assigned the symbol +, and its suppressors, among them FC7 and FC9, are assigned the symbol —. It does not matter here whether FC0 is really an insertion and FC7 and FC9 are really deletions; it is important only that a mutation and its suppressor be of opposite sign. Accordingly, the suppressors to the suppressors of type — are again assigned the symbol + (see Fig. 15-2).

It follows from these considerations that all combinations of two mutants of the same sign, such as ++ or — —, brought into the same genome should still be of mutant phenotype, a prediction which could be verified. It might also be expected, on first thought, that all combinations of + and — should be wild or pseudowild phenotypes, just like the original double mutants in which the suppressors were first isolated. This is not so, however, since any long sequence of nucleotide triplets can be read correctly in only one way, but can be read incorrectly in two different ways, depending on whether the "reading frame" is shifted one place to the right or one place to the left. We must refer the reader to the original paper (150) for a detailed discussion of the theoretical consequences of alternative shifts in reading frame, as well as of the occurrence of so-called "unacceptable triplets"; we can state here only that if proper account is taken of these complications, recombinational juxtapositions of appropriate + and — mutations do indeed generate wild or pseudowild T4 phenotypes.

Although the foregoing considerations assumed that each amino acid is coded by a nucleotide triplet, they did not really depend on this assumption and would be equally applicable if the coding ratio were four or five nucleotides per amino acid or any other larger number. It was only essential that the reading of the comma-less code proceed from one end of the cistron to the other, code word by code word, so that juxtaposition of insertions and deletions of single nucleotides restores the correct reading frame to regions of the cistron outside the two mutant sites. But it was possible to obtain further evidence that showed that the coding ratio is actually three, by constructing *triple* mutants of the type +++ or — — —. *Such triple mutants manifest the wild or pseudowild phenotype*, provided that the rules of shift direction and "unacceptable triplets" have been observed in the choice of the three mutant sites. For instance, the triple +++ mutant carrying FC0 and two suppressors of suppressors to FC0 forms plaques on strain K, even though either singly or in pairs each of these mutant sites produces an *r*II mutant virus that is quite unable to grow on strain K. It is thus the combination of all three mutations of the same sign within the same DNA polynucleotide chain that restores function, or partial function, to the mutant B cistron. This result could be expected only if the coding ratio is really *three*, since only if the code words are triplets could the net result of deletion or insertion of three nucleotides be the restoration of the correct reading frame outside the three mutant sites (Fig. 15-4). Strictly speaking, this result

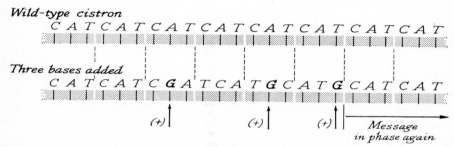

Wild-type cistron
C A T C A T C A T C A T C A T C A T C A T C A T

Three bases added
C A T C A T C G A T C A T G C A T G C A T C A T

(+)   (+)   (+)   *Message in phase again*

Fig. 15-4.   Insertion of three nucleotides at closely situated sites distorts the genetic message over a short stretch of the genetic segment but leaves the remainder of the message unaffected. Deletion of three neighboring nucleotides produces the same result. [From Crick, *Scientific American* **207**, No. 4: 74 (1962).]

proved only that the code word is a *multiple* of three, since the whole analysis departed from the assumption that the original FC0 mutant had suffered the insertion or deletion of a *single* nucleotide. Thus a more conservative inference from these observations would be that the coding ratio is $3n$, where n is the number of nucleotides that are inserted or deleted at a time by the mutagenic action of acridines. In the following discussions, we will continue to pretend, however, that the code words are simply triplets, or that $n = 1$.

These experiments suggest, finally, that it is unlikely that only 20 of the 64 possible nucleotide triplets represent the "standard" set of 20 amino acids and that the remaining 44 triplets are "nonsense," corresponding to no amino acid at all. If this were the case, then the genetic region over which suppressor mutations of the FC0 family could occur should be very much smaller than that actually found. For if most of the possible nucleotide triplets were nonsense, then the shift in reading frame that obtains between any + and − mutant sites separated by more than a very few nucleotides would invariably lead to at least one nonsense triplet that would interrupt the continuity of transcription of the polypeptide chain and hence would prevent the reading process from ever reaching those regions of the cistron to which the correct reading frame had been restored. It is therefore very likely that the code is degenerate, many of the 20 "standard" amino acids being represented by more than one kind of nucleotide triplet. Since only a minor fraction of the 64 possible nucleotide triplets would then be nonsense, rather lengthy shifts in reading frame could thus be tolerated without the generation of nonsense triplets that interrupt the continuity of the transcription process.

The Messenger

After having considered the *formal* interrelations by which the structure of the viral proteins is inscribed in the hereditary substance of the infecting phage, we may now proceed to examine the nature of the "black box" which actually effects the translation of the DNA nucleotide sequence into polypeptide amino acid sequence. Where in the infected cell, first of all, does the synthesis of proteins take place? Short transient exposure of bacteria to radioactive C^{14}- or S^{35}-labeled amino acids reveals that the radioactive amino acids "flow" through the *ribosomes* (468), the small ribonucleoprotein particles that contain the bulk of the RNA of the bacterial cell (542). In such experiments, the C^{14} or S^{35} tracer atoms first appear in protein bound to ribosomes and later pass out of the ribosomes into the "soluble" (nonribosomal or general) protein of the cell. Since the rate at which the amino acid tracer atoms flow in and out of the ribosome-bound nascent polypeptides suffices to account for the whole synthesis of bacterial protein, it may be inferred that the ribosomes are in fact the very sites at which amino acids are assembled into specific polypeptides of predetermined order.

How then is the information for specific amino acid permutations encoded in the DNA cistrons made available in the ribosomes for this assembly process? One hypothesis (149) that held sway for about four or five years—a lifetime apparently long enough to earn for it the name "classical" model (92)—supposed that each DNA cistron serves as the template for the synthesis of molecules of RNA onto which the precise nucleotide sequence of the cistron and hence its coded information is transcribed. After their formation on the DNA cistron surface, these RNA molecules were imagined to migrate to the cytoplasm, where they would provide the RNA moieties for nascent ribosomal particles and, henceforth, act as the immediate templates for the ordered amino acid copolymerization. According to this view, each cistron would control the synthesis of one specialized kind of ribosome, which, in turn, would direct the synthesis of one and only one kind of protein, "a scheme which can be epitomized as the one gene–one ribosome–one protein hypothesis" (98).

The finding of S. S. Cohen (138) in 1948—that after infection of bacteria with T2 phage net synthesis of RNA comes to a stop, whereas net synthesis of protein continues at its preinfection rate—seemed, however, at first difficult to reconcile with the "classical" model. For, as described in Chapters 6 and 7, the kinds of proteins made after T-even phage infection are radically different from the proteins previously made by the uninfected cell. One would expect, therefore, an acceleration, rather than a halt, of RNA synthesis, as the cytoplasm of the host bacterium is renovated for future production of polypeptides encoded in the viral DNA. However, the demonstration (288, 651) that bacterio-phages do induce in the infected cell the synthesis of a small but signifi-cant amount of virus-specific RNA in a state of rapid metabolic turnover (see pp. 156–157) renewed the lease on life of this "classical" model, particularly after it was realized that the purine-pyrimidine base composition of the phage RNA resembles that of the phage DNA (see Table 7-II). It could now be imagined that the viral DNA induces the formation in its image of new ribosomal RNA specially fit for viral protein synthesis, although it would have to be supposed that the phage-specific ribosomes, unlike the stable ribosomes of uninfected bacteria (289), are in a state of rapid metabolic turnover. Indeed, Nomura, Hall, and Spiegelman (495) believed that they had gained support for this idea when they showed that most of the RNA synthesized in T2-infected cells possesses the sedimentation characteristics of ribo-somes. Though they noticed that in low Mg^{++} concentrations the phage-induced RNA, in contrast to normal ribosomal RNA, is released from the ribosomal particles as the free nucleic acid, and that in this free form the phage RNA manifests a considerably lower sedimentation velocity and higher electrophoretic mobility than the normal ribosomal RNA, they nevertheless interpreted their observations in terms of a postinfection synthesis of new phage-specific ribosomes. Nomura et al. reasoned that the observed rate of phage-induced RNA synthesis in

T2-infected bacteria might allow the construction of about 170 ribosomes per cell every 2 minutes, a figure which they thought sufficient "to take care of the needs generated by the requirement to form the relatively restricted variety of protein molecules relevant to virus production."

But this "classical" model of the ribosomal RNA as the template for protein synthesis in an autonomous, differentiated ribonucleoprotein particle had to face also other conceptual difficulties. (a) Ribosomal RNA molecules are very homogeneous in size (262, 389) and nucleotide composition (47), and thus, contrary to what would have been expected from the template molecules, reflect neither the range of size of polypeptide chains synthesized nor the variation in nucleotide composition of the DNA of different bacterial species (47, 406). (b) The capacity of ribosomes to synthesize proteins, contrary to what would have been expected for fully autonomous biosynthetic sites, does not survive radiochemical destruction of the bacterial DNA (465, 526). (c) The regulation of synthesis of specific bacterial proteins (for instance, of inducible or repressible enzymes) is achieved in time periods much too short to allow any corresponding change in the character of the ribosome population in the bacterial cytoplasm. These facts led Jacob and Monod (331) to propose that, contrary to the image of the "classical" model, ribosomes are not congenitally differentiated in their capacity to synthesize this or that polypeptide. Instead of regarding the ribosomal RNA as the direct template for the orderly assembly of amino acids, they proposed that each DNA cistron causes the synthesis of *messenger* RNA molecules, which harbor the amino acid sequence information of a particular polypeptide encoded in the cistronic nucleotide sequence. Jacob and Monod further envisaged that these messenger RNA molecules then enter into temporary combination with *undifferentiated* ribosomal particles already endowed with their own ribosomal RNA and that it is the messenger-ribosome complex that is competent to synthesize the polypeptide corresponding to the phenotypic product of the DNA cistron represented by a particular messenger RNA molecule. From this viewpoint, the ribosome is the "workshop" for protein synthesis and the messenger RNA the "blueprint." Jacob and Monod proposed, finally, that the messenger RNA has only a limited lifetime, and hence can serve for the construction of only a few polypeptide molecules; thus, during active protein synthesis the messenger RNA molecules are in a state of rapid turnover. One and the same ribosome may, therefore, synthesize one kind of protein molecule at one moment and another kind at the next, depending on the kind of messenger the ribosome happens to have engaged.

Before these a priori conceptions of Jacob and Monod had even appeared in print, Brenner, Jacob, and Meselson (98) could demonstrate their applicability to the events attending protein synthesis in T4-infected *E. coli*. Cultures of *E. coli* were grown in a medium containing N^{15} and C^{13} as the only nitrogen and carbon sources, so that all cell constituents were labeled with these heavy isotopes. After growth in the "heavy" medium, the bacteria were infected with T4 phage and immediately transferred to a medium containing the ordinary isotopes N^{14} and C^{12}, so that all cell constituents synthesized after infection were labeled with light nitrogen and carbon atoms. Radioactive $P^{32}O_4^=$ or $S^{35}O_4^=$ was also added to the infected cultures, so that the density distribution of newly synthesized, postinfection RNA and protein among the cell components liberated by artificial lysis of the infective centers 7 minutes after the onset of intra-cellular phage growth could be followed by means of equilibrium sedimentation in density gradients of concentrated cesium chloride solutions (475, 476).

The result of this experiment confirmed the previous inference that most of the virus-induced RNA is associated with bacterial ribosomes. But, in conflict with the "classical" notion that this RNA reflects the formation of new species of ribosomes, density analysis of the ribosomal particles carrying the P^{32}-labeled postinfection RNA revealed here that they contain the heavy, preinfection isotopes N^{15} and C^{13} rather than the light, postinfection isotopes N^{14} and C^{12} (Fig. 15-5). In other words, this experiment showed that *the virus-induced, postinfection RNA enters old ribosomes that are already present in the cell before its infection with T4 phage;* indeed, no ribosomes at all corresponding to the N^{14}-C^{12} density appear in the infected cell, showing that the T-even phage infection really brings ribosomal synthesis to term. This experiment showed also that the S^{35}-labeled amino acids "flow" through ribosomes corresponding to the higher, preinfection particle density, confirming the inference that pre-existing rather than newly formed ribosomes are the sites of synthesis of the nascent proteins that arise in the T-even phage-infected bacterium. Thus, it is altogether excluded that the amino acid permutation for polypeptide synthesis is encoded in the ribosomal RNA, since the ribosomes of the uninfected bacterium could hardly possess the plans for the construction of viral proteins *before* the viral DNA, the permanent

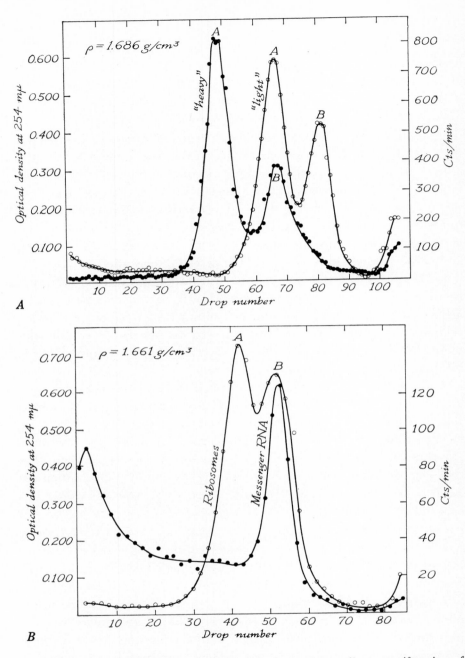

Fig. 15-5. The messenger RNA. Cesium chloride density gradient centrifugation of ribosomes of normal and phage-infected bacteria, and of the virus-induced, postinfection RNA. Open circles represent the optical density at a wavelength of 254 mμ, and hence total nucleic acid content, and solid circles the radioactivity, and hence labeled RNA content, of drops collected through the bottom of the centrifuge tube. **A.** Density of "heavy" and "light" bacterial ribosomes. *E. coli* cells, grown in an N¹⁵-C¹³-P³²-labeled medium, are mixed with a fiftyfold excess of cells grown in nutrient broth. The ribosomes of this mixed bacterial population are extracted from the cells by alumina grinding, isolated from the extract by differential centrifugation, and centrifuged into bands in a concentrated cesium chloride solution. Each of the two species of ribosomes can be seen

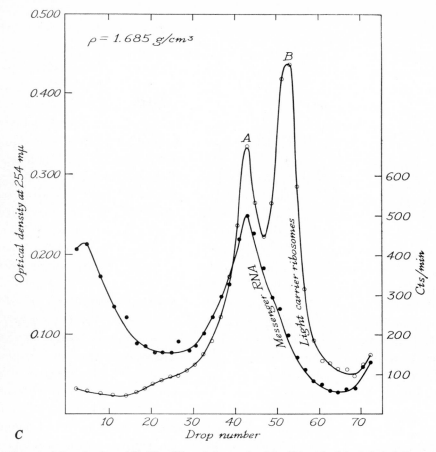

$\rho = 1.685 \; g/cm^3$

to form two bands, A and B. The P^{32} activity peak of the B band of the labeled "heavy" ribosomes falls just under the optical density peak of the A band of the unlabeled "light" ribosomes. **B.** Association of postinfection RNA with ribosomes. A culture of *E. coli* is infected with an average of thirty T4 particles per cell and exposed to C^{14}-labeled uracil in its medium from the third to the fifth minute of intracellular phage growth. The ribosomes are then extracted, purified, and centrifuged in concentrated cesium chloride solution, as above. It can be seen that the C^{14}-activity peak of the postinfection RNA falls just under the optical-density peak of the band. Hence the virus-induced RNA appears to be associated only with the ribosomes of the B band, which, as independent experiments show, is the band of ribosomes actively engaged in protein synthesis. **C.** Density of postinfection RNA formed in bacteria switched from "heavy" to "light" medium immediately after infection. *E. coli*, grown in an N^{15}-C^{13}-labeled "heavy" medium, are infected with an excess of T4 phages and immediately brought into ordinary, "light" broth. The infected bacteria are exposed to P^{32} in their growth medium from the second to the seventh minute of intracellular phage growth and then mixed with a fiftyfold excess of nonlabeled "light," T4-infected bacteria. The ribosomes are then extracted from this mixed culture, purified, and centrifuged in concentrated cesium chloride solution, as above. It can be seen that the P^{32}-activity peak of the labeled postinfection RNA falls just under the optical density-peak of the A band of the "light" carrier ribosomes. That position, as was seen in **A**, corresponds to the B band of the "heavy" ribosomes. Since, as was evident in **B**, the postinfection RNA is associated with the B band, it can be concluded that here the P^{32}-labeled postinfection RNA enters the "heavy" N^{15}-C^{13}-labeled ribosomes constructed before infection during growth of the culture in the "heavy" medium. [From Brenner, Jacob, and Meselson (98).]

repository of this knowledge, has even entered the cell. Instead, it may be concluded that the virus-induced, postinfection RNA appears to play the very role of the postulated messengers to whom the viral DNA devolves the task of bringing the amino acid sequence information encoded in its cistrons to the nondifferentiated bacterial ribosomes, the sites at which the viral messenger molecules preside over the assembly of the viral polypeptides. It now becomes easy to comprehend why "autark" phages such as T2 and T4 make short shrift of synthesis of all bacterial proteins and enzymes: since these viruses destroy the host DNA at the outset of their intracellular growth, they cut off formation of bacterial messengers at their source. At the same time, the viral DNA generates its own messenger RNA molecules, which then have a clear field for taking over the ready-made bacterial ribosomes for the parasitic synthesis of viral rather than bacterial proteins.

The actual molecular mechanism by which the viral cistrons preside over the synthesis of their messenger RNA still remains to be clarified. Though *RNA polymerase* enzymes that appear to be responsible for the DNA-template-directed polymerization of ribonucleotides into specific RNA molecules have already been isolated from a variety of cells (319, 678), it is not yet known whether it is the normal *E. coli* RNA polymerase that functions in the T4-infected cell, or whether a phage-specific enzyme is required for transcription of the viral cistrons. If synthesis of T4 phage messenger RNA, like synthesis of T4 phage DNA, *is* catalyzed by a phage-specific polymerase, it would be necessary that the viral RNA polymerase be carried also by the free, infective phage particle and injected together with the viral DNA into the host cell at the moment of infection. Otherwise no synthesis of viral messenger, and hence of viral proteins, could ever get under way.

Other, as yet unresolved, problems concern the manner in which the viral DNA carries out its template function. Do the two complementary polynucleotide strands of the viral DNA double helix temporarily unwind for messenger synthesis to expose the hydrogen bonding sites of their purine and pyrimidine bases? Are the ribonucleotides of the nascent messenger molecules assembled into their particular order by formation of Watson-Crick type complementary hydrogen bonds between their bases and the bases of the DNA template? Most important, do *both* complementary polynucleotide strands of the viral DNA really figure as templates for messenger synthesis, either jointly or individually, or is the nucleotide sequence of only one of them, the "phenotypically active" strand, transcribed into the messenger? It can hardly be very long until the answers to these questions will have been provided.

The Adaptor

Granted that the viral messenger RNA molecules provide the templates for protein synthesis in the bacterial ribosomes, how are the amino acids actually assembled by the messenger into a sequence of the correct predetermined order? In 1958, Crick (149) analyzed this problem in these terms: "One's first naive idea is that the RNA will take up a configuration capable of forming twenty different 'cavities,' one for the side-chain of each of the twenty amino acids . . . [but] on physical-chemical grounds, the idea does not seem in the least plausible. Apart from the phosphate-sugar backbone, which we have assumed to be regular and perhaps linked to the structural protein of the [ribosome] particles, RNA presents mainly a sequence of sites where hydrogen bonding could occur. One would expect, therefore, that whatever went on to the template in a *specific* way did so by forming hydrogen bonds. It is therefore a natural hypothesis that the amino acid is carried to the template by an *adaptor* molecule, and that the adaptor is the part which actually fits on to the RNA. In its simplest form [this hypothesis] would require twenty adaptors, one for each amino acid."

Though "what sort of molecules such adaptors might be is anybody's guess," Crick thought that "there is one possibility which seems more likely than any other—that they might contain nucleotides. This would enable them to join on to the RNA template by the same 'pairing' of bases as is found in DNA, or in polynucleotides." Crick imagined further that "a separate enzyme would be required to join each adaptor to its own amino acid and that the specificity required to distinguish between, say, leucine, isoleucine and valine would be provided by these enzyme molecules, instead of by cavities in the RNA. Enzymes, being made of protein, can probably make such distinctions more easily than can nucleic acid."

The adaptor hypothesis thus leads to the following image of the amino acid assembly process (Fig. 15-6): before its incorporation into the nascent polypeptide chain, each amino acid molecule is fitted out with a nucleotide adaptor that contains a nucleotide triplet *complementary* in its nucleotide sequence to the nucleotide triplet that codes for the same amino acid in the messenger RNA. The amino acid–nucleotide complexes then diffuse into the ribosomes, where they are held in their proper places on the messenger template by pairs of hydrogen bonds between

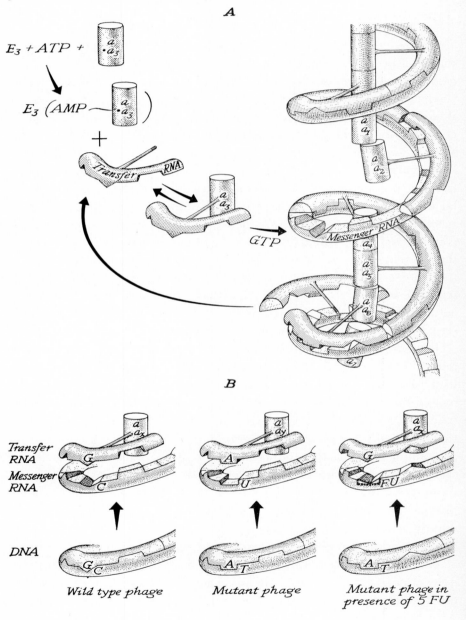

A

$E_3 + ATP +$

$E_3 \left(AMP \quad \begin{array}{c} a \\ \cdot a_3 \end{array} \right)$

$+$

Transfer *RNA*

GTP

Messenger RNA

B

Transfer
RNA

Messenger
RNA

DNA

Wild type phage   Mutant phage   Mutant phage in
                                                presence of 5 FU

complementary purines and pyrimidines of adaptor and messenger RNA molecules. Once lined up in this way along the messenger RNA in the "correct" order, the individual amino acid residues are joined to each other through peptide bonds, by means of a chemical rearrangement that simultaneously liberates the amino acid from its bond to the nucleotide adaptor and solders it into the nascent polypeptide chain. In this model, the set of twenty postulated enzymes that match each amino acid with its cognate adaptor represent the "dictionary"—the agency that "knows" the code. (Since the amino acid sequence of these enzymes, and hence the specificity of their structure, must of course be also inscribed in some cistrons, the DNA is, in the last analysis, also privy to the code.)

While these notions were taking form in the minds of Crick and his friends, students of the enzymology of protein biosynthesis started to encounter an ensemble of specific reactions that gradually resembled more and more the postulated adaptor system. It was found, first of all, that one of the initial steps in protein synthesis is the "activation" of each amino acid (63, 311, 313) by means of a special activating enzyme that catalyzes the reaction

amino acid $+$ adenosine triphosphate $\longrightarrow$

$\qquad$ amino acid–adenosine monophosphate $+$ pyrophosphate.

Fig. 15-6. The adaptor hypothesis. **A.** The specific enzyme, E_3, "activates" its cognate amino acid, aa_3, by catalyzing the reaction between aa_3 and adenosine triphosphate (ATP) to yield the aminoacyl derivative of adenosine monophosphate, or AMP $\sim aa_3$. The same enzyme then "transfers" the activated aa_3 to its cognate species of transfer RNA. The complex transfer RNA-aa_3 then enters the ribosome, a process that appears to involve guanosine triphosphate (GTP), where aa_3 is brought into position along the messenger RNA template for incorporation into the nascent polypeptide chain by its polynucleotide adaptor. The contours of the transfer RNA molecules shown here represent the specific nucleotide sequence by which the adaptor molecules are "recognized" by their complementary nucleotide triplets on the messenger RNA, depicted here as a helix. **B.** Detail of the relation of DNA, messenger, transfer RNA, and amino acid, and the proposed mechanism by which 5-fluorouracil (FU) restores normal function to a mutant phage by promoting errors in the transcription process. The GC pair in the DNA of the wild type phage is translated as C in the messenger RNA, and a complementary transfer-RNA adaptor pairs with the latter, thus specifying amino acid X. For a mutant arising by a GC $\rightarrow$ AT transition, the base in the messenger RNA becomes U, specifying the incorrect amino acid Y. In the presence of FU, however, U may be replaced by FU, which, when occasionally pairing like C, restores the correct amino acid X to the mutant polypeptide. [From Champe and Benzer (130).]

In this reaction, each kind of amino acid is activated only by its own homologous enzyme, and twenty such specific activating enzymes corresponding to the "standard" set of amino acids can be isolated from *E. coli* (492). Second, it was found that these selfsame activating enzymes catalyze also the attachment of the activated amino acid to a special type of RNA, the "soluble" or **transfer** RNA (314). This transfer RNA comprises about 10% of the total RNA of *E. coli* bacteria (392); it is not only of considerably lower molecular weight than either messenger or ribosomal RNA, being made up of only about 100 nucleotide units, but it also contains some unusual nucleotides, such as pseudo–uridine and ribothymidine, not present in the ribosomal RNA (312). The transfer RNA is itself heterogeneous, representing a mixture of different classes of molecules, of which each kind accepts only one kind of amino acid (64, 554); amino acids attached to transfer RNA molecules appear to be direct intermediates of protein biosynthesis in bacteria (392).

Since the transfer RNA molecules thus behave just like the postulated adaptors, it came to be generally believed that they *are* the adaptors, a belief which we shall also embrace here. In that case, it must be supposed that each transfer RNA molecule incorporates at some particular site in its polynucleotide chain the nucleotide sequence that recognizes, and hence is complementary to, the proper nucleotide triplet on the RNA messenger template. Once an amino acid has been brought into union with its homologous transfer RNA molecule by the specific activating enzyme, it has been "recognized" for the purposes of protein synthesis and can now fall into the proper place in the polypeptide assembly on the messenger RNA template.

The synthesis of transfer RNA, like that of ribosomal RNA, ceases upon infection of *E. coli* by T-even phages (495). It may be presumed, therefore, that the infecting virus utilizes the same adaptor-activating system as the bacterium itself. Hence the viral messenger RNA molecules that preside over the synthesis of viral proteins in the "old" ribosomes of the host receive amino acids for protein synthesis that are still being activated and "recognized" by the "old" transfer RNA molecules present in the cell before infection.

Synthetic Messengers

Some years before the discovery of the messenger RNA, Grunberg-Manago and Ochoa (258) found an enzyme, polynucleotide phosphorylase, in bacteria that catalyzes the in vitro synthesis of high molecular weight ribopolynucleotides from nucleoside–5'–diphosphates. Synthetic polymers can be prepared by use of this enzyme that, depending on the starting mixture of monomeric nucleoside diphosphates, contain either one or several kinds of ribonucleotides, in any desired proportion. Since such artificial ribopolynucleotide chains (particularly those composed of the four common nucleotides—adenylic, guanylic, cytidylic, and uridylic acids) bear a strong chemical resemblance to natural RNA, it was Ochoa's belief that polynucleotide phosphorylase "may be generally concerned with the intracellular synthesis of RNA" (498). But the natural role of this enzyme is probably connected not with RNA synthesis but rather with the *reversal* of the polymerization reaction —that is, with phosphorolytic cleavage of ribonucleotide diester bonds— and more particularly with the breakdown of spent messenger RNA molecules into nucleotide monomers reutilizable by the real RNA polymerizing enzymes (319, 678).

Though their availability as model substances proved to be of great value in the study of the chemistry of natural nucleic acids (591), synthetic polyribonucleotides came to play a much more important role in 1961, when Nirenberg and Matthaei (491) managed to develop a "cell-free" system capable of protein biosynthesis containing ribosomes, transfer RNA, and the relevant "soluble" enzymes, all extracted from *E. coli* cells. This particular cell-free system was by no means the first to be developed, but it had one very great advantage over its predecessors (311, 702): here the incorporation of radioactive amino acids into protein, the usual test reaction for detecting protein synthesis in such in vitro experiments, depended on the addition of *messenger RNA* to the mixture. Thus this kind of bacterial extract not only provided a way of assaying messenger RNA but also made possible the willful direction of the synthesis of specific polypeptides by introducing into this brew different species of messenger RNA molecules carrying different amino acid sequences encoded in their polynucleotide chains. When an artificial polyribonucleotide synthesized from nucleoside diphosphates by means of polynucleotide phosphorylase was added to this system instead of natural messenger RNA, a most surprising result was obtained. Introduction of polyuridylic acid, an RNA whose bases are all uracil, as an artificial messenger into the cell-free system stimulates the in vitro synthesis of polyphenylalanine, a polypeptide whose amino acids are all phenylalanine. This result could have but one meaning: a sequence of uridylic acids, that is, a UUU triplet in the messenger polynucleotide codes for the amino acid phenylalanine.

Thus, at one stroke, the breaking of the genetic code now became accessible to direct chemical methods, since it was evident that the nucleotide composition of the code words of other amino acids ought to be decipherable by examining the stimulatory effect of various artificial ribonucleotide homo- and copolymers on the in vitro incorporation into protein of other radioactive amino acids in this cell-free system. When Nirenberg (464) proceeded to do this, he found that the uridylic–cytidylic copolymer (poly UC) stimulates the incorporation not only of phenylalanine but also of leucine, serine, and proline, making it appear that the coding triplets for these latter three amino acids contain cytidylic as well as uridylic acid. Furthermore, by varying the relative amounts of cytidylic and uridylic acids in the artificial messenger copolymer and by observing the effect of this compositional variation of the template on the relative incorporation of the radioactive amino acids stimulated by the various copolymers, it could be ascertained whether each of the nucleotide triplets coding for leucine, serine, and proline is of composition U_2C or UC_2. For the incorporation of an amino acid that contains UC_2 in its coding triplet should be reduced much more by a decreased C content of the synthetic poly UC messenger than the incorporation of an amino acid coded by U_2C. In this way, it was possible to show that leucine and serine appear to be coded by different isomers of U_2C and proline by an isomer of UC_2. Entirely analogous experiments with other artificial polynucleotide copolymers, such as poly UA, poly UG, poly UAC, poly UGC, and poly UGA, made it possible to infer also the nucleotide compositions of code words of other amino acids (464). It should be noted, of course, that these experiments with mixed copolymers yielded only the nucleotide *composition* of code words but not the *order* of nucleotides within them.

Another entirely analogous set of experiments was carried out by Ochoa and his collaborators (409, 580). They also added various artificial nucleotide polymers and copolymers to Nirenberg and Matthaei's "cell-free" amino acid incorporation system and thus secured an independent determination of the nucleotide compositions of the code words for many of the "standard" set of amino acids that turned out to be in general agreement with those obtained in Nirenberg's laboratory. Hence in the autumn of 1961, within the short space of a few months, not only the general nature of the genetic code but also the chemical composition of some specific coding units and at least one actual code word of the dictionary relating nucleotides to amino acids—UUU = phenylalanine—suddenly became known, a research goal that had previously been thought likely to provide employment for many future generations of molecular biologists.

Ambivalence

Another important paper relevant to the heterocatalytic function of bacteriophage DNA appeared in 1961, the year in which the first reports describing the messenger RNA and the nature of the genetic code were published. In this paper, Benzer and Champe (56) deal with variations in *fidelity* of translation from cistron polynucleotide sequence into polypeptide amino acid sequence. Earlier discussions on mutation in phage had shown that the appearance of mutant genomes is, in effect, a reflection of the limits of fidelity of replication of the viral DNA: the mechanism of DNA replication, though of high fidelity, is not perfect and is subject to rare errors that generate polynucleotide chains slightly different in purine and pyrimidine base sequence, and hence information content, from the parent molecules. What about the fidelity of *protein synthesis?* Do there also occur errors in the transcription of the hereditary message that result in the construction of polypeptide chains whose amino acid sequence differs slightly from the "true" sequence coded in the relevant DNA cistron? Conceivably, such errors might occur at several stages of the transcription process. For instance, an "incorrect" nucleotide could be introduced into the nascent messenger RNA molecule, producing an incorrect polypeptide "blueprint"; or a molecule of an amino acid of type α could become attached to an adaptor cognate with another type of amino acid, β, and then be incorporated into a polypeptide at a site intended for the amino acid type β whose adaptor it bears.

In contrast to errors in DNA replication, errors in protein synthesis are not self-perpetuating, and hence they are rather more difficult to detect. But Benzer and Champe discovered a way in which the physiological consequences of transcription errors of the viral genome can be so amplified as to render them easily observable. The point of departure of this work was a re-examination of the ability of different T4rII mutants to grow on the three substrains KB, KT, and KB-1 of *E. coli*, strain K. These tests revealed that although, in principle, no *r*II mutant ought to be able to multiply on any bacterium of strain K, among the many *r*II mutants there exist subsets whose members *can* grow on one but not on another substrain of K. This is illustrated in Fig. 15-7. It can be seen that the T4*r*⁺ standard type lyses the bacteria of all three strains and hence

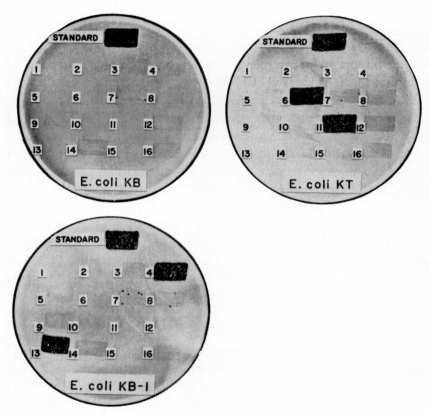

Fig. 15-7. Ambivalence of certain *r*II mutants of bacteriophage T4, as revealed by spot tests for activity on three bacterial strains. Each plate shown here was seeded with 10^8 bacteria. Streaks of the wild type T4*r*⁺ (designated here "standard") and sixteen different *r*II mutants were added (to the right of each number), by means of a sterile paper strip dipped into a stock of the mutant phage, and the plates were incubated overnight. The *r*⁺ wild type is active on all three bacterial strains. Ambivalent mutants of subset 1 are illustrated by spots 6 and 11. Spots 4 and 13 are ambivalent mutants of subset 3. The occasional plaques are due to *r*⁺ revertants present in the mutant stocks. [From Benzer and Champe (56).]

produces clearing on the test plate; that of the sixteen different rII mutants tested none is active on KB; and that two mutants (spots 6 and 11) are active on KT, and two mutants (spots 4 and 13) are active on KB-1. There exist also some rII mutants (not shown in Fig. 15-7) that are active on KB but not on KT or KB-1. This pattern of growth defines three subsets of **ambivalent** rII mutants: subset 1 can grow only on KT, subset 2 can grow only on KB, and subset 3 can grow only on KB-1. Similar tests carried out with several thousand different rII mutants showed that each ambivalent subset includes about one out of every thirty mutant sites in both rII cistrons and that the distribution of the mutant sites belonging to one subset is not restricted to any particular portion of the genetic map, or to one cistron.

Why can an ambivalent rII mutant grow in cells of one substrain of strain K but not in cells of another? What is the difference between the three closely related bacterial strains that define the ambivalent subsets? Benzer and Champe at once recognized the significance of this phenomenon: "The most striking aspect of the effects described is their extreme specificity. Since all rII mutants within a given cistron are defective in a unitary function, the change in the host bacterium cannot concern its response to the function *per se*, or it would effect all the rII mutants of the cistron similarly. This does happen if the bacterium loses its λ prophage, in which case all rII mutants become active." Following an idea of Yanofsky and St. Lawrence (700) for explaining "allele-specific suppression" in various organisms in which a mutation outside a genetic region suppresses the phenotype of some mutants within that region, Benzer and Champe proposed that there exist some differences between the three bacterial strains in regard to the specificity of their system for activating amino acids and attaching them to transfer RNA. "Suppose, for example, that one of the [amino acid] activating enzymes were altered, so that it had some tendency to couple the wrong amino acid to a given acceptor RNA. The result could be the occasional insertion of amino acid α in positions where amino acid β belongs. While such a fault in the translation of the genetic information would tend to reduce to some degree the activity of all enzymes, it could greatly increase the activity of an inactive one in which the defect were due to a mutation of just the right kind, namely one which has caused amino acid β to replace the normal α. A similar result might also be effected by modification of the acceptor [transfer] RNA's."

Thus the ambivalence pattern of the T4 phage mutants could be explained by assuming that each of the three subsets of ambivalent rII mutants owes its mutant phenotype—that is, lack of the rII enzyme activity required for growth in K bacteria—to the replacement of one amino acid in the rII$^+$ wild type polypeptide by another, say α replaced by β in subset 1, α' replaced by β' in subset 2, and α'' replaced by β'' in subset 3. Suppose there exists in each of the substrains of *E. coli*, strain K, a different hereditary defect in the specific coupling amino acid to transfer RNA, so that in KT bacteria amino acid α is sometimes coupled to the transfer RNA cognate to β, in KB bacteria amino acid α' is sometimes coupled to transfer RNA cognate to β', and in KB-1 bacteria amino acid α'' is sometimes coupled to transfer RNA cognate to β''. If this were true, it would follow that each rII mutant subset can grow only on that type of K bacterium in which there occurs the proper compensating error in the translation of the mutant messenger RNA that allows production of some rII wild type enzyme.

This ingenious notion of error correction might at first seem rather farfetched. But it was possible to secure enough supporting evidence to render it rather likely that this proposal is indeed the correct explanation of ambivalence. Above all, it turned out that among the members of a collection of mutants of the *E. coli* host unable to synthesize the enzyme *alkaline phosphatase* (235, 420), there can be found subsets of ambivalent phosphatase mutants that match the subsets of ambivalent rII mutants of the virus. That is to say, although none of the phosphataseless mutations allow formation of any phosphatase activity in the genetic background of the *E. coli* strain in which they were isolated, a few of these mutant genes do produce significant amounts of alkaline phosphatase when transferred by conjugation into one of the bacterial strains in which one set of ambivalent rII mutants is also able to grow (58). It may be inferred, therefore, that in the matching sets of ambivalent T4rII and phosphataseless *E. coli* mutants the mutant phenotypes derive from replacement of the same amino acid α of the normal wild type protein by the incorrect amino acid β, and that the hereditary defect in the specificity of amino acid activation system of the particular bacterial strain occasionally restores α to its normal place in the polypeptide chains coded by messenger RNA representing the mutant cistron of either viral or cellular DNA.

It is likely that the physiological basis of the phenotype of the *amber* (*am*) mutants of T4 discussed in Chapter 9 is to be explained in these same terms. That is, an *am* mutant may be thought to carry a mutation in one of its cistrons that engenders the replacement of an amino acid α at some particular site of the normal wild type polypeptide by the incorrect amino acid β. This replacement renders the mutant polypeptide functionally defective, so that the mutant virus is unable to grow in the nonpermissive *E. coli*, strain B. In bacterial strains, like *E. coli*, K12, that are permissive for the *am* mutant there obtains a reduced specificity of activation for protein synthesis that allows the occasional erroneous replacement of amino acid β by amino acid α in the construction of the viral polypeptide chains. In such bacteria the reduced fidelity of amino acid activation allows the *am* mutant to produce enough of the functional form of the mutant polypeptide to complete successfully the reactions essential for intracellular phage growth.

The foregoing interpretation of the nature of ambivalent and amber mutants is undoubtedly an oversimplification. Further analysis of the transmission pattern of *r*II and *am* mutants on different host strains suggests that the growth of these mutants on the permissive host is not necessarily rendered possible by the occasional restoration of the "correct" amino acid α present in the original wild type polypeptide. Instead, it is probably the occasional replacement of the pernicious mutant amino acid β by an "acceptable" amino acid γ that restores full or partial function to the defective mutant polypeptide. Thus one permissive host strain might allow growth of a phage mutant because the cellular amino acid activation system allows the occasional replacement of the pernicious mutant amino acid by one kind of acceptable amino acid; another permissive strain might allow growth because of the insertion of another kind of acceptable amino acid; and, finally, a third permissive strain might allow growth because here the wild type amino acid is really restored to the mutant polypeptide site.

Benzer and Champe (56, 130) also demonstrated that there can occur not only hereditary but also *physiological* variations in the fidelity of the polynucleotide-polypeptide translation process. Thus they found that if strain K bacteria infected with *certain* T4*r*II mutants are subjected to transient exposures of the pyrimidine analogue 5-fluorouracil, the fraction of infective centers that gives rise to at least an *r*II progeny phage particle is raised more than several hundredfold from the very low *transmission coefficient* that normally obtains in the absence of 5-fluorouracil.

However, the majority of T4rII mutants do not respond to this treatment and produce no infective progeny on *E. coli* K, whether the infected bacteria are exposed to the pyrimidine analogue or not. This indicates that the effect of 5-fluorouracil, like the hereditary difference between substrains KB, KT, and KB-1, is a specific one and not just a general facilitation of growth of *r*II mutants in strain K bacteria, such as that produced, for instance, by high concentrations of Mg^{++} (236). Instead, it appears that 5-fluorouracil, which is known to replace uracil in RNA (317), exerts its specific effect by being incorporated into the viral messenger RNA molecules synthesized in its presence. The 5-fluorouracil, like uracil, should generally pair with adenine in the template-adaptor bonding scheme shown in Fig. 15-6. But the presence of the fluorine atom (just like the presence of the bromine atom in the mutagenic thymine analogue 5-bromouracil) should raise the chance that in the messenger RNA polynucleotide the halogenated uracil temporarily acts like cytosine, and hence pairs with an adaptor that contains guanylic rather than adenylic acid in its coding triplet. This false pairing would, of course, result in the insertion of an incorrect amino acid into the growing polypeptide chain. In this way, the presence of 5-fluorouracil could restore some *r*II$^+$ wild type activity to those *r*II mutants that owe their mutant genotype to the mutational transition of a guanine-cytosine base pair into an adenine-thymine base pair at some particular site of the normal wild type cistron. Indeed, the pattern of reverse mutation induced by various specific mutagens (see pp. 259–273) shows that almost all *r*II mutants whose phenotype is sensitive to suppression by 5-fluorouracil actually appear to be represented by an adenine-thymine base pair at the mutant site in the viral DNA (130).

Thus the *r*II region of the T-even phage genome provided the experimental material for defining the limits not only of the resolving power of recombinational and mutational analysis but also of the fidelity of translation of the hereditary message in the heterocatalytic function of the viral DNA.

Regulation

Besides determining the primary structure of the proteins over whose synthesis it presides in the infected bacterial cell, the viral DNA performs also another task essential in the morphogenesis of the progeny viruses.

This task is to govern the actual *rate* at which different cistrons produce the polypeptides whose amino acid sequence is encoded in their nucleotide sequence. For instance, it has been noted that synthesis of the phage-induced "early" enzymes of viral DNA metabolism begins at the outset of T-even phage infection and comes to a halt toward the end of the eclipse period; but synthesis of the phage-precursor proteins and phage lysozyme commences only much later and continues unabated throughout the remaining course of intracellular phage growth. How is this precise temporal sequence of intracellular accumulation of various phage-specific polypeptides programed into the phage genome? It has also been noted that when a temperate phage such as λ infects an *immune* bacterium carrying a prophage homologous to the infecting phage, the presence of a specific repressor—the "immunity substance"— prevents the infecting viral genome from synthesizing any of the proteins necessary for its conversion to the vegetative state. What is the source of this repressor, and how is its repressive action exerted on the function of the viral cistrons?

Once the role of messenger RNA in protein synthesis had been understood, it became possible to comprehend how the functional regulation of the cistrons of the viral DNA is accomplished. The way toward this comprehension was shown by Jacob and Monod (331)— in a review which also happened to appear in 1961, that vintage year of molecular biology. Though Jacob and Monod's ideas are based mostly on physiologic-genetic observations on bacterial synthesis of inducible and repressible enzymes, they have equal applicability to the function of the viral genome. These ideas are summarized graphically in Fig. 15-8. According to Jacob and Monod, a set of one or more cistrons, all closely linked on the genetic map and hence residing in contiguous sectors of the DNA, form an **operon** by virtue of the joint control of their function by a common gene, their **operator**. The operator, whose site is closely linked to the operon which it controls, can exist in two states: *open* or *closed*. In the open state of the operator, every cistron of its operon synthesizes messenger RNA, and hence gives rise to the polypeptide whose structural information is encoded into it. In the closed state of the operator no cistron of its operon synthesizes its messenger RNA. The operator closes whenever it is engaged by a specific cytoplasmic **repressor**; this repressor is itself the product of another cistron, the **regulator gene.** There exist at least two different kinds of repressors. One kind is *neutralized* by a specific metabolite, or *inducer*, that prevents reaction of the repressor with the operator, and thus induces the otherwise repressed synthesis of the polypeptides coded in all cistrons of the relevant operon. Another kind of repressor must be *activated* by a specific metabolite, or *corepressor*, before it

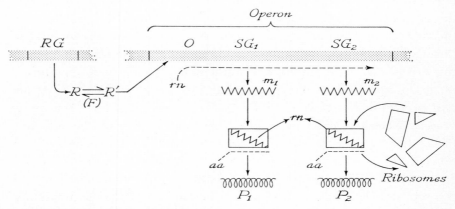

Fig. 15-8. Diagrammatic representation of the activity of cistrons and of the regulation of protein synthesis in bacteria. The two cistrons (SG_1 and SG_2) are under the control of a single operator (o) and form therefore an operon. The transfer of amino acid sequence information from structural genes (SG_1 and SG_2) to proteins involves the production of two messengers (m_1 and m_2, probably polyribonucleotides, rn). The messengers associate with ribosomal particles, and they direct the assembly of amino acids (aa) into polypeptide chains. Once completed, the polypeptides fold, forming proteins P_1 and P_2 which are detached from ribosomal particles. These particles are set free for a new cycle, involving the same or any other specific messenger. The synthesis of the two messengers m_1 and m_2 is a polarized process along the operon and is initiated in the operator region. A regulator gene (RG) produces a specific repressor (R) which interacts with specific small molecules (F = inducing or repressing metabolite, depending on the system) thus producing an altered repressor (R'). The active form of the repressor (R in inducible systems, R' in repressible systems) interacts specifically with the operator (O) and thus blocks the production of the two messengers m_1 and m_2. [From Jacob and Wollman (342).]

can react with its homologous operator and thus shut off function of all the cistrons of the operon.

The notion of the operon explains why, as had been learned from transductional fine-structure mapping, functionally related genetic loci are often closely linked on the bacterial chromosome. For instance, in *Salmonella typhimurium* the cistrons coding the four enzymes concerned with the terminal steps of tryptophan biosynthesis (see Fig. 13-3) cluster in one operon in order that their function can be regulated jointly by the intracellular supply of a single metabolite: tryptophan, the end product of the reaction sequence catalyzed by the four enzymes. Whenever tryptophan, the corepressor necessary for activation of the repressor of the tryptophan enzyme operon, is in short supply, the repressor is inactive and the operator is open; under these conditions, rapid synthesis of the relevant messenger RNA, and hence of tryptophan enzymes, may proceed. Whenever tryptophan is abundant, the repressor is activated, the operator is closed, and formation of all four of the now redundant tryptophan-synthesizing enzymes is held in abeyance.

The nature of some of the mutants of the temperate phage λ may now be considered in the light of this theory. It was stated in Chapter 12 that λc mutants carry a hereditary defect that prevents effective synthesis of the immunity repressor, and hence maintenance of the lysogenic state. In mixed infection of sensitive bacteria with λc^+ phage, or in super-infection of lysogenic K12(λ) bacteria, λc mutants are, however, still subject to the regulatory action of the normal repressor elaborated by the wild type phage genome. The λc mutants therefore represent an example of a mutation in a regulator gene responsible for the failure to synthesize an effective repressor. Two other instances of mutation of the c regulator gene of λ are known, which give rise to phage phenotypes somewhat different from that of the c mutants. One kind of such mutant is the *noninducible*, or $\lambda\ ind^-$, mutant that in its prophage state does not respond to the action of the usual inducing agents, such as UV or X-rays (328). In mixed infection or in polylysogeny, the $\lambda\ ind^-$ mutant is *dominant* over the $\lambda\ ind^+$ wild type and appears to carry a mutation in the c gene that results in the synthesis of a *more abundant* or *more efficient* immunity repressor substance. Another kind of regulation mutant is represented by λcI857, a genotype that can maintain the normal lysogenic state at 32°C but becomes induced and lyses its host cell as soon as a culture of *E. coli*, strain K12 carrying its prophage is brought to 40°C (618). The λcI857 appears to carry a mutation in the c regulator gene that results in the synthesis of a *heat-labile* repressor unable to exert its repressive action at temperatures above 38°C. In addition to these types, there also exist mutants of λ that carry mutations in the operator gene of the virus on which the immunity repressor normally acts. These are the *virulent* or λv mutants that, like λc mutants, are incapable of giving the lysogenic response. But unlike λc mutants, λv mutants are *dominant* over the wild type since, upon infection of $K12(\lambda^+)$ bacteria, λv mutants proceed to multiply and lyse the cells immune to the λ^+ wild type (332). Evidently, the immunity operator of λv mutants has mutated to a state that is no longer receptive to the immunity repressor elaborated by the c regulator gene.

Finally, the regulation of the biosynthetic events in the growth of the T-even phages may be interpreted in terms of the operator-repressor concept. It was seen in Chapter 9 that the disposition of the genetic loci of T4 on the circular genetic map of phage T4 appears to be correlated with the time in intracellular phage growth at which the product of each locus makes its appearance, or starts to function. This spatial distribution of the phage genes probably reflects the evolutionary amalgamation into operons of cistrons whose temporal function is to be coordinated. In this way, neutralization (or activation) of a single repressor species in the cytoplasm of the T4-infected cell suffices to turn on (or off) synthesis of messenger RNA by cistrons of contemporaneous function. Jacob (327, 342) also explained in these terms the nature of the physiological "clock" by which the vegetative phage tells the time at which particular functions are to be turned on or off. His idea is based on an earlier proposal of Stanier (584), who pointed out that there occurs a sequential induction of the synthesis of a series of enzymes if the metabolic product of the first enzyme is an inducer (neutralizes the repressor) of the synthesis of the second enzyme, and the metabolic product of the second enzyme is an inducer of the synthesis of the third, and so on. Jacob reasoned that a sequential functional activation of the phage genome can be achieved if, at the outset of phage growth, messenger RNA synthesis by "late" operons is first held in abeyance by specific repressors, and that these repressors are later neutralized by metabolic products of "early" operons. For instance, it could be imagined that the operon containing the phage tail-fiber cistron is initially repressed, until induced to form its messenger RNA by one of the compounds of phage DNA metabolism synthesized by the "early" enzymes of Fig. 7-3. Conversely, it could be imagined that the cessation of messenger RNA synthesis by the cistrons of an "early" operon at a later stage of the latent period results from the synthesis or activation of a specific repressor by a metabolic product of a "later" operon. For instance, it is possible that synthesis of the "early" enzymes of phage DNA metabolism ceases halfway through the latent period because a structural phage component—for example, the tail-fiber polypeptide—acts as a specific repressor or corepressor of the relevant operon.

This image of the regulation process can also account for the observations of Chapter 11 that though T2 or T4 phages inactivated by UV can still elicit the synthesis of the enzymes of phage DNA metabolism, they are no longer capable of giving rise to the structural proteins of the phage tail or head. Thus the functional expression of "late" operons of the phage is much more UV-sensitive than that of "early" operons. This inference is supported also by the relatively low sensitivity to UV of the function of the genes coding for the internal protein and for the u and rII^+ phenotypes, all "early" functions of the T-even phage genome (266, 383, 488). That the UV sensitivity of "late" functions should be greater than that of "early" functions becomes comprehensible when it is considered that UV inactivation of the function of an "early" cistron entrains an interruption of the specific induction sequence. Such a stoppage of the physiological clock would have the result that synthesis of messenger RNA by "late" operons of the irradiated viral genome is never turned on. Or, restating this proposition in more general terms, the UV "target" whose inactivation results in the loss of a particular function is represented not only by the cistron coding the polypeptide entrusted with this function but also by all other "earlier" cistrons that code polypeptides involved at an anterior point in the sequential induction chain. That synthesis of the "early" enzymes of phage DNA metabolism initiated by a population of UV-inactivated T2 phages does not cease at the normal time and results in abnormally high intracellular concentrations of these enzymes (178) is a very strong supporting argument for the conception that UV irradiation stops the working of the physiological clock.

Further Reading

Crick, F. H. C., "On protein synthesis" (149). Probably the first general outline of the mechanism by which the hereditary substance directs the synthesis of specific proteins; a clairvoyant analysis.

Hoagland, M. B., "The relationship of nucleic acid and protein synthesis as revealed by studies in cell-free systems" (312); Gros, F., "Biosynthesis of proteins in intact bacterial cells" (257); Berg, P., "Specificity in protein synthesis" (62). More detailed discussions on the role of nucleic acids and polynucleotides in protein synthesis.

Crick, F. H. C., Barnett, L., Brenner, S., and Watts-Tobin, R. J., "The general nature of the genetic code" (150). The study of the pattern of T4rII suppressor mutations that revealed the general nature of the code.

Brenner, S., Jacob, F., and Meselson, M., "An unstable intermediate carrying information from genes to ribosomes for protein synthesis" (98). A demonstration of the validity of the messenger RNA concept by use of the flow of radioisotope through density-labeled ribosomes of phage-infected bacteria.

Benzer, S. and Champe, S. P., "Ambivalent rII mutants of phage T4" (56); Champe, S. P. and Benzer, S., "Reversal of mutant phenotypes of 5-fluorouracil: an approach to nucleotide sequences in messenger RNA" (130). On the limits of fidelity of protein synthesis.

Jacob, F. and Monod, J., "Genetic regulatory mechanisms in the synthesis of proteins" (331). An admirable exposition of the facts and ideas that have exerted a profound influence on latter-day physiological genetics. One of the most important supplementary readings for this text.

Crick, F. H. C., "The recent excitement in the coding problem" (149a). A cool appreciation that separates the wheat from the chaff.

Postscript

IT SHOULD BE pointed out, before closing this account, that interpretations and theories have sometimes been presented here in rather a more positive manner than a cautious appreciation of the available facts might have actually warranted. This is particularly true for the treatment of the expression of the hereditary message in Chapter 15. Most of the important discoveries recounted in that chapter are of such recent date and rest on so few, albeit brilliant, key experiments that they cannot yet have been put to the test of time. Nevertheless, it would seem quite improbable that the present general picture of how the viral DNA achieves its autocatalytic and heterocatalytic functions should be very far off the mark.

The attainment of understanding biological self-reproduction in molecular terms marks another milestone in the march against vitalism, the 18th century doctrine which held that, in the last analysis, the phenomena of life can only be explained by a mystical "vital force," neither physical nor chemical in nature. Although the embrace of vitalism implied acceptance of an essentially idealistic belief, adherence to the materialistic tenet that the complexities of the structure, function, and variety of living forms could eventually be accounted for in purely mechanical terms required as great an act of faith. Admittedly, since the middle of the 19th century one biological enigma after another has been successfully explained without the necessity of appeal to metaphysical vital forces, beginning with Wöhler's synthesis of organic chemicals and Darwin's rational account of organic evolution. But as late as the first two or three decades of this century it still must have seemed an impossibly difficult task to give a wholly physical account of the mechanisms of heredity. As the developments described in this text have finally shown, however, it is unnecessary to resort to forces more mysterious than the hydrogen bond to explain how like begets like.

427

What fundamental questions remain after the solution of the problem of self-reproduction to which the molecular biologist might now address himself? Foremost among these are the origin of life itself and the processes responsible for the orderly morphogenesis of single germ cells into amazingly complex and highly differentiated multicellular organisms. Great strides have, of course, already been made in the study of these problems and, in fact, more or less reasonable outlines of their ultimate solutions can be at least imagined; it seems not unlikely that the insights brought by molecular genetics will help to accelerate their eventual comprehension. But one major frontier of biological inquiry would still remain even after origin of life and morphogenesis have also been satisfactorily accounted for—the higher nervous system. Its fantastic attributes now seem to pose as hopelessly difficult and intractably complex a problem as did the phenomena of heredity half a century ago. Perhaps just because of the challenge constituted by the present impossibility of even imagining any reasonable molecular explanation for such manifestations of life as consciousness and memory, the neuron bids fair to become the phage of the future.

Bibliography and Citation Index

A reference number in **boldface** indicates that the article has been reprinted in the collection *Papers on Bacterial Viruses* (595). Numbers in brackets following each reference indicate the text pages where the reference has been cited. Citation numbers with letter (as 652a) indicate references added in proof.

1. Adams, J. N., and Luria, S. E. Transduction by bacteriophage P1. Abnormal phage function of the transducing particles. *Proc. Nat. Acad. Sci. U.S.A.*, **44:**590 (1958). [363]

2. Adams, M. H. *Bacteriophages*, Interscience, New York, 1959. [ix, 30, 69, 174, 201, 236, 305, 340]

3. Adams, M. H., and Wade, E. Classification of bacterial viruses: characteristics of the T1, D20 species of coli-dysentery phages. *J. Bacteriol.*, **70:**253 (1955). [57]

4. Alexander, P. A., and Stacey, K. A. Production of "hidden" breaks in DNA by the direct action of ionizing radiation. In *Progress in Radiobiology* (J. S. Mitchell, B. E. Holmes, and C. L. Smith, eds.), p. 105. Oliver and Boyd, London, 1956. [300]

5. Alper, T. Hydrogen peroxide and the indirect effect of ionizing radiations. *Nature*, **162:**615 (1948). [298]

6. Ames, B. N., and Dubin, D. T. Role of polyamines in the neutralization of bacteriophage deoxyribonucleic acid. *J. Biol. Chem.*, **235:**769 (1960). [68]

7. Ames, B. N., Dubin, D. T., and Rosenthal, S. M. Presence of polyamines in certain bacterial viruses. *Science*, **127:**814 (1958). [68]

8. Anderson, E. S., and Felix, A. Variation in Vi-phage II of *Salmonella typhi*. *Nature*, **170:**492 (1952). [377]

9. Anderson, H. W. A bacteriophage of *B. pruni*. *Phytopathology*, **18:**144 (1928). [25]

10. Anderson, T. F. On a bacteriolytic substance associated with a purified virus. *J. Cellular Comp. Physiol.*, **25:**1 (1945). [81]

11. Anderson, T. F. The role of tryptophane in the adsorption of two bacterial viruses on their host *Escherichia coli*. *J. Cellular Comp. Physiol.*, **25:**17 (1945). [107, 186]

12. Anderson, T. F. The activation of bacterial virus T4 by L-tryptophan. *J. Bacteriol.*, **55:**637 (1948). [107]

13. Anderson, T. F. The inheritance of requirements for adsorption cofactors in bacterial virus T4. *J. Bacteriol.*, **55:**651 (1948). [107]

14. Anderson, T. F. The growth of T2 virus on ultraviolet-killed host cells. *J. Bacteriol.*, **56:**403 (1948). [371]

15. Anderson, T. F. The reactions of bacterial viruses with their host cells. *Botan. Rev.*, **15:**464 (1949). [63, 110] — 505

16. Anderson, T. F. Destruction of bacterial viruses by osmotic shock. *J. Appl. Phys.*, **21:**70 (1950). [63]

17. Anderson, T. F. Techniques for the preservation of three dimensional structure in preparing specimens for the electron microscope. *Trans. New York Acad. Sci.*, **13**:130 (1951). [47, 104]

18. Anderson, T. F. The morphology and osmotic properties of bacteriophage systems. *Cold Spring Harbor Symp. Quant. Biol.*, **18**:197 (1953). [63, 104]

19. Anderson, T. F., and Doermann, A. H. The intracellular growth of bacteriophages. II. The growth of T3 studied by sonic disintegration and by T6-cyanide lysis of infected cells. *J. Gen. Physiol.*, **35**:657 (1952). [85]

20. Anderson, T. F., Rappaport, C., and Muscatine, A. On the structure and osmotic properties of phage particles. *Ann. Inst. Pasteur*, **84**:5 (1953). [63, 121]

21. Andrewes, C. H., and Elford, W. J. Observations on antiphage sera: I. "The percentage law." *Brit. J. Exp. Pathol.*, **14**:367 (1933). [61]

22. Andrewes, C. H., and Elford, W. J. Observations on antiphage sera: II. Properties of incompletely neutralized phage. *Brit. J. Exp. Pathol.*, **14**:377 (1933). [61]

23. Anfinsen, C. B., and Redfield, R. R. Protein structure in relation to function and biosynthesis. *Adv. Protein Chem.*, **11**:1 (1956). [250]

24. Appelmans, R. Quelques applications de la méthode de dosage du bactériophage. *C. R. Soc. Biol.*, **86**:508 (1922). [277]

25. Appleyard, R. Segregation of lambda lysogenicity during bacterial recombination in *Escherichia coli* K12. *Genetics*, **39**:429 (1954). [321]

26. Appleyard, R. Segregation of new lysogenic types during growth of a doubly lysogenic strain derived from *Escherichia coli* K12. *Genetics*, **39**:440 (1954). [332]

27. Appleyard, R. The transfer of defective lambda lysogeny between strains of *Escherichia coli*. *J. Gen. Microbiol.*, **14**:573 (1956). [333]

28. Arber, W. Transduction des charactères Gal par le bactériophage λ. *Arch. sci.* (Geneva), **11**:259 (1958). [361]

29. Arber, W. Polylysogeny for bacteriophage lambda. *Virology*, **11**:250 (1960). [332]

30. Arber, W., and Dussoix, D. Host specificity of DNA produced by *Escherichia coli*. I. Host controlled modification of bacteriophage λ. *J. Mol. Biol.*, **5**:18 (1962). [332, 378, 380]

31. Arber, W., Kellenberger, G., and Weigle, J. J. La défectuosité du phage λ transducteur. *Schweiz. Z. allgem. Pathol. Bakteriol.*, **20**:659 (1957). [361]

32. Astrachan, L., and Volkin, E. Properties of ribonucleic acid turnover in T2-infected *Escherichia coli*. *Biochim. Biophys. Acta*, **29**:536 (1958). [157]

33. Avery, O. T., MacLeod, C. M., and McCarty, M. Studies on the chemical nature of the substance inducing transformation of pneumococcal types. Induction of transformation by a desoxyribonucleic acid fraction isolated from pneumococcus type III. *J. Exp. Med.*, **79**:137 (1944). [114, 343]

34. Bail, O. Der Colistamm 88 von Gildemeister und Herzberg. *Med. Klin.* (Munich), **21**:1271 (1925). [307, 312]

35. Bail, O., and Matusmoto, T. Die Anhäufungsmöglichkeit von Bakteriophagen und Bakterien. *Med. Klin.* (Munich), **19**:1579 (1923). [79]

36. Baricelli, N. A. A "chromosomic" recombination theory for multiplicity reactivation in phages. *Acta biotheoretica* (Leiden), **11**:107 (1956). [291]

37. Barksdale, L. W. Lysogenic conversions in bacteria. *Bacteriol. Rev.*, **23**:202 (1959). [336, 338]

38. Barksdale, L. W. and Pappenheimer, A. M., Jr. Phage host relationships in non-toxigenic and toxigenic diphtheria bacilli. *J. Bacteriol.*, **67**:220 (1954). [337]

39. Barner, H. D., and Cohen, S. S. The induction of thymine synthesis by T2 infection of a thymine requiring mutant of *Escherichia coli*. *J. Bacteriol.*, **68**:80 (1954). [149]

40. Barner, H. D., and Cohen, S. S. Virus-induced acquisition of metabolic function. IV. Thymidylate synthetase in thymine-requiring *Escherichia coli* infected by T2 and T5 bacteriophages. *J. Biol. Chem.*, **234**:2987 (1959). [149]

41. Barrington, L. F., and Kozloff, L. M. Action of bacteriophage on isolated host cell walls. *J. Biol. Chem.*, **223**:615 (1956). [80, 81]

42. Bautz, E., and Freese, E. On the mutagenic effect of alkylating agents. *Proc. Nat. Acad. Sci. U.S.A.*, **46**:1585 (1960). [265]

43. Baylor, M. D., Hurst, D., Allen, S. L., and Bertani, E. T. The frequency and distribution of loci affecting host range in the coliphage T2H. *Genetics*, **42**:104 (1957). [186, 208]

44. Bayne-Jones, S., and Sandholzer, L. A. Changes in the shape and size of *Bacterium coli* and *Bacillus megaterium* under the influence of bacteriophage. A motion photo-micrographic analysis of the mechanism of lysis. *J. Exp. Med.*, **57**:279 (1933). [80]

45. Beijerinck, M. W. Über ein contagium vivum fluidum als Ursache der Flecken-krankheit der Tabaksblätter. *Zentr. Bakteriol. Parasitenk. (II)*, **5**:27 (1899). [1]

46. Belling, J. Crossing over and gene rearrangement in flowering plants. *Genetics*, **18**:388 (1933). [224]

47. Belozersky, A. N., and Spirin, A. S. Chemistry of the nucleic acid of microorganisms. In *The Nucleic Acids* (E. Chargaff and J. N. Davidson, eds.), Vol. III, p. 147. Academic Press, New York, 1960. [291, 404]

48. Bentzon, M. W., Maaløe, O., and Rasch, G. Analysis of the mode of increase in number of intracellular phage particles at different temperatures. *Acta Pathol. Microbiol. Scand.*, **30**:243 (1951). [82, 85]

49. Benzer, S. Resistance to ultraviolet light as an index to the reproduction of bacteriophage. *J. Bacteriol.*, **63**:59 (1952). [301, 305, 371, 374]

50. Benzer, S. Induced synthesis of enzymes in bacteria analyzed at the cellular level. *Biochim. Biophys. Acta*, **11**:383 (1953). [140]

51. Benzer, S. Fine structure of a genetic region in bacteriophage. *Proc. Nat. Acad. Sci. U.S.A.*, **41**:344 (1955). [190, 239, 241, 276]

52. Benzer, S. The elementary units of heredity. In *The Chemical Basis of Heredity* (W. D. McElroy and B. Glass, eds.), p. 70. The Johns Hopkins Press, Baltimore, 1957. [239, 257, 276]

53. Benzer, S. On the topology of the genetic fine structure. *Proc. Nat. Acad. Sci. U.S.A.*, **45**:1607 (1959). [276]

54. Benzer, S. Genetic fine structure. *Harvey Lectures*, Vol. 56, p. 1. Academic Press, New York, 1961. [263]

55. Benzer, S. On the topography of the genetic fine structure. *Proc. Nat. Acad. Sci. U.S.A.*, **47**:403 (1961). [248, 249, 257, 258, 268, 276]

56. Benzer, S., and Champe, S. P. Ambivalent rII mutants of phage T4. *Proc. Nat. Acad. Sci. U.S.A.*, **47**:1025 (1961). [415, 416, 419, 426]

57. Benzer, S., and Champe, S. P. An active cistron fragment. *J. Mol. Biol.*, **4**:288 (1962). [256]

58. Benzer, S., Champe, S. P., Garen, A., and Siddiqi, O. In press. [418]

59. Benzer, S., Delbrück, M., Dulbecco, R., Hudson, W., Stent, G. S., Watson, J. D., Weidel, W., Weigle, J. J., and Wollman, E. L. A Syllabus on Procedures, Facts and Interpretations in Phage. In *Virus 1950* (M. Delbrück, ed.). Calif. Inst. of Tech., Pasadena, 1950. [ix]

60. Benzer, S., and Freese, E. Induction of specific mutations with 5-bromouracil. *Proc. Nat. Acad. Sci. U.S.A.*, **44**:112 (1958). [263, 268, 276]

61. Benzer, S., and Jacob, F. Étude du développement du bactériophage au moyen d'irradiations par la lumière ultraviolette. *Ann. Inst. Pasteur*, **84**:186 (1953). [372, 373]

62. Berg, P. Specificity in protein synthesis. *Ann. Rev. Biochem.*, **30**:293 (1961). [426]

63. Berg, P., and Newton, G. The interaction of adenosinetriphosphate and L-methionine. *J. Biol. Chem.*, **222**:1025 (1956). [411]

64. Berg, P., and Ofengand, E. J. An enzymatic mechanism for linking amino acids to ribonucleic acid (RNA). *Proc. Nat. Acad. Sci. U.S.A.*, **44**:78 (1958). [412]

65. Bernheimer, A. W. Differentiation of ribonucleic acids by inhibition of streptococcal desoxyribonuclease. *Biochem. J.*, **53**:53 (1953). [141]

65a. Bertani, G. Studies on lysogenesis. I. The mode of phage liberation by lysogenic *Escherichia coli*. *J. Bacteriol.*, **62**:293 (1951). [347]

66. Bertani, G. Lysogenic versus lytic cycle of phage multiplication. *Cold Spring Harbor Symp. Quant. Biol.*, **18**:65 (1953). [319, 337]

67. Bertani, G. Infections bactériophagiques secondaires des bactéries lysogènes. *Ann. Inst. Pasteur*, **84**:273 (1953). [319]

68. Bertani, G. Studies on lysogenesis. III. Superinfection of lysogenic *Shigella dysenteriae* with temperate mutants of the carried phage. *J. Bacteriol.*, **67**:696 (1954). [316]

69. Bertani, G. Lysogeny. *Adv. Virus Research*, **5**:151 (1958). [49, 315, 323, 340]

70. Bertani, G., and Weigle, J. J. Host controlled variation in bacterial viruses. *J. Bacteriol.*, **65**:113 (1953). [377, 378]

71. Bertani, L. E. The effect of the inhibition of protein synthesis on the establishment of lysogeny. *Virology*, **4**:53 (1957). [313]

72. Bessman, M. J. Deoxyribonucleotide kinases in normal and virus-infected *Escherichia coli*. *J. Biol. Chem.*, **234**:2735 (1959). [150, 151]

73. Bessman, M. J., and Van Bibber, M. J. A change in the properties of deoxyguanylate kinase of *Escherichia coli* caused by viral infection. *Biochem. Biophys. Research Commun.*, **1**:101 (1959). [150, 151]

74. Beukers, R., and Berends, W. Isolation and identification of the irradiation product of thymine. *Biochim. Biophys. Acta*, **41**:550 (1960). [282]

75. Blair, J. E. A lytic principle (bacteriophage) for *Corynebacterium diphtheriae*. *J. Infectious Diseases*, **35**:401 (1924). [25]

76. Bonét-Maury, P., and Bulgakov, N. Recherches sur la taille et la structure du bactériophage φX-174. Actions des rayons alpha du radon. *C. R. Soc. Biol.*, **138**:499 (1944). [384]

77. Bonifas, V., and Kellenberger, E. Étude de l'action des membranes du bactériophage T2 sur *Escherichia coli. Biochim. Biophys. Acta*, **16**:330 (1955). [65, 370]

78. Bordet, J. Concerning the theories of the so-called "bacteriophage." *Brit. Med. J.* (2), August 19, 1922, p. 296. [13, 21]

79. Bordet, J. Le problème de l'autolyse microbienne transmissible ou du bactériophage. *Ann. Inst. Pasteur*, **39**:711 (1925). [87, 307, 312, 347]

80. Bordet, J. The theories of the bacteriophage. *Proc. Roy. Soc. London, Ser. B*, **83**:398 (1931). [13, 21]

81. Bordet, J., and Ciuca, M. Exudats leucocytaires et autolyse microbienne transmissible. *C. R. Soc. Biol.*, **83**:1293 (1920). [80]

82. Bordet, J., and Ciuca, M. Le bactériophage de d'Hérelle, sa production, et son interpretation. *C. R. Soc. Biol.*, **83**:1296 (1920). [80]

83. Bordet, J., and Ciuca, M. Déterminisme de l'autolyse microbienne transmissible. *C. R. Soc. Biol.*, **84**:276 (1921). [25, 58]

84. Bordet, J., and Ciuca, M. Évolution des cultures de coli lysogènes. *C. R. Soc. Biol.*, **84**:747 (1921). [306]

85. Bowen, G. H. Studies of ultraviolet irradiation phenomena—an approach to the problems of bacteriophage reproduction. *Cold Spring Harbor Symp. Quant. Biol.*, **18**:245 (1953). [283]

86. Bowen, G. H. Kinetic studies on the mechanism of photoreactivation of bacteriophage T2 inactivated by ultraviolet light. *Ann. Inst. Pasteur*, **84**:218 (1953). [283]

87. Boyd, J. S. K. The role of mutation in the survival and multiplication of bacterial viruses. In *The Nature of Virus Multiplication*, Symposium of the Society for General Microbiology (P. Fildes and W. E. Van Heyningen, eds.), p. 119. Cambridge University Press, London, 1952. [313]

88. Brenner, S. Tryptophan biosynthesis in *Salmonella typhimurium. Proc. Nat. Acad. Sci. U.S.A.*, **41**:862 (1955). [350]

89. Brenner, S. Impossibility of all overlapping triplet codes in information transfer from nucleic acid to proteins. *Proc. Nat. Acad. Sci. U.S.A.*, **43**:687 (1957). [393]

90. Brenner, S. Genetic control and phenotypic mixing of the adsorption cofactor requirement in bacteriophages T2 and T4. *Virology*, **3**:560 (1957). [136, 186, 201]

91. Brenner, S. Physiological aspects of bacteriophage genetics. *Adv. Virus Research*, **6**:137 (1959). [237]

92. Brenner, S. RNA, ribosomes and protein synthesis. *Cold Spring Harbor Symp. Quant. Biol.*, **26**:101 (1961). [402]

93. Brenner, S., and Barnett, L. Genetic and chemical studies on the head protein of bacteriophages T2 and T4. In *Structure and Function of Genetic Elements*, Brookhaven Symposia in Biology, No. 12, p. 86 (1959). [187]

94. Brenner, S., Barnett, L., Crick, F. H. C., and Orgel, A. The theory of mutagenesis. *J. Mol. Biol.*, **3**:121 (1961). [272, 398]

95. Brenner, S., Benzer, S., and Barnett, L. Distribution of proflavin-induced mutation in the genetic fine structure. *Nature*, **182**:983 (1958). [264]

96. Brenner, S., Champe, S. P., Streisinger, G., and Barnett, L. On the interaction of adsorption cofactors with bacteriophages T2 and T4. *Virology*, **17**:30 (1962). [107]

97. Brenner, S., and Horne, R. W. Negative staining method for high-resolution electron microscopy of viruses. *Biochim. Biophys. Acta*, **34:**103 (1959). [47]

98. Brenner, S., Jacob, F., and Meselson, M. An unstable intermediate carrying information from genes to ribosomes for protein synthesis. *Nature*, **190:**576 (1961). [403, 405, 407, 426]

99. Brenner, S., and Smith, J. D. Induction of mutations in the deoxyribonucleic acid of phage T2 synthesized in the presence of chloramphenicol. *Virology*, **8:**124 (1959). [144]

100. Brenner, S., and Stent, G. S. Bacteriophage growth in protoplasts of *Bacillus megaterium. Biochim. Biophys. Acta*, **17:**473 (1955). [102]

101. Brenner, S., Streisinger, G., Horne, R. W., Champe, S. P., Barnett, L., Benzer, S., and Rees, M. W. Structural components of bacteriophage. *J. Mol. Biol.*, **1:**281 (1959). [65, 105, 106, 109]

102. Bresch, C. Zum Paarungsmechanismus von Bakteriophagen. *Z. Naturforsch.*, **10b:**545 (1955). [224]

103. Bresch, C. Recombination in bacteriophage. *Ann. Rev. Microbiol.*, **13:**313 (1959). [237]

104. Bresch, C., and Starlinger, P. Zum Problem der genetischen Rekombination von Bakteriophagen. *Z. Vererbungsl.*, **89:**459 (1958). [89, 224]

105. Bronfenbrenner, J. J. In *Filtrable Viruses* (T. Rivers, ed.), p. 373. Williams & Wilkins, Baltimore, 1928. [14, 80, 89]

106. Brown, D. M., and Schell, P. The reaction of hydroxylamine with cytosine and related compounds. *J. Mol. Biol.*, **3:**709 (1961). [268]

107. Burgi, E., and Hershey, A. D. A relative molecular weight series derived from the nucleic acid of bacteriophage T2. *J. Mol. Biol.*, **3:**458 (1961). [67]

108. Burnet, F. M. The relationship between heat-stable agglutinogens and sensitivity to bacteriophage in the Salmonella group. *Brit. J. Exp. Pathol.*, **8:**121 (1927). [382]

109. Burnet, F. M. A method for the study of bacteriophage multiplication in broth. *Brit. J. Exp. Pathol.*, **10:**109 (1929). [16, 71]

110. Burnet, F. M. "Smooth rough" variation in bacteria in its relation to bacteriophage. *J. Pathol. Bacteriol.*, **32:**15 (1929). [16]

111. Burnet, F. M. A specific soluble substance from bacteriophages. *Brit. J. Exp. Pathol.*, **14:**100 (1933). [119]

112. Burnet, F. M. Specific agglutination of bacteriophage particles. *Brit. J. Exp. Pathol.*, **14:**302 (1933). [61]

113. Burnet, F. M. The classification of dysentery coli-bacteriophages. II. The serological classification of coli-dysentery phages. *J. Pathol. Bacteriol.*, **37:**107 (1933). [57, 61]

114. Burnet, F. M. The bacteriophages. *Biol. Rev. Cambridge Phil. Soc.*, **9:**332 (1934). [11, 16, 21, 57]

115. Burnet, F. M. The phage-inactivating agent of bacterial extracts. *J. Pathol. Bacteriol.*, **38:**285 (1934). [97, 195]

116. Burnet, F. M., and Freeman, M. A comparative study of the inactivation of a bacteriophage by immune serum and by a bacterial polysaccharide. *Austral. J. Exp. Biol. Med. Sci.*, **15:**49 (1937). [97]

117. Burnet, F. M., Keogh, E. V., and Lush, D. The immunological reactions of the filterable viruses. *Austral. J. Exp. Biol. Med. Sci.*, **15**:227 (1937). [59]

118. Burnet, F. M., and Lush, D. Induced lysogenicity and mutation of bacteriophage within lysogenic bacteria. *Austral. J. Exp. Biol. Med. Sci.*, **14**:27 (1936). [16, 176]

119. Burnet, F. M., and McKie, M. Observations on a permanently lysogenic strain of *B. enteritidis gaertner*. *Austral. J. Exp. Biol. Med. Sci.*, **6**:277 (1929). [16, 307, 308]

120. Burnet, F. M., and McKie, M. The classification of dysentery-coli bacteriophages. I. The differentiation by Bail's method of phages lysing a typical coli strain. *J. Pathol. Bacteriol.*, **36**:299 (1933). [181]

121. Burton, K. The relation between the synthesis of deoxyribonucleic acid and the synthesis of protein in the multiplication of bacteriophage T2. *Biochem. J.*, **61**:473 (1955). [143]

122. Buschke, A., and Harry, F. Färberische Versuche über die Degeneration von Gonokokken und Gonovaccinen. *Deut. med. Wschr.*, p. 1068 (1922). [25]

123. Cairns, J. An estimate of the length of the DNA molecule of T2 bacteriophage by autoradiography. *J. Mol. Biol.*, **3**:756 (1961). [67]

124. Calef, E., and Licciardello, G. Recombination experiments on prophage host relationships. *Virology*, **12**:81 (1960). [331]

125. Campbell, A. Transduction and segregation in *E. coli* K12. *Virology*, **4**:366 (1957). [361]

126. Campbell, A. The different kinds of transducing particles in the λ-gal system. *Cold Spring Harbor Symposia Quant. Biol.*, **23**:83 (1958). [361]

127. Campbell, A. M. Episomes. *Adv. Genet.*, **11**:101 (1962). [330]

128. Cancik, J. Über Pyozyanensbakteriophagen. *Časopis ces. lek.*, **62**:183 (1923). [25]

129. Cavalli, L. L. La sessualita nei batteri. *Boll. Ist. sierotera, Milano*, **29**:281 (1950). [321]

130. Champe, S. P. and Benzer, S. Reversal of mutant phenotypes by 5-fluorouracil: an approach to nucleotide sequences in messenger RNA. *Proc. Nat. Acad. Sci. U.S.A.*, **48**:532 (1962). [411, 419, 420, 426]

131. Chargaff, E. Chemical specificity of nucleic acids and mechanism of their enzymatic degradation. *Experientia*, **6**:201 (1950). [55]

132. Chase, M., and Doermann, A. H. High negative interference over short segments of the genetic structure of bacteriophage T4. *Genetics*, **43**:332 (1958). [230, 231]

133. Christensen, J. R. On the process of host-controlled modification of bacteriophage. *Virology*, **13**:40 (1961). [378]

134. Christensen, J. R. The fate of genes from restricted T1 in lysogenic *Shigella dysenteriae*, Sh(P1). *Virology*, **16**:133 (1962). [378]

135. Clarke, N. A. Studies on the host-virus-relationship in a lysogenic strain of *Bac. megatherium*. II. The growth of *Bac. megatherium* in synthetic medium. *J. Bacteriol.*, **63**:187 (1952). [315]

136. Cocito, C., and Hershey, A. D. Transfer of DNA-glucose from parental to offspring phage T2. *Biochim. Biophys. Acta*, **37**:543 (1960). [199]

137. Cohen, S. S. Synthesis of bacterial viruses in infected cells. *Cold Spring Harbor Symp. Quant. Biol.*, **12**:35 (1947). [123, 130]

138. Cohen, S. S. Synthesis of bacterial viruses; synthesis of nucleic acid and protein in *Escherichia coli* infected with T2r^+ bacteriophage. *J. Biol. Chem.*, **174:**281 (1948). [123, 130, 155, 403]

139. Cohen, S. S. Synthesis of bacterial viruses; origin of phosphorus found in desoxyribonucleic acids of T2 and T4 bacteriophages. *J. Biol. Chem.*, **174:**295 (1948). [126, 138, 140]

140. Cohen, S. S. Growth requirements of bacterial viruses. *Bacteriol. Rev.*, **13:**1 (1949). [140]

141. Cohen, S. S. Studies on controlling mechanisms in the metabolism of virus-infected bacteria. *Cold Spring Harbor Symp. Quant. Biol.*, **18:**221 (1953). [127]

142. Cohen, S. S., and Anderson, T. F. Chemical studies on host virus interactions. I. The effect of bacteriophage adsorption on the multiplication of its host *Escherichia coli* B. *J. Exp. Med.*, **84:**511 (1946). [139, 141]

143. Cohen, S. S., and Arbogast, R. Chemical studies in host virus interaction. VIII. The mutual reactivation of T2r^+ virus inactivated by ultraviolet light and the synthesis of desoxyribosenucleic acid. *J. Exp. Med.*, **91:**637 (1950). [282]

144. Cohen, S. S., Flaks, J. G., Barner, H. D., Loeb, M. R., and Lichtenstein, J. The mode of action of 5-fluorouracil and its derivatives. *Proc. Nat. Acad. Sci. U.S.A.*, **44:**1004 (1958). [390]

145. Cohen, S. S., and Fowler, C. B. Chemical studies on host virus interactions. IV. Tryptophan requirements in stages of virus multiplication in the *Escherichia coli*-T2 bacteriophage system. *J. Exp. Med.*, **85:**771 (1947). [142]

146. da Costa Cruz, J. La lyse par le bactériophage observée au microscope. *C. R. Soc. Biol.*, **95:**1501 (1926). [80]

147. Combiesco, D., and Margheru, A. Sur la lyse du bacille pyocyanique. *C. R. Soc. Biol.*, **88:**912 (1923). [25]

148. Cowles, P. B. A bacteriophage for *Cl. tetani*. *J. Bacteriol.*, **27:**163 (1934). [25]

149. Crick, F. H. C. On protein synthesis. In *The Biological Replication of Macromolecules*, Symposium of the Society for Experimental Biology, XII, p. 138, Cambridge University Press, London, 1958. [250, 402, 409, 425]

149a. Crick, F. H. C. The recent excitement in the coding problem. In *Progress in Nucleic Acid Research* (J. N. Davidson and W. E. Cohn, eds.) Vol. I (in press), Academic Press, New York, 1963. [426]

150. Crick, F. H. C., Barnett, L., Brenner, S., and Watts-Tobin, R. J. The general nature of the genetic code. *Nature*, **192:**1227 (1961). [395, 400, 426]

151. Crick, F. H. C., Griffith, J. S., and Orgel, L. E. Codes without commas. *Proc. Nat. Acad. Sci. U.S.A.*, **43:**416 (1957). [394, 395]

152. Davidson, J. N. *The Biochemistry of the Nucleic Acids*. 3rd ed. Methuen, London; Wiley, New York, 1957. [69]

153. Davis, B. D. Nonfilterability of the agents of genetic recombination in *Escherichia coli*. *J. Bacteriol.*, **60:**507 (1950). [342]

154. Davison, P. F. The effect of hydrodynamic shear on the deoxyribonucleic acid from T2 and T4 bacteriophages. *Proc. Nat. Acad. Sci. U.S.A.*, **45:**1560 (1959). [67]

155. Davison, P. F., Freifelder, D., Hede, R., and Levinthal, C. The structural unity of the DNA of T2 bacteriophage. *Proc. Nat. Acad. Sci. U.S.A.*, **47:**1123 (1961). [67]

156. Dekker, C. A., and Schachman, H. K. On the macromolecular structure of deoxyribonucleic acid: an interrupted two-strand model. *Proc. Nat. Acad. Sci. U.S.A.*, **40**:894 (1954). [167]

157. Delaporte, B. Cytology of bacteria. *Carnegie Inst. Wash. Yearbook*, **48**:166 (1948). [133, 370]

158. Delbrück, M. Adsorption of bacteriophages under various physiological conditions of the host. *J. Gen. Physiol.*, **23**:631 (1940). [19, 90]

159. Delbrück, M. The growth of bacteriophage and lysis of the host. *J. Gen. Physiol.*, **23**:643 (1940). [74, 79, 87]

160. Delbrück, M. Bacterial viruses. *Adv. Enzymol.*, **2**:1 (1942). [21]

161. Delbrück, M. The burst size distribution in the growth of bacterial viruses. *J. Bacteriol.*, **50**:131 (1945). [76]

162. Delbrück, M. Effects of specific antisera on the growth of bacterial viruses. *J. Bacteriol.*, **50**:137 (1945). [61, 88]

163. Delbrück, M. Interference between bacterial viruses. III. The mutual exclusion effect and the depressor effect. *J. Bacteriol.*, **50**:151 (1945). [183, 374]

164. Delbrück, M. Bacterial viruses or bacteriophages. *Biol Rev.*, **21**:30 (1946). [309]

165. Delbrück, M. Experiments with bacterial viruses. *Harvey Lectures*, **41**:161 (1946). [60]

166. Delbrück, M. Biochemical mutants of bacterial viruses. *J. Bacteriol.*, **56**:1 (1948). [186]

167. Delbrück, M., and Bailey, W. T. Induced mutations in bacterial viruses. *Cold Spring Harbor Symp. Quant. Biol.*, **11**:33 (1946). [136, 195, 198, 199, 202]

168. Delbrück, M., and Luria, S. E. Interference between two bacterial viruses acting upon the same host, and mechanism of virus growth. *Arch. Biochem.*, **1**:111 (1942). [74, 78, 201, 374]

169. Delbrück, M., and Stent, G. S. On the mechanism of DNA replication. In *The Chemical Basis of Heredity* (W. D. McElroy and B. Glass, eds.), p. 699. The Johns Hopkins Press, Baltimore, 1957. [160, 165, 174, 225, 392]

170. DeMars, R. I. Chemical mutagenesis in bacteriophage T2. *Nature*, **172**:964 (1953). [261]

171. DeMars, R. I. The production of phage-related material when bacteriophage development is interrupted by proflavine. *Virology*, **1**:83 (1955). [119, 138]

172. DeMars, R. I., Luria, S. E., Fisher, H., and Levinthal, C. The production of incomplete bacteriophage particles by the action of proflavine and the properties of the incomplete particles. *Ann. Inst. Pasteur*, **84**:113 (1953). [121, 138]

173. Demerec, M., Blomstrand, I., and Demerec, Z. E. Evidence of complex loci in *Salmonella*. *Proc. Nat. Acad. Sci. U.S.A.*, **41**:359 (1955). [350]

174. Demerec, M., and Demerec, Z. E. Analysis of linkage relations in *Salmonella* by transduction techniques. In *Mutation*, Brookhaven Symposia in Biology, No. 8, p. 75 (1956). [350]

175. Demerec, M., and Fano, U. Bacteriophage-resistant mutants in *Escherichia coli*. *Genetics*, **30**:119 (1945). [19, 99]

176. Demerec, M., and Hartman, P. E. Complex loci in microorganisms. *Ann. Rev. Microbiol.*, **13**:377 (1959). [353]

177. Demerec, M., and Hartman, Z. Tryptophan mutants in *Salmonella typhimurium*. In *Genetic Studies with Bacteria. Carnegie Inst. Wash. Publ.* No. 612, p. 5. Washington, D.C., 1956. [350, 351]

178. Dirksen, M. L., Wiberg, J. S., Koerner, J. F., and Buchanan, J. M. Effect of ultraviolet irradiation of bacteriophage T2 on enzyme synthesis in host cells. *Proc. Nat. Acad. Sci. U.S.A.*, **46**:1425 (1960). [282, 289, 425]

179. Doermann, A. H. Intracellular growth of bacteriophage. *Carnegie Inst. Wash. Yearbook*, **47**:176 (1948). [83]

180. Doermann, A. H. Lysis and lysis inhibition with *Escherichia coli* bacteriophage. *J. Bacteriol.*, **55**:257 (1948). [79, 82, 178, 179]

181. Doermann, A. H. The intracellular growth of bacteriophages. I. Liberation of intracellular bacteriophage T4 by premature lysis with another phage or with cyanide. *J. Gen. Physiol.*, **35**:645 (1952). [73, 83, 84]

182. Doermann, A. H. The vegetative state in the life cycle of bacteriophage: Evidence for its occurrence and its genetic characterization. *Cold Spring Harbor Symp. Quant. Biol.*, **18**:3 (1953). [87, 210]

183. Doermann, A. H. The analysis of ultraviolet lesions in bacteriophage T4 by cross reactivation. *J. Cell Comp. Physiol.*, **58**, Suppl. 1:79 (1961). [286]

184. Doermann, A. H., Chase, M., and Stahl, F. W. Genetic recombination and replication in bacteriophage. *J. Cell. Comp. Physiol.*, **45**, Suppl. 2:51 (1955). [285, 286]

185. Doermann, A. H., and Hill, M. B. Genetic structure of bacteriophage T4 as described by recombination studies of factors influencing plaque morphology. *Genetics*, **38**:79 (1953). [186, 210]

186. Dooren de Jong, L. E. den. Studien über Bakteriophagie. I. Über *Bac. megatherium* und den darin anwesenden Bakteriophagen. *Zentr. Bakteriol. Parasitenk.* (I), **120**:1 (1931). [307, 315]

187. Drexler, H., and Christensen, J. R. Genetic crosses between restricted and unrestricted phage T1 in lysogenic and nonlysogenic hosts. *Virology*, **13**:31 (1961). [378]

188. Dreyer, W. J., Crumpton, M., Koch, G., and Streisinger, G. In press. [82]

189. Dulbecco, R. The number of particles of bacteriophage T2 that can participate in intracellular growth. *Genetics*, **34**:126 (1949). [196]

190. Dulbecco, R. Experiments on photoreactivation of bacteriophages inactivated with ultraviolet radiation. *J. Bacteriol.*, **59**:329 (1950). [282, 284, 305]

191. Dulbecco, R. A critical test for the recombination theory of multiplicity reactivation. *J. Bacteriol.*, **63**:199 (1952). [290, 291]

192. Dulbecco, R. Mutual exclusion between related phages. *J. Bacteriol.*, **63**:209 (1952). [153]

193. Dulbecco, R., and Vogt, M. Biological properties of poliomyelitis virus as studied by the plaque technique. *Ann. New York Acad. Sci.*, **61**:790 (1955). [43]

194. Dunn, D. B., and Smith, J. D. Incorporation of halogenated pyrimidines into deoxyribonucleic acids of *Bacterium coli* and its bacteriophages. *Nature*, **174**:305 (1954). [262]

195. Dussoix, D., and Arber, W. Host specificity of DNA produced by *Escherichia coli*. II. Control over acceptance of DNA from infecting phage λ. *J. Mol. Biol.*, **5**:37 (1962). [378]

196. Edgar, R. S. High negative interference and heterozygosis: a study of the mechanism of recombination in bacteriophage. *Virology*, **13**:1 (1961). [232]

197. Edgar, R. S., and Epstein, R. H. Inactivation by ultraviolet light of an acriflavine-sensitive gene function in phage T4D. *Science*, **134**:327 (1961). [187]

198. Edgar, R. S., and Susman, M. In press. [187, 219, 220]

199. Elford, W. J. The sizes of viruses and bacteriophages and methods for their determination. In *Handbuch der Virusforschung* (R. Doerr and C. Hallauer, eds.), p. 126. Springer, Wien, 1938. [44]

200. Elford, W. J., and Andrewes, C. H. The sizes of different bacteriophages. *Brit. J. Exp. Pathol.*, **13**:446 (1932). [44, 45, 382]

201. Ellis, E. L., and Delbrück, M. The growth of bacteriophage. *J. Gen. Physiol.*, **22**:365 (1939). [19, 42, 43, 72, 74, 75, 76, 87, 391]

202. Epstein, R. H. In press [187, 218, 220]

203. Fermi, G., and Stent, G. S. Protein synthesis and the onset of intracellular bacteriophage growth. III. Replication of the genome of a secondary phage. *J. Mol. Biol.*, **4**:179 (1962). [152]

204. Fernandez, B., Haas, F. L., and Wyss, O. Induced host range mutations in bacteriophage. *Proc. Nat. Acad. Sci. U.S.A.*, **39**:1052 (1953). [261]

205. Flaks, J. G., and Cohen, S. S. Virus-induced acquisition of metabolic function. I. Enzymatic formation of 5-hydroxymethyldeoxycytidylate. *J. Biol. Chem.*, **234**:1501 (1959). [141, 148]

206. Flaks, J. G., and Cohen, S. S. Virus-induced acquisition of metabolic function. III. Formation and some properties of thymidylate synthetase of bacteriophage-infected *Escherichia coli*. *J. Biol. Chem.*, **234**:2981 (1959). [149]

207. Flaks, J. G., Lichtenstein, J., and Cohen, S. S. Virus-induced acquisition of metabolic function. II. Studies on the origin of the deoxycytidylate hydroxymethylase of bacteriophage-infected *E. coli*. *J. Biol. Chem.* **234**:1507 (1959). [148]

208. Fleming, A. On a remarkable bacteriolytic element found in tissues and secretions. *Proc. Roy. Soc. London, Ser. B*, **93**:306 (1922). [82]

209. Flu, P. C. Over cholerabacteriophagen. *Tijdschr. Vergl. Geneesk.*, **10**:196 (1924). [25]

210. Foster, R. A. C. An analysis of the action of proflavine on bacteriophage growth. *J. Bacteriol.*, **56**:795 (1948). [136]

211. Fraenkel-Conrat, H. The role of the nucleic acid in the reconstitution of active tobacco mosaic virus. *J. Am. Chem. Soc.*, **78**:882 (1956). [115]

212. Franklin, N. C., Jerne, N. K., and Kellenberger, E. Unpublished observations [107]

213. Fraser, D. Bursting bacteria by release of gas pressure. *Nature*, **167**:33 (1951). [85]

214. Fraser, D. Comparison of the amino acid composition of T2 and T3 bacteriophages. *J. Biol. Chem.*, **227**:711 (1957). [50]

215. Fraser, D., Mahler, H. R., Shug, A. L., and Thomas, C. A., Jr. The infection of sub-cellular *Escherichia coli*, strain B, with a DNA preparation from T2 bacteriophage. *Proc. Nat. Acad. Sci. U.S.A.*, **43**:939 (1957). [103]

216. Fraser, D., and Williams, R. C. Electron microscopy of the nucleic acid released from individual bacteriophage particles. *Proc. Nat. Acad. Sci. U.S.A.*, **39**:750 (1953). [64]

217. Fraser, D. K. Host range mutants and semi-temperate mutants of bacteriophage T3. *Virology*, **3**:527 (1957). [375]

218. Frédéricq, P. Emploi du chloroforme pour mesurer le taux de fixation des entéro-bactériophages par les bactéries vivantes. *C. R. Soc. Biol.*, **146**:327 (1952). [89]

219. Frédéricq, P. Localisation du prophage sur le chromosome. Son intervention dans le taux de ségrégation apparent des récombinants d'*Escherichia coli* K12. *C. R. Soc. Biol.*, **148**:1501 (1954). [321]

220. Freeman, V. J. Studies on the virulence of bacteriophage infected strains of *Corynebacterium diphtheriae*. *J. Bacteriol.*, **61**:675 (1951). [337]

221. Freese, E. On the molecular explanation of spontaneous and induced mutations. In *Structure and Function of Genetic Elements*, Brookhaven Symposia in Biology, No. 12, p. 63 (1959). [266]

222. Freese, E. The difference between spontaneous and base-analogue induced mutations of phage T4. *Proc. Nat. Acad. Sci. U.S.A.*, **45**:622 (1959). [268, 269, 271]

223. Freese, E. The specific mutagenic effect of base analogues on phage T4. *J. Mol. Biol.*, **1**:87 (1959). [264]

224. Freese, E. The molecular mechanism of mutations. 5th International Congress of Biochemistry, Moscow, 1961. [267, 268, 269, 276]

225. Freese, E., Bautz, E., and Bautz-Freese, E. The chemical and mutagenic specificity of hydroxylamine. *Proc. Nat. Acad. Sci. U.S.A.*, **47**:845 (1961). [268]

226. Freese, E., Bautz-Freese, E., and Bautz, E. Hydroxylamine as a mutagenic and inactivating agent. *J. Mol. Biol.*, **3**:133 (1961). [268]

227. French, R. C. The contribution of protein from parent to progeny in T2 coliphage. *J. Bacteriol.*, **67**:45 (1954). [113]

228. French, R. C., Lesley, S. M., Graham, A. F., and van Rooyen, C. E. Studies on the relationship between virus and host cell. III. The breakdown of P^{32} labelled $T2r^+$ bacteriophage adsorbed to *E. coli* previously infected by other coliphages of the T group. *Canad. J. Med. Sci.*, **29**:144 (1951). [371]

229. French, R. C., Graham, A. F., Lesley, S. M., and van Rooyen, C. E. The contribution of phosphorus from $T2r^+$ bacteriophage to progeny. *J. Bacteriol.*, **64**:597 (1952). [153, 161, 163]

230. French, R. C., and Siminovitch, L. The action of T2 bacteriophage ghosts on *Escherichia coli* B. *Canad. J. Microbiol.*, **1**:757 (1955). [65]

231. Gamow, G. Possible relation between deoxyribonucleic acid and protein structure. *Nature*, **173**:318 (1954). [393]

232. Gamow, G., Rich, A., and Yčas, M. Problem of information transfer from nucleic acids to proteins. *Adv. Biol. Med. Phys.*, **4**:23 (1955). [393]

233. Gardner, G. M., and Weiser, R. S. A bacteriophage for *Mycobacterium smegmatis*. *Proc. Soc. Exp. Biol. Med.*, **66**:205 (1947). [25]

234. Garen, A. Thermodynamic and kinetic studies on the attachment of T1 bacterio-phage to bacteria. *Biochim. Biophys. Acta*, **14**:163 (1954). [93]

235. Garen, A. Genetic control of the specificity of the bacterial enzyme, alkaline phos-phatase. In *Microbial Genetics* (W. Hayes and R. C. Clowes, eds.), p. 239. Cambridge University Press, London, 1960. [418]

236. Garen, A. Physiological effects of rII mutations in bacteriophage T4. *Virology*, **14**:151 (1961). [240, 304, 420]

237. Garen, A., and Kozloff, L. M. The initiation of bacteriophage infection. In *The Viruses* (F. M. Burnet and W. M. Stanley, eds.), Vol. II, p. 204. Academic Press, New York, 1959. [115]

238. Garen, A., and Puck, T. T. The first two steps of the invasion of host cells by bacterial viruses. *J. Exp. Med.*, **94**:177 (1951). [93, 100]

239. Garen, A., and Zinder, N. D. Radiological evidence for partial genetic homology between bacteriophage and host bacteria. *Virology*, **1**:347 (1955). [372, 373, 378]

240. Gates, F. L. Results of irradiating *Staphylococcus aureus* bacteriophage with monochromatic ultraviolet light. *J. Exp. Med.*, **60**:179 (1934). [279]

241. Gierer, A., and Mundry, K. W. Production of mutants of tobacco mosaic virus by chemical alteration of its ribonucleic acid *in vitro*. *Nature*, **182**:1457 (1958). [266]

242. Gierer, A., and Schramm, G. Infectivity of ribonucleic acid from tobacco mosaic virus. *Nature*, **177**:702 (1956). [115]

243. Gildemeister, E. Über das d'Hérellesche Phänomen. *Berlin. klin. Wochschr.*, **58**:1355 (1921). [306]

244. Gildemeister, E. Weitere Untersuchungen über das d'Hérellesche Phänomen. *Zentr. Bakteriol. Parasitenk.* (*I*), **89**:181 (1922). [277]

245. Gildemeister, E., and Herzberg, K. Zur Theorie der Bakteriophagen (d'Hérelle Lysine). 6. Mitteilung über das d'Hérellsche Phänomen. *Zentr. Bakteriol. Parasitenk.* (*I*), **93**:402 (1924). [126, 306]

246. Goodgal, S. H., Rupert, C. S., and Herriott, R. M. Photoreactivation of *Hemophilus influenzae* transforming factor for streptomycin resistance by an extract of *Escherichia coli* B. In *The Chemical Basis of Heredity* (W. D. McElroy and B. Glass, eds.), p. 341. The Johns Hopkins Press, Baltimore, 1957. [282]

247. Goodman, F., Saukkonnen, J. J., and Chargaff, E. Patterns of cellular controls operating in bacteriophage reproduction. I. Effect of 5-fluorouracil on the multiplication of several coliphages. *Biochim. Biophys. Acta*, **44**:458 (1960). [390]

248. Graham, A. F. The fate of the infecting phage particle. *Ann. Inst. Pasteur*, **84**:90 (1953). [153]

249. Gratia, A. Concerning the theories of the so-called "bacteriophage." *Brit. Med. J.* (2), August 19, 1922, p. 296. [12, 13, 21]

250. Gratia, A. Des relations numériques entre bactéries lysogènes et particules de bactériophagie. *C. R. Soc. Biol.*, **122**:812 (1936). [40]

251. Gratia, A. Le phénomène du halo et la synergie des bactériophages. *C. R. Soc. Biol.*, **126**:418 (1937). [81]

252. Green, D. M., and Krieg, D. R. The delayed origin of mutants induced by exposure of extracellular phage T4 to ethyl methane sulfonate. *Proc. Nat. Acad. Sci. U.S.A.*, **47**:64 (1961). [266]

253. Grinjs, A. Waarnemingen omtrent den bacteriophaag bij *Bac. danicus* en *B. radiciola*. Dissertation, Wageningen, 1926. [25]

254. Groman, N. B. Evidence for the induced nature of the change from nontoxigenicity to toxigenicity in *Corynebacterium diphtheriae* as a result of exposure to specific bacteriophage. *J. Bacteriol.*, **66**:184 (1953). [336, 337]

255. Groman, N. B. Evidence for the active role of bacteriophage in the conversion of nontoxigenic *Corynebacterium diphtheriae* to toxin production. *J. Bacteriol.*, **69**:9 (1955). [337]

256. Groman, N. B., Eaton, M., and Booker, Z. Studies of mono- and polylysogenic *Corynebacterium diphtheriae*. *J. Bacteriol.*, **75**:320 (1958). [337]

257. Gros, F. Biosynthesis of proteins in intact bacterial cells. In *The Nucleic Acids* (E. Chargaff and J. N. Davidson, eds.), Volume III, p. 409. Academic Press, New York, 1960. [426]

258. Grunberg-Manago, M., and Ochoa, S. Enzymic synthesis and breakdown of polynucleotides: polynucleotide phosphorylase. *J. Am. Chem. Soc.*, **77**:3165 (1955). [412]

259. Guthrie, G. D., and Sinsheimer, R. L. Infection of protoplasts of *Escherichia coli* by subviral particles of bacteriophage φX174. *J. Mol. Biol.*, **2**:297 (1960). [386]

260. Hadley, P. The action of the lytic principle on capsulated bacteria. *Proc. Soc. Exp. Biol. Med.*, **23**:443 (1926). [25]

261. Haldane, J. B. S. The combination of linkage values, and the calculation of distances between loci of linked factors. *J. Genet.*, **8**:299 (1919). [212, 230]

262. Hall, B. D., and Doty, P. The preparation and physical chemical properties of ribonucleic acid from microsomal particles. *J. Mol. Biol.*, **1**:111 (1959). [404]

263. Hall, C. E., Maclean, E. C., and Tessman, I. Structure and dimensions of bacteriophage φX174 from electron microscopy. *J. Mol. Biol.*, **1**:192 (1959). [385]

264. Harm, W. On the mechanism of multiplicity reactivation in bacteriophage. *Virology*, **2**:559 (1956). [291]

265. Harm, W. Untersuchungen zur Wirkungsweise eines die UV-Empfindlichkeit bestimmenden Gens der Bakteriophagen T2 und T4. *Z. Vererbungslehre*, **90**:428 (1959). [278, 284]

266. Harm, W. Gene-controlled reactivation of ultraviolet-inactivated bacteriophage. *J. Cellular Comp. Physiol.*, **58,** Suppl. 1:69 (1961). [425]

267. Hartman, P. E. Linked loci in the control of consecutive steps in the primary pathway of histidine synthesis in *Salmonella typhimurium*. *Carnegie Inst. Wash. Publ.*, No. 612, p. 35 (1956). [353]

268. Hartman, P. E. Transduction: a comparative review. In *The Chemical Basis of Heredity* (W. D. McElroy and B. Glass, eds.), p. 408. The Johns Hopkins Press, Baltimore, 1957. [367]

269. Hayes, W. The mechanism of genetic recombination in *E. coli. Cold Spring Harbor Symp. Quant. Biol.*, **18**:75 (1953). [321]

270. Heagy, F. C. The effect of 2,4-dinitrophenol and phage T2 on *E. coli* B. *J. Bacteriol.*, **59**:367 (1950). [80]

271. Hedén, C. G. Studies of the infection of *E. coli* B with the bacteriophage T2. *Acta Pathol. Microbiol. Scand.*, Suppl. No. 88, 1951. [74]

272. Herčik, F. Some observations about the morphology of bacteriophage. *Experientia*, **6**:64 (1950). [121]

273. d'Hérelle, F. Sur un microbe invisible antagoniste des bacilles dysentériques. *C. R. Acad. Sci. Paris*, **165**:373 (1917). [5, 25]

274. d'Hérelle, F. Sur le rôle du microbe filtrant bactériophage dans la dysenterie bacillaire. *C. R. Acad. Sci. Paris*, **167**:970 (1918). [6]

275. d'Hérelle, F. Technique de la recherche du microbe filtrant bactériophage (*Bacteriophagum intestinale*). *C. R. Soc. Biol.*, **81**:1160 (1918). [25]

276. d'Hérelle, F. Le microbe bactériophage, agent d'immunité dans la peste et le barbone. *C. R. Acad. Sci. Paris*, **172**:99 (1921). [25]

277. d'Hérelle, F. *Le bactériophage. Son role dans l'immunité.* Masson, Paris, 1921. English translation: *The Bacteriophage; its Role in Immunity.* Williams & Wilkins, Baltimore, 1922. [9, 80]

278. d'Hérelle, F. The nature of bacteriophage. *Brit. Med. J.* (2), August 19, 1922, p. 289. [21]

279. d'Hérelle, F. *Le bactériophage et son comportement.* Masson, Paris, 1926. English translation: *The Bacteriophage and its Behaviour.* Williams & Wilkins, Baltimore, 1926. [9, 64, 70, 92, 376]

280. d'Hérelle, F. The bacteriophage. *Science News*, No. 14, p. 44. Penguin, Harmondsworth, 1949. [4, 21]

281. Herriott, R. M. Nucleic acid-free T2 virus "ghosts" with specific biological action. *J. Bacteriol.*, **61**:752 (1951). [110]

282. Herriot, R. M., and Barlow, J. L. Preparation, purification and properties of *E. coli* virus T2. *J. Gen. Physiol.*, **36**:17 (1952). [50]

283. Hershey, A. D. Experiments with bacteriophages supporting the lattice-hypothesis. *J. Immunol.*, **47**:77 (1943). [59]

284. Hershey, A. D. Mutation of bacteriophage with respect to type of plaque. *Genetics*, **31**:620 (1946). [176, 186, 190, 195]

285. Hershey, A. D. Spontaneous mutations in bacterial viruses. *Cold Spring Harbor Symp. Quant. Biol.*, **11**:67 (1946). [183, 185, 186, 188, 195, 202]

286. Hershey, A. D. Reproduction of bacteriophage. *Intern. Rev. Cytol.*, Vol. I. (1952), p. 119. [224]

287. Hershey, A. D. Inheritance in bacteriophage. *Adv. Genet.*, **5**:89 (1953). [201]

288. Hershey, A. D. Nucleic acid economy in bacteria infected with bacteriophage T2. II. Phage precursor nucleic acid. *J. Gen. Physiol.*, **37**:1 (1953). [125, 129, 138, 156, 163, 164, 403]

289. Hershey, A. D. Conservation of nucleic acids during bacterial growth. *J. Gen. Physiol.*, **38**:145 (1954). [157, 403]

290. Hershey, A. D. An upper limit to the protein content of the germinal substance of bacteriophage T2. *Virology*, **1**:108 (1955). [64, 67]

291. Hershey, A. D. Chemistry and viral growth. In *Currents in Biochemical Research* (D. E. Green, ed.), p. 1. Interscience, New York, 1956. [163]

292. Hershey, A. D. Bacteriophages as genetic and biochemical systems. *Adv. Virus Research*, **4**:25 (1957). [93, 112, 115, 132]

293. Hershey, A. D. Bacteriophage T2: parasite or organelle? *Harvey Lectures*, **51**:229 (1957). [110]

294. Hershey, A. D. Some minor components of bacteriophage T2 particles. *Virology*, **4**:237 (1957). [67, 113]

295. Hershey, A. D. The production of recombinants in phage crosses. *Cold Spring Harbor Symp. Quant. Biol.*, **23**:19 (1958). [230, 237]

296. Hershey, A. D., and Burgi, E. Genetic significance of the transfer of nucleic acid from parental to offspring phage. *Cold Spring Harbor Symp. Quant. Biol.*, **21:**91 (1956). [144, 161, 162, 163, 167, 174, 233]

297. Hershey, A. D., and Burgi, E. Molecular homogeneity of the deoxyribonucleic acid of phage T2. *J. Mol. Biol.*, **2:**143 (1960). [67, 113]

298. Hershey, A. D., Burgi, E., and Streisinger, G. Genetic recombination between phages in the presence of chloramphenicol. *Virology*, **6:**287 (1958). [292, 293]

299. Hershey, A. D., Burgi, E., Garen, A., and Melechen, N. E. Growth and inheritance in bacteriophage. *Carnegie Inst. Wash. Yearbook*, **54:**216 (1955). [119]

300. Hershey, A. D., and Chase, M. Genetic recombination and heterozygosis in bacteriophage. *Cold Spring Harbor Symp. Quant. Biol.*, **16:**471 (1951). [209, 210, 226, 237]

301. Hershey, A. D., and Chase, M. Independent functions of viral protein and nucleic acid in growth of bacteriophage. *J. Gen. Physiol.*, **36:**39 (1952). [110, 113, 161, 386, 391]

302. Hershey, A. D., Dixon, J., and Chase, M. Nucleic acid economy in bacteria infected with bacteriophage T2. I. Purine and pyrimidine composition. *J. Gen. Physiol.*, **36:**777 (1953). [124, 127]

303. Hershey, A. D., Garen, A., Fraser, D. K., and Hudis, J. D. Growth and inheritance in bacteriophage. *Carnegie Inst. Wash. Yearbook*, **53:**210 (1954). [127, 130, 162, 233, 375]

304. Hershey, A. D., Kalmanson, G., and Bronfenbrenner, J. Quantitative methods in the study of phage-antiphage reaction. *J. Immunol.*, **46:**281 (1943). [40, 62]

305. Hershey, A. D., Kalmanson, G., and Bronfenbrenner, J. Coordinate effects of electrolyte and antibody on infectivity of bacteriophage. *J. Immunol.*, **48:**221 (1944). [92, 93]

306. Hershey, A. D., Kamen, M. D., Kennedy, J. W., and Gest, H. The mortality of bacteriophage containing assimilated radioactive phosphorus. *J. Gen. Physiol.*, **34:**305 (1951). [115, 293]

307. Hershey, A. D., and Melechen, N. E. Synthesis of phage-precursor nucleic acid in the presence of chloramphenicol. *Virology*, **3:**207 (1957). [143]

308. Hershey, A. D., Roesel, C., Chase, M., and Forman, S. Growth and inheritance in bacteriophage. *Carnegie Inst. Wash. Yearbook*, **50:**195 (1951). [136, 163, 201]

309. Hershey, A. D., and Rotman, R. Linkage among genes controlling inhibition of lysis in a bacterial virus. *Proc. Nat. Acad. Sci. U.S.A.*, **34:**89 (1948). [203]

310. Hershey, A. D., and Rotman, R. Genetic recombination between host range and plaque-type mutants of bacteriophage in single bacterial cells. *Genetics*, **34:**44 (1949). [186, 203, 204, 208, 209, 222, 223, 237]

311. Hoagland, M. B. Enzymic mechanism for amino acid activation in animal tissues. *Biochim. Biophys. Acta*, **16:**288 (1955). [411, 413]

312. Hoagland, M. B. The relationship of nucleic acid and protein synthesis as revealed by studies in cell free systems. In *The Nucleic Acids* (E. Chargaff and J. N. Davidson, eds.), Vol. III, p. 349. Academic Press, New York, 1960. [412, 426]

313. Hoagland, M. B., Keller, E. B., and Zamecnik, P. C. Enzymic carboxyl activation of amino acids. *J. Biol. Chem.*, **218:**345 (1956). [411]

314. Hoagland, M. B., Zamecnik, P. C., and Stephenson, M. L. Intermediate reactions in protein biosynthesis. *Biochim. Biophys. Acta*, **24:**215 (1957). [412]

315. Hofschneider, P. H. Über ein infektiöses Desoxyribonucleinsäure Agens aus dem Phagen φX174. *Z. Naturforsch.*, **15b**:441 (1960). [386]

316. Holmes, F. O. *The Filtrable Viruses*, Williams & Wilkins, Baltimore, 1948. [21]

317. Horowitz, J., and Chargaff, E. Massive incorporation of 5-fluorouracil into a bacterial ribonucleic acid. *Nature*, **184**:1213 (1959). [420]

318. Horowitz, N. H., and Leupold, V. Some recent studies bearing on the one gene-one enzyme hypothesis. *Cold Spring Harbor Symp. Quant. Biol.*, **16**:65 (1951). [219]

319. Hurwitz, J., Furth, J. J., Anders, M., Ortiz, P. J., and August, J. T. The enzymatic incorporation of ribonucleotides into RNA and the role of DNA. *Cold Spring Harbor Symp. Quant. Biol.*, **26**:91 (1961). [408, 413]

320. Iseki, S., and Sakai, T. Artificial transformation of O antigens in Salmonella E group. I. Transformation by antiserum and bacterial autolysate. *Proc. Japan Acad.*, **29**:121 (1953). [337]

321. Jacob, F. Induction de la lyse et de la production de bactériophages chez un *Pseudomonas pyocyanea* lysogène. *C. R. Acad. Sci. Paris*, **231**:1585 (1950). [332]

322. Jacob, F. Production de bactériophages par action de la methylbio (chloroethyl) amine sur des bactéries lysogènes. *C. R. Acad. Sci. Paris*, **234**:2238 (1952). [312, 370]

323. Jacob, F. Influence du régime carbone sur le développement des bactériophages chez un *Pseudomonas pyocyanea*. *Ann. Inst. Pasteur*, **82**:578 (1952). [370]

324. Jacob, F. Mutation d'un bactériophage induite par l'irradiation des seules bactéries-hôtes avant l'infection. *C. R. Acad. Sci. Paris*, **238**:732 (1954). [372, 376]

325. Jacob, F. *Les bactéries lysogènes et la notion de provirus.* Monographies de l'Institut Pasteur. Masson, Paris, 1954. [316, 317]

326. Jacob, F. Transduction of lysogeny in *Escherichia coli*. *Virology*, **1**:207 (1955). [347, 367]

327. Jacob, F. Genetic control of viral functions. *Harvey Lectures*, **54**:1 (1960). [323, 336, 367, 424]

328. Jacob, F., and Campbell, A. Sur le système de répression assurant l'immunité chez les bactéries lysogènes. *C. R. Acad. Sci. Paris*, **248**:3219 (1959). [323, 423]

328a. Jacob, F., and Fuerst, C. R. The mechanism of lysis studied with defective lysogenic bacteria. *J. Gen. Microbiol.*, **18**:518 (1958). [80, 81, 311]

329. Jacob, F., Fuerst, C., and Wollman, E. L. Recherches sur les bactéries lysogènes défectives. II. Les types physiologiques liés aux mutations du prophage. *Ann. Inst. Pasteur*, **93**:724 (1957). [334, 371]

330. Jacob, F., Lwoff, A., Siminovitch, L., and Wollman, E. Définition de quelques termes relatifs à la lysogénie. *Ann. Inst. Pasteur*, **84**:222 (1953). [313]

331. Jacob, F., and Monod, J. Genetic regulatory mechanisms in the synthesis of proteins. *J. Mol. Biol.*, **3**:318 (1961). [323, 324, 404, 421, 426]

332. Jacob, F., and Wollman, E. L. Induction of phage development in lysogenic bacteria. *Cold Spring Harbor Symp. Quant. Biol.*, **18**:101 (1953). [312, 319, 424]

333. Jacob, F., and Wollman, E. L. Induction spontanée du développement du bactériophage au cours de la récombinaison génétique, chez *Escherichia coli* K12. *C. R. Acad. Sci. Paris*, **239**:317 (1954). [English translation in (595).] [323]

334. Jacob, F., and Wollman, E. L. Etude génétique d'un bactériophage tempéré d'*Escherichia coli*. I. Le système génétique du bactériophage λ. *Ann. Inst. Pasteur*, **87**:653 (1954). [234, 328]

335. Jacob, F., and Wollman, E. L. Étude génétique d'un bactériophage temperé d'*Escherichia coli*. III. Effet du rayonnement ultraviolet sur la récombinaison génétique. *Ann. Inst. Pasteur*, **88**:724 (1955). [292]

336. Jacob, F., and Wollman, E. Recherches sur les bactéries lysogènes défectives. I. Déterminisme génétique de la morphogenèse chez un bactérie tempéré. *Ann. Inst. Pasteur*, **90**:282 (1956). [332, 333, 334]

337. Jacob, F., and Wollman, E. L. Genetic aspects of lysogeny. In *The Chemical Basis of Heredity* (W. D. McElroy and B. Glass, eds.), p. 468. The Johns Hopkins Press, Baltimore, 1957. [321, 324, 340]

338. Jacob, F., and Wollman, E. L. Les épisomes, éléments génétiques ajoutés. *C. R. Acad. Sci. Paris*, **247**:154 (1958). [338]

339. Jacob, F., and Wollman, E. L. Sur les processus de conjugaison et de récombinaison génétique chez *Escherichia coli*. IV. Prophages inductibles et mesure des segments génétiques transférés au cour de la conjugaison. *Ann. Inst. Pasteur*, **95**:497 (1958). [324]

340. Jacob, F., and Wollman, E. L. Genetic and physical determinations of chromosomal segments in *E. coli*. In *The Biological Replication of Macromolecules*. Symposia of the Society for Experimental Biology, **12**:75 (1958). [218]

341. Jacob, F., and Wollman, E. L. The relationship between the prophage and the bacterial chromosome in lysogenic bacteria. In *Recent Progress in Microbiology* (G. Tuneval, ed.), p. 15. Almqvist & Wiksell, Stockholm, 1959. [218, 328, 329, 340, 364]

342. Jacob, F., and Wollman, E. L. *Sexuality and the Genetics of Bacteria*. Academic Press, New York, 1961. [322, 326, 327, 338, 366, 422, 424]

343. Jeney, A. V. Bakteriophage Erscheinungen au einem Wasserbakterium. *Bacterium cloacae Szegediensis crystalliformans*. *Zentr. Bakteriol. Parasitenk.* (*I*), **102**:263 (1927). [25]

344. Jerne, N. K. Bacteriophage inactivation by antiphage serum in distilled water. *Nature*, **169**:117 (1952). [59]

345. Jerne, N. K. The presence in normal serum of specific antibody against bacteriophage T4 and its increase during the earliest stages of immunization. *J. Immunol.*, **76**:209 (1956). [61, 107]

346. Jerne, N. K., and Avegno, P. The development of phage inactivating properties of serum during the course of specific immunization of an animal: reversible and irreversible inactivation. *J. Immunol.*, **76**:200 (1956). [59]

347. Jesaitis, M. A. Differences in the chemical composition of the phage nucleic acids. *Nature*, **178**:637 (1956). [56]

348. Jesaitis, M. A. Nucleic acids of T2, T4, and T6 bacteriophages. *J. Exp. Med.*, **106**:233 (1957). [56]

349. Jesaitis, M. A., and Goebel, W. F. Lysis of T4 phage by the specific lipocarbohydrate of phase II *Shigella sonnei*. *J. Exp. Med.*, **102**:733 (1955). [101]

350. Kaiser, A. D. A genetic study of the temperate coliphage λ. *Virology*, **1**:424 (1955). [234, 326]

351. Kaiser, A. D. Mutations in a temperate bacteriophage affecting its ability to lysogenize *E. coli*. *Virology*, 3:42 (1957). [325]

352. **Kaiser, A. D., and Jacob, F.** Recombination between related temperate bacteriophages and the genetic control of immunity and prophage localization. *Virology*, 4:509 (1957). [326, 340]

353. Keck, K., Mahler, H. R., and Fraser, D. Synthesis of deoxycytidine-5'-phosphate deaminase in *Escherichia coli* infected by T2 bacteriophage. *Arch. Biochem. Biophys.*, 86:85 (1960). [149]

354. Kellenberger, E. Les formes charactéristiques des nucleoïdes de *E. coli* et leurs transformations dues à l'action d'agents mutagènes-inducteurs et de bactériophages. Symposium: Bacterial Cytology. Istituto Superiore di Sanita, Rome, 1953, p. 45. [370]

355. Kellenberger, E. The physical state of the bacterial nucleus. In *Microbial Genetics*, Tenth Symposium of the Society for General Microbiology, p. 39. Cambridge University Press, London, 1960. [132, 369, 370]

356. Kellenberger, E. Vegetative bacteriophage and the maturation of virus particles. *Adv. Virus Research*, 8:1 (1962). [49, 106, 133, 138, 369]

357. Kellenberger, E., and Arber, W. Die Struktur des Schwanzes der Phagen T2 and T4 und der Mechanismus der irreversiblen Adsorption. *Z. Naturforsch.*, 10b:698 (1955). [108, 109, 133]

358. Kellenberger, E., Ryter, A., and Séchaud, J. Electron microscope study of DNA-containing plasms. II. Vegetative and mature phage DNA as compared with normal bacterial nucleoids in different physiological states. *J. Biophys. Biochem. Cytol.*, 4:671 (1958). [144, 145]

359. Kellenberger, E., and Séchaud, J. Electron microscopical studies of phage multiplication. II. Production of phage-related structures during multiplication of phages T2 and T4. *Virology*, 3:256 (1957). [106, 121, 122, 138]

360. Kellenberger, E., Séchaud, J., and Ryter, A. Electron microscopical studies of phage multiplication. IV. The establishment of the DNA pool of vegetative phages and the maturation of phage particles. *Virology*, 8:478 (1959). [133, 138]

361. Kellenberger, G., and Kellenberger, E. Electron microscopical studies of phage multiplication. III. Observation of single cell bursts. *Virology*, 3:275 (1957). [138]

362. Kellenberger, G., and Weigle, J. Étude au moyen des rayons ultraviolets de l'interaction entre bactériophage tempéré et bactérie hôte. *Biochim. Biophys. Acta*, 30:112 (1958). [372]

363. Kellenberger, G., Zichichi, M. L., and Weigle, J. Exchange of DNA in the recombination of bacteriophage λ. *Proc. Nat. Acad. Sci. U.S.A.*, 47:869 (1961). [234]

364. Kellenberger, G., Zichichi, M. L., and Weigle, J. A mutation affecting the DNA content of bacteriophage lambda and its lysogenizing properties. *J. Mol. Biol.*, 3:399 (1961). [326, 327]

365. Kelner, A. Growth, respiration and nucleic acid synthesis in ultraviolet-irradiated and in photoreactivated *Escherichia coli*. *J. Bacteriol.*, 65:252 (1953). [372]

365a. Kleinschmidt, A. K., Lang, D., Jacherts, D., and Zahn, R. K. Darstellung und Längenmessungen des gesamten Deoxyribonucleinsäure-Inhalts von T2 Bakteriophagen. *Biochim. Biophys. Acta*, 61:857 (1962). [frontispiece]

366. Koch, G., and Dreyer, W. J. Characterization of an enzyme of phage T2 as a lysozyme. *Virology*, 6:291 (1958). [82]

367. Koch, G., and Hershey, A. D. Synthesis of phage precursor protein in bacteria infected with T2. *J. Mol. Biol.*, **1:**260 (1959). [131, 138]

368. Koch, G., and Jordan, E. M. Killing of *Escherichia coli* B by phage-free T2 lysates. *Biochim. Biophys. Acta*, **25:**437 (1957). [80]

369. Koch, G., and Weidel, W. Abspaltung chemischer Komponenten der Coli-Membran durch daran absorbierte Phagen. I. Mitt: Allgemeine Charakterisierung des Effekts und Partial Analyse einer der abgespaltenen Komponenten. *Z. Naturforsch.*, **11b:**345 (1956). [81, 100]

370. Koerner, J. F., Smith, M. S., and Buchanan, J. M. A deoxycytidine triphosphate splitting enzyme and the synthesis of the deoxyribosenucleic acid of T2 bacteriophage. *J. Am. Chem. Soc.*, **81:**2594 (1959). [148]

371. Kornberg, A. Biological synthesis of deoxyribonucleic acid. *Science*, **131:**1503 (1960). [148]

372. Kornberg, A., Zimmerman, S. B., Kornberg, S. R., and Josse, J. Enzymatic synthesis of deoxyribonucleic acid. VI. Influence of bacteriophage T2 on the synthetic pathway in host cells. *Proc. Nat. Acad. Sci. U.S.A.*, **45:**722 (1959). [148, 150, 151, 174, 199]

373. Kornberg, S. R., Zimmerman, S. B., and Kornberg, A. Glucosylation of deoxyribonucleic acid by enzymes from bacteriophage-infected *Escherichia coli*. *J. Biol. Chem.*, **236:**1487 (1961). [150]

374. Kozinski, A. W. Fragmentary transfer of P^{32}-labeled parental DNA to progeny phage. *Virology*, **13:**124 (1961). [169, 173, 392]

375. Kozinski, A. W., and Uchida, H. Phage DNA subunits in the phage precursor pool. *J. Mol. Biol.*, **3:**267 (1961). [167]

376. Kozloff, L. M. Biochemical studies of virus reproduction. VII. The appearance of parent nitrogen and phosphorus in the progeny. *J. Biol. Chem.*, **194:**95 (1952). [161]

377. Kozloff, L. M. Origin and fate of bacteriophage material. *Cold Spring Harbor Symp. Quant. Biol.*, **18:**209 (1953). [127, 140, 161]

378. Kozloff, L. M. Structure and function in T2 bacteriophage. In *Sulfur in Proteins* (R. Benesch et al., eds.), p. 347. Academic Press, New York, 1959. [109]

379. Kozloff, L. M., and Henderson, K. Action of complexes of the zinc group metals on the tail protein of bacteriophage $T2r^+$. *Nature*, **176:**1169 (1955). [109]

380. Kozloff, L. M., Knowlton, K., Putnam, F. W., and Evans, E. A., Jr. Biochemical studies on virus reproduction. V. The origin of bacteriophage nitrogen. *J. Biol. Chem.*, **188:**101 (1951). [130]

381. Kozloff, L. M., and Lute, M. A contractile protein in the tail of bacteriophage T2. *J. Biol. Chem.*, **234:**534 (1959). [109]

382. Kozloff, L. M., Lute, M., and Henderson, K. Viral invasion. I. Rupture of thiol ester bonds in the bacteriophage tail. *J. Biol. Chem.*, **228:**511 (1957). [108]

383. Krieg, D. A study of gene action in ultraviolet-irradiated bacteriophage T4. *Virology*, **8:**80 (1959). [287, 288, 425]

384. Krueger, A. P. The sorption of bacteriophage by living and dead susceptible bacteria. *J. Gen. Physiol.*, **14:**493 (1931). [89]

385. Krueger, A. P. The mechanism of bacteriophage production. *Science*, **86:**379 (1937). [126]

386. Krueger, A. P., and Northrop, J. H. The kinetics of the bacterium-bacteriophage reaction. *J. Gen. Physiol.*, **14:**233 (1931). [14, 79]

387. Krueger, A. P., and Scribner, E. J. Nature of intracellular phage precursor. *J. Gen. Physiol.*, **22:**699 (1939). [126]

388. Kunkee, R. E., and Pardee, A. B. Studies on the role of deoxyribonuclease in T2 bacteriophage development. *Biochim. Biophys. Acta*, **19:**236 (1956). [140, 150]

389. Kurland, C. G. Molecular characterization of ribonucleic acid from *Escherichia coli* ribosomes. I. Isolation and molecular weights. *J. Mol. Biol.*, **2:**83 (1960). [404]

390. Labaw, L. W., Mosley, V. M., and Wyckoff, R. W. G. Electron microscopy of ultraviolet irradiated bacteria and their interaction with bacteriophage. *Biochim. Biophys. Acta*, **5:**327 (1950). [371]

391. Labaw, L. W., Mosley, V. M., and Wyckoff, R. W. G. Development of bacteriophage in X-ray inactivated bacteria. *J. Bacteriol.*, **65:**330 (1953). [373]

392. Lacks, S., and Gros, F. A metabolic study of the RNA-amino acid complexes in *Escherichia coli*. *J. Mol. Biol.*, **1:**301 (1959). [412]

393. Lanni, F., and Lanni, Y. T. Antigenic structure of bacteriophage. *Cold Spring Harbor Symp. Quant. Biol.*, **18:**159 (1953). [61, 120]

394. Latarjet, R. Intracellular growth of bacteriophages studied by roentgen irradiation. *J. Gen. Physiol.*, **31:**529 (1948). [299]

395. Latarjet, R. Mutation induite chez un virus par irradiation ultraviolette de cellules infectées. *C. R. Acad. Sci. Paris*, **228:**1354 (1949). [261]

396. Latarjet, R. Induction par les rayons X de la production d'un bactériophage chez *B. megatherium* lysogène. *Ann. Inst. Pasteur*, **81:**389 (1951). [312]

397. Latarjet, R. Multiplication of bacterial viruses studies by radiobiological methods. In *The Nature of Virus Multiplication*, Second Symposium of the Society for General Microbiology (P. Fildes and W. E. van Heyningen, eds.), p. 175. Cambridge University Press, Cambridge, 1953. [304]

398. Lawley, P. D. The action of alkylating agents on deoxyribonucleic acid. *J. Chim. Phys.*, **58:**1011 (1961). [265]

399. Lea, D. E. *Actions of Radiations on Living Cells*. Cambridge University Press, Cambridge, 1947. [300, 382]

400. Lea, D. E., and Salaman, M. H. Experiments on inactivation of bacteriophage by radiations, bearing on the nature of bacteriophage. *Proc. Roy. Soc. London, Ser. B*, **133:**434 (1946). [382]

401. Lederberg, E. M. Lysogenicity in *E. coli* K-12. *Genetics*, **36:**560 (1951). [315, 319]

402. Lederberg, E. M., and Lederberg, J. Genetic studies of lysogenicity in *Escherichia coli*. *Genetics*, **38:**51 (1953). [321]

403. Lederberg, J. Recombination mechanisms in bacteria. *J. Cellular Comp. Physiol.*, **45,** Suppl. 2:75 (1955). [224]

404. Lederberg, J., and Tatum, E. L. Novel genotypes in mixed cultures of biochemical mutants of bacteria. *Cold Spring Harbor Symp. Quant. Biol.*, **11:**113 (1946). [319, 341]

405. Lederberg, S. Suppression of the multiplication of heterologous bacteriophages in lysogenic bacteria. *Virology*, **3:**496 (1957). [337, 378]

406. Lee, K. Y., Wahl, R., and Barbu, E. Contenu en bases puriques et pyrimidiques des acides desoxyribonucléiques des bactéries. *Ann. Inst. Pasteur*, **91:**212 (1956). [404]

407. Lehmann, I. R., Bessman, M. J., Simms, E. S., and Kornberg, A. Enzymatic synthesis of deoxyribonucleic acid. I. Preparation of substrates and partial purification of an enzyme from *Escherichia coli*. *J. Biol. Chem.*, **233:**163 (1958). [158]

408. Lehmann, I. R., and Pratt, E. A. On the structure of glucosylated hydroxymethyl-cytosine nucleotides of coliphages T2, T4, and T6. *J. Biol. Chem.*, **235:**3254 (1960). [56, 58, 148, 199]

409. Lengyel, P., Speyer, J. F., and Ochoa, S. Synthetic polynucleotides and the amino acid code. *Proc. Nat. Acad. Sci. U.S.A.*, **47:**1936 (1961). [414]

410. Lennox, E. S. Transduction of linked genetic characters of the host by bacterio-phage P1. *Virology*, **1:**190 (1955). [347]

411. Lennox, E. S., Luria, S. E., and Benzer, S. On the mechanism of photoreactivation of ultraviolet inactivated bacteriophage. *Biochim. Biophys. Acta*, **15:**471 (1954). [283]

412. Lerman, L. Structural considerations in the interaction of DNA and acridines. *J. Mol. Biol.*, **3:**18 (1961). [273]

413. Lesley, S. M., French, R. C., and Graham, A. F. Breakdown of infecting coliphage by the host cell. *Arch. Biochem.*, **28:**149 (1950). [153]

414. Lesley, S. M., French, R. C., Graham, A. F., and van Rooyen, C. E. Studies on the relationship between virus and host cell. II. The breakdown of T2r^+ bacteriophage upon infection of its host *Escherichia coli*. *Canad. J. Med. Sci.*, **29:**128 (1951). [153]

415. Levine, L., Barlow, J. L., and Van Vunakis, H. An internal protein of T2 and T4 bacteriophages. *Virology*, **6:**702 (1958). [68, 113]

416. Levine, P., and Frisch, A. W. On specific inhibition of bacteriophage action by bacterial extracts. *J. Exp. Med.*, **59:**213 (1934). [97]

417. Levinthal, C. Recombination in phage T2; its relation to heterozygosis and growth. *Genetics*, **39:**169 (1954). [228]

418. Levinthal, C. The mechanism of DNA replication and genetic recombination in phage. *Proc. Nat. Acad. Sci. U.S.A.*, **42:**394 (1956). [65, 166]

419. Levinthal, C. Bacteriophage genetics. In *The Viruses* (F. M. Burnet and W. M. Stanley, eds.), Vol. II, p. 281. Academic Press, New York, 1959. [230]

420. Levinthal, C. Genetic and chemical studies with alkaline phosphatase of *Escherichia coli*. *Brookhaven Symp. Biol.*, **12:**76 (1959). [418]

421. Levinthal, C., and Fisher, H. The structural development of a bacterial virus. *Biochim. Biophys. Acta*, **9:**419 (1952). [121]

422. Levinthal, C., and Fisher, H. Maturation of phage and the evidence of phage precursors. *Cold Spring Harbor Symp. Quant. Biol.*, **18:**29 (1953). [113]

423. Levinthal, C., and Thomas, C. A., Jr. Molecular autoradiography: The β-ray counting from single virus particles and DNA molecules in nuclear emulsions. *Biochim. Biophys. Acta*, **23:**453 (1957). [66, 67]

424. Levinthal, C., and Visconti, N. Growth and recombination in bacterial viruses. *Genetics*, **38:**500 (1953). [83, 210, 216]

425. Lewis, E. B. Pseudo-allelism and gene evolution. *Cold Spring Harbor Symp. Quant. Biol.*, **16:**159 (1951). [254]

426. Lieb, M. The establishment of lysogeny in *E. coli*. *J. Bacteriol.*, **65:**642 (1953). [313]

427. Litman, R. M., and Pardee, A. B. Production of bacteriophage mutants by a dis-turbance of deoxyribosenucleic acid metabolism. *Nature*, **178:**529 (1956). [261]

428. Litman, R. M., and Pardee, A. B. Mutations of bacteriophage T2 induced by bromouracil in the presence of chloramphenicol. *Virology*, **8**:125 (1959). [144]

429. Loeb, T. The isolation of a bacteriophage specific for the F^+ and Hfr mating types of *Escherichia coli* K12. *Science*, **131**:932 (1960). [389]

430. Loeb, T., and Zinder, N. D. A bacteriophage containing RNA. *Proc. Nat. Acad. Sci. U.S.A.*, **47**:282 (1961). [389]

431. Loveless, A. Increased rate of plaque-type and host-range mutation following treatment of bacteriophage *in vitro* with ethyl methane sulphonate. *Nature*, **181**:1212 (1958). [265]

432. Loveless, A. The influence of radiomimetic substances on deoxyribonucleic acid synthesis and function studied in *Escherichia coli*/phage systems. III. Mutation of T2 bacteriophage as a consequence of alkylation *in vitro:* the uniqueness of ethylation. *Proc. Roy. Soc. London, Ser. B*, **150**:497 (1959). [265]

433. Luria, S. E. Mutations of bacterial viruses affecting their host range. *Genetics*, **30**:84 (1945). [181, 186, 188]

434. Luria, S. E. Reactivation of irradiated bacteriophage by transfer of self-reproducing units. *Proc. Nat. Acad. Sci. U.S.A.*, **33**:253 (1947). [289]

435. Luria, S. E. Recent advances in bacterial genetics. *Bacteriol. Rev.*, **11**:1 (1947). [376]

436. Luria, S. E. Bacteriophage: An essay on virus reproduction. *Science*, **111**:507 (1950). [85, 87]

437. Luria, S. E. The frequency distribution of spontaneous bacteriophage mutants as evidence for the exponential rate of phage reproduction. *Cold Spring Harbor Symp. Quant. Biol.*, **16**:463 (1951). [190, 193, 201]

438. Luria, S. E. Reactivation of ultraviolet-irradiated bacteriophage by multiple infection. *J. Cellular Comp. Physiol.*, **39,** Suppl. 1:119 (1952). [285, 291]

439. Luria, S. E. Host-induced modifications of bacterial viruses. *Cold Spring Harbor Symp. Quant. Biol.*, **18**:237 (1953). [378, 390]

440. Luria, S. E. *General Virology*. Wiley, New York, 1953. [x]

441. Luria, S. E. Radiation and viruses. In *Radiation Biology* (A. Hollaender, ed.), Vol. 11, p. 333. McGraw-Hill, New York, 1955. [298, 300, 305]

442. Luria, S. E., Adams, J. N., and Ting, R. C. Transduction of lactose-utilizing ability among strains of *E. coli* and *S. dysenteriae* and the properties of the transducing phage particles. *Virology*, **12**:348 (1960). [365]

443. Luria, S. E., and Anderson, T. F. Identification and characterization of bacteriophages with the electron microscope. *Proc. Nat. Acad. Sci. U.S.A.*, **28**:127 (1942). [47]

444. Luria, S. E., and Delbrück, M. Interference between bacterial viruses: II. Interference between inactivated bacterial virus and active virus of the same strain and of a different strain. *Arch. Biochem.*, **1**:207 (1942). [282]

445. Luria, S. E., and Delbrück, M. Mutations of bacteria from virus sensitivity to virus resistance. *Genetics*, **28**:491 (1943). [39, 190, 194]

446. Luria, S. E., Delbrück, M., and Anderson, T. F. Electron microscope studies of bacterial viruses. *J. Bacteriol.*, **46**:57 (1943). [47]

447. Luria, S. E., and Dulbecco, R. Genetic recombinations leading to production of active bacteriophage from ultraviolet inactivated bacteriophage particles. *Genetics*, **34**:93 (1949). [291, 305]

448. Luria, S. E., and Exner, F. M. The inactivation of bacteriophages by X-rays; influence of the medium. *Proc. Nat. Acad. Sci. U.S.A.*, **27**:370 (1941). [298]

449. Luria, S. E., and Human, M. L. Chromatin staining of bacteria during bacteriophage infection. *J. Bacteriol.*, **59**:551 (1950). [133, 282, 370]

450. Luria, S. E., and Human, M. L. A non-hereditary host-induced variation of bacterial viruses. *J. Bacteriol.*, **64**:557 (1952). [377]

451. Luria, S. E., and Latarjet, R. Ultraviolet irradiation during intracellular growth. *J. Bacteriol.*, **53**:149 (1947). [300]

452. Luria, S. E., Williams, R. C., and Backus, R. C. Electron micrographic counts of bacteriophage particles. *J. Bacteriol.*, **61**:179 (1951). [43]

453. Lwoff, A. Lysogeny. *Bacteriol. Rev.*, **17**:269 (1953). [308, 313, 316, 339]

454. Lwoff, A. Bacteriophage as a model of host-virus relationship. In *The Viruses* (F. M. Burnet and W. M. Stanley, eds.), Vol. II, p. 187. Academic Press, New York, 1959. [21]

455. Lwoff, A., and Gutmann, A. Recherches sur un *Bacillus megathérium* lysogène. *Ann. Inst. Pasteur*, **78**:711 (1950). [English translation in (595).] [309, 310, 339]

456. Lwoff, A., and Jacob, F. Induction de la production de bactériophages et d'une colicine par les peroxydes, les éthylèneimines et les halogenoalcoylamines. *C. R. Acad. Sci. Paris*, **234**:2308 (1952). [312]

457. Lwoff, A., and Siminovitch, L. Induction de la lyse d'une bactérie lysogène sans production de bactériophage. *C. R. Acad. Sci. Paris*, **233**:1397 (1951). [332]

458. Lwoff, A., Siminovitch, L., and Kjeldgaard, N. Induction de la lyse bactériophagique de la totalité d'une population microbienne lysogène. *C. R. Acad. Sci. Paris*, **231**:190 (1950). [English translation in (595).] [311]

459. Lwoff, A., Siminovitch, L., and Kjeldgaard, N. Induction de la production de bactériophages chez une bactérie lysogène. *Ann. Inst. Pasteur*, **79**:815 (1950). [311]

460. Maaløe, O. Some effects of changes of temperature on intracellular growth of the bacterial virus T4r. *Acta Pathol. Microbiol. Scand.*, **27**:680 (1950). [74, 82]

461. Maaløe, O., and Stent, G. S. Radioactive phosphorus tracer studies on the reproduction of T4 bacteriophage. I. Intracellular appearance of phage-like material. *Acta Pathol. Microbiol. Scand.*, **30**:149 (1952). [63, 123]

462. Maaløe, O., and Symonds, N. Radioactive sulfur tracer studies on the reproduction of T4 bacteriophage. *J. Bacteriol.*, **65**:177 (1953). [63, 117, 119]

463. Maaløe, O., and Watson, J. D. The transfer of radioactive phosphorus from parental to progeny phage. *Proc. Nat. Acad. Sci. U.S.A.*, **37**:507 (1951). [161, 163]

464. Martin, R. G., Matthaei, J. H., Jones, O. W., and Nirenberg, M. W. Ribonucleotide composition of the genetic code. *Biochem. Biophys. Res. Comm.*, **6**:410 (1961). [414]

465. McFall, E., Pardee, A. B., and Stent, G. S. Effects of radiophosphorus decay on some synthetic capacities of bacteria. *Biochim. Biophys. Acta*, **27**:282 (1958). [404]

466. McFall, E., and Stent, G. S. Three star mutants of coliphage T2. *J. Gen. Microbiol.*, **18**:346 (1958). [180, 186, 208, 272]

467. McKinley, E. B. Sérum antilytique obtenu par immunisation contre une bactérie normale. *C. R. Soc. Biol.*, **93**:1050 (1925). [307]

468. McQuillen, K., Roberts, R. B., and Britten, R. J. Synthesis of nascent protein by ribosomes in *Escherichia coli*. *Proc. Nat. Acad. Sci. U.S.A.*, **45**:1437 (1959). [402]

469. Mahler, H. R., and Fraser, D. Reproduction of bacteriophage T3 in protoplasts of *Escherichia coli*, strain B. *Biochim. Biophys. Acta*, **22**:197 (1956). [103]

470. Marshak, A. Absence of cytosine in bacteriophage T2. *Proc. Nat. Acad. Sci. U.S.A.*, **37**:299 (1951). [55]

471. Matsumoto, T., and Sawada, Y. Bacteriophage specific for *Bacillus aroideae*. *Trans. Nat. Hist. Soc. Formosa*, **28**:247 (1938). [25]

472. Maxted, W. R. The active agent in nascent phage lysis of Streptococci. *J. Gen. Microbiol.*, **16**:584 (1957). [81]

473. Meissner, G. Über Bakteriophagen gegen Choleravibrionen. *Zentr. Bakteriol. Parasitenk. (I)*, **91**:149 (1924). [25]

474. Melechen, N. E. The relationship of phage DNA synthesis to protein synthesis in replication of bacteriophage T2. *Genetics*, **40**:585 (1955). [143]

475. Meselson, M., and Stahl, F. W. The replication of DNA in *Escherichia coli*. *Proc. Nat. Acad. Sci. U.S.A.*, **44**:671 (1958). [167, 169, 174, 388, 392, 405]

476. Meselson, M., Stahl, F. W., and Vinograd, J. Equilibrium sedimentation of macromolecules in density gradients. *Proc. Nat. Acad. Sci. U.S.A.*, **43**:581 (1957). [167, 405]

477. Meselson, M., and Weigle, J. J. Chromosome breakage accompanying genetic recombination in bacteriophage. *Proc. Nat. Acad. Sci. U.S.A.*, **47**:857 (1961). [234, 236]

478. Meuli, H. Studien zum Bakteriophagen-problem. II. Die Konzentration des lytischen Prinzips und ihre Beziehung zum Ablauf der Bakteriophagenreaktion. *Z. Hyg. Infektionskrankh.*, **99**:46 (1923). [79]

479. Miller, E. M., and Goebel, W. F. The nature of prophage in lysogenic *Bacillus megatherium*. *J. Exp. Med.*, **100**:525 (1954). [317]

480. Minagawa, T. Some characteristics of the internal protein of phage T2. *Virology*, **13**:515 (1961). [113, 130]

481. Monod, J., and Wollman, E. L. L'inhibition de la croissance et de l'adaption enzymatique chez les bactéries infectées par le bactériophage. *Ann. Inst. Pasteur*, **73**:937 (1947). [140]

482. Morrison, J. *Bacteriophage in the Treatment and Prevention of Cholera*, Lewis, London, 1932. [8]

483. Morse, M. L., Lederberg, E. M., and Lederberg, J. Transduction in *Escherichia coli* K12. *Genetics*, **41**:142 (1956). [358]

484. Morse, M. L., Lederberg, E. M., and Lederberg, J. Transductional heterogenotes in *Escherichia coli*. *Genetics*, **41**:758 (1956). [358]

485. Mühlens, K. Beobachtungen über Bakteriophagenwirkung bei aeroben Aktinomyceten. *Zbl. Bakteriol. (I)*, **138**:256 (1940). [25]

486. Mukai, F., Streisinger, G., Miller, B., and Dreyer, W. In press. [154]

487. Muller, H. J. Variation due to change in the individual gene. *Am. Naturalist*, **56**:32 (1922). [175]

488. Murakami, W. T., Van Vunakis, H., and Levine, L. Synthesis of T2 internal protein in infected *Escherichia coli*, strain B. *Virology*, **9**:624 (1959). [118, 120, 289, 425]

489. Murray, R. G. E., Gillen, D. H., and Heagy, F. C. Cytological changes in *Escherichia coli* produced by infection with phage T2. *J. Bacteriol.*, **59**:603 (1950). [133, 370]

490. Mutsaars, W. Multiplication du bactériophage dans les protoplastes de *B. subtilis*. *Ann. Inst. Pasteur*, **89**:166 (1955). [102]

491. Nirenberg, M. W., and Matthaei, J. H. The dependence of cell-free protein synthesis in *E. coli* upon naturally occurring or synthetic polyribonucleotides. *Proc. Nat. Acad. Sci. U.S.A.*, **47**:1588 (1961). [413]

492. Nismann, B., Bergmann, F., and Berg, P. Observations on amino acid-dependent exchanges of inorganic pyrophosphate and ATP. *Biochim. Biophys. Acta*, **26**:639 (1957). [412]

493. Nomura, M. DNA synthesized in *Escherichia coli* K12 (λ) after infection with an *r*II mutant of bacteriophage T4. *Virology*, **14**:164 (1961). [240]

494. Nomura, M., and Benzer, S. The nature of the "deletion" mutants in the *r*II region of phage T4. *J. Mol. Biol.*, **3**:684 (1961). [244, 245]

495. Nomura, M., Hall, B. D., and Spiegelman, S. Characterization of RNA synthesized in *Escherichia coli* after bacteriophage T2 infection. *J. Mol. Biol.*, **2**:306 (1960). [403, 412]

496. Northrop, J. H. Increase in bacteriophage and gelatinase concentration in cultures of *Bacillus megatherium*. *J. Gen. Physiol.*, **23**:59 (1939). [79, 308]

497. Novick, A., and Szilard, L. Virus strains of identical phenotype but different genotype. *Science*, **113**:34 (1951). [136, 199]

498. Ochoa, S. Biosynthesis of ribonucleic acid. In *Recent Progress in Microbiology* (G. Tunevall, ed.), p. 122. Almqvist & Wiksell, Stockholm, 1959. [413]

499. Ozeki, H. Abortive transduction in purine-requiring mutants of *Salmonella typhimurium*. In *Genetic Studies with Bacteria*, Carnegie Inst. Wash. Publ. 612, p. 97 (1956). [355, 366]

500. Pardee, A. B. Enzyme activity and bacteriophage infection. *J. Gen. Physiol.*, **34**:619 (1951). [140]

501. Pardee, A. B., and Kunkee, R. E. Enzymatic activity and bacteriophage infection. II. Activities before and after virus infection. *J. Biol. Chem.*, **199**:9 (1952). [140]

502. Pardee, A. B., and Williams, I. Increase in desoxyribonuclease of virus-infected *E. coli*. *Arch. Biochem.*, **40**:222 (1952). [140, 150, 370]

503. Pardee, A. B., and Williams, I. Enzymatic activity and bacteriophage infection. III. Increase of deoxyribonuclease. *Ann. Inst. Pasteur*, **84**:147 (1953). [371]

504. Pfeifer, D. Genetische Untersuchungen am Bakteriophagen φX174. I. Aufbau eines Selektiven Systems und Nachweis Genetischer Rekombination. *Z. Verebungsl.*, **92**:317 (1961). [389]

505. Piorkowski, G. Beitrag zur Streptokokkenfrage. Anwendung des d'Hérelleschen Phänomens auf Streptokokken. *Med. Klin.*, **18**:474 (1922). [25]

506. Poisson, S. D. Recherches sur la probabilité des jugements en matière criminelle et en matière civile, précedées des règles générales du calcul des probabilités. Paris, 1837. [75]

507. Pons, R. Bactériophage du pyocyanique. *C. R. Soc. Biol.*, **89**:77 (1923). [25]

508. Pontecorvo, G. Genetic formulation of gene structure and gene action. *Adv. Enzymol.*, **13**:121 (1952). [254]

509. Pontecorvo, G. *Trends in Genetic Analysis*, Columbia University Press, New York, 1958. [232, 239]

510. Pratt, D., and Stent, G. S. Mutational heterozygotes in bacteriophages. *Proc. Nat. Acad. Sci. U.S.A.*, **45**:1507 (1959). [263, 274, 392]

511. Pratt, D., Stent, G. S., and Harriman, P. D. Stabilization to P³² decay and onset of DNA replication of T4 bacteriophage. *J. Mol. Biol.*, **3**:409 (1961). [152, 303, 304]

512. Primosigh, J., Pelzer, H., Maass, D., and Weidel, W. Chemical characterization of mucopeptides released from the *E. coli* B cell wall by enzymic action. *Biochim. Biophys. Acta*, **46**:68 (1961). [100]

513. Puck, T. T. The first steps of virus invasion. *Cold Spring Harbor Symp. Quant. Biol.*, **18**:149 (1953). [80, 93]

514. Puck, T. T., Garen, A., and Cline, J. The mechanism of virus attachment to host cells. I. The role of ions in the primary reaction. *J. Exp. Med.*, **93**:65 (1951). [92, 100]

515. Puck, T. T., and Lee, H. Mechanism of cell wall penetration by viruses. I. An increase in host cell permeability induced by bacteriophage infection. *J. Exp. Med.*, **99**:481 (1954). [101]

516. Puck, T. T., and Lee, L. H. Mechanism of cell wall penetration by viruses. II. Demonstration of cyclic permeability change accompanying virus infection of *Escherichia coli* B cells. *J. Exp. Med.*, **101**:151 (1955). [101]

517. Puck, T. T., and Tolmach, L. J. The mechanisms of virus attachment to host cells. IV. Physicochemical studies on virus and cell surface groups. *Arch. Biochem. Biophys.*, **51**:229 (1954). [92]

518. Putnam, F. W. Bacteriophages: Nature and reproduction. *Adv. Protein Chem.*, **8**:177 (1953). [46, 157]

519. Putnam, F. W. Ultracentrifugation of bacterial viruses. *J. Polymer. Sci.*, **12**:391 (1954). [46, 91]

520. Putnam, F. W., and Kozloff, L. M. Biochemical studies of virus reproduction. IV. The fate of the infecting virus particle. *J. Biol. Chem.*, **182**:243 (1950). [160]

521. Putnam, F. W., Kozloff, L. M., and Neil, J. C. Biochemical studies of virus reproduction: I. Purification and properties of *E. coli* bacteriophage T6. *J. Biol. Chem.*, **179**:303 (1949). [50]

522. Raettig, H. *Bakteriophagie, 1917 bis 1956*. Gustav Fischer, Stuttgart, 1958. [x, 24]

523. Ralston, D. J., and Krueger, A. P. The isolation of a staphylococcal phage variant susceptible to an unusual host control. *J. Gen. Physiol.*, **37**:685 (1954). [377]

524. Ralston, D. J., Liebermann, M., Baer, B., and Krueger, A. P. Staphylococcal virolysin, a phage-induced lysin. Its differentiation from the autolysin of normal cells. *J. Gen. Physiol.*, **40**:791 (1957). [81]

525. Reilly, H. C., Harris, D. A., and Waksman, S. A. An actinophage for *Streptomyces grisens*. *J. Bacteriol.*, **54**:451 (1947). [25]

526. Riley, M., Pardee, A. B., Monod, J., and Jacob, F. On the expression of a structural gene. *J. Mol. Biol.*, **2**:216 (1960). [404]

527. Robinow, C. F. The chromatin bodies of bacteria. *Bacteriol. Rev.*, **20**:207 (1956). [369]

528. Roller, A. Studies on the replication and transfer to progeny of the DNA of the bacteriophage T4. Unpublished Ph.D. thesis, California Institute of Technology, Pasadena, 1961. [169]

529. Rouyer, M., and Latarjet, R. Augmentation du nombre de bactériophages en présence de bactéries stérilisées par irradiation. *Ann. Inst. Pasteur*, **72**:89 (1946). [373]

530. Rubenstein, I., Thomas, C. A., Jr., and Hershey, A. D. The molecular weights of T2 bacteriophage and its first and second breakage products. *Proc. Nat. Acad. Sci. U.S.A.*, **47**:1113 (1961). [67]

531. Rubin, H., and Temin, H. M. A radiological study of cell-virus interaction in the Rous sarcoma. *Virology*, **7**:75 (1959). [304]

532. Ruska, H. Die Sichtbarmachung der bakteriophagen Lyse im Übermikroskop. *Naturwiss.*, **28**:45 (1940). [47]

533. Sadron, C. L. Deoxyribonucleic acids as macromolecules. In *The Nucleic Acids* (E. Chargaff and J. N. Davidson, eds.), Vol. III, p. 1. Academic Press, New York, 1960. [65]

534. Salton, M. R. J. Bacterial cell walls. In *Bacterial Anatomy*, Sixth Symposium of the Society for General Microbiology, p. 81. Cambridge University Press, Cambridge, 1956. [97]

535. Salton, M. R. J., and McQuillen, K. Bacterial photoplasts. II. Bacteriophage multiplication in protoplasts of sensitive and lysogenic strains of *Bacillus megaterium*. *Biochim. Biophys. Acta*, **17**:465 (1955). [102]

536. Sanderson, E. S. Bacteriophage tests on the meconium of aborted fetuses. *J. Exp. Med.*, **42**:561 (1925). [25]

537. Sato, G. H. Activation of bacteriophage by urea. *Science*, **123**:891 (1956). [107]

538. Sato, G. H., and Stent, G. S. [Unpublished experiments, cited in (169) and (603).] [234]

539. Saudek, E. C., and Collingsworth, D. R. A bacteriophage in the streptomycin fermentation. *J. Bacteriol.*, **54**:41 (1947). [25]

540. Sauer, L. W., and Hambrecht, L. Bacteriophage of *Bacillus pertussis*. *J. Infect. Diseases*, **53**:197 (1933). [25]

541. Saukkonnen, J. J., Goodman, F., and Chargaff, E. Patterns of cellular controls operating in bacteriophage reproduction. II. Effect of 5-fluorouracil on metabolic events in bacteria infected with coliphage T2r$^+$. *Biochim. Biophys. Acta*, **44**:469 (1960). [390]

542. Schachman, H. K., Pardee, A. B., and Stanier, R. Y. Investigations on the macromolecular organization of microbial cells. *Arch. Biochem. Biophys.*, **38**:245 (1952). [155, 383, 402]

543. Schlesinger, M. Ueber die Bindung des Bakteriophagen an homologe Bakterien. I. Die Unterscheidung von Gruppen von verschiedener Bindungsaffinitaet innerhalb der Bakterien des selben Lysats. Die Frage der Reversibilitaet oder Irreversibilitaet der Bindung. *Z. Hyg. Infektionskrankh.*, **114**:136 (1932). [17, 93]

544. Schlesinger, M. Ueber die Bindung des Bakteriophagen an homologe Bakterien. II. Quantitative Untersuchungen ueber die Bindungsgeschwindigkeit und die Saettigung. Berechnung der Teilchengroesse des Bakteriophagen aus deren Ergebnissen. *Z. Hyg. Infektionskrankh.*, **114**:149 (1932). [English translation in (595).] [17, 90]

545. Schlesinger, M. Die Bestimmung von Teilchengrösse und spezifischem Gewicht des Bakteriophagen durch Zentrifugierversuche. *Z. Hyg. Infektionskrankh.*, **114**:161 (1932). [46, 382]

546. Schlesinger, M. Beobachtung und Zählung von Bakteriophagenteilchen im Dunkelfeld. Die Form der Teilchen. *Z. Hyg. Infektionskrankh.*, **115**:774 (1933). [17, 44]

547. Schlesinger, M. Reindarstellung eines Bakteriophagen in mit freiem Auge sichtbaren Mengen. *Biochem. Z.*, **264:**6 (1933). [17, 49]

548. Schlesinger, M. Zur Frage der chemischen Zusammensetzung des Bakteriophagen. *Biochem. Z.*, **273:**306 (1934). [17, 51]

548a. Schlesinger, M. The Feulgen reaction of the bacteriophage substance. *Nature*, **138:**508 (1936). [17, 51]

549. Schmoluchowski, M. von. Versuch einer mathematischen Theorie der Koagulationskinetik Kolloider Lösungen. *Z. Physik. Chem.*, **92:**129 (1917). [90]

550. Schuster, H. The reaction of nitrous acid with deoxyribonucleic acid. *Biochem. Biophys. Res. Comm.*, **2:**320 (1960). [266]

551. Schuster, H. The reaction of tobacco mosaic virus ribonucleic acid with hydroxylamine. *J. Mol. Biol.*, **3:**447 (1961). [268]

552. Schuster, H., and Schramm, G. Bestimmung der biologisch wirksamen Einheit in der Ribonucleinsäure des Tabakmosaikvirus auf chemischem Wege. *Z. Naturforsch.*, **13b:**697 (1958). [266]

553. Schuurman, C. J. Bakteriophagen produzieren lytische Fermente: Es sind selbständige Organismen. *Zentr. Bakteriol. Parasitenk.* (*I*), **137:**438 (1936). [81]

554. Schweet, R. S., Bovard, F. C., Allen, E., and Glassman, E. The incorporation of amino acids into ribonucleic acid. *Proc. Nat. Acad. Sci. U.S.A.*, **44:**173 (1958). [412]

555. Séchaud, J. Développement intracellulaire du coliphage lambda. *Arch. Sci.* (*Geneva*), **13:**427 (1960). [370]

556. Séchaud, J., and Kellenberger, E. Lyse précoce, provoquée par le chloroforme, chez les bactéries infectées par du bactériophage. *Ann. Inst. Pasteur*, **90:**102 (1956). [85]

557. Séchaud, J., Ryter, A., and Kellenberger, E. Considérations quantitatives sur des coupes ultraminces de bactéries infectées par un bactériophage. *J. Biophys. Biochem. Cytol.*, **5:**469 (1959). [133]

558. Sekiguchi, M., Taketo, A., and Takagi, Y. An infective deoxyribonucleic acid from bacteriophage ϕX174. *Biochim. Biophys. Acta*, **45:**199 (1960). [386]

559. Sertic, V. Untersuchungen über einen Lysinzonen bildenden Bakteriophagen. I. Mitteilung: Der Aufbau der Bakteriophagen Kolonien. *Zentr. Bakteriol. Parasitenk.* (*I*), **110:**125 (1929). [80, 81]

560. Sertic, V. Origine de la lysine d'une race du bactériophage. *C. R. Soc. Biol.*, **100:**477 (1929). [80]

561. Sertic, V. Procédé d'obtention de variantes de bactériophage adaptées a lyser des formes bactériennes secondaires. *C. R. Soc. Biol.*, **100:**612 (1929). [176]

562. Sertic, V. Sur l'action inhibitrice des cations monovalents sur la multiplication d'une race de bactériophage. *C. R. Soc. Biol.*, **124:**14 (1937). [92]

563. Sertic, V. Sur la différence d'actions des électrolytes sur le développement des diverses races de bactériophages. *C. R. Soc. Biol.*, **124:**98 (1937). [92]

564. Sertic, V., and Boulgakov, N. Lysines de bactériophages présentant différentes thermorésistances. *C. R. Soc. Biol.*, **108:**948 (1931). [81]

565. Sertic, V., and Boulgakov, N. Classification et identification des typhiphages. *C. R. Soc. Biol.*, **119:**1270 (1935). [384]

566. Sher, I. H., and Malette, M. F. The adaptive nature of the formation of lysine decarboxylase in *Escherichia coli* B. *Arch. Biochem. Biophys.*, **52**:331 (1954). [140]

567. Siddiqi, M. S. H., Kozloff, L. M., Putnam, F. W., and Evans, E. A., Jr. Biochemical studies of virus reproduction. IX. Nature of the host cell contributions. *J. Biol. Chem.*, **199**:165 (1952). [130]

568. Siegel, A., Ginoza, W., and Wildman, S. G. The early events of infection with tobacco mosaic virus nucleic acid. *Virology*, **3**:554 (1957). [304]

569. Siegel, A., and Wildman, S. G. The inactivation of the infectious centers of tobacco mosaic virus by ultraviolet light. *Virology*, **2**:69 (1956). [304]

570. Silvestri, L. Studi sull' azione dell' azotoiprite (metildibetachloroetilammina) sul batteriofago anticoli T2. *Boll. Ist. Sieroter. Milan.*, **28**:193 (1949). [261]

571. Siminovitch, L., and Jacob, F. Biosynthèse induite d'un enzyme pendant le développement des bactériophages chez *Escherichia coli* K12. *Ann. Inst. Pasteur*, **83**:745 (1952). [370]

572. Sinsheimer, R. L. Nucleotides from T2r^+ bacteriophage. *Science*, **120**:551 (1954). [56]

573. Sinsheimer, R. L. The glucose content of the deoxyribonucleic acids of certain bacteriophages. *Proc. Nat. Acad. Sci. U.S.A.*, **42**:502 (1956). [199]

574. Sinsheimer, R. L. Purification and properties of bacteriophage ϕX174. *J. Mol. Biol.*, **1**:37 (1959). [384]

575. Sinsheimer, R. L. A single-stranded deoxyribonucleic acid from bacteriophage ϕX174. *J. Mol. Biol.*, **1**:43 (1959). [386]

576. Sinsheimer, R. L. The nucleic acids of the bacterial viruses. In *The Nucleic Acids* (E. Chargaff and J. N. Davidson, eds.), Vol. III, p. 187. Academic Press, New York, 1960. [58]

577. Sinsheimer, R. L. The replication of bacteriophage ϕX174. *J. Chim. Phys.*, **58**:986 (1961). [386, 387]

578. Sinsheimer, R. L., Starman, B., Nagler, C., and Guthrie, S. The process of infection with bacteriophage ϕX174. I. Evidence for a "replicative form." *J. Mol. Biol.*, **4**:142 (1962). [386]

579. Somerville, R., Ebisuzaki, K., and Greenberg, G. R. Hydroxylmethyldeoxycytidylate kinase formation after bacteriophage infection of *Escherichia coli*. *Proc. Nat. Acad. Sci. U.S.A.*, **45**:1240 (1959). [148]

580. Speyer, J. F., Lengyel, P., Basilio, C., and Ochoa, S. Synthetic polynucleotides and the amino acid code II. *Proc. Nat. Acad. Sci. U.S.A.*, **48**:63 (1962). [414]

581. Srb, A. M., and Owen, R. D. *General Genetics*. Freeman, San Francisco, 1952. [201]

582. Stahl, F. W. The effects of the decay of incorporated radioactive phosphorus on the genome of bacteriophage T4. *Virology*, **2**:206 (1956). [297]

583. Stahl, F. W. Radiobiology of bacteriophage. In *The Viruses* (F. M. Burnet and W. M. Stanley, eds.), Vol. II, p. 353. Academic Press, New York, 1959. [277, 305]

584. Stanier, R. Y. Enzymatic adaptation in bacteria. *Ann. Rev. Microbiol.*, **5**:35 (1951). [424]

585. Stanier, R. Y., Doudoroff, M., and Adelberg, E. A. *The Microbial World*, Prentice-Hall, Englewood Cliffs, N.J., 1957. [22, 23, 26]

586. Starlinger, P. Über ein Defekt des transduzierenden Salmonella Phagen P22. *Z. Naturforsch.*, **14b**:489 (1958). [363]

587. Steinberg, C., and Edgar, R. S. A critical test of a current theory of genetic recombination in bacteriophage. *Genetics*, **47**:187 (1962). [232]

588. Steinberg, C., and Epstein, R. H. In press. [218]

589. Steinberg, C., and Stahl, F. The theory of formal phage genetics. *Cold Spring Harbor Symp. Quant. Biol.*, **23**:42 (1958). [224]

590. Steinberg, C., and Stahl, F. The clone-size distribution of mutants arising from a steady state pool of vegetative phage. *J. Theoret. Biol.*, **1**:488 (1961). [77, 195]

591. Steiner, R. F., and Beers, R. F., Jr. *Polynucleotides.* Elsevier, Amsterdam, 1961. [413]

592. Stent, G. S. Cross reactivation of genetic loci of T2 bacteriophage after decay of incorporated radioactive phosphorus. *Proc. Nat. Acad. Sci. U.S.A.*, **39**:1234 (1953). [297]

593. Stent, G. S. Decay of incorporated radioactive phosphorus during reproduction of bacteriophage T2. *J. Gen. Physiol.*, **38**:853 (1955). [152, 302, 304]

594. Stent, G. S. Mating in the reproduction of bacterial viruses. *Adv. Virus Res.*, **5**:95 (1958). [152, 299, 304, 372, 390, 392]

595. Stent, G. S. (ed.). *Papers on Bacterial Viruses.* Little, Brown, Boston, 1960. [x, 115]

596. Stent, G. S. Stabilization to P^{32} decay and onset of replication of bacteriophage DNA. *J. Chim. Phys.* **58**:1028 (1961). [339]

597. Stent, G. S., and Fuerst, C. R. Inactivation of bacteriophages by decay of incorporated radioactive phosphorus. *J. Gen. Physiol.*, **38**:441 (1955). [294, 295]

598. Stent, G. S., and Fuerst, C. R. Decay of incorporated radioactive phosphorus during development of a temperate bacteriophage. *Virology*, **2**:737 (1956). [304, 305, 325, 373]

599. Stent, G. S., and Fuerst, C. R. Genetic and physiological effects of the decay of incorporated radioactive phosphorus in bacterial viruses and bacteria. *Adv. Biol. Med. Physics*, **7**:1 (1960). [296, 305]

600. Stent, G. S., Fuerst, C. R., and Jacob, F. Inactivation d'un prophage par la désintégration du radiophosphore. *C. R. Acad. Sci. Paris*, **244**:1840 (1957). [317]

601. Stent, G. S., and Jerne, N. K. The distribution of parental phosphorus atoms among bacteriophage progeny. *Proc. Nat. Acad. Sci. U.S.A.*, **41**:704 (1955). [166]

602. Stent, G. S., and Maaløe, O. Radioactive phosphorus tracer studies on the reproduction of T4 bacteriophage. II. Kinetics of phosphorus assimilation. *Biochim. Biophys. Acta*, **10**:55 (1953). [83, 128, 129, 179]

603. Stent, G. S., Sato, G. H., and Jerne, N. K. Dispersal of the parental nucleic acid of bacteriophage T4 among its progeny. *J. Mol. Biol.*, **1**:134 (1956). [163, 166]

604. Stent, G. S., and Wollman, E. L. Studies on activation of T4 bacteriophage by cofactor. II. The mechanism of activation. *Biochim. Biophys. Acta*, **6**:307 (1950). [107]

605. Stent, G. S., and Wollman, E. L. Studies on activation of T4 bacteriophage by cofactor. III. Conditions affecting the activation process. *Biochim. Biophys. Acta*, **6**:374 (1951). [107]

606. Stent, G. S., and Wollman, E. L. On the two-step nature of bacteriophage adsorption. *Biochim. Biophys. Acta*, **8**:260 (1952). [90, 93, 94]

607. Stocker, B. A. D. Abortive transduction of motility in *Salmonella;* a nonreplicated gene transmitted through many generations to a single descendant. *J. Gen. Microbiol.*, **15:**575 (1956). [353, 355]

608. Stocker, B. A. D., Zinder, N. D., and Lederberg, J. Transduction of flagellar characters in *Salmonella. J. Gen. Microbiol.*, **9:**410 (1953). [346, 353]

609. Stone, A. B., and Burton, K. The deoxyribonucleases of bacteriophage-infected *Escherichia coli. Biochem. J.*, **85:**600 (1962). [141, 151]

610. Streisinger, G. The genetic control of ultraviolet sensitivity levels in bacteriophage T2 and T4. *Virology*, **2:**1 (1956). [187, 283]

611. Streisinger, G. The genetic control of host range and serological specificity in bacteriophages T2 and T4. *Virology*, **2:**377 (1956). [136]

612. Streisinger, G. Phenotypic mixing of host range and serological specificities in bacteriophages T2 and T4. *Virology*, **2:**388 (1956). [200]

613. Streisinger, G., and Bruce, V. Linkage of genetic markers in phages T2 and T4. *Genetics*, **45:**1289 (1960). [208]

614. Streisinger, G., Edgar, R. H., and Denhardt, G. H. The gross structure of the genome of phage T4. I. The circularity of the linkage map. *Proc. Nat. Acad. Sci. U.S.A.*, **49,** in press. (1963). [217]

615. Streisinger, G., and Franklin, N. C. Mutation and recombination at the host range genetic region of phage T2. *Cold Spring Harbor Symp. Quant. Biol.*, **21:**103 (1956). [190, 201, 276]

616. Streisinger, G., Mukai, F., Dreyer, W. J., Miller, B., and Horiuchi, S. Mutations affecting the lysozyme of phage T4. *Cold Spring Harbor Symp. Quant. Biol.*, **26:**25 (1961). [82, 187]

617. Streisinger, G., and Weigle, J. Properties of bacteriophages T2 and T4 with unusual inheritance. *Proc. Nat. Acad. Sci. U.S.A.*, **42:**504 (1956). [199]

618. Sussman, R., and Jacob, F. Sur un système de repression thermosensible chez le bactériophage λ d'*Escherichia coli. C. R. Acad. Sci. Paris*, **254:**1517 (1962). [423]

619. Symonds, N. The properties of a star mutant of phage T2. *J. Gen. Microbiol.*, **18:**330 (1958). [186]

620. Symonds, N., and Ritchie, D. A. Multiplicity reactivation after the decay of incorporated radioactive phosphorus in phage T4. *Virology*, **3:**61 (1961). [304]

621. Taylor, N. W., Epstein, H. T., and Lauffer, M. A. The particle weight, hydration and shape of the T2 bacteriophage of *Escherichia coli. J. Am. Chem. Soc.*, **77:**1270 (1955). [46]

622. Terada, M. T., Tomii, T., and Kurosaka, K. A doubly lysogenic strain of *S. typhi murium. Virus (Osaka)*, **6:**274 (1956). [337]

623. Terzaghi, B. E., Streisinger, G., and Stahl, F. W. The mechanism of 5-bromouracil mutagenesis in bacteriophage T4. *Proc. Nat. Acad. Sci. U.S.A.*, **48:**1519 (1962). [263]

624. Tessman, E. S. Growth and mutation of phage T1 on ultraviolet-irradiated host cells. *Virology*, **2:**679 (1956). [371, 372, 376]

625. Tessman, E. S., and Tessman, J. Genetic recombination in phage S13. *Virology*, **7:**465 (1959). [389]

626. Tessman, I. Some unusual properties of the nucleic acid in bacteriophages S13 and φX-174. *Virology*, **7:**263 (1959). [384, 386]

627. Tessman, I. Mutagenesis in phages φX-174 and T4 and properties of the genetic material. *Virology*, **9**:375 (1959). [266, 275]

628. Tessman, I., Tessman, E. S., and Stent, G. S. The relative radiosensitivity of bacteriophages S13 and T2. *Virology*, **4**:209 (1957). [383]

629. Thomas, C. A., Jr. The release and stability of the large subunit of DNA from T2 and T4 bacteriophage. *J. Gen. Physiol.*, **42**:503 (1959). [67, 296]

630. Thomas, C. A., Jr. The organization of DNA in bacteriophage and bacteria. In *Molecular Genetics*, Chapter III. Academic Press, New York, 1962. [69]

631. Thomas, R. Effects of chloramphenicol on genetic replication in bacteriophage λ. *Virology*, **9**:275 (1959). [152, 371]

632. Timoféeff-Ressovsky, N. W., Zimmer, K. G., and Delbrück, M. Gen Mutation und Gen Struktur. *Nachr. Ges. Wiss. Göttingen*, **1**:189 (1935). [18]

633. Tobin, J. O'H. Some observations on the effect of X-rays on the behaviour of a temperate phage in two strains of *Ps. pyocyanea*. *Brit. J. Exp. Pathol.*, **34**:635 (1953). [373]

634. Tolmach, L. J. Attachment and penetration of cells by viruses. *Adv. Virus Res.*, **4**:63 (1957). [115]

635. Tolmach, L. J., and Puck, T. T. The mechanism of virus attachment to host cells. III. *J. Am. Chem. Soc.*, **74**:5551 (1952). [92]

636. Tomizawa, J. Sensitivity of phage precursor nucleic acid synthesized in the presence of chloramphenicol to ultraviolet irradiation. *Virology*, **6**:55 (1958). [143, 167]

637. Tomizawa, J., and Sunakawa, S. The effect of chloramphenicol on deoxyribonucleic acid synthesis and the development of resistance to ultraviolet irradiation in *E. coli* infected with bacteriophage T2. *J. Gen. Physiol.*, **39**:553 (1956). [143, 144, 152, 304]

638. Trautner, T. A. Untersuchungen am Heterozygoten des Phagen T1. *Z. Vererbungsl.*, **89**:264 (1958). [229]

639. Twort, F. W. An investigation on the nature of the ultramicroscopic viruses. *Lancet* (2), **189**:1241 (1915). [3, 25]

640. Twort, F. W. The bacteriophage: the breaking down of bacteria by associated filter-passing lysins. *Brit. Med. J.* (2), August 19, 1922, p. 293 [21]

641. Twort, F. W. The discovery of the bacteriophage. *Science News*, No. 14, p. 33. Penguin, Harmondsworth, 1949. [3, 21]

642. Uchida, H., and Stent, G. S. Protein synthesis and the onset of intracellular bacteriophage growth. I. Stabilization of the infecting phage to P^{32} decay. *J. Mol. Biol.*, **2**:251 (1960). [152]

643. Uchida, H., and Stent, G. S. Protein synthesis and the onset of intracellular bacteriophage growth. II. Stabilization to P^{32} decay of the genome of a secondary phage. *J. Mol. Biol.*, **2**:262 (1960). [152]

644. Uetake, H., Luria, S. E., and Burrous, J. W. Conversion of somatic antigens in *Salmonella* by phage infection leading to lysis or lysogeny. *Virology*, **5**:68 (1958). [337]

645. Uetake, H., Nakagawa, T., and Akiba, T. The relationship of bacteriophage to antigenic changes in group E *Salmonellas*. *J. Bacteriol.*, **69**:571 (1955). [337]

646. Van Vunakis, H., Baker, W. H., and Brown, R. K. Structural studies on the proteins of bacteriophages. I. Alkaline dissociation of the protein coat "ghost" of bacteriophage T2r^+. *Virology*, **5**:327 (1958). [65]

647. Vielmetter, W., and Schuster, H. The base specificity of mutation induced by nitrous acid in phage T2. *Biochem. Biophys. Res. Comm.*, **2**:324 (1960). [266]

648. Vielmetter, W., and Wieder, C. M. Mutagene und inaktivierende Wirkung salpetriger Säure auf freie Partikel des Phagen T2. *Z. Naturforsch.*, **14b**:312 (1959). [266, 275]

649. Visconti, N. Resistance to lysis from without in bacteria infected with T2 bacteriophage. *J. Bacteriol.*, **66**:247 (1953). [153, 154]

650. Visconti, N., and Delbrück, M. The mechanism of genetic recombination in phage. *Genetics*, **38**:5 (1953). [210, 211, 216]

651. Volkin, E., and Astrachan, L. Phosphorus incorporation in *Escherichia coli* ribonucleic acid after infection with bacteriophage T2. *Virology*, **2**:149 (1956). [156, 403]

652. Volkin, E., and Astrachan, L. The absence of ribonucleic acid in bacteriophage T2r^+. *Virology*, **2**:594 (1956). [157]

652a. Wacker, A. Strahlenchemische Veränderungen von Pyrimidinen in vivo und in vitro. *J. Chim. Phys.*, **58**:1041 (1961). [281, 282]

653. Wacker, A., Dellweg, H., and Weinblum, D. Strahlenchemische Veränderung der Bakterien-Desoxyribonucleinsaüre in vivo. *Naturwiss.*, **47**:477 (1960). [282]

654. Watanabe, I. The effect of ultraviolet light on the production of bacterial virus protein. *J. Gen. Physiol.*, **40**:521 (1957). [118, 119, 282, 372]

655. Watanabe, I. Formation of non-phage-antigenic protein in *E. coli* infected with T2 phage. *Biochim. Biophys. Acta*, **25**:665 (1957). [142]

656. Watanabe, I., Stent, G. S., and Schachman, H. K. On the state of parental phosphorus during reproduction of bacteriophage T2. *Biochim. Biophys. Acta*, **15**:38 (1954). [163, 164]

656a. Watson, J. D. The properties of X-ray-inactivated bacteriophage. I. Inactivation by direct effect. *J. Bacteriol.*, **60**:697 (1950). [300]

657. Watson, J. D. The properties of X-ray inactivated bacteriophage. II. Inactivation by indirect effects. *J. Bacteriol.*, **63**:473 (1952). [298]

658. Watson, J. D., and Crick, F. H. C. A structure for deoxyribose nucleic acid. *Nature*, **171**:737 (1953). [53]

659. Watson, J. D., and Crick, F. H. C. Genetical implications of the structure of deoxyribonucleic acid. *Nature*, **171**:964 (1953). [53, 158, 259]

660. Watson, J. D., and Crick, F. H. C. The structure of DNA. *Cold Spring Harbor Symp. Quant. Biol.*, **18**:123 (1953). [53, 174, 392]

661. Watson, J. D., and Maaløe, O. Nucleic acid transfer from parental to progeny bacteriophage. *Biochim. Biophys. Acta*, **10**:432 (1953). [161, 163, 174]

662. Weed, L. L., and Cohen, S. S. Utilization of host pyrimidines in the synthesis of bacterial viruses. *J. Biol. Chem.*, **192**:693 (1951). [127]

663. Weibull, C. The isolation of protoplasts from *Bacillus megaterium* by controlled treatment with lysozyme. *J. Bacteriol.*, **66**:688 (1953). [102]

664. Weidel, W. Über die Zellmembran von *Escherichia coli* B. I. Preparierung der Membran; analytische Daten, Morphologie, Verhalten der Membran gegenüber den Bakteriophagen der T-Serie. *Z. Naturforsch.*, **6b**:251 (1951). [80, 97, 100]

665. Weidel, W. Further studies on the membrane of *E. coli*, B. *Ann. Inst. Pasteur*, **84**:60 (1951). [97]

666. Weidel, W. L-Gala-D-manno-heptose als Baustein von Bakterienzellwänden. *Hoppe-Seyler's Z. physiol. Chem.*, **299**:253 (1954). [99]

667. Weidel, W. Bacterial viruses (with particular reference to adsorption penetration). *Ann. Rev. Microbiol.*, **12**:27 (1958). [115]

668. Weidel, W., Frank, H., and Martin, H. H. The rigid layer of the cell wall of *Escherichia coli* strain B. *J. Gen. Microbiol.*, **22**:158 (1960). [97]

669. Weidel, W., and Katz, W. Reindarstellung und Charakterisierung des für die lyse T2-infizierter Zellen verantwortlichen Enzyms. *Z. Naturforsch.*, **166**:156 (1961). [82]

670. Weidel, W., and Kellenberger, E. The *E. coli* B receptor for the phage T5. II. Electron microscopic studies. *Biochim. Biophys. Acta*, **17**:1 (1955). [99, 100, 101, 104]

671. Weidel, W., Koch, G., and Bobosch, K. Über die Rezeptorsubstanz für den Phagen T5. I. Reindarstellung aus *E. col* B. Physikalische, chemische und funktionelle Charakterisierung. *Z. Naturforsch.*, **9b**:573 (1954). [99]

672. Weidel, W., and Primosigh, J. Die gemeinsame Wurzel der Lyse von *Escherichia coli* durch Penicillin oder durch Phagen. *Z. Naturforsch.*, **12b**:421 (1957). [100]

673. Weigle, J. J. Induction of mutations in a bacterial virus. *Proc. Nat. Acad. Sci. U.S.A.*, **39**:628 (1953). [314, 376]

674. Weigle, J. Transduction by coliphage λ of the galactose marker. *Virology*, **4**:14 (1957). [360]

675. Weigle, J. J., and Bertani, G. Multiplicity reactivation of bacteriophage inactivated by ionizing radiation. *Virology*, **2**:344 (1956). [299]

676. Weigle, J. J., and Delbrück, M. Mutual exclusion between an infecting phage and a carried phage. *J. Bacteriol.*, **62**:301 (1951). [339, 374]

677. Weigle, J. J., Meselson, M., and Paigen, K. Density alterations associated with transducing ability in the bacteriophage λ. *J. Mol. Biol.*, **1**:379 (1959). [362, 363]

678. Weiss, S. B. Enzymatic incorporation of ribonucleoside triphosphates into the inter-polynucleotide linkages of ribonucleic acid. *Proc. Nat. Acad. Sci. U.S.A.*, **46**:1020 (1960). [408, 413]

679. Whitfield, J. F., and Murray, R. G. E. A cytological study of the lysogenization of *Shigella dysenteriae* with P1 and P2 bacteriophages. *Canad. J. Microbiol.*, **1**:216 (1955). [370]

680. Wiberg, J. F., Dirksen, M. L., Epstein, R. H., Luria, S. E., and Buchanan, J. M. Early enzyme synthesis and its control in *E. coli* infected with some amber mutants of bacteriophage T4. *Proc. Nat. Acad. Sci. U.S.A.*, **48**:293 (1962). [218]

681. Wilkins, M. H. F., Stokes, A. R., Wilson, H. R. Molecular structure of deoxy-pentose nucleic acids. *Nature*, **171**:738 (1953). [53]

682. Williams, R. C. The shapes and sizes of purified viruses as determined by electron microscopy. *Cold Spring Harbor Symp. Quant. Biol.*, **18**:185 (1953). [47]

683. Williams, R. C., and Fraser, D. Morphology of the seven T-bacteriophages. *J. Bacteriol.*, **66**:458 (1953). [47, 48, 49]

684. Williams, R. C., and Fraser, D. Structural and functional differentiation in T2 bacteriophage. *Virology*, **2**:289 (1956). [106]

685. Williams, R. C., and Wyckoff, R. W. G. Applications of metallic shadow-casting to microscopy. *J. Appl. Phys.*, **17**:23 (1946). [47]

686. Wollman, E. Bactériophagie et processus similaires. Hérédité ou infection? *Bull. Inst. Pasteur*, **26:**1 (1928). [15]

687. Wollman, E., and Wollman, E. Bactériophage et lyse secondaire. *C. R. Soc. Biol.*, **112:**164 (1933). [80]

688. Wollman, E., and Wollman, E. Régénération des bactériophages chez le *B. megatherium* lysogène. *C. R. Soc. Biol.*, **122:**190 (1936). [308]

689. Wollman, E., and Wollman, E. Les "phases" des bactériophages (facteurs lysogènes). *C. R. Soc. Biol.*, **124:**931 (1937). [85, 308]

690. Wollman, E. L. Sur le déterminisme génétique de la lysogénie. *Ann. Inst. Pasteur*, **84:**281 (1953). [321]

691. Wollman, E. L., and Jacob, F. Lysogénie et récombinaison génétique chez *Escherichia coli* K12. *C. R. Acad. Sci. Paris*, **239:**455 (1954). [English translation in (595).] [321]

692. Wollman, E. L., and Jacob, F. Étude génétique d'un bactériophage temperé d'*Escherichia coli*. II. Mécanisme de la récombinaison génétique. *Ann. Inst. Pasteur*, **87:**674 (1954). [234]

693. Wollman, E. L., and Jacob, F. Sur le mécanisme de transfert de matériel génétique au cours de la récombinaison chez *Escherichia coli* K12. *C. R. Acad. Sci. Paris*, **240:**2449 (1955). [321]

694. Wollman, E. L., and Jacob, F. Sur les processus de conjugation et de récombinaison chez *Escherichia coli*. II. La localisation chromosomique du prophage et les conséquences de l'induction zygotique. *Ann. Inst. Pasteur*, **93:**323 (1957). [323]

695. Wollman, E. L., Jacob, F., and Hayes, W. Conjugation and genetic recombination in *Escherichia coli* K-12. *Cold Spring Harbor Symp. Quant. Biol.*, **21:**141 (1956). [38, 321]

696. Wollman, E. L., and Stent, G. S. Studies on activation of T4 bacteriophage by cofactor. I. The degree of activity. *Biochim. Biophys. Acta*, **6:**292 (1950). [107]

697. Work, E., and Dewey, D. L. The distribution of $\alpha\epsilon$-diaminopimelic acid among various microorganisms. *J. Gen. Microbiol.*, **9:**394 (1953). [97]

698. Wyatt, G. R., and Cohen, S. S. The bases of the nucleic acids of some bacterial and animal viruses: The occurrence of 5-hydroxymethylcytosine. *Biochem. J.*, **55:**774 (1953). [55, 124]

699. Wyckoff, R. W. G. The electron microscopy of developing bacteriophage. II. Growth of T4 in liquid culture. *Biochim. Biophys. Acta*, **2:**246 (1948). [121]

700. Yanofsky, C., and St. Lawrence, P. Gene action. *Ann. Rev. Microbiol.*, **14:**311 (1960). [272, 417]

701. Zahler, S. A. Some biological properties of bacteriophages S13 and ϕX-174. *J. Bacteriol.*, **75:**310 (1958). [384, 388]

702. Zamecnik, P. C., Keller, E. B., Littlefield, J. W., Hoagland, M. B., and Loftfield, R. B. Mechanism of incorporation of labeled amino acids into protein. *J. Cellular Comp. Physiol.*, **47,** Suppl. 1:81 (1956). [413]

703. Zamenhof, S., Leidy, G., Hahn, E., and Alexander, H. E. Inactivation and unstabilization of the transforming principle by mutagenic agents. *J. Bacteriol.*, **72:**1 (1956). [300]

704. Zelle, M., and Hollaender, A. Monochromatic ultraviolet action spectra and quantum yields for inactivation of T1 and T2 *Escherichia coli* bacteriophages. *J. Bacteriol.*, **68:**210 (1954). [280]

705. Zichichi, M. L., and Kellenberger, G. Two distinct functions in the lysogenization process: the repression of phage multiplication and the incorporation of the prophage in the bacterial genome. *Virology*, in press. (1963). [327]

706. Zinder, N. D. Infective heredity in bacteria. *Cold Spring Harbor Symp. Quant. Biol.*, **18:**261 (1953). [343]

707. Zinder, N. D. Genetic interaction between bacteriophage and bacteria. In *Perspectives in Virology* (M. Pollard, ed.), p. 43. Wiley, New York, 1959. [363]

708. Zinder, N. D. Hybrids of *Escherichia* and *Salmonella*. *Science*, **131:**813 (1960). [378]

709. Zinder, N. D., and Lederberg, J. Genetic exchange in *Salmonella*. *J. Bacteriol.*, **64:**679 (1952). [341, 364]

Index

Abortive infection, 155
Abortive transduction, 353–357, 366
Absolute plating efficiency, 17, 43
Acid-soluble peptide (of T-even phage), 67–68
Acridine dyes, 82, 187, 261, 264–265, 269, 272–273, 398
Action spectrum (ultraviolet), 279–281
Activating enzyme (amino acid), 411–412, 417
Actomyosin, 109
Adaptor (in protein synthesis), 409–412, 415
Adenine:
    action of alkylating agents on, 265–266
    action of nitrous acid on, 266
    content of various phage strains, 56
    hydrogen bonding in DNA, 259
    structure of, 51
Adenosine triphosphate (ATP), 109
Adenylic acid, 51, 156, 158
Adsorption, 10, 16, 61, 88–109
    bacterial receptor sites, 16, 96–102
    capacity, 17, 90
    cations, 92
    cofactors, 107
    irreversible, 93, 94–96
    kinetics, 89–96
    organ, 103–109, 181
    pH effect on, 92
    rate constant of, 89–90
    reversible, 93, 94–96, 100
    temperature effect on, 94–96, 108
    tryptophan requirement for, 107
    two-step nature of, 94–96, 108
Aeration, 31–32
Aerobe, 31–32
Agar, 31, 40
Agglutination, 61
Alanine, 50, 251
Alkaline phosphatase, 418
Alkylating agents, 265–266, 268–270
Allele, 205
Amber mutants, 187, 218–222, 418–419
Ambivalent mutants, 415–420
Amino acids:
    activation, 411–412, 417
    coding relation, 252–253, 392–402, 409–411

cofactors (adsorption), 107
composition of T2 and T3, 50
peptide bonds, 250
polypeptide, 250, 252
standard set, 251–252, 392–393, 401–402, 412
Aminopurine, 264–265, 268–270
Anaerobe, 31–32
Anlage (of phage), 16, 307
Anthranilic acid, 350
Antibodies (antiphage), 57–58, 62, 107, 117
Antigens:
    internal protein, 68, 130
    phages as, 16, 58, 114, 317
    surplus, 119, 131, 132, 221
Arrowsmith, 8
Attachment: *see* Adsorption
Autarky, 374
Autocatalytic function (of DNA), 391–392
Autolysin, 15
Autoradiography, 65–67, 166
Auxotroph, 36–37, 341–342, 356–357

Bacterial contribution, 126–127, 129–130, 162, 370
Bacterial receptor sites, 16, 96–102
Bacteriophage:
    ghosts, 64, 110, 112
    historical, 1–21
    incomplete, 117–124
    name, 5–6, 12
    nature of, 3, 9–15
    nomenclature, 20–21
    precursors, 83, 123–125
    size, 17, 43–46, 49, 382–384
    strains (Note. References to the T strains, λ, and P22 are too numerous for inclusion in this index):
        C16, 46
        D12, 45
        f2, 389–390
        Fcz, 80–81
        P1, 347–348, 370, 378–381
        S13, 45, 382–383, 388–389
        WLL, 49
        ϕX174, 383–389
    strain 363, 347–348
    taxonomy of, 20, 58, 60

Bacteriophage (*continued*)
    therapy, 6–9
Base analogue mutagens, 269–271
Base pairing in DNA, 53–55, 260, 267
Base plate (of phage tail), 106
β-galactosidase, 140
Bipartite structure of phage DNA, 67, 167
Blendor experiment, 110
Breakage and reunion (recombination by), 222, 224, 225, 232–236
Breakdown of infecting phage DNA, 153, 198, 381
Bromouracil, 169–171, 261–265, 269, 270–271, 273–275
Burst size, 72, 74–76. 83, 389

Capacity:
    adsorption, 17, 90
    for phage reproduction (radio-sensitivity of), 371–374
Cell count, 33
Cell membrane, 26
Cell structure (bacterial), 26–29
Cell wall (bacterial), 26
    chemical structure, 97, 99–100
    lysozyme action on, 100–101
    phage receptors, 96–100
    stimulation of synthesis by phage, 154
Cesium chloride density gradient, 167–169, 235, 379, 386–387, 405
Chemical composition (of phage), 17–18, 49–56, 62, 384, 389
Chloramphenicol, 142–143, 304, 324, 370
Chloroform, 85, 88–89
Chromatin body, 369, 370
Chromosome, 17–18, 39, 204, 206, 207–208, 211–212, 319, 321, 322, 325, 328–332, 353, 422
Circular genetic map, 39, 217–222, 322, 331
Cis-trans test, 254–256, 356–357
Cistron:
    definition, 256, 356–357
    length, 256
    regulation of function, 421–423
    ultraviolet light target, 287–289
Clear plaque phage mutants, 176, 325, 423
Clone, 36, 71–72, 180
Coding ratio, 394, 400
Cofactor requirement (adsorption), 107
Colicinogenic factors, 338
Collodion filter membrane, 44, 49

Colony, 33, 40
Colony count, 33
Commaless code, 395
Complementary recombinants, 203, 222
Complementation test, 254–255, 356–357
Condensation of phage DNA, 133
Condensation principle, 133–134
Confluent lysis, 182
Conjugation (bacterial), 37, 318
    circular linkage group, 39, 322
    fertility mutants (Hfr), 39, 321
    recombinants, 37–39, 321
    sex factor, 39, 338
Conservative replication, 160, 275
Contractile organ (phage tail as), 108
Conversion, 336–338
Copy choice recombination, 222–225, 229, 234
Copy error:
    mutation as, 189
Core (of phage tail), 106, 113
Corepressor, 422–423
Cotransduction of linked markers, 346–348
Crossover, 205–206
Crossreaction (serological), 58, 59–60
Cross reactivation:
    after P^{32} decay, 296–297
    after ultraviolet light, 285–287
Cryptophagic phase, 85
Cultivation (of bacteria), 28–32
Curing (prophage), 315, 317–318
Cyanide, 82, 83, 100, 102, 108
Cysteine, 50, 111, 251, 353
Cytidylic acid, 156, 158
Cytoplasmic inheritance, 318
Cytosine:
    action of nitrous acid on, 266
    content of various phage strains, 56
    hydrogen bonding in DNA, 53–54, 260, 267
    structure of, 51

Dalton (definition), 46
Dark field microscope, 17, 44
Deamination, 266
Defective lysogenic strains, 332–336, 361–363
Degeneracy (of code), 393, 402
Deletions, 247–250, 253, 272, 398
Density gradient sedimentation, 167–171, 234, 235, 379, 380, 386–387, 405, 406
Density mutants, 327
Density of transducing phage, 362–363

Deoxycytidine pyrophosphatase, 148
Deoxycytidylate hydroxymethylase, 148, 218
Deoxycytidylic deaminase, 149
Deoxyribonuclease, 110, 112, 140–141, 150, 153, 343
Deoxyribonucleic acid:
  absorption spectrum (UV), 280
  as germinal substance, 114, 386
  assimilation of phage, 127
  bipartite structure of phage, 67, 167
  breakage by shear, 67, 171
  breakdown of bacterial, 127, 282, 370
  breakdown of infecting phage, 153, 198, 381
  chemical structure, 52–56, 386
  condensation of phage, 133
  content and composition of phages, 17–18, 51, 53–57, 64, 124–125, 384
  enzymes for replication of phage, 144–150
  in bacterial nuclei, 28–29, 369–370
  incomplete phage, 123–125, 138
  injection of phage, 110–114, 282
  molecular weight, 65–67, 384
  phage precursor, 143–144, 164–165
  polymerase, 148, 158, 218
  pool in infected bacteria, 126–128, 133
  replication, 157–160, 386, 391–392
  single-stranded, 384, 386
  transfer from parent to progeny phage, 160–172, 232–236, 379–380
Deoxyribose, 53, 389
Diaminopimelic acid, 96
Diffusion constant (of phage), 46, 90, 91, 94
Diphtheria toxin, 337
Direct effects (X-rays), 298–299
"Disease" (of bacteria), 2, 4, 13
Dispersive transfer of DNA, 165, 166–167, 235
DNA: *see* Deoxyribonucleic acid
DNase: *see* Deoxyribonuclease
Dominance, 254
Dose (radiation), 279, 298–299
"Doughnuts," 121
Dynamics of growth (bacterial), 34–36

Early protein, 141–144, 152, 304, 323–324, 421
Eclipse, 83–87, 103, 114, 117, 312
Efficiency of killing (in P³² decay), 294, 382–383, 384, 386

Efficiency of plating (E.O.P.), 17, 43
Electron microscopy, 26, 44, 46–49, 62, 63, 107, 120–122, 133
EMB agar, 345
Empty phage heads, 120–121, 135
Enzymes:
  effect of phage on bacterial, 140–141, 370–371
  inducible, 140, 421–422
  phage-induced, 81, 140, 144–152
  repressible, 140, 421–422
Episome, 338–339
Epistatic, 207
Ethyl ethane sulfonate (EES), 265, 269–270
Ethyl methane sulfonate (EMS), 265–266, 268
Eubacteria, 23–25
Excitations, 279, 300
Exclusion:
  by autark phages, 374
  "key enzyme" hypothesis, 195
  of superinfecting phage, 153–154, 318–319, 371
  partial, 198–199
Exogenote, 355, 357
Exponential growth phase, 34

Fidelity (of translation), 415, 419
Filtrable agent (FA) in transduction, 342–344
Filtration end point, 44–45, 383
Fine-structure genetic map, 239–242, 256–259, 350
Fixation: *see* Adsorption
Flagella, 23, 346–347, 353
Fluorodeoxyuridine, 389–390
Fluorouracil, 419–420
Functional survival (after UV), 287–289
Functional unit (genetic), 250–256

Gamete, 37
Gene, 18, 204, 207–208, 238–239
Generation time, 35
Genetic code, 252, 392–402, 411, 414
Genetic equilibrium, 210, 214
Genetic locus, 204
Genetic map, 203–209, 220, 322
  circular, 217–222, 330–331
  fine structure of, 239–242, 256–259, 348–351
  topography of, 256–259

Genetic recombination, 142, 202, 203–209
  between phage and host, 373–376
  breakage and reunion, 222, 223, 225, 232–236
  copy choice, 222, 224–225, 229, 234
  discovery in phage, 202–203
  effect of ultraviolet light, 292–293, 388–389
  role of heterozygotes, 228–230, 232
Genome, 114, 180
Genotype, 179–180
Germicidal lamp, 278
Ghosts (phage), 64, 110, 112, 370
Glassy transformation, 2, 11–12
Glucose, content of T-even DNA, 56–57, 149–150
Glucoseamine, 97, 101
Glucosyl transferase, 148–149
Glucosylation:
  and partial exclusion, 198–199
  pattern of T-even DNA, 56–58, 198–199
Glutamic acid, 50, 97, 251
Gram-negative bacteria, 26, 103
Gram-positive bacteria, 26, 102
Growth cycle of phage, 10–11, 70–87
Growth medium, 29–31
Guanine, 53–56
  action of alkylating agents on, 265
  action of nitrous acid on, 266
  content of various phage strains, 56
  hydrogen bonding in DNA, 54, 260
  structure of, 51
Guanylic acid, 156, 158

Head (of phage), 47, 49, 112
Head, protein, 65, 106, 282
Heat-labile repressor, 423
Heavy isotopes, 169, 235, 379, 386–387, 405
Helper phage, 333, 361, 365
Heterocatalytic function (of DNA), 391
Heteroduplex, 229–230, 273–274, 275
Heterogenote, 355, 358–363, 364
Heterozygotes:
  mutational, 273–275
  recombinational, 225–230, 232
Hfr fertility mutants (of bacteria), 39, 321
HFT lysate, 360–365
Histidine, 50, 251, 353
Hit, lethal, 279
HMC: see Hydroxymethylcytosine
Homogenote, 364

Homology (genetic), 328, 346, 365
Host-controlled (or host-induced) modification (or host-controlled variation), 376–382
Host range mutants, 180–183, 375–376
Hot spots (mutational), 257, 264
Hydrogen peroxide, 108, 312, 324
Hydroxylamine, 266, 268, 269
Hydroxymethylcytidylic acid, 52, 156
Hydroxymethylcytosine, 55, 124–125
  action of hydroxylamine on, 268
  action of nitrous acid on, 266
  content of various phage strains, 56
  glucosylation, 56–57, 149–150, 198–199
  structure of, 51
Hydroxymethyluracil, 266
Hypoxanthine, 266–267

Immune precipitate, 60–61, 117
Immunity (against disease), role of phage in, 7
Immunity (of lysogenic bacteria), 16, 315–317
  genetic control, 325–328
  substance, 233–234, 421, 423–424
Immunology (of phage): see Serology
Incomplete phage, 117–124
Indicator strains, 14
  mixed, 183, 198
Indirect effects (X-rays), 100
Indole glycerol phosphate, 350
Induced mutation:
  in vitro, 265–268
  in vivo, 261–265
Inducer (of enzyme synthesis), 421–424
Induction of prophage, 311–312, 324, 332–336
Infective center, 74, 198
Injection of phage DNA, 110–114, 282
Insertions (genetic), 272–273, 329, 398–401
Integration of genetic markers, 349–350
Internal protein, 67, 68, 113, 120, 130, 138
Internal structure (of phage), 63–68
Intracellular phage growth, kinetics of, 86

Key-enzyme, 195
Killing titer (of phage suspension), 33, 77–78
Kinase, 148, 150–151

Lamarckism, 376
Latent period, 19, 72, 83, 312

Leakage (of infected cell), 101
Lesion (ultraviolet light), 282, 283–284, 287
Lethal hit, 279
LFT lysate, 360
Limit of participation (in phage growth), 196–198
Limiting dilution (assay), 9
Linkage, 39, 205–209, 211–212
Lipopolysaccharide, 97
Lipoprotein, 97
Locus, genetic, 204, 208
Logarithmic phase, 34
Long-span phage mutants, 245
Luria-Latarjet experiment, 300–304
Lysine, 50, 113, 251
Lysins (*see also* Lysozyme), 80–82,
Lysis, 5, 9, 10–11, 12, 14, 70, 77–83, 101, 306, 308, 310, 311
    artificial, 83, 85, 312
    from within, 80, 82, 101
    from without, 79–80, 83, 101–102, 154, 198
    inhibition, 82–83, 178–179
    transmissible, 11, 12, 13, 70
Lysogenic bacteria (*see also* Prophage, Immunity, Transduction, Induction), 13–14, 16, 20, 306–339
    artificial strains, 312–313, 314
    bacteriophage production by, 309–311
    conjugation of, 319–322
    conversion, 336–338
    defective, 332–336, 361–366
    definition, 306–307, 310–311
    history, 13–15, 306–311
    liberation of phage by, 308, 309
    superinfection of, 318–319, 332, 333–334
Lysogenic response, 313, 325
    abortive, 327–328
Lysogeny: *see* Lysogenic bacteria
Lysozyme, 28, 81–82, 85, 100–102, 113, 154–155, 308
Lytic response, 313

Majority parent, 210
Male-specific phage, 389
Map: *see* Genetic map
Map unit, 208, 216
Marker rescue, 285–287, 297, 381
Mating, 211–212
Mating pool, 211–212
Maturation of phage, 86, 117, 132–138, 335

Messenger RNA, 156, 402–409, 412–415
Methionine, 50, 111, 113, 251
5-methyl tryptophan, 142
Minimum recombinational distance, 242
Minor components (of phage), 67–68
Minority parent, 210
Minute colonies, 355–356
Minute phages, 382–390
Mixed indicators, 183, 198
Mixed infection, 195–198
Morphology (of phage), 47–49, 121
Mottled plaque, 196, 225–226, 273–274, 275
Mucopolymer, 97, 101, 113
Multiplicity of infection, 77, 79
Multiplicity reactivation, 289–291, 303
Muramic acid, 97, 100
Mutagenesis: *see* Mutation
Mutagens, 36, 261–273
    base analogue, 264–265, 269
Mutants (bacterial):
    definition, 36
    phage-resistant, 16, 91–92, 99, 180–183
    suppressor, 417
    thymine-requiring (phage growth on), 149–150
Mutants (phage), 16, 174–188
    amber, 218–222, 418–419
    ambivalent, 415–418
    clear plaque, 176, 325, 423
    deletion, 244–250, 398–400
    density, 327
    host range, 180–183
    long-span, 245
    noninducible, 423
    rapid lysis, 177–180
    spontaneous, 263–264, 269–270
    temperature-sensitive, 219
    virulent, 423–424
Mutation, 143, 180, 188–195
    frequency, 190, 194
    hot spots, 257, 264
    index, 190
    induced, 261–269
    molecular explanation, 259–261
    of first kind, 269–270, 272
    of second kind, 269–270, 272
    point, 243
    reverse, 188, 243, 268–269, 271–272, 396
    spontaneous, 261, 263
    suppressor, 271–272, 396–398
    unit of, 242–245
    vegetative phage, 188–190

Mutational heterozygotes, 273–275
Mutilat strain, 307, 310

Negative interference, 230–232
Nephelometer, 34
Neutralization, 58–61
Nitrogen mustard, 261, 312
Nitrous acid, 266, 268, 269, 275
Nomenclature (of phage), 20–21
Noninducible phage mutants, 423
Nonsense (genetic), 244, 253, 395, 401–402
Nucleic acid: see Deoxyribonucleic acid
    and Ribonucleic acid
Nucleoids, 369
Nucleotide, 51, 52, 53, 242, 245
Nucleus, bacterial, 22, 28, 133, 141, 282,
    369–371
Nutrient broth, 30
Nutrition (of bacteria), 29–30, 74

One-step growth, 19, 72–74, 83
Operator, 421–423, 424–425
Operon, 421–423, 424–425
Osmotic shock, 63
Overlapping code, 393

P³² decay inactivation: see Radioactive
    decay
Partial replicas, 224–225, 229
Persistent complex, 375–376
Petri plate, 31, 40–41
Phage: see Bacteriophage
Phage unit (definition), 117–119
Phenotype, 179–180, 250, 253
Phenotypic mixing, 136, 199–201, 239
Phosphorus:
    assimilation of phage, 126–128
    transfer of phage, 160–172, 232–236,
        379–380
Photometer, 33
Photoreactivable sector, 282–283
Photoreactivation, 282–283
Physiological clock (of phage), 424–425
P.I.A. (phage-inhibiting agent), 97
Plaque, 9, 40
    assay, 40–43
    turbid, 183, 314
    type mutant, 178, 235
Point mutation, 83
Poisson law, 75, 279
Polyamines, 68, 113, 135
Polylysogenic bacteria, 332, 362

Polymerase:
    DNA, 148, 158, 218
    RNA, 408
Polynucleotide, 53, 157, 250, 252
Polynucleotide phosphorylase, 413
Polyphenylalanine, 413–414
Polyuridylic acid, 413–414
Precursors, phage, 83, 123–125, 130
Proflavine, 82, 136, 138, 261, 264–265,
    269, 272–273
Prophage, 239, 309–311
    as "hook," 330
    chromosomal attachment, 321, 328–
        332
    curing, 315, 317–318
    defective, 332–336, 360
    induction, 311–312, 324, 333–336
    nature of, 317–323, 328–332
    recombination, 333–336
    segregation in genetic crosses, 321
    specific site of, 319, 324–325, 364
    transduction of, 348
    zygotic induction of, 323
Protein:
    early, 141–144, 152, 282, 304
    fate of phage in infection, 110
    incomplete phage, 117–123
    internal phage, 68, 113, 120, 130, 135
    non-precursor, 141–143
    phage precursor, 130, 131–132, 141–
        143
    pool of precursor, 129–132
    regulation of synthesis, 420–425
    synthesis in infected cell, 129–132, 141–
        142, 282
Protoplasts, 26, 102–103
Prototroph, 37, 341, 357
Pseudolysogeny, 309
Pseudowild phenotype, 396, 400
Purification (of phage), 17, 49–50, 384

Quantum yield (of ultraviolet light), 278,
    279, 283

R layer (of cell wall), 97, 103
Radioactive decay, inactivation by, 166,
    233–234, 279, 293–297, 301–302, 317,
    373, 379, 383
Radiosensitivity of capacity for phage
    reproduction, 371–374
Rapid lysis mutants, 176–180
Reactivation:
    cross, 285–287, 296–297
    multiplicity, 289–291

Reactivation (*continued*)
photo, 282–283
Recombinant frequency, 203, 204, 213
Recombination: *see* Genetic recombination
Regulation (of protein synthesis), 420–425
Replication, 157–160, 386
conservative, 160, 275
follow-the-leader, 191–194
geometric, 191–194
semiconservative, 160, 167–169, 235, 273, 274, 388
stamping machine, 191–194
Replicative form, 388
Repressor, 323–324, 420–425
Resealing (of infected cell), 101
Resistance (of bacteria to phage), 16, 91–92, 99, 180–183, 315–316
Respiration rate of infected bacteria, 139–140
Reversal of phenotype, 419–420
Reverse mutation, 188, 243, 268–269, 271–272, 335, 396
Reversion index, 243–244, 267
RF: *see* Replicative form
Ribonucleic acid:
as genetic material, 115, 266, 389
as inhibitor of DNase, 140–141
composition of postinfection, 156
messenger, 156, 402–409, 412–415
polymerase, 408
synthesis in infected cell, 155–157, 282, 403–409, 412
transfer, 29, 412, 417
Ribosomes, 29, 155, 402–408
Rise period, 72
RNA: *see* Ribonucleic acid
Rods (phage precursor), 121–122
Roentgen, 298
Rounds of matnig, 213–216, 234,

Sedimentation velocity (of phage), 17, 46, 383
Segmental classification (of genetic map), 247–248
Semiconservative replication, 160, 167–169, 235, 273, 274, 388
Sensitive volume, 298–299, 382–383
Serology, 16, 58–63, 68, 107, 117–120, 317
Serum-blocking-power (SBP), 117, 119–120, 135, 221
Sex factor (of bacteria), 39, 338
Sheath (of phage tail), 106, 108–109, 113
Single burst, 16, 74–77, 85, 193

Size of bacteriophage, 17, 43–46, 49
"Soft" agar, 40
Spheroplasts, 28, 103
Spontaneous phage mutants, 263–264, 269–270
Stationary phase, 36
Stepwise multiplication, 71
Streptomycin, 261
Substrate transition, 260, 263
Sulfur, assimilation of phage, 130–132
Superinfection breakdown, 153, 198
Suppressor mutation, 271–272, 396–402, 417
Surplus antigens, 119, 121, 132, 135
Synapsis, 222, 331
Synthetic medium, 30
Synthetic messenger RNA, 412–415

Tail (of phage), 47, 49, 61, 64, 65, 103–109, 112, 120
fibers, 106, 107
proteins, 106, 282
Target theory, 279, 382
Tautomeric forms (of purines and pyrimidines), 259, 270–271
Taxonomy of bacteriophage, 20–21, 57–59, 60
Temperate phages, 313
Temperature effect on:
adsorption, 94–96, 108
bacterial growth, 32
efficiency of killing, in P^{32} decay, 294
lysogenization, 324
latent period, 74
Temperature-sensitive phage mutants, 219
Template transition, 262–263
Thymidylate synthetase, 149
Thymidylic acid, 52, 156, 158
Thymine:
content of various phage strains, 56
dimerization of, 281–282, 283
hydrogen bonding in DNA, 54, 260
new pathway of synthesis, 149–150
replacement by 5-bromouracil, 262–263
structure of, 51
Titration:
of antiphage serum, 59
of phage, 9–10, 40–43
Tobacco mosaic virus, 1, 115, 266
Topography of genetic map, 263, 268
Topology of genetic map, 276, 329

Transduction, 37, 341–366
  abortive, 353–357, 366
  discovery, 341–344
  fine-structure mapping, 348–353
  generalized, 357, 363–366
  high frequency (HFT), 360–364
  integration of exogenote, 349–350
  low frequency, 360
  of linked markers, 346–353
  of lysogeny, 348
  specialized, 357–366
  stable, 357
Transfer of phage DNA, 113, 160–172
  association with genetic markers, 233–236
  distribution of transferred material, 165–172
  extent and specificity, 160–165
  kinetics, 163
Transfer of phage protein, 113
Transfer RNA, 29, 412, 417
Transformation (bacterial), 38, 114–115
Transition (mutational), 270
Transmissible lysis, 11, 12, 13, 70
Transmission coefficient, 419
Transmutation, 295–296
Transversion, 271, 273
Triplet (nucleotide), 253, 392–402, 412
True linkage, 211–212, 292
Tryptophan, 50, 252, 350–352, 422
  as adsorption cofactor, 107
Turbidity (of bacterial cultures), 33–34, 35, 79, 101, 311

U-tube, 342
Ultrafiltration, 44, 45, 49, 119
Ultraviolet light (UV), 277–293
  action spectrum, 279–280
  as mutagen, 261, 375
  effect on capacity, 371–374
  effect on DNA, 281–282
  effect on genetic recombination, 292–293, 389
  effect on physiological clock, 425
  functional survival after, 287–289
  inactivation kinetics, 279
  prophage induction, 311 324 ,333–336, 360–361
  quantum yield, 278, 279

Ultraviolet sensitivity:
  definition, 279
  genetic control of, 283–285
  of capacity, 371–374
  of vegetative phage, 300–304
Unit (genetic):
  of function, 250–256
  of mutation, 242–245
  of recombination, 239–242
Uracil, 266, 267–268, 389, 420
Uridylic acid, 156, 414

Vegetative phage, 86–87, 312
  mutation, 188–190
  pool, 194, 211
  radiosensitivity, 300–304
Viable count, 33
Virulent mutants, 423–424
Virulent phages, 313
Virus (theory), 1, 3, 5, 6, 9, 11, 12, 13, 15, 16, 45, 116–117
Visconti-Delbrück theory, 209–217, 222–224, 230
Vitalism, 428
von Schmoluchowski equation, 90
Vulnerable centers, 291

Watson-Crick structure of DNA, 53–55, 158–159, 296, 388, 392
Wild type, 178

Xanthine, 267
X-rays, 297–300
  direct effects, 298
  excitations, 298, 300
  inactivation kinetics, 298–299
  indirect effects, 298
  ionizations, 298, 300
  prophage induction, 312
  sensitivity of capacity, 373
  sensitivity of various phages, 299–300, 382–383

Zygotic induction, 323–324